Student Edition

SpringBoard®

Mathematics

Geometry

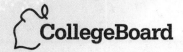

About the College Board

The College Board is a mission-driven not-for-profit organization that connects students to college success and opportunity. Founded in 1900, the College Board was created to expand access to higher education. Today, the membership association is made up of more than 5,900 of the nation's leading educational institutions and is dedicated to promoting excellence and equity in education. Each year, the College Board helps more than seven million students prepare for a successful transition to college through programs and services in college readiness and college success—including the SAT® and the Advanced Placement Program®. The organization also serves the education community through research and advocacy on behalf of students, educators, and schools.

For further information, visit www.collegeboard.org.

ISBN: 1-4573-0152-0
ISBN: 978-1-4573-0152-0

1 2 3 4 5 6 7 8   14 15 16 17 18
Printed in the United States of America

Acknowledgments

The College Board gratefully acknowledges the outstanding work of the classroom teachers and writers who have been integral to the development of this revised program. The end product is testimony to their expertise, understanding of student learning needs, and dedication to rigorous but accessible mathematics instruction.

Michael Allwood
Brunswick School
Greenwich, Connecticut

Bonnie Fenwick
Atlantic High School
Port Orange, Florida

Brian Kotz
Montgomery College
Monrovia, Maryland

Floyd Bullard
North Carolina School of Science
and Mathematics
Durham, North Carolina

Kathy Fritz
Plano Independent School District
Plano, Texas

Chris Olsen
Prairie Lutheran School
Cedar Rapids, Iowa

Marcia Chumas
East Mecklenburg High School
Charlotte, North Carolina

Marie Humphrey
David W. Butler High School
Charlotte, North Carolina

Dr. Roxy Peck
California Polytechnic Institute
San Luis Obispo, California

Wendy DenBesten
Hoover High School
Fresno, California

Andrew Kearns
Dr. Michael Krop Senior High
Miami, Florida

Andrea Sukow
Mathematics Consultant
Nashville, Tennessee

Product Development

Betty Barnett
Executive Director, SpringBoard

Robert Sheffield
Sr. Director, SpringBoard Implementation

Allen Dimacali
Editorial Director, Mathematics
SpringBoard

Kimberly Sadler
Senior Math Product Manager
SpringBoard

John Nelson
Editor, SpringBoard

Alex Chavarry
Sr. Director, SpringBoard Strategic Accounts

Acknowledgments *continued*

Research and Planning Advisors

We also wish to thank the members of our SpringBoard Advisory Council and the many educators who gave generously of their time and their ideas as we conducted research for both the print and online programs. Your suggestions and reactions to ideas helped immeasurably as we planned the revisions. We gratefully acknowledge the teachers and administrators in the following districts.

ABC Unified
Cerritos, California

Albuquerque Public Schools
Albuquerque, New Mexico

Amarillo School District
Amarillo, Texas

Baltimore County Public Schools
Baltimore, Maryland

Bellevue School District 405
Bellevue, Washington

Charlotte Mecklenburg Schools
Charlotte, North Carolina

Clark County School District
Las Vegas, Nevada

Cypress Fairbanks ISD
Houston, Texas

District School Board of
    Collier County
Collier County, Florida

Denver Public Schools
Denver, Colorado

Frisco ISD
Frisco, Texas

Gilbert Unified School District
Gilbert, Arizona

Grand Prairie ISD
Grand Prairie, Texas

Hillsborough County Public
    Schools
Tampa, Florida

Houston Independent School
    District
Houston, Texas

Hobbs Municipal Schools
Hobbs, New Mexico

Irving Independent School
    District
Irving, Texas

Kenton County School District
Fort Wright, Kentucky

Lee County Public Schools
Fort Myers, Florida

Newton County Schools
Covington, Georgia

Noblesville Schools
Noblesville, Indiana

Oakland Unified School District
Oakland, California

Orange County Public Schools
Orlando, Florida

School District of Palm Beach
    County
Palm Beach, Florida

Peninsula School District
Gig Harbor, Washington

Polk County Public Schools
Bartow, Florida

Quakertown Community School
    District
Quakertown, Pennsylvania

Rio Rancho Public Schools
Rio Rancho, New Mexico

Ronan School District
Ronan, Montana

St. Vrain Valley School District
Longmont, Colorado

Scottsdale Public Schools
Phoenix, Arizona

Seminole County Public Schools
Sanford, Florida

Southwest ISD
San Antonio, Texas

Spokane Public Schools
Spokane, Washington

Volusia County Schools
DeLand, Florida

Contents

Contents *continued*

Contents *continued*

Contents *continued*

To the Student

Welcome to the SpringBoard program.

This program has been created with you in mind: the content you need to learn, the tools to help you learn, and the critical thinking skills that help you build confidence in your own knowledge of mathematics. The College Board publishes the SpringBoard program. It also publishes the PSAT/NMSQT, the SAT, and the Advanced Placement exams—all exams that you are likely to encounter in your student years. Preparing you to perform well on those exams and to develop the mathematics skills needed for high school success is the primary purpose of this program.

Standards-Based Mathematics Learning

The SpringBoard program is based on learning standards that identify the mathematics skills and knowledge that you should master to succeed in high school and in future college-level work. In this course, the standards follow these broad areas of mathematics knowledge:

- Mathematical practices
- Number and quantity
- Algebra
- Functions
- Modeling
- Statistics and probability

Mathematical practice standards guide your study of mathematics. They are actions you take to help you understand mathematical concepts rather than just mathematical procedures. For example, the mathematical practice standards state the following:

MP.1 Make sense of problems and persevere in solving them.

MP.2 Reason abstractly and quantitatively.

MP.3 Construct viable arguments and critique the reasoning of others.

MP.4 Model with mathematics.

MP.5 Use appropriate tools strategically.

MP.6 Attend to precision.

MP.7 Look for and make use of structure.

MP.8 Look for and express regularity in repeated reasoning.

As you continue your studies from middle school, you will examine expressions, equations, and functions, which will allow you to make comparisons between relations and functions. Expressions and equations connect with functions. Understanding the concept of functions is critical to future success in your study of algebra and the rest of the high school mathematics curriculum.

See pages xiii–xvi for a complete list of the College and Career Readiness Standards for Mathematics for this course.

Strategies for Learning Mathematics

Some tools to help you learn are built into every activity. At the beginning of each activity, you will see suggested learning strategies. Each of these strategies is explained in full in the Resources section of your book. As you learn to use each strategy, you'll have the opportunity to decide which strategies work best for you. Suggested learning strategies include:

- Reading strategies
- Writing strategies
- Problem-solving strategies
- Collaborative strategies

Building Mathematics Knowledge and Skills

The SpringBoard program is built around the following.

Problem Solving Many of the problems in this book require you to *analyze* the situation and the information in a problem, *make decisions, determine the strategies* you'll use to solve the problem, and *justify* your solution.

Reasoning and Justification You will be asked to explain the reasoning behind how you solved problems, the mathematics concepts involved, and why your approach was appropriate.

Communication Communicating about mathematics, orally and in writing, with your classmates and teachers helps you organize your learning and explain mathematics concepts.

Mathematics Connections As you develop your mathematics knowledge, you will see the many connections between mathematics concepts and between mathematics and your own life.

Representations In mathematics, representations can take many forms, such as numeric, verbal, graphic, or symbolic. In this course, you are encouraged to use representations to organize problem information, present possible solutions, and communicate your reasoning.

We hope you enjoy your study of mathematics using the SpringBoard program.

College and Career Readiness Standards

HSG-CO Congruence

HSG-CO.A.1 Know precise definitions of angle, circle, perpendicular line, parallel line, and line segment, based on the undefined notions of point, line, distance along a line, and distance around a circular arc.

HSG-CO.A.2 Represent transformations in the plane using, e.g., transparencies and geometry software; describe transformations as functions that take points in the plane as inputs and give other points as outputs. Compare transformations that preserve distance and angle to those that do not (e.g., translation versus horizontal stretch).

HSG-CO.A.3 Given a rectangle, parallelogram, trapezoid, or regular polygon, describe the rotations and reflections that carry it onto itself.

HSG-CO.A.4 Develop definitions of rotations, reflections, and translations in terms of angles, circles, perpendicular lines, parallel lines, and line segments.

HSG-CO.A.5 Given a geometric figure and a rotation, reflection, or translation, draw the transformed figure using, e.g., graph paper, tracing paper, or geometry software. Specify a sequence of transformations that will carry a given figure onto another.

HSG-CO.B.6 Use geometric descriptions of rigid motions to transform figures and to predict the effect of a given rigid motion on a given figure; given two figures, use the definition of congruence in terms of rigid motions to decide if they are congruent.

HSG-CO.B.7 Use the definition of congruence in terms of rigid motions to show that two triangles are congruent if and only if corresponding pairs of sides and corresponding pairs of angles are congruent.

HSG-CO.B.8 Explain how the criteria for triangle congruence (ASA, SAS, and SSS) follow from the definition of congruence in terms of rigid motions.

HSG-CO.C.9 Prove theorems about lines and angles. *Theorems include: vertical angles are congruent; when a transversal crosses parallel lines, alternate interior angles are congruent and corresponding angles are congruent; points on a perpendicular bisector of a line segment are exactly those equidistant from the segment's endpoints.*

HSG-CO.C.10 Prove theorems about triangles. *Theorems include: measures of interior angles of a triangle sum to 180°; base angles of isosceles triangles are congruent; the segment joining midpoints of two sides of a triangle is parallel to the third side and half the length; the medians of a triangle meet at a point.*

HSG-CO.C.11 Prove theorems about parallelograms. *Theorems include: opposite sides are congruent, opposite angles are congruent, the diagonals of a parallelogram bisect each other, and conversely, rectangles are parallelograms with congruent diagonals.*

HSG-CO.D.12 Make formal geometric constructions with a variety of tools and methods (compass and straightedge, string, reflective devices, paper folding, dynamic geometric software, etc.). *Copying a segment; copying an angle; bisecting a segment; bisecting an angle; constructing perpendicular lines, including the perpendicular bisector of a line segment; and constructing a line parallel to a given line through a point not on the line.*

HSG-CO.D.13 Construct an equilateral triangle, a square, and a regular hexagon inscribed in a circle.

HSG-SRT Similarity, Right Triangles, and Trigonometry

HSG-SRT.A.1 Verify experimentally the properties of dilations given by a center and a scale factor:

>**HSG-SRT.A.1a** A dilation takes a line not passing through the center of the dilation to a parallel line, and leaves a line passing through the center unchanged.

>**HSG-SRT.A.1b** The dilation of a line segment is longer or shorter in the ratio given by the scale factor.

HSG-SRT.A.2 Given two figures, use the definition of similarity in terms of similarity transformations to decide if they are similar; explain using similarity transformations the meaning of similarity for triangles as the equality of all corresponding pairs of angles and the proportionality of all corresponding pairs of sides.

HSG-SRT.A.3 Use the properties of similarity transformations to establish the AA criterion for two triangles to be similar.

HSG-SRT.B.4 Prove theorems about triangles. *Theorems include: a line parallel to one side of a triangle divides the other two proportionally, and conversely; the Pythagorean Theorem proved using triangle similarity.*

HSG-SRT.B.5 Use congruence and similarity criteria for triangles to solve problems and to prove relationships in geometric figures.

HSG-SRT.C.6 Understand that by similarity, side ratios in right triangles are properties of the angles in the triangle, leading to definitions of trigonometric ratios for acute angles.

HSG-SRT.C.7 Explain and use the relationship between the sine and cosine of complementary angles.

HSG-SRT.C.8 Use trigonometric ratios and the Pythagorean Theorem to solve right triangles in applied problems.*

HSG-SRT.D.9 (+) Derive the formula $A = \frac{1}{2} ab \sin (C)$ for the area of a triangle by drawing an auxiliary line from a vertex perpendicular to the opposite side.

HSG-SRT.D.10 (+) Prove the Laws of Sines and Cosines and use them to solve problems.

HSG-SRT.D.11 (+) Understand and apply the Law of Sines and the Law of Cosines to find unknown measurements in right and non-right triangles (e.g., surveying problems, resultant forces).

HSG-C Circles

HSG-C.A.1 Prove that all circles are similar.

HSG-C.A.2 Identify and describe relationships among inscribed angles, radii, and chords. *Include the relationship between central, inscribed, and circumscribed angles; inscribed angles on a diameter are right angles; the radius of a circle is perpendicular to the tangent where the radius intersects the circle.*

HSG-C.A.3 Construct the inscribed and circumscribed circles of a triangle, and prove properties of angles for a quadrilateral inscribed in a circle.

HSG-C.A.4 (+) Construct a tangent line from a point outside a given circle to the circle.

HSG-C.B.5 Derive using similarity the fact that the length of the arc intercepted by an angle is proportional to the radius, and define the radian measure of the angle as the constant of proportionality; derive the formula for the area of a sector.

HSG-GPE Expressing Geometric Properties with Equations

HSG-GPE.A.1 Derive the equation of a circle of given center and radius using the Pythagorean Theorem; complete the square to find the center and radius of a circle given by an equation.

HSG-GPE.A.2 Derive the equation of a parabola given a focus and directrix.

HSG-GPE.B.4 Use coordinates to prove simple geometric theorems algebraically. *For example, prove or disprove that a figure defined by four given points in the coordinate plane is a rectangle; prove or disprove that the point $(1, \sqrt{3})$ lies on the circle centered at the origin and containing the point (0, 2).*

HSG-GPE.B.5 Prove the slope criteria for parallel and perpendicular lines and use them to solve geometric problems (e.g., find the equation of a line parallel or perpendicular to a given line that passes through a given point).

HSG-GPE.B.6 Find the point on a directed line segment between two given points that partitions the segment in a given ratio.

HSG-GPE.B.7 Use coordinates to compute perimeters of polygons and areas of triangles and rectangles, e.g., using the distance formula.*

HSG-GMD Geometric Measurement and Dimension

HSG-GMD.A.1 Give an informal argument for the formulas for the circumference of a circle, area of a circle, volume of a cylinder, pyramid, and cone. *Use dissection arguments, Cavalieri's principle, and informal limit arguments.*

HSG-GMD.A.3 Use volume formulas for cylinders, pyramids, cones, and spheres to solve problems.*

HSG-GMD.B.4 Identify the shapes of two-dimensional cross-sections of three-dimensional objects, and identify three-dimensional objects generated by rotations of two-dimensional objects.

HSG-MG Modeling with Geometry

HSG-MG.A.1 Use geometric shapes, their measures, and their properties to describe objects (e.g., modeling a tree trunk or a human torso as a cylinder).*

HSG-MG.A.2 Apply concepts of density based on area and volume in modeling situations (e.g., persons per square mile, BTUs per cubic foot).*

HSG-MG.A.3 Apply geometric methods to solve design problems (e.g., designing an object or structure to satisfy physical constraints or minimize cost; working with typographic grid systems based on ratios).*

HSS-CP Conditional Probability and the Rules of Probability

HSS-CP.A.1 Describe events as subsets of a sample space (the set of outcomes) using characteristics (or categories) of the outcomes, or as unions, intersections, or complements of other events ("or," "and," "not").

HSS-CP.A.2 Understand that two events A and B are independent if the probability of A and B occurring together is the product of their probabilities, and use this characterization to determine if they are independent.

HSS-CP.A.3 Understand the conditional probability of A given B as $P(A \text{ and } B)/P(B)$, and interpret independence of A and B as saying that the conditional probability of A given B is the same as the probability of A, and the conditional probability of B given A is the same as the probability of B.

HSS-CP.A.4 Construct and interpret two-way frequency tables of data when two categories are associated with each object being classified. Use the two-way table as a sample space to decide if events are independent and to approximate conditional probabilities. *For example, collect data from a random sample of students in your school on their favorite subject among math, science, and English. Estimate the probability that a randomly selected student from your school will favor science given that the student is in tenth grade. Do the same for other subjects and compare the results.*

HSS-CP.A.5 Recognize and explain the concepts of conditional probability and independence in everyday language and everyday situations. *For example, compare the chance of having lung cancer if you are a smoker with the chance of being a smoker if you have lung cancer.*

HSS-CP.B.6 Find the conditional probability of A given B as the fraction of B's outcomes that also belong to A, and interpret the answer in terms of the model.

HSS-CP.B.7 Apply the Addition Rule, $P(A \text{ or } B) = P(A) + P(B) - P(A \text{ and } B)$, and interpret the answer in terms of the model.

HSS-CP.B.8 (+) Apply the general Multiplication Rule in a uniform probability model, $P(A \text{ and } B) = P(A)P(B|A) = P(B)P(A|B)$, and interpret the answer in terms of the model.

HSS-CP.B.9 (+) Use permutations and combinations to compute probabilities of compound events and solve problems.

HSS-MD Using Probability to Make Decisions

HSS-MD.B.6 (+) Use probabilities to make fair decisions (e.g., drawing by lots, using a random number generator).

HSS-MD.B.7 (+) Analyze decisions and strategies using probability concepts (e.g., product testing, medical testing, pulling a hockey goalie at the end of a game).

Proof, Parallel and Perpendicular Lines

Unit Overview
In this unit you will begin the study of an axiomatic system, Geometry. You will investigate the concept of proof and discover the importance of proof in mathematics. You will extend your knowledge of the characteristics of angles and parallel and perpendicular lines and explore practical applications involving angles and lines.

Key Terms
As you study this unit, add these and other terms to your math notebook. Include in your notes your prior knowledge of each word, as well as your experiences in using the word in different mathematical examples. If needed, ask for help in pronouncing new words and add information on pronunciation to your math notebook. It is important that you learn new terms and use them correctly in your class discussions and in your problem solutions.

Academic Vocabulary
- compare and contrast
- justify
- argument
- interchange
- negate
- format
- confirm

Math Terms
- inductive reasoning
- conjecture
- deductive reasoning
- proof
- theorem
- axiomatic system
- undefined terms
- two-column proof
- conditional statement
- hypothesis
- conclusion
- counterexample
- converse
- inverse
- contrapositive
- truth value
- biconditional statement
- postulates
- midpoint
- congruent
- bisect
- bisector of an angle
- parallel
- transversal
- same-side interior angles
- alternate interior angles
- corresponding angles
- perpendicular
- perpendicular bisector

ESSENTIAL QUESTIONS

? Why are properties, postulates, and theorems important in mathematics?

? How are angles and parallel and perpendicular lines used in real-world settings?

EMBEDDED ASSESSMENTS

These assessments, following Activities 3, 5, and 8 will give you an opportunity to demonstrate what you have learned about reasoning, proof, and some basic geometric figures.

Embedded Assessment 1:

Geometric Figures and Basic Reasoning   p. 37

Embedded Assessment 2:

Distance, Midpoint, and Angle Measurement   p. 61

Embedded Assessment 3:

Angles, Parallel Lines, and Perpendicular Lines   p. 99

Write your answers on notebook paper.
Show your work.

1. Solve each equation.
   a. $5x - 2 = 8$
   b. $4x - 3 = 2x + 9$
   c. $6x + 3 = 2x + 8$

2. Graph $y = 3x - 3$ and label the x- and y-intercepts.

3. Tell the slope of a line that contains the points $(5, -3)$ and $(7, 3)$.

4. Write the equation of a line that has slope $\frac{1}{3}$ and y-intercept 4.

5. Write the equation of the line graphed below.

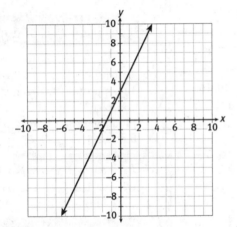

6. Describe a pattern shown in this sequence, and use the pattern to find the next two terms.

   7, 15, 23, 31, 39, __?__, __?__, . . .

7. Draw a right triangle and label the hypotenuse and legs.

8. Use a protractor to find the measure of each angle.

   a.

   b.
   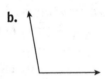

   c.

1a) $x = 2 \rightarrow 5(2) - 2 = 8 \checkmark$

1b) $x = 6$

1c) $x = 2\,3/4$

2) x-interce[
     y-interce[

$4x - 3 = 2x + 9$
$ +3 +3$
$4x = 2x + 12$
$-2x -2x$
$\dfrac{2x}{2} = \dfrac{12}{2}$
$\boxed{x = 6}$

Geometric Figures

What's My Name?
Lesson 1-1 Basic Geometric Figures

Learning Targets:

- Identify, describe, and name points, lines, line segments, rays, and planes using correct notation.
- Identify and name angles.

SUGGESTED LEARNING STRATEGIES: Activating Prior Knowledge, Think-Pair-Share, Group Presentation, Interactive Word Wall, Think Aloud, Debriefing, Self Revision/Peer Revision

Below are some types of figures you have seen in earlier mathematics courses. Describe each figure using your own words. If you can recall the mathematical terms that identify the figures, you can use them in your descriptions.

1.

2.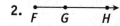

3.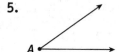

4.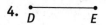

5.

6.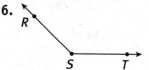

7.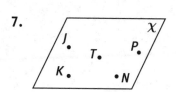

ACTIVITY 1
continued

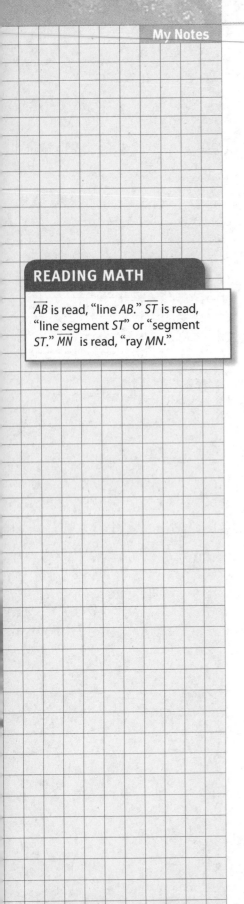

READING MATH

$\overleftrightarrow{AB}$ is read, "line *AB*." $\overline{ST}$ is read, "line segment *ST*" or "segment *ST*." $\overrightarrow{MN}$ is read, "ray *MN*."

Naming Geometric Figures

Geometric Figure	Naming	Example
point	Named with a capital letter	point *P* P•
line	Named using any two points on the line, in any order, with a line symbol drawn above OR Named using a lowercase letter	$\overleftrightarrow{AB}$, $\overleftrightarrow{BA}$, or line *m*
line segment	Named using the two endpoints, in any order, with a segment symbol drawn above	$\overline{ST}$ or $\overline{TS}$
ray	Named using the endpoint and one other point, with a ray symbol drawn above; the endpoint is always listed first	$\overrightarrow{MN}$
plane	Named using any three points in the plane that are not on the same line, in any order OR Named using a capital cursive letter	plane *FGH* or plane *Q*

8. Identify each geometric figure. Then give all possible names for the figure.

   a. •——————•
      Q   *P*

   b. ←•————•→
      N   *C*

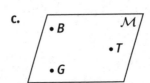

   c.

   d. *D* •

My Notes

9. Draw $\overrightarrow{FE}$. Explain where the points F and E lie on the ray.

10. **Critique the reasoning of others.** Caleb says that the figure below can be named $\overrightarrow{KJ}$. Jen says the figure can be named $\overrightarrow{JL}$. Who is correct? Explain.

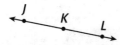

Check Your Understanding

11. Is $\overrightarrow{SR}$ a possible name for the figure at the right? Explain.

12. Graham draws a point. Describe how he could label and name the point.

There are three different ways to name an angle.

- Use the angle symbol and a number.
- Use the angle symbol and the vertex of the angle.
- Use the angle symbol and three points on the angle. The first point is on one side of the angle, the second point is the vertex, and the third point is on the other side of the angle.

MATH TIP

The *vertex* of an angle is the point where the sides of the angle meet, or intersect.

Example A
Give all possible names for the angle.

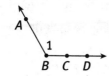

Use a number: $\angle 1$.

Use the vertex: $\angle B$.

Use three points. The second point should be the vertex. Be sure the first and third points are not on the same side.

$$\angle ABC, \angle ABD, \angle CBA, \angle DBA$$

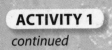

My Notes

Try These A
Give all possible names for each angle.

a.

b.

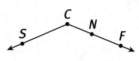

TECHNOLOGY TIP

You can make your drawing for
Item 13 by using a pencil and a
straightedge or by using geometry
software.

Check Your Understanding

13. Draw a figure that could be named ∠*LMN*.

14. Is ∠*FDE* a possible name for the figure at the right? Explain.

15. How many different line segments does the figure at the right include? Name them.

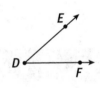

LESSON 1-1 PRACTICE

16. Identify each geometric figure. Then give all possible names for the figure.

a.

b.

c.

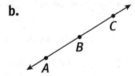

d.

The diagram below includes $\overrightarrow{RU}$. Use the figure for Items 17–19.

17. How many different rays does the figure include? Name them.

18. **Reason abstractly.** Explain why ∠*S* is not an appropriate name for ∠1.

19. Give the other possible appropriate names for ∠2.

20. Draw $\overleftrightarrow{LM}$. Then draw $\overrightarrow{NP}$ so that point *N* lies on $\overleftrightarrow{LM}$.

Learning Targets:
- Describe angles and angle pairs.
- Identify and name parts of circles.

> **SUGGESTED LEARNING STRATEGIES:** Think-Pair-Share, Self Revision/Peer Revision, Discussion Groups, Create Representations

As you share your ideas, be sure to use mathematical terms and academic vocabulary precisely. Make notes to help you remember the meaning of new words and how they are used to describe mathematical ideas.

1. Draw four angles with different characteristics. Describe each angle. Name the angles using numbers and letters.

2. *Compare and contrast* each pair of angles.

a.

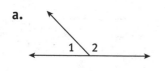

b.

c.

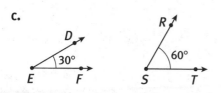

d.

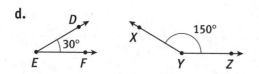

My Notes

ACADEMIC VOCABULARY

When you *compare and contrast* two figures, you describe how they are alike or different.

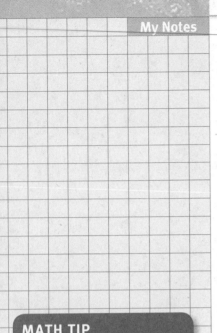

Recall that the sum of the measures of *complementary angles* is 90° and the sum of the measures of *supplementary angles* is 180°.

3. a. The figure below shows two intersecting lines. Name two angles that are supplementary to ∠4.

   b. Reason quantitatively. Explain why the angles you named in part a must have the same measure.

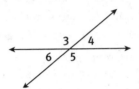

4. Complete the chart by naming all the listed angle types in each figure.

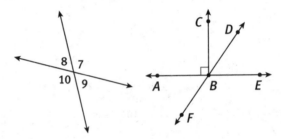

MATH TIP

Angles can be classified by their measures.

- An *acute angle* measures greater than 0° and less than 90°.
- A *right angle* measures 90°.
- An *obtuse angle* measures greater than 90° and less than 180°.
- A *straight angle* measures 180°.

Acute angles		
Obtuse angles		
Angles with the same measure		
Supplementary angles		
Complementary angles		

A *chord* of a circle is a segment with both endpoints on the circle.

A *diameter* is a chord that passes through the center of a circle.

A *radius* is a segment with one endpoint on the circle and one endpoint at the center of the circle.

5. In the circle below, draw and label each geometric term.

   a. radius *OA*

   b. chord *BA*

   c. diameter *CA*

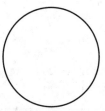

6. Refer to your drawings in the circle above. What is the geometric term for point *O*?

7. The circles below are concentric, meaning that they have the same center. The center of both circles is point *P*.

   a. Construct viable arguments. Explain why circle *P* is not an appropriate name for the smaller circle.

   b. Propose an alternate name for the smaller circle that would be appropriate. *Justify* your choice.

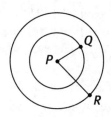

ACADEMIC VOCABULARY

When you *justify* a choice, you provide evidence that shows that your choice is correct or reasonable.

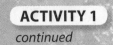
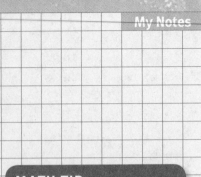

MATH TIP

You can use a compass to draw a circle. You can also use geometry software.

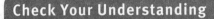

Check Your Understanding

8. Compare and contrast the terms *acute angle*, *obtuse angle*, *right angle*, and *straight angle*.

9. The measure of $\angle A$ is 42°.
   a. What is the measure of an angle that is complementary to $\angle A$?
   b. What is the measure of an angle that is supplementary to $\angle A$?

10. Draw a circle *P*.
    a. Draw a segment that has one endpoint on the circle but is not a chord.
    b. Draw a segment that intersects the circle in two points and contains the center but is not a radius, diameter, or chord.

LESSON 1-2 PRACTICE

11. Classify each segment in circle *O*. Use all terms that apply.

    a. $\overline{AF}$

    b. $\overline{BO}$

    c. $\overline{CO}$

    d. $\overline{DO}$

    e. $\overline{EO}$

    f. $\overline{CE}$

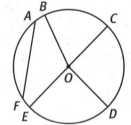

The figure below includes $\overleftrightarrow{PL}$ and $\overleftrightarrow{JM}$. Use the figure for Items 12–13.

12. Name three pairs of supplementary angles.

13. Name two angles that appear to be obtuse.

14. **Make sense of problems.** Can two obtuse angles be complementary to each other? Explain.

15. **Model with mathematics.** Is it possible for a pair of nonadjacent angles to share vertex *A* and arm $\overline{AB}$? If it is possible, draw an example. If it is not possible, explain your answer.

ACTIVITY 1 PRACTICE
Write your answers on notebook paper.
Show your work.

Lesson 1-1

1. Which is a correct name for this line?

    G   *E*   *M*

  A. $\vec{G}$ **B.** $\overline{GM}$

  C. $\overline{MG}$ **D.** $\overline{ME}$

2. Draw each figure.
  a. point *L*
  b. $\overrightarrow{MN}$
  c. $\overline{PQ}$
  d. plane $\mathcal{R}$
  e. $\overrightarrow{ST}$
  f. $\angle U$

3. Identify each geometric figure. Then give all possible names for the figure.
  a.

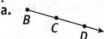

  b.

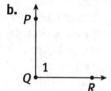

  c.

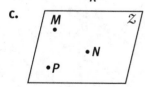

  d.

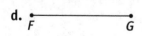

  e.

4. Describe all of the acceptable ways to name a plane.

5. What are some acceptable ways to name an angle?

6. Describe all of the acceptable ways to name a line.

7. **a.** How many rays are in the figure below? Name them.
    b. How many different angles are in the figure? Name them.

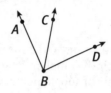

8. Describe the diagram below using correct geometric names.

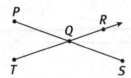

9. **a.** Explain why plane *JKL* is not an appropriate name for the plane below.
    b. Give three names for the plane that would be appropriate.

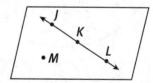

10. How can you use the figures in this activity to describe real-world objects and situations? Give examples.

Lesson 1-2

11. In this diagram, $m\angle SUT = 25°$.

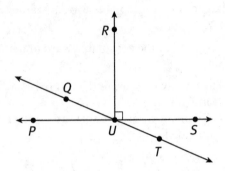

a. Name another angle that measures 25°.
b. Name a pair of complementary angles.
c. Name a pair of supplementary angles.

Use circle Q for Items 12–15.

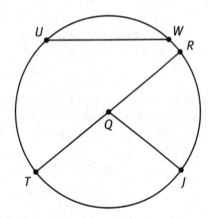

12. Name the radii of circle Q.

13. Name the diameter(s) in circle Q.

14. Name the chord(s) in circle Q.

15. Which statement below must be true about circle Q?
A. The distance from U to W is the same as the distance from R to T.
B. The distance from U to W is the same as the distance from Q to J.
C. The distance from R to T is half the distance from Q to R.
D. The distance from R to T is twice the distance from Q to J.

16. Two angles have the same measure. The angles are also supplementary. Are the angles acute, right, or obtuse? How do you know?

17. This diagram includes $\overleftrightarrow{KN}$, $\overleftrightarrow{SP}$, and $\overrightarrow{MR}$.

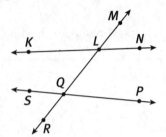

a. Name three angles that appear to be acute.
b. Name three angles that appear to be obtuse.
c. Name three straight angles.

18. $\angle F$ and $\angle G$ are complementary. The measure of $\angle F$ is four times the measure of $\angle G$. What is the measure of each angle?

19. Compare and contrast a chord and a diameter of a circle.

MATHEMATICAL PRACTICES
Construct Viable Arguments and Critique the Reasoning of Others

20. a. Lucinda describes the angle below as $\angle BAC$. Ahmad describes the angle as $\angle CBD$. State whether each of these names is appropriate for the angle, and explain why or why not.
b. Give another name for the angle, and explain why the name you chose is appropriate.

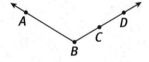

Logical Reasoning
Riddle Me This
Lesson 2-1 Inductive Reasoning

Learning Targets:

- Make conjectures by applying inductive reasoning.
- Recognize the limits of inductive reasoning.

> SUGGESTED LEARNING STRATEGIES: Interactive Word Wall, Vocabulary Organizer, Think-Pair-Share, Look for a Pattern, Visualization, Discussion Groups, Self Revision/Peer Revision

The ability to recognize patterns is an important aspect of mathematics. But when is an *observed* pattern actually a *real* pattern that continues beyond just the observed cases? In this activity, you will explore patterns and check to see if the patterns hold true beyond the observed cases.

Inductive reasoning is the process of observing data, recognizing patterns, and making a generalization. This generalization is a **conjecture**.

1. Five students attended a party and ate a variety of foods. Something caused some of them to become ill. JT ate a hamburger, pasta salad, and coleslaw. She became ill. Guy ate coleslaw and pasta salad but not a hamburger. He became ill. Dean ate only a hamburger and felt fine. Judy didn't eat anything and also felt fine. Cheryl ate a hamburger and pasta salad but no coleslaw, and she became ill. Use inductive reasoning to make a conjecture about which food probably caused the illness.

2. **Reason quantitatively.** Use inductive reasoning to make a conjecture about the next two terms in each sequence. Explain the pattern you used to determine the terms.

   a. A, 4, C, 8, E, 12, G, 16, _____, _____

   b. 3, 9, 27, 81, 243, _____, _____

   c. 3, 8, 15, 24, 35, 48, _____, _____

   d. 1, 1, 2, 3, 5, 8, 13, _____, _____

CONNECT TO HISTORY

The sequence of numbers in Item 2d is named after Leonardo of Pisa, who was known as Fibonacci. Fibonacci's 1202 book *Liber Abaci* introduced the sequence to Western European mathematics.

My Notes

3. Use the four circles below. From each of the given points, draw all possible chords. These chords will form a number of nonoverlapping regions in the interior of each circle. For each circle, count the number of these regions. Then enter this number in the appropriate place in the table below.

Number of Points on the Circle	Number of Nonoverlapping Regions Formed
2	
3	
4	
5	

4. Look for a pattern in the table above.

   a. Describe, in words, any patterns you see for the numbers in the column labeled Number of Nonoverlapping Regions Formed.

   b. Use the pattern that you described to predict the number of nonoverlapping regions that will be formed if you draw all possible line segments that connect six points on a circle.

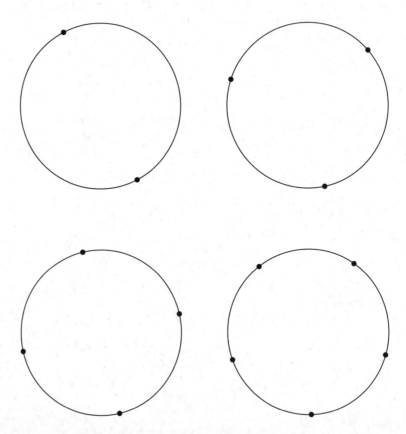

Check Your Understanding

5. **Critique the reasoning of others.** The diagram shows the first three figures in a pattern. Mario conjectures that the fourth figure in the pattern will be the third figure rotated 90° clockwise. Is Mario's conjecture reasonable? Explain.

6. Anya is training for a 10K race. The table shows the distance she ran during the first 3 weeks of training.

   a. Make a conjecture about the distance Anya will run during each practice of the fourth week.

   b. How could you test your conjecture?

Week	Distance per Practice (mi)
1	0.5
2	1.0
3	2.0

7. Use the circle on the next page. Draw all possible chords connecting any two of the six points.

   a. What is the number of nonoverlapping regions formed by chords connecting the points on this circle?

   b. Is the number you obtained above the same number you predicted from the pattern in the table in Item 4b?

   c. Describe what you would do to further investigate the pattern in the number of regions formed by chords joining *n* points on a circle, where *n* represents any number of points placed on a circle.

MATH TIP

Number the nonoverlapping regions as you count them. That way, you'll be sure not to skip any or count any more than once.

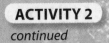

My Notes

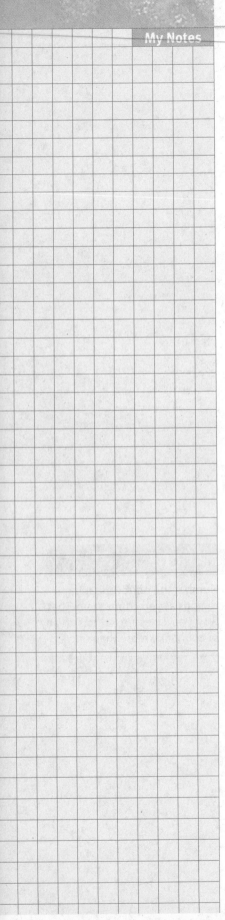

d. Make use of structure. Try to find a new pattern for predicting the number of regions formed by chords joining points on a circle when two, three, four, five, and six points are placed on a circle. Describe the pattern in algebraic terms or in words.

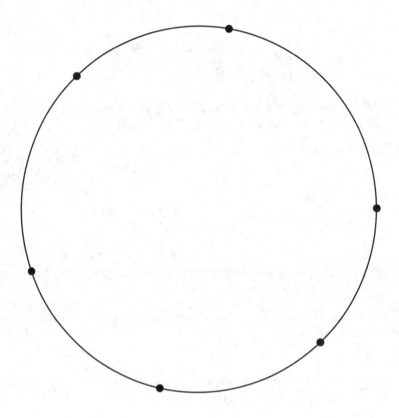

Check Your Understanding

8. Zack writes a conjecture that is true for the first few terms of a sequence. Is the conjecture necessarily true for *all* terms of the sequence? Explain.

9. The table below represents the function $f(x) = 2x + 5$. Based on the table, Trent conjectures that the value of $f(x)$ is always positive. Is Trent's conjecture true? Explain how you know.

x	−2	−1	0	1	2
$f(x)$	1	3	5	7	9

10. Monique tosses a coin three times. She gets heads each time. Based on this pattern, she makes a conjecture that she will always get heads when she tosses the coin. Do you think Monique's conjecture is reasonable? Why or why not?

> **MATH TIP**
>
> Recall that a *sequence* is an ordered list of numbers or other items. For example, 2, 4, 6, 8, 10, . . . is a sequence.

LESSON 2-1 PRACTICE

11. Use inductive reasoning to determine the next two terms in each sequence.

    a. $\dfrac{1}{2}, \dfrac{1}{4}, \dfrac{1}{8}, \dfrac{1}{16}, \ldots$

    b. A, B, D, G, K, . . .

12. Write the first five terms of two different sequences that have 10 as the second term. Describe the pattern in each of your sequences.

13. **Make sense of problems.** Generate a sequence using this description: The first term in the sequence is 4, and each other term is three more than twice the previous term.

14. The diagram shows the first three figures in a pattern. Each figure is made of small triangles. How many small triangles will be in the sixth figure of the pattern? Support your answer.

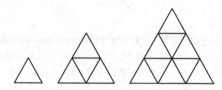

15. **Critique the reasoning of others.** The first two terms of a number pattern are 2 and 4. Alicia conjectures that the next term will be 6. Mario conjectures that the next term will be 8. Whose conjecture is reasonable? Explain.

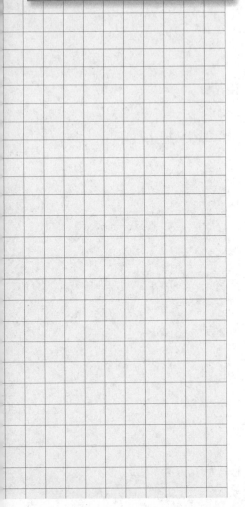

My Notes

ACADEMIC VOCABULARY

In this context, an argument is not a disagreement. Instead, an **argument** is a series of reasons or facts that support a given statement.

Learning Targets:

- Use deductive reasoning to prove that a conjecture is true.
- Develop geometric and algebraic arguments based on deductive reasoning.

> **SUGGESTED LEARNING STRATEGIES:** Interactive Word Wall, Vocabulary Organizer, Marking the Text, Think-Pair-Share, Look for a Pattern, Use Manipulatives, Discussion Groups, Summarizing, Paraphrasing, Create Representations, Group Presentation

In this activity, you have described patterns and made conjectures about how these patterns would extend beyond your observed cases, based on collected data. Some of your conjectures were probably shown to be untrue when additional data were collected. Other conjectures took on a greater sense of certainty as more confirming data were collected.

In mathematics, there are certain methods and rules of *argument* that mathematicians use to convince someone that a conjecture is true, even for cases that extend beyond the observed data set. These rules are called rules of logical reasoning or rules of *deductive reasoning*. An argument that follows such rules is called a *proof*. A statement or conjecture that has been proven, that is, established as true without a doubt, is called a *theorem*. A proof transforms a conjecture into a theorem.

Below are some definitions from arithmetic.

Even integer: An integer that has a remainder of 0 when it is divided by 2.

Odd integer: An integer that has a remainder of 1 when it is divided by 2.

Express regularity in repeated reasoning. In the following items, you will make some conjectures about the sums of even and odd integers.

1. Calculate the sum of some pairs of even integers. Show the examples you use and make a conjecture about the sum of two even integers.

2. Calculate the sum of some pairs of odd integers. Show the examples you use and make a conjecture about the sum of two odd integers.

3. Calculate the sum of pairs of integers consisting of one even integer and one odd integer. Show the examples you use and make a conjecture about the sum of an even integer and an odd integer.

The following items will help you write a convincing argument (a proof) that supports each of the conjectures you made in Items 1–3.

4. Figures A, B, C, and D are puzzle pieces. Each figure represents an integer determined by counting the square pieces in the figure. Use these figures to answer the following questions.

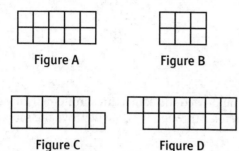

Figure A   Figure B

Figure C   Figure D

a. Which of the figures can be used to model an even integer?

b. Which of the figures can be used to model an odd integer?

c. Compare and contrast the models of even and odd integers.

5. **Model with mathematics.** Which pairs of puzzle pieces can fit together to form rectangles? Make sketches to show how they fit.

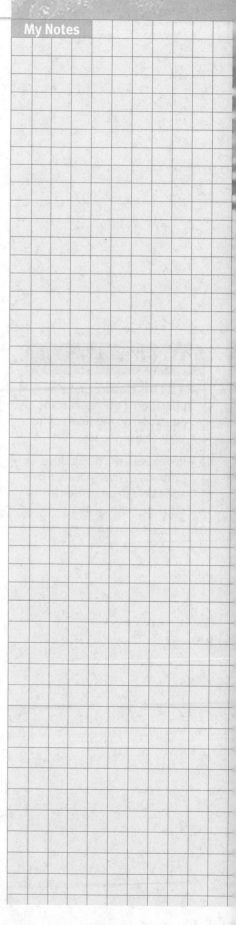

My Notes

6. Explain how the figures (when used as puzzle pieces) can be used to show that each of the conjectures in Items 1 through 3 is true.

In Items 5 and 6, you proved the conjectures in Items 1 through 3 geometrically. In Items 7 through 9, you will prove the same conjectures algebraically.

This is an algebraic definition of even integer: An integer is *even* if and only if it can be written in the form $2p$, where p is an integer. (You can use other variables, such as $2m$, to represent an even integer, where m is an integer.)

7. Reason abstractly. Use the expressions $2p$ and $2m$, where p and m are integers, to confirm the conjecture that the sum of two even integers is an even integer.

MATH TIP

- A set has **closure** under an operation if the result of the operation on members of the set is also in the same set.

- In symbols, the distributive property of multiplication over addition can be written as $a(b + c) = a(b) + a(c)$.

This is an algebraic definition of odd integer: An integer is *odd* if and only if it can be written in the form $2t + 1$, where t is an integer. (Again, you do not have to use t as the variable.)

8. Use expressions for odd integers to confirm the conjecture that the sum of two odd integers is an even integer.

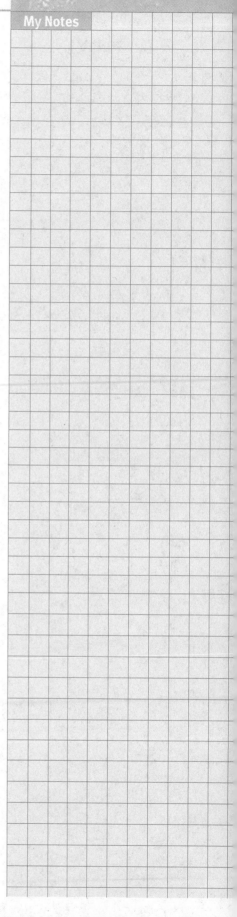

9. Use expressions for even and odd integers to confirm the conjecture that the sum of an even integer and an odd integer is an odd integer.

In Items 5 and 6, you developed a geometric puzzle-piece argument to confirm conjectures about the sums of even and odd integers. In Items 7–9, you developed an algebraic argument to confirm these same conjectures. Even though one method is considered geometric and the other algebraic, they are often seen as the same basic argument.

10. Construct viable arguments. Explain the link between the geometric and the algebraic methods of the proof.

11. State three theorems that you have proved about the sums of even and odd integers.

Check Your Understanding

12. Compare and contrast a theorem and a conjecture.

13. Todd knows that 3, 5, 7, 11, and 13 are prime numbers. Based on this evidence, he concludes that all prime numbers are odd.

    a. Is this an example of inductive or deductive reasoning? Explain.

    b. Is Todd's conclusion correct? Support your answer.

14. Shayla knows that all rectangles have four right angles. She also knows that figure *ABCD* is a rectangle. She concludes that figure *ABCD* has four right angles.

    a. Is this an example of inductive or deductive reasoning? Explain.

    b. **Critique the reasoning of others.** Is Shayla's conclusion correct? Support your answer.

LESSON 2-2 PRACTICE

15. Use expressions for even and odd integers to confirm the conjecture that the product of an even integer and an odd integer is an even integer.

16. **Reason abstractly.** Prove this conjecture geometrically: Any odd integer can be expressed as the sum of an even integer and an odd integer.

17. Use deductive reasoning to prove that the solution of the equation $x - 5 = -2$ is $x = 3$. Be sure to justify each step in your proof.

18. **Reason quantitatively.** Based solely on the pattern in the table, Andre states that the number of sides of a polygon is equal to its number of angles. Is Andre's statement a conjecture or a theorem? Explain.

Polygon	Sides	Angles
Triangle	3	3
Quadrilateral	4	4
Pentagon	5	5

19. Hairs found at a crime scene are consistent with those of a suspect. Based on this evidence, an investigator concludes that the suspect was at the crime scene. Is this an example of inductive or deductive reasoning? Explain.

ACTIVITY 2 PRACTICE
Write your answers on notebook paper.
Show your work.

Lesson 2-1

1. Use inductive reasoning to determine the next two terms in the sequence.
   a. 1, 3, 7, 15, 31, …
   b. 3, −6, 12, −24, 48, …

2. Write the first five terms of two different sequences for which 24 is the third term.

3. Generate a sequence using this description: The first term in the sequence is 2, and the terms increase by consecutive odd numbers beginning with 3.

4. Use this picture pattern.

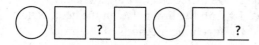

   a. Draw the next shape in the pattern.
   b. Write a sequence of numbers that could be used to express the pattern.
   c. Verbally describe the pattern of the sequence.

5. Two shapes are missing from the sequence below.

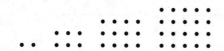

   a. Based on the given shapes, make a conjecture about the missing shapes. Explain the pattern you used to make your conjecture.
   b. Now suppose that you learn that the first missing shape is a triangle. Would this additional information change your conjecture about the other missing shape? Explain.

6. Describe a situation from your everyday life in which you applied inductive reasoning.

7. Kristen divides each convex polygon below into triangles by drawing all diagonals from a single vertex. She conjectures that the number of triangles is always two less than the number of sides of the convex polygon.

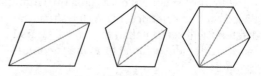

   a. Is Kristen's conjecture reasonable? Explain.
   b. Provide an additional example that supports your answer to Item 7a.

8. Which rule describes how to find the next term of the following sequence?

   64, 40, 28, 22, 19, . . .

   A. Subtract 24 from the previous term.
   B. Divide the previous term by 2 and add 8.
   C. Divide the previous term by 4 and add 16.
   D. Multiply the previous term by 5 and divide by 8.

9. Explain how you know that the rules you did not choose in Item 8 are incorrect.

10. Use this picture pattern.

   a. Draw the next shape in the pattern.
   b. Write a sequence of numbers that could be used to express the pattern.
   c. Verbally describe the pattern of the sequence.

Lesson 2-2

11. Use expressions for odd integers to confirm the conjecture that the product of two odd integers is an odd integer.

12. For the first four weeks of school, the cafeteria served either spaghetti or lasagna on Thursday. Based on this evidence, Liam states that the cafeteria will serve Italian food next Thursday. Is Liam's statement a conjecture or a theorem? Explain.

13. Use deductive reasoning to prove that $x = -3$ is not in the solution set of the inequality $-4x < 8$. Be sure to justify each step in your proof.

14. David notices this pattern.

$$19 = 1 \times 9 + 1 + 9$$
$$29 = 2 \times 9 + 2 + 9$$
$$39 = 3 \times 9 + 3 + 9$$

Based on this pattern, David concludes that any two-digit number ending in 9 is equal to $n \times 9 + n + 9$, where n is the tens digit of the number.
  a. Is this an example of inductive or deductive reasoning? Explain.
  b. Is David's conclusion correct? Support your answer.

15. The density of gold is 19.3 grams per cubic centimeter. Rachel determines that the density of a coin is 18.7 grams per cubic centimeter. Based on this evidence, she concludes that the coin is not gold or at least not entirely gold. Is this an example of inductive or deductive reasoning? Explain.

16. Consider the expression $3p + 5$. Bethany states that this expression is even for any integer p because $3p + 5 = 8$ when $p = 1$ and $3p + 5 = 20$ when $p = 5$. Is Bethany's conclusion correct? Support your answer.

17. Consider these true statements.

  All amphibians are cold blooded.

  All frogs are amphibians.

  Chris has a pet frog.

Based on deductive reasoning, which of the following statements is *not* necessarily true?
  A. Chris has a cold-blooded pet.
  B. Chris has a pet amphibian.
  C. All frogs are cold blooded.
  D. All amphibians are frogs.

18. Consider this conjecture: An integer that is divisible by 9 is also divisible by 3.
  a. Prove the conjecture geometrically. (Hint: You can represent an integer divisible by 9 by using a rectangle composed of groups of 9 squares, as shown below.)

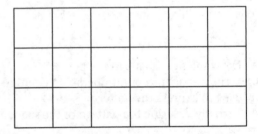

  b. Prove the conjecture algebraically.
  c. Explain the link between the geometric and the algebraic methods of the proof.

MATHEMATICAL PRACTICES
Construct Viable Arguments and Critique the Reasoning of Others

19. a. Construct a viable argument for this conjecture: If two angles are complementary, both angles must be acute.
  b. What type of reasoning—inductive or deductive—did you use in your argument? Explain.
  c. Compare your argument with the argument another student in your group or class has written. Do you agree with this student's argument? Why or why not?

The Axiomatic System of Geometry

Back to the Beginning

Lesson 3-1 Geometric Definitions and Two-Column Proofs

Learning Targets:

- Distinguish between undefined and defined terms.
- Use properties to complete algebraic two-column proofs.

SUGGESTED LEARNING STRATEGIES: Close Reading, Quickwrite, Think-Pair-Share, Vocabulary Organizer, Interactive Word Wall, Group Presentation, Discussion Groups, Self Revision/Peer Revision

Geometry is an *axiomatic system*. That means that from a small, basic set of agreed-upon assumptions and premises, an entire structure of logic is devised. Many interactive computer games are designed with this kind of structure. A game may begin with a basic set of scenarios. From these scenarios, a gamer can devise tools and strategies to win the game.

In geometry, it is necessary to agree on clear-cut meanings, or definitions, for words used in a technical manner. For a definition to be helpful, it must be expressed in words whose meanings are already known and understood.

Compare the following definitions.

Fountain: a roundel that is barry wavy of six argent and azure

Guige: a belt that is worn over the right shoulder and used to support a shield

1. Which of the two definitions above is easier to understand? Why?

For a new vocabulary term to be helpful, it should be defined using words that have already been defined. The *first* definitions used in building a system, however, cannot be defined in terms of other vocabulary words, because no other vocabulary words have been defined yet. In geometry, it is traditional to start with the simplest and most fundamental terms—without trying to define them—and use these terms to define other terms and develop the system of geometry. These fundamental *undefined terms* are **point**, **line**, and **plane**.

2. Define each term using the undefined terms.
   a. **Ray**

   b. **Collinear points**

   c. **Coplanar points**

MATH TERMS

The term *line segment* can be defined in terms of **undefined terms:** A *line segment* is part of a line bounded by two points on the line called *endpoints*.

My Notes

MATH TIP

The common endpoint of the rays that form an angle is the *vertex* of the angle.

After a term has been defined, it can be used to define other terms. For example, an **angle** is defined as a figure formed by two rays with a common endpoint.

3. Define each term using the already defined terms.
   a. **Complementary angles**

   b. **Supplementary angles**

The process of deductive reasoning, or deduction, must have a starting point. A conclusion based on deduction cannot be made unless there is an established assertion to work from. To provide a starting point for the process of deduction, a number of assertions are accepted as true without proof.

When you solve algebraic equations, you are using deduction. You can use properties to support your reasoning without having to prove that the properties are true.

4. Using one operation or property per step, show how to solve the equation $4x + 9 = 18 - \frac{1}{2}x$. Name each operation or property used to justify each step.

CONNECT TO ALGEBRA

Addition Property of Equality
If $a = b$ and $c = d$,
then $a + c = b + d$.

Subtraction Property of Equality
If $a = b$ and $c = d$,
then $a - c = b - d$.

Multiplication Property of Equality
If $a = b$, then $ca = cb$.

Division Property of Equality
If $a = b$ and $c \neq 0$, then $\frac{a}{c} = \frac{b}{c}$.

Distributive Property
$a(b + c) = ab + ac$

Reflexive Property
$a = a$

Symmetric Property
If $a = b$, then $b = a$.

Transitive Property
If $a = b$ and $b = c$, then $a = c$.

Substitution Property
If $a = b$, then a can be substituted for b in any equation or inequality.

You can organize the steps and the reasons used to justify the steps in two columns with statements (steps) on the left and reasons (properties) on the right. This format is called a *two-column proof*.

Example A

Given: $3(x + 2) - 1 = 5x + 11$ **Prove:** $x = -3$

Statements	Reasons
1. $3(x + 2) - 1 = 5x + 11$	1. Given equation
2. $3(x + 2) = 5x + 12$	2. Addition Property of Equality
3. $3x + 6 = 5x + 12$	3. Distributive Property
4. $6 = 2x + 12$	4. Subtraction Property of Equality
5. $-6 = 2x$	5. Subtraction Property of Equality
6. $-3 = x$	6. Division Property of Equality
7. $x = -3$	7. Symmetric Property of Equality

Try These A

a. Supply the reasons to justify each statement in the proof below.

Given: $\dfrac{x - 3}{2} = \dfrac{6 + x}{5}$ **Prove:** $x = 9$

Statements	Reasons
1. $\dfrac{x - 3}{2} = \dfrac{6 + x}{5}$	1. _____
2. $10\left(\dfrac{x - 3}{2}\right) = 10\left(\dfrac{6 + x}{5}\right)$	2. _____
3. $5(x - 3) = 2(6 + x)$	3. _____
4. $5x - 15 = 12 + 2x$	4. _____
5. $3x - 15 = 12$	5. _____
6. $3x = 27$	6. _____
7. $x = 9$	7. _____

b. Complete the *Prove* statement and write a two-column proof for the equation given in Item 4. Number each statement and corresponding reason.

Given: $4x + 9 = 18 - \dfrac{1}{2}x$

Prove:

DISCUSSION GROUP TIP

As you read and discuss the two-column proof in Example A, ask and answer questions to be sure you have a clear understanding of not only all the terminology used, but also how the two-column proof is formed.

MATH TIP

In Item b, the *Prove* statement should be the solution of the given equation. In this case, it may be easier to write the statements and reasons of the proof before writing the *Prove* statement.

My Notes

Check Your Understanding

5. Explain why undefined terms are necessary in geometry.

6. **Express regularity in repeated reasoning.** What is the relationship between a conjecture, a theorem, and a two-column proof?

7. Jeffrey wrote a two-column proof to solve the equation $3(x + 5) = -6x + 6$. In addition to an incorrectly written *Prove* statement, what error did Jeffrey make in his proof? Rewrite the proof so that it correctly shows how to solve the given equation.

Given: $3(x + 5) = -6x + 6$ **Prove:** $x = -81$

Statements	Reasons
1. $3(x + 5) = -6x + 6$	**1.** Given equation
2. $3x + 15 = -6x + 6$	**2.** Distributive Property
3. $9x + 15 = 6$	**3.** Addition Property of Equality
4. $\quad 9x = -9$	**4.** Subtraction Property of Equality
5. $\quad x = -81$	**5.** Multiplication Property of Equality

LESSON 3-1 PRACTICE

8. Identify the property that justifies the statement: If $4x - 3 = 7$, then $4x = 10$.

9. Complete the prove statement and write a two-column proof for the equation:

   Given: $x - 2 = 3(x - 4)$ Prove:

10. **Construct viable arguments.** Explain why *line segment* is considered a defined term in geometry.

11. Complete the prove statement and write a two-column proof for the equation:

    Given: $2n - 21 = \dfrac{n}{4}$ Prove:

12. **Look for and make use of structure.** Suppose you are given that $a = b + 2$ and $b + 2 = 5$. What can you prove by using these statements and the Transitive Property?

Learning Targets:

- Identify the hypothesis and conclusion of a conditional statement.
- Give counterexamples for false conditional statements.

> **SUGGESTED LEARNING STRATEGIES:** Vocabulary Organizer, Interactive Word Wall, Marking the Text, Self Revision/Peer Revision, Discussion Groups

Rules of logical reasoning involve using a set of given statements along with a valid argument to reach a conclusion. Statements to be proved are often written in if-then form. An if-then statement is called a ***conditional statement***. In such statements, the *if* clause is the ***hypothesis***, and the *then* clause is the ***conclusion***.

Example A

| Conditional statement: If $3(x + 2) - 1 = 5x + 11$, then $x = -3$. ||
Hypothesis	**Conclusion**
$3(x + 2) - 1 = 5x + 11$	$x = -3$

Try These A

Use the conditional statement: If $x + 7 = 10$, then $x = 3$.
a. What is the hypothesis?

b. What is the conclusion?

c. State the property of equality that justifies the conclusion of the statement.

Conditional statements may not always be written in if-then form. You can restate such conditional statements in if-then form.

1. **Make use of structure.** Restate each conditional statement in if-then form.
   a. I'll go if you go.

   b. There is smoke only if there is fire.

   c. $x = 4$ implies $x^2 = 16$.

WRITING MATH

The letters p and q are often used to represent the hypothesis and conclusion, respectively, in a conditional statement. The basic form of an if-then statement would then be, "If p, then q."

READING MATH

Forms of conditional statements include:
- If p, then q.
- p only if q
- p implies q.
- q if p

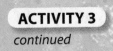

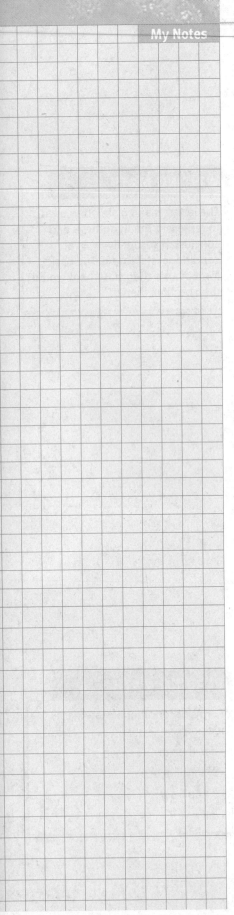

An if-then statement is false if an example can be found for which the hypothesis is true and the conclusion is false. This type of example is a **counterexample**.

2. This is a false conditional statement.

   If two numbers are odd, then their sum is odd.

   a. Identify the hypothesis of the statement.

   b. Identify the conclusion of the statement.

   c. Give a counterexample for the conditional statement and justify your choice for this example.

Check Your Understanding

3. **Reason abstractly.** If you can find an example for which both the hypothesis and the conclusion of a conditional statement are true, is the conditional statement itself necessarily true? Explain.

4. Give an example of a true conditional statement that includes this hypothesis: An angle is named $\angle ABC$.

5. Give an example of a true conditional statement that includes this conclusion: The angles share a vertex.

6. Cesar conjectures that the quotient of any two even numbers greater than 0 is odd.

   a. Write Cesar's conjecture as a conditional statement.

   b. Give a counterexample to show that Cesar's conjecture is false.

7. Write the definition of *collinear points* as a conditional statement.

LESSON 3-2 PRACTICE

8. Write the statement in if-then form:

Two angles have measures that add up to 90° only if they are complements of each other.

9. Which of the following is a counterexample of this statement?

If an angle is acute, then it measures 80°.

A. a 100° angle   **B.** a 90° angle
C. an 80° angle   **D.** a 70° angle

10. Identify the hypothesis and the conclusion of the statement:

If it is not raining, then I will go to the park.

11. Critique the reasoning of others. Joanna says that $4 + 7 = 11$ is a counterexample that shows that the following conditional statement is false. Is Joanna correct? Explain.

If two integers are even, then their sum is even.

12. Construct viable arguments. Why do you only need a single counterexample to show that a conditional statement is false?

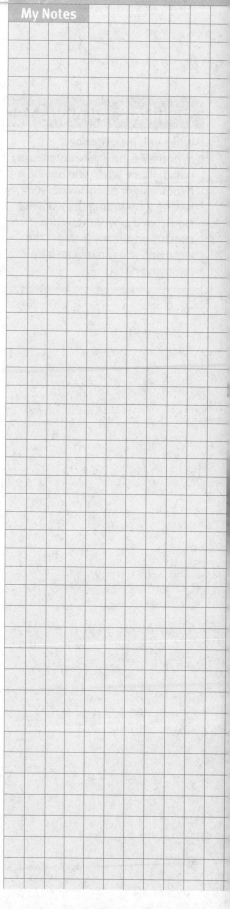

ACTIVITY 3
continued

Learning Targets:

- Write and determine the truth value of the converse, inverse, and contrapositive of a conditional statement.
- Write and interpret biconditional statements.

SUGGESTED LEARNING STRATEGIES: Vocabulary Organizer, Interactive Word Wall, Think-Pair-Share, Group Presentation, Discussion Groups

Every conditional statement has three related conditionals. These are the *converse*, the *inverse*, and the *contrapositive* of the conditional statement. The converse of a conditional is formed by *interchanging* the hypothesis and conclusion of the statement. The inverse is formed by *negating* both the hypothesis and the conclusion. Finally, the contrapositive is formed by interchanging *and* negating both the hypothesis and the conclusion.

Conditional:	If p, then q.
Converse:	If q, then p.
Inverse:	If not p, then not q.
Contrapositive:	If not q, then not p.

1. Given the conditional statement:

If a figure is a triangle, then it is a polygon.

Complete the table.

Form of the statement	Write the statement	True or False?	If the statement is false, give a counterexample.
Conditional statement	If a figure is a triangle, then it is a polygon.		
Converse of the conditional statement			
Inverse of the conditional statement			
Contrapositive of the conditional statement			

ACADEMIC VOCABULARY

When you *interchange* a hypothesis and a conclusion, you switch them. When you *negate* a hypothesis or a conclusion, you rewrite it by adding the word *not*. Note that if a hypothesis or a conclusion already includes the word *not*, you can negate it by removing *not*.

If a given conditional statement is true, the converse and inverse are not necessarily true. However, the contrapositive of a true conditional is always true, and the contrapositive of a false conditional is always false. Likewise, the converse and inverse of a conditional are either both true or both false. Statements with the same ***truth values*** are *logically equivalent*.

2. Write a true conditional statement whose inverse is false.

3. Write a true conditional statement that is logically equivalent to its converse.

When a statement and its converse are both true, they can be combined into one statement using the words "if and only if." An "if and only if" statement is a ***biconditional statement***. All definitions you have learned can be written as biconditional statements.

4. Write the definition of perpendicular lines in biconditional form.

5. Consider the statement: *Numbers that do not end in 2 are not even.*
   a. Rewrite the statement in if-then form and state whether it is true or false.

   b. Write the converse and state whether it is true or false. If false, give a counterexample.

   c. Write the inverse and state whether it is true or false.

   d. Write the contrapositive and state whether it is true or false. If false, give a counterexample.

   e. Can you write a biconditional statement for the original statement? Why or why not?

MATH TERMS

The **truth value** of a statement is the truth or falsity of that statement.

MATH TIP

Given the biconditional statement "p if and only if q," then the following conditional statements are true.

- If p, then q.
- If q, then p.
- If not p, then not q.
- If not q, then not p.

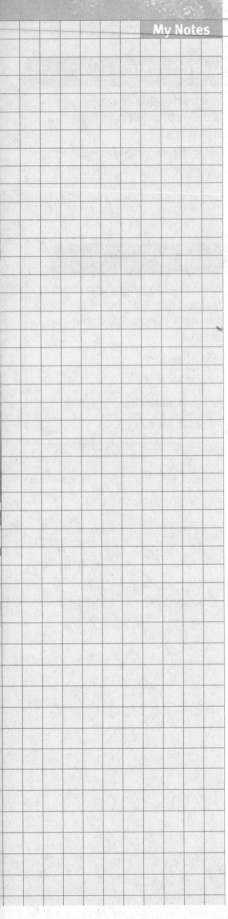

Check Your Understanding

6. Write four true conditional statements based on this biconditional statement.

   An angle is a right angle if and only if it measures 90°.

7. A conditional statement is true, and its inverse is false. What can you conclude about the converse and the contrapositive of the conditional statement?

8. **Make use of structure.** Are these two statements logically equivalent? Explain.

   If a polygon is a square, then it is a quadrilateral.

   If a polygon is a quadrilateral, then it is a square.

9. **Critique the reasoning of others.** Toby says that the converse of the following statement is true. Is Toby's reasoning correct? Explain.

   If a number is divisible by 6, then it is divisible by 2.

10. Consider this statement.

    All birds have wings.

    a. Write the statement as a conditional statement.

    b. Can you write the statement as a biconditional statement? Explain.

LESSON 3-3 PRACTICE

Use the following statement for Items 11–13.

If a vehicle has four wheels, then it is a car.

11. Write the converse.

12. Write the inverse.

13. Write the contrapositive.

14. Write the definition of the vertex of an angle as a biconditional statement.

15. Give an example of a true statement that has a false converse.

16. **Reason abstractly.**

    Given: (1) If *X* is blue, then *Y* is gold.

    (2) *Y* is not gold.

    Which of the following *must* be true?
    A. *Y* is blue.   **B.** *Y* is not blue.
    C. *X* is not blue.   **D.** *X* is gold.

ACTIVITY 3 PRACTICE
Write your answers on notebook paper.
Show your work.

Lesson 3-1

1. Identify the property that justifies the statement:
   $5(x - 3) = 5x - 15$
   A. multiplication **B.** transitive
   C. subtraction **D.** distributive

2. **a.** Give an example of an undefined term and a defined term in geometry.
   b. Explain the difference between an undefined term and a defined term.

3. How is a definition different from a theorem?

4. What are the missing reasons and statements in the two-column proof?

Given: $\dfrac{2x}{4} = \dfrac{5x + 8}{2}$ **Prove:** $x = -2$

Statements	Reasons
1. _____a._____	1. Given equation
2. $2x = 2(5x + 8)$	2. _____b._____
3. _____c._____	3. Distributive Property
4. $0 = 8x + 16$	4. _____d._____
5. _____e._____	5. Subtraction Property of Equality
6. $-2 = x$	6. _____f._____
7. _____g._____	7. Symmetric Property

For Items 5 and 6, complete the prove statement and write a two-column proof for the equation.

5. Given: $5(x - 2) = 2x - 4$ Prove:

6. Given: $\dfrac{4c - 6}{3} = 8$ Prove:

7. Suppose you are given that $a = 5$ and $4a + b = 6$. What can you prove by using these statements and the Substitution Property?

Lesson 3-2

For Items 8–10, write each statement in if-then form.

8. Dianna will go to the movie if she finishes her homework.

9. $m\angle G = 40°$ implies $\angle G$ is acute.

10. A figure is a triangle only if it is a polygon with three sides.

11. State the hypothesis and the conclusion of this conditional statement.

    If the temperature drops below 65°F, then the swimming pool closes.

12. Given the false conditional statement, "If a vehicle is built to fly, then it is an airplane," write a counterexample.

13. Dustin says that $8 \cdot -1 = 8$ is a counterexample that shows that the following conditional statement is false. Is Dustin correct? Explain.

    If two integers are multiplied, then the product is greater than both integers.

14. Given that the hypothesis of the following conditional statement is true, which statement must also be true?

    If Margo wears gloves or a scarf, then she wears a coat.
    A. Margo is wearing a coat.
    B. Margo is wearing gloves.
    C. Margo is not wearing a coat.
    D. Margo is not wearing gloves.

15. **a.** Write a true conditional statement that includes this hypothesis: $-3x + 10 = -5$.
    b. Write a two-column proof to prove that your conditional statement is true.

Lesson 3-3

Use this statement for Items 16–19.

If today is Thursday, then tomorrow is Friday.

16. Write the converse of the statement.

17. Write the inverse of the statement.

18. Write the contrapositive of the statement.

19. Can the conditional statement be written as a biconditional statement? If so, write the biconditional statement. If not, explain why not.

20. A certain conditional statement is true. Which of the following must also be true?
  A. converse   **B.** inverse
  C. contrapositive   **D.** all of the above

21. Give an example of a statement that is false and logically equivalent to its inverse.

22. Compare and contrast a true conditional statement and a biconditional statement.

For Items 23–26, tell whether each statement is true or false. If it is false, give a counterexample.

23. If a number is a multiple of 8, then it is a multiple of 4.

24. the converse of the statement in Item 23

25. the inverse of the statement in Item 23

26. the contrapositive of the statement in Item 23

27. The following statement is the contrapositive of a conditional statement. What is the original conditional statement?

  If a parallelogram does not have four right angles, then it is not a rectangle.

28. Consider this conditional statement.

  If two numbers are negative, then their sum is less than both numbers.

  Lorenzo says that the inverse of the statement can be written as follows.

  If two numbers are positive, then their sum is greater than both numbers.

  Is Lorenzo's reasoning correct? Explain.

Use this statement for Items 29–32.

If the sum of the measures of two angles is 90°, then the angles are complementary.

29. Write the inverse of the converse of the statement.

30. What is another name for the inverse of the converse?

31. Write the contrapositive of the inverse of the statement.

32. What is another name for the contrapositive of the inverse?

MATHEMATICAL PRACTICES
Attend to Precision

33. Write a clear definition of the term *adjacent angles.* Then use your definition to explain why ∠KJL and ∠LJM are adjacent angles but ∠KJL and ∠KJM are not adjacent angles.

Geometric Figures and Basic Reasoning

THE ART AND MATH OF FOLDING PAPER

Origami is the art of paper folding. In traditional origami, a single sheet of paper is folded to create a three-dimensional design, such as a crane, a dragon, or a flower. Origami also has practical applications. For example, origami has been used to fold car airbags efficiently so that they will inflate correctly in an accident.

Origami designs make use of geometric figures such as points, lines, rays, segments, and angles.

1. The diagrams at the right show how you can use origami to construct an equilateral triangle from a rectangular sheet of paper. Describe each step in words as precisely as possible, using correct geometric notation. The first step has been done for you.

    Step 1: Fold rectangle $ABCD$ along a line so that $\overline{AB}$ aligns on top of $\overline{CD}$. Then unfold. The fold creates $\overline{EF}$.

2. The diagram below shows $\triangle GAD$ from the beginning of Step 3. Based on this diagram, $m\angle AGD + 90° + 30° = 180°$.

    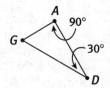

    Complete the *Prove* statement and write a two-column proof for the equation.

    Given: $m\angle AGD + 90° + 30° = 180°$

    Prove:

3. Consider this statement: "A triangle is equilateral if it has three sides with the same length."
    a. Write the statement in if-then form. Identify the hypothesis and conclusion.
    b. Write the converse, inverse, and contrapositive of the conditional statement. Which are true?
    c. Can the conditional statement be written as a biconditional statement? Explain.

Step 1

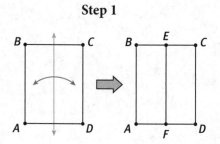

Step 2

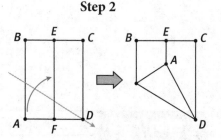

Step 3

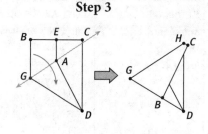

Step 4

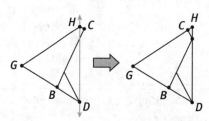

$\triangle GHD$ is equilateral.

4. Suppose you start with a stack of printer paper that is 0.02 inch thick. The table shows the thickness of the stack after folding the paper in half several times.

Number of Folds	1	2	3	4	5
Thickness (in.)	0.04	0.08	0.16	0.32	0.64

a. Make a conjecture about the thickness of the stack after folding the paper in half six times. Explain the pattern you used to determine your answer.

b. Did you use inductive or deductive reasoning to make your conjecture? Explain.

c. Ellis claims that he could fold a sheet of printer paper in half 25 times. Is his claim realistic? Support your answer.

Scoring Guide	Exemplary	Proficient	Emerging	Incomplete
	The solution demonstrates these characteristics:			
Mathematics Knowledge and Thinking (Items 1, 3, 4b)	• Clear and accurate use of geometric vocabulary and notation, including line and line segment • Accuracy in writing the converse, inverse, and contrapositive of a statement • Clear and accurate understanding of hypothesis, conclusion, bi-conditional statements, and inductive and deductive reasoning	• A functional understanding of geometric vocabulary and notation, including line and line segment • Mostly correct statements of converse, inverse and contrapositive of a statement • Adequate understanding of hypothesis, conclusion, bi-conditional statements, and inductive and deductive reasoning	• Partial understanding of geometric vocabulary and notation, including line and line segment • Somewhat correct statements of converse, inverse and contrapositive of a statement • Partial understanding of hypothesis, conclusion, bi-conditional statements, and inductive and deductive reasoning	• Inaccurate or incomplete explanation of steps needed to construct an equilateral triangle • Incorrect or incomplete statements of converse, inverse and contrapositive of a statement • Little or no understanding of hypothesis, conclusion, bi-conditional statements, and inductive and deductive reasoning
Problem Solving (Items 2, 4a, 4c)	• An appropriate and efficient strategy that results in a correct answer	• A strategy that may include unnecessary steps but results in a correct answer	• A strategy that results in some incorrect answers	• No clear strategy when solving problems
Mathematical Modeling / Representations (Items 3a, 4a)	• Effective understanding of how to write a conditional statement, and how to interpret and make conjectures from a data table	• Largely correct understanding of how to write a conditional statement, and how to interpret and make conjectures from a data table	• Partial understanding of writing a conditional statement, and making a conjecture from a data table	• Inaccurate or incomplete understanding of how to write a conditional statement, and how to make a conjecture from a data table.
Reasoning and Communication (Items 1, 2)	• Precise use of appropriate math terms and language to describe the steps necessary to fold the paper • Clear and accurate prove statement and proof	• Adequate understanding of geometric vocabulary and notation needed to describe the steps necessary to fold the paper • Mostly correct prove statement and proof	• Misleading or confusing geometric vocabulary and notation needed to describe the steps necessary to fold the paper • Partially correct prove statement and proof	• Incomplete or inaccurate vocabulary and notation needed to describe the steps necessary to fold the paper • Inaccurate or incomplete prove statement and proof

Segment and Angle Measurement

It All Adds Up
Lesson 4-1 Segments and Midpoints

Learning Targets:
- Apply the Segment Addition Postulate to find lengths of segments.
- Use the definition of midpoint to find lengths of segments.

> **SUGGESTED LEARNING STRATEGIES:** Close Reading, Look for a Pattern, Think-Pair-Share, Vocabulary Organizer, Interactive Word Wall, Create Representations, Marking the Text, Visualization, Identify a Subtask, Discussion Groups

In geometry, axioms, or *postulates*, are statements that are accepted as true without proof in order to provide a starting point for deductive reasoning.

Like *point, line,* and *plane, distance along a line* is an undefined term in geometry used to define other geometric terms. For example, the length of a line segment is the distance between its endpoints.

If two points are no more than 1 foot apart, you can find the distance between them by using an ordinary ruler. (The inch rulers below have been reduced to fit on the page.)

In the figure, the distance between point *A* and point *B* is 5 inches. Of course, there is no need to place the zero of the ruler on point *A*. In the figure below, the 2-inch mark is on point *A*. In this case, *AB*, measured in inches, is $|7 - 2| = |2 - 7| = 5$, as before.

The number obtained as a measure of distance depends on the unit of length. For example, the distance between two points in inches will be a different number than the distance between the two points in centimeters.

1. Determine the length of each segment in centimeters.

a. $DE =$ **b.** $EF =$ **c.** $DF =$

MATH TERMS

To prove a rule, at least one other rule must be used. So in order to develop geometry, some rules, called **postulates,** are accepted without proof.

READING MATH

AB denotes the distance between points *A* and *B*. If *A* and *B* are the endpoints of a segment ($\overline{AB}$), then *AB* denotes the length of $\overline{AB}$.

MATH TERMS

The **Ruler Postulate**

a. To every pair of points there corresponds a unique positive number called the distance between the points.

b. The points on a line can be matched with the real numbers so that the distance between any two points is the absolute value of the difference of their associated numbers.

My Notes

2. **Attend to precision.** Determine the length of each segment in centimeters (to the nearest tenth).

G   H   K

a. $KH =$ b. $HG =$ c. $GK =$

3. Using your results from Items 1 and 2, describe any patterns that you notice.

MATH TERMS

Item 4 and your answer together form a statement of the **Segment Addition Postulate**.

4. Given that N is a point between endpoints M and P of line segment MP, describe how to determine the length of $\overline{MP}$, without measuring, if you are given the lengths of $\overline{MN}$ and $\overline{NP}$.

MATH TIP

For each part of Item 5, make a sketch so that you can identify the parts of the segment.

5. Use the Segment Addition Postulate and the given information to complete each statement.

a. If B is between C and D, $BC = 10$ in., and $BD = 3$ in., then $CD =$ _____.

b. If Q is between R and T, $RT = 24$ cm, and $QR = 6$ cm, then $QT =$ _____.

c. If P is between L and A, $PL = x + 4$, $PA = 2x - 1$, and $LA = 5x - 3$, then $x =$ _____ and $LA =$ _____.

CONNECT TO AP

You will frequently be asked to find the lengths of horizontal, vertical, and diagonal segments in the coordinate plane in AP Calculus.

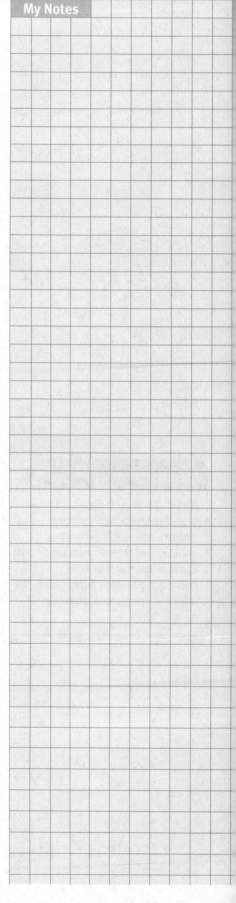

The ***midpoint*** of a segment is the point on the segment that divides it into two ***congruent*** segments. For example, if B is the midpoint of $\overline{AC}$, then $\overline{AB} \cong \overline{BC}$.

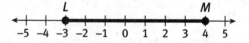

A   3   B   3   C

6. Given: M is the midpoint of $\overline{RS}$. Complete each statement.

   a. If $RS = 10$, then $SM = $ _____.

   b. If $RM = 12$, then $MS = $ _____, and $RS = $ _____.

Check Your Understanding

7. Points D and E are aligned with a ruler. Point D is at the mark for 4.5 cm, and the distance between points D and E is 3.4 cm. At which two marks on the ruler could point E be located?

8. Point N is the midpoint of $\overline{FG}$. If $FN = 2x$, what expression represents FG?

9. **Reason abstractly.** Does a ray have a midpoint? Explain.

10. Give an example that illustrates the Segment Addition Postulate. Include a sketch with your example.

You can also use a number line to find the distance between two points.

11. What is LM?

My Notes

The midpoint of a segment is halfway between its endpoints. So, if you know the coordinates of the endpoints, you can average them to find the coordinate of the midpoint.

12. What is the coordinate of the midpoint M of $\overline{PQ}$?

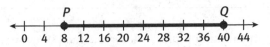

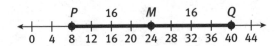

Check Your Understanding

13. Use the number line to solve each problem.

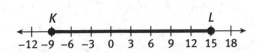

a. What is KL?

b. What is the coordinate of the midpoint of $\overline{KL}$?

c. Point C lies between points K and L. The distance between points K and C is $\frac{1}{3}$ of KL. What is the coordinate of point C?

d. Point N lies between points C and L. The distance between points C and N is $\frac{3}{4}$ of CL. What is the coordinate of point N?

MATH TIP

A number line represents a one-dimensional coordinate system. You will explore the concepts of distance and midpoint using a two-dimensional coordinate system when you work with the coordinate plane in the next activity.

You can use the definition of midpoint and properties of algebra to determine the length of a segment.

My Notes

Example A

If Q is the midpoint of $\overline{PR}$, $PQ = 4x - 5$, and $QR = 11 + 2x$, determine the length of $\overline{PQ}$.

Because Q is the midpoint of $\overline{PR}$, you know that $\overline{PQ} \cong \overline{QR}$ and $PQ = QR$.

$PQ = QR$	
$4x - 5 = 11 + 2x$	Substitution Property
$2x - 5 = 11$	Subtraction Property of Equality
$2x = 16$	Addition Property of Equality
$x = 8$	Division Property of Equality

WRITING MATH

Use $\overline{AB}$ when you talk about segment AB.

Use AB when you talk about the measure, or length, of $\overline{AB}$.

Now substitute 8 for x in the expression for PQ.

$PQ = 4x - 5 = 4(8) - 5 = 27$

Make a sketch of $\overline{PR}$ and its midpoint Q. Label the lengths of $\overline{PR}$, $\overline{PQ}$, and $\overline{QR}$.

Try These A

a. If Y is the midpoint of $\overline{WZ}$, $YZ = x + 3$, and $WZ = 3x - 4$, determine the length of $\overline{WZ}$.

Given: M is the midpoint of $\overline{RS}$. Use the given information to find the missing values.

b. $RM = x + 3$ and $MS = 2x - 1$

$x = $ _____ and $RM = $ _____

c. $RM = x + 6$ and $RS = 5x + 3$

$x = $ _____ and $SM = $ _____

When you **bisect** a geometric figure, you divide it into two equal or congruent parts.

14. Reason abstractly. Line segment WZ bisects $\overline{XY}$ at point Z. What are two conclusions you can draw from this information?

MATH TERMS

A geometric figure that **bisects** another figure divides it into two equal or congruent parts.

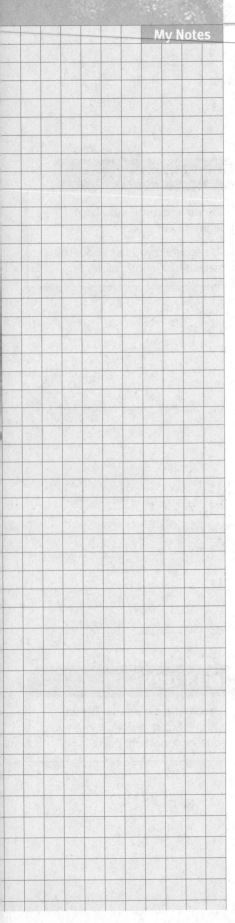

My Notes

Check Your Understanding

15. Explain how to find the distance between two points on a number line.

16. Mekhi knows that $GH = 7$ and $HJ = 7$. Based on this information, he claims that point H is the midpoint of $\overline{GJ}$. Is Mekhi's claim necessarily true? Make a sketch that supports your answer.

17. Given: T is the midpoint of $\overline{JK}$, $JK = 5x - 3$, and $JT = 2x + 1$. Determine the length of $\overline{JK}$.

18. **Reason quantitatively.** $\overline{AB}$ lies on a number line. The coordinate of point A is -6. Given that $AB = 20$, what are the two possible coordinates for point B?

LESSON 4-1 PRACTICE

19. Given: Point K is between points H and J, $HK = x - 5$, $KJ = 5x - 12$, and $HJ = 25$. Find the value of x.

20. If B is the midpoint of $\overline{AC}$, $AB = x + 6$, and $AC = 5x - 6$, then what is BC?

21. Point P is between points F and G. The distance between points F and P is $\frac{1}{4}$ of FG. What is the coordinate of point P?

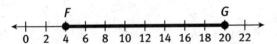

22. **Use appropriate tools strategically.** Anne has a broken ruler. It starts at the 3-inch mark and ends at the 12-inch mark. Explain how Anne could use the ruler to measure the length of a line segment in inches.

23. If P is the midpoint of $\overline{ST}$, $SP = x + 4$, and $ST = 4x$, determine the length of $\overline{ST}$.

24. Compare and contrast a postulate and a conjecture.

Learning Targets:

- Apply the Angle Addition Postulate to find angle measures.
- Use the definition of angle bisector to find angle measures.

SUGGESTED LEARNING STRATEGIES: Think-Pair-Share, Look for a Pattern, Quickwrite, Vocabulary Organizer, Interactive Word Wall, Create Representations, Debriefing, Identify a Subtask, Group Presentation

You measure angles with a protractor. The number of degrees in an angle is called its measure.

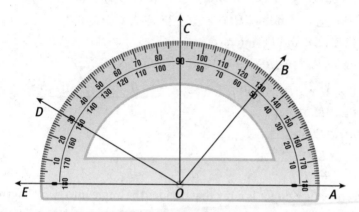

1. **Use appropriate tools strategically.** Determine the measure of each angle.

   a. $m\angle AOB = \underline{50°}$ **b.** $m\angle BOC = \underline{}$ **c.** $m\angle AOC = \underline{}$

   d. $m\angle EOD = \underline{}$ **e.** $m\angle BOD = \underline{}$ **f.** $m\angle BOE = \underline{}$

2. Use a protractor to determine the measure of each angle.

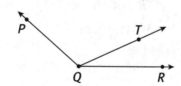

   a. $m\angle TQP = \underline{}$ **b.** $m\angle TQR = \underline{}$ **c.** $m\angle RQP = \underline{}$

3. **Express regularity in repeated reasoning.** Using your results from Items 1 and 2, describe any patterns that you notice.

4. Given that point D is in the interior of $\angle ABC$, describe how to determine the measure of $\angle ABC$, without measuring, if you are given the measures of $\angle ABD$ and $\angle DBC$.

CONNECT TO ASTRONOMY

The astronomer Claudius Ptolemy (about 85–165 CE) based his observations of the solar system on a unit that resulted from dividing the distance around a circle into 360 parts. This later became known as a degree.

MATH TERMS

The **Protractor Postulate**

a. To each angle there corresponds a unique real number between 0 and 180 called the measure of the angle.

b. The measure of an angle formed by a pair of rays is the absolute value of the difference of their associated numbers.

MATH TERMS

Item 4 and your answer together form a statement of the **Angle Addition Postulate**.

My Notes

5. Use the Angle Addition Postulate and the given information to complete each statement.

   a. If P is in the interior of $\angle XYZ$, $m\angle XYP = 25°$, and $m\angle PYZ = 50°$, then $m\angle XYZ =$ _____.

   b. If M is in the interior of $\angle RTD$, $m\angle RTM = 40°$, and $m\angle RTD = 65°$, then $m\angle MTD =$ _____.

   c. If H is in the interior of $\angle EFG$, $m\angle EFH = 75°$, and $m\angle HFG = (10x)°$, and $m\angle EFG = (20x - 5)°$, then $x =$ _____ and $m\angle HFG =$ _____.

   d. Lines DB and EC intersect at point F. If $m\angle BFC = 44°$ and $m\angle AFB = 61°$, then

   $m\angle AFC =$ _____

   $m\angle AFE =$ _____

   $m\angle EFD =$ _____

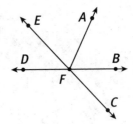

The ***bisector of an angle*** is a ray that divides the angle into two congruent adjacent angles. For example, if $\overrightarrow{BD}$ bisects $\angle ABC$, then $\angle ABD \cong \angle DBC$.

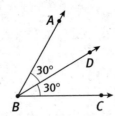

6. Given: $\overrightarrow{AH}$ bisects $\angle MAT$. Determine the missing measure.

   a. $m\angle MAT = 70°$, $m\angle MAH =$ _____

   b. $m\angle HAT = 80°$, $m\angle MAT =$ _____.

You can use definitions, postulates, and properties of algebra to determine the measures of angles.

Example A

If $\overrightarrow{QP}$ bisects $\angle DQL$, $m\angle DQP = 5x - 7$, and $m\angle PQL = 11 + 2x$, determine the measure of $\angle DQL$.

Because $\overrightarrow{QP}$ is the angle bisector of $\angle DQL$, you know that $\angle DQP \cong \angle PQL$ and $m\angle DQP = m\angle PQL$.

$m\angle DQP = m\angle PQL$	
$5x - 7 = 11 + 2x$	Substitution Property
$3x - 7 = 11$	Subtraction Property of Equality
$3x = 18$	Addition Property of Equality
$x = 6$	Division Property of Equality

Substitute 6 for x in the expressions for $m\angle DQP$ and $m\angle PQL$.

$m\angle DQP = 5(6) - 7 = 23°$ $m\angle PQL = 11 + 2(6) = 23°$

By the Angle Addition Postulate, $m\angle DQL = m\angle DQP + m\angle PQL$, so $m\angle DQL = 23° + 23° = 46°$.

Make a sketch of $\angle DQL$ and its angle bisector $\overrightarrow{QP}$. Label the measures of $\angle DQP$ and $\angle PQL$.

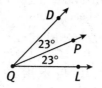

Try These A

Given: $\overrightarrow{FL}$ bisects $\angle AFM$. Determine each missing value.

a. $m\angle LFM = 11x + 4$ and $m\angle AFL = 12x - 2$

$x = $ _____ , $m\angle LFM = $ _____, and $m\angle AFM = $ _____

b. $m\angle AFM = 6x - 2$ and $m\angle AFL = 4x - 10$

$x = $ _____ and $m\angle LFM = $ _____

7. $\angle A$ and $\angle B$ are complementary, $m\angle A = 3x + 7$, and $m\angle B = 6x + 11$. Determine the measure of each angle.

MATH TIP

In Item 7, you know that $\angle A$ and $\angle B$ are complementary, so the sum of their measures is 90°. Use this fact to write an equation that you can solve for x. Once you know the value of x, you can find the measures of the angles.

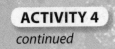

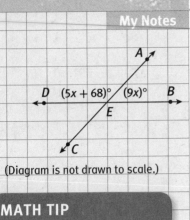

(Diagram is not drawn to scale.)

MATH TIP

Angles 1 and 3 are vertical angles. Vertical angles have the same measure.

READING MATH

The symbol ⊥ is read "is perpendicular to."

8. In the diagram at the left, $\overleftrightarrow{AC}$ and $\overleftrightarrow{DB}$ intersect as shown. Determine the measure of ∠CEB.

Check Your Understanding

9. $\overrightarrow{KN}$ is the angle bisector of ∠JKL. Explain how you could find $m\angle JKN$ if you know $m\angle JKL$.

10. In this diagram, $m\angle 1 = 4x + 30$ and $m\angle 3 = 2x + 48$. Write a step-by-step explanation for an absent classmate showing how to find $m\angle 2$.

11. **Construct viable arguments.** ∠RST is adjacent to ∠TSU, $m\angle RST = 40°$, and $m\angle TSU = 50°$. Explain how you can use the Angle Addition Postulate to show that ∠RSU is a right angle.

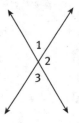

LESSON 4-2 PRACTICE

12. Point D is in the interior of ∠ABC, $m\angle ABC = 10x - 7$, $m\angle ABD = 6x + 5$, and $m\angle DBC = 36°$. What is $m\angle ABD$?

13. $\overrightarrow{QS}$ bisects ∠PQR. If $m\angle PQS = 5x$ and $m\angle RQS = 2x + 6$, then what is $m\angle PQR$?

14. ∠L and ∠M are complementary, $m\angle L = 2x + 25$, and $m\angle M = 4x + 11$. Determine the measure of each angle.

15. In this diagram, $\overrightarrow{EA} \perp \overrightarrow{ED}$ and $\overrightarrow{EB}$ bisects ∠AEC. Given that $m\angle AEB = 4x + 1$ and $m\angle CED = 3x$, determine the missing measures.
    a. $x =$ _____
    b. $m\angle BEC =$ _____

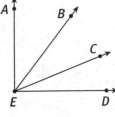

16. **Critique the reasoning of others.** Penny knows that point W is in the interior of ∠XYZ. Based on this information, she claims that ∠XYW ≅ ∠WYZ. Is Penny's claim necessarily true? Explain. Make a sketch that supports your answer.

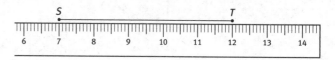
ACTIVITY 4 PRACTICE
Write your answers on notebook paper.
Show your work.

Lesson 4-1

1. If Q is between A and M and $MQ = 7.3$ and $AM = 8.5$, then $QA = \underline{\ ?\ }$.
   A. 5.8   B. 1.2
   C. 7.3   D. 14.6

2. Given: K is between H and J, $HK = 2x - 5$, $KJ = 3x + 4$, and $HJ = 24$. What is the value of x?
   A. 9   B. 5
   C. 19   D. 3

3. If K is the midpoint of $\overline{HJ}$, $HK = x + 6$, and $HJ = 4x - 6$, then $KJ = \underline{\ ?\ }$.
   A. 15   B. 9
   C. 4   D. 10

4. State the Segment Addition Postulate in your own words.

5. Explain what *distance along a line* means as an undefined term in geometry.

Use the number line for Items 6–9.

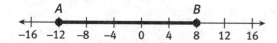

6. What is AB?

7. What is the coordinate of the midpoint of $\overline{AB}$? Explain how you found your answer.

8. Point M is the midpoint of $\overline{AB}$. What is the coordinate of the midpoint of $\overline{AM}$?

9. Point C is between points A and B. The distance between points B and C is $\frac{1}{4}$ of AB. What is the coordinate of point C?

10. $\overline{FG}$ lies on a number line. The coordinate of point F is 8. Given that $FG = 16$, what are the two possible coordinates for point G?

11. In the diagram, $\overline{ST}$ is aligned with a centimeter ruler. What is the length of $\overline{ST}$ in centimeters?

12. Compare and contrast a *postulate* and a *theorem*.

13. What are two conclusions you can draw from this statement? Support your answers.

    Point P is the midpoint of $\overline{QR}$.

14. If D is the midpoint of $\overline{CE}$, $CD = x + 7$, and $CE = 5x - 1$, determine each missing value.
    a. $x = \underline{\ ?\ }$
    b. $CD = \underline{\ ?\ }$
    c. $CE = \underline{\ ?\ }$
    d. $DE = \underline{\ ?\ }$

15. Leo is running in a 5-kilometer race along a straight path. If he is at the midpoint of the path, how many kilometers does he have left to run?

16. Point S is between points R and T. Given that $\overline{RS} \cong \overline{ST}$ and $RS = 16$, what is RT?

Lesson 4-2

17. P lies in the interior of $\angle RST$. $m\angle RSP = 40°$ and $m\angle TSP = 10°$. $m\angle RST = \underline{\ ?\ }$
    A. 100°   B. 50°
    C. 30°   D. 10°

18. $\overrightarrow{QS}$ bisects $\angle PQR$. If $m\angle PQS = 3x$ and $m\angle RQS = 2x + 6$, then $m\angle PQR = \underline{\ ?\ }$.
    A. 18°   B. 36°
    C. 30°   D. 6°

19. $\angle P$ and $\angle Q$ are supplementary. $m\angle P = 5x + 3$ and $m\angle Q = x + 3$. $x = \underline{\ ?\ }$
    A. 14   B. 0
    C. 29   D. 30

20. In this figure, $m\angle 3 = x + 18$, $m\angle 4 = x + 15$, and $m\angle 5 = 4x + 3$. Show all work for parts a, b, and c.

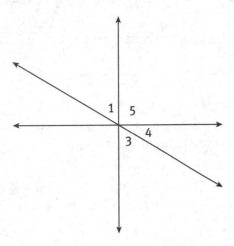

   a. What is the value of x?
   b. What is the measure of $\angle 1$?
   c. Is $\angle 3$ complementary to $\angle 1$? Explain.

21. $\overrightarrow{MP}$ is the angle bisector of $\angle LMN$. Given that $\angle LMP$ is a right angle, what type of angle is $\angle LMN$? Explain how you know.

22. State the Angle Addition Postulate in your own words.

23. A protractor is properly aligned with the vertex of $\angle KLM$. $\overrightarrow{LK}$ passes through the mark for 38° on the protractor and $\overrightarrow{LM}$ passes through the mark for 126°. What is $m\angle KLM$?

24. $\angle GFH$ and $\angle HFJ$ are adjacent and congruent. What are two conclusions you can draw from this information? Support your answers.

25. In this figure, $m\angle 1 = 4x + 50$ and $m\angle 3 = 2x + 66$. Show all work for parts a, b, and c.

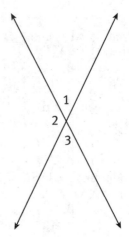

   a. What is the value of x?
   b. What is the measure of $m\angle 3$?
   c. What is the measure of $m\angle 2$?

26. Given: $\overrightarrow{AE} \perp \overrightarrow{AB}$, $\overrightarrow{AD}$ bisects $\angle EAC$, $m\angle CAB = 2x - 4$ and $m\angle CAE = 3x + 14$. Show all work for parts a and b.

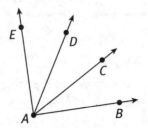

   a. What is the value of x?
   b. What is the measure of $m\angle DAC$?

MATHEMATICAL PRACTICES
Look for and Express Regularity in Repeated Reasoning

27. $\angle CDF$ is one of the congruent angles formed by the angle bisector of $\angle CDE$. Write a formula that can be used to determine $m\angle CDF$ given $m\angle CDE$.

Distance and Midpoint Formulas

We ♥ Descartes

Lesson 5-1 Distance on the Coordinate Plane

Learning Targets:
- Derive the Distance Formula.
- Use the Distance Formula to find the distance between two points on the coordinate plane.

SUGGESTED LEARNING STRATEGIES: Create Representations, Simplify the Problem, Think-Pair-Share, Think Aloud, Visualization, Look for a Pattern, Graphic Organizer, Discussion Groups, Identify a Subtask

In the previous activity, you used number lines to determine distance and to locate the midpoint of a segment. A number line is a one-dimensional coordinate system.

In this activity, you will explore the concepts of distance and midpoint on a two-dimensional coordinate system, or coordinate plane.

Use the coordinate plane and follow the steps below to determine the distance between points $P(1, 4)$ and $Q(13, 9)$.

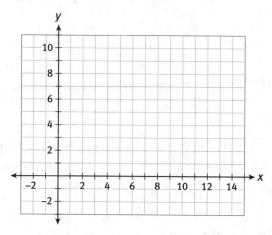

1. **Model with mathematics.** Plot the points $P(1, 4)$ and $Q(13, 9)$ on the coordinate plane. Then draw $\overline{PQ}$.

2. Draw horizontal segment PR and vertical segment QR to create right triangle PQR, with a right angle at vertex R.

3. **Attend to precision.** What are the coordinates of point R?

CONNECT TO HISTORY

The Cartesian coordinate system was developed by the French philosopher and mathematician René Descartes in 1637 as a way to specify the position of a point or object on a plane.

READING MATH

The notation $P(1, 4)$ means point P with coordinates $(1, 4)$ on the coordinate plane.

My Notes

4. a. What is *PR*, the length of the horizontal leg of the right triangle?

b. What is *QR*, the length of the vertical leg of the right triangle?

c. Explain how you determined your answers to parts a and b.

5. Use the Pythagorean Theorem to find *PQ*. Show your work.

MATH TIP

The *Pythagorean Theorem* states that the square of the length of the hypotenuse of a right triangle is equal to the sum of the squares of the lengths of the legs of the right triangle. In other words, for a right triangle with hypotenuse *c* and legs *a* and *b*, $c^2 = a^2 + b^2$.

6. Attend to precision. What is the distance between points $P(1, 4)$ and $Q(13, 9)$? How do you know?

7. How do you know that the triangle you drew in Item 2 is a right triangle?

8. What relationship do you notice among the coordinates of points *P*, *Q*, and *R*?

Check Your Understanding

9. Explain how you would find the distance between points $J(-3, 6)$ and $K(3, 14)$.

10. What is the distance between $M(9, -5)$ and $N(-11, 10)$?

Although the method you just learned for finding the distance between two points will always work, it may not be practical to plot points on a coordinate plane and draw a right triangle each time you want to find the distance between them.

Instead, you can use algebraic methods to derive a formula for finding the distance between any two points on the coordinate plane. Start with any two points (x_1, y_1) and (x_2, y_2) on the coordinate plane. Visualize using these points to draw a right triangle with a horizontal leg and a vertical leg.

My Notes

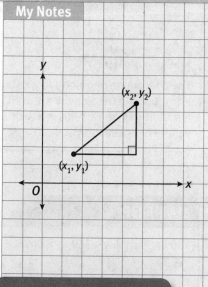

11. What are the coordinates of the point at the vertex of the right angle of the triangle?

12. Write an expression for the length of the horizontal leg of the right triangle.

> **MATH TIP**
>
> In Item 12, you can think of the *x*-coordinates of the endpoints of the horizontal leg as values on a horizontal number line.
>
> In Item 13, you can think of the *y*-coordinates of the endpoints of the vertical leg as values on a vertical number line.

13. Write an expression for the length of the vertical leg of the right triangle.

14. Use the Pythagorean Theorem to write an expression for the length of the hypotenuse of the right triangle.

15. Express regularity in repeated reasoning. Write a formula that can be used to find *d*, the distance between two points (x_1, y_1) and (x_2, y_2) on the coordinate plane.

> **MATH TIP**
>
> Squaring a difference and then taking the square root has the same effect as taking the absolute value of the difference. Both result in nonnegative quantities. That means that the absolute value symbols are not needed in your formula to find the distance between two points.

My Notes

CONNECT TO AP

The coordinate geometry formulas introduced in this activity are used frequently in AP calculus in a wide variety of applications.

MATH TIP

You can simplify $\sqrt{369}$ as follows.

$$\sqrt{369} = \sqrt{9 \cdot 41}$$
$$= \sqrt{9} \cdot \sqrt{41}$$
$$= 3\sqrt{41}$$

MATH TIP

A Venn diagram illustrates logical relationships. Think about the commonalities between the Pythagorean Theorem and the Distance Formula. These similarities are placed in the overlapping circles of the Venn diagram. The differences are shown in the nonoverlapping parts.

16. Use the formula you wrote in Item 15 to find the distance between the points with coordinates $(12, -5)$ and $(-3, 7)$.

Check Your Understanding

17. Find the distance between the points with the coordinates shown.
    a. $(-8, 5)$ and $(7, -3)$
    b. $(3, 8)$ and $(8, 3)$

18. Create a Venn diagram that compares and contrasts the Pythagorean Theorem and the Distance Formula.

19. **Reason abstractly.** Suppose two points lie on the same vertical line. Can you use the Distance Formula to find the distance between them? Explain.

20. Write and simplify a formula for the distance d between the origin and a point (x, y) on the coordinate plane.

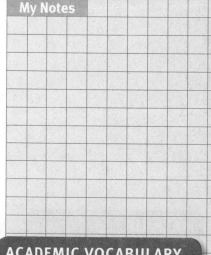

LESSON 5-1 PRACTICE

Find the distance between the points with the given coordinates.

21. $(-8, -6)$ and $(4, 10)$

22. $(5, 14)$ and $(-3, -9)$

23. **Reason quantitatively.** Explain how you know that your answer to Item 22 is reasonable. Remember to use complete sentences and words such as *and, or, since, for example, therefore, because of, by the,* to make connections between your thoughts.

24. Use your Venn diagram from Item 18 to write a RAFT.

Role: Teacher

Audience: A classmate who was absent for the lesson on distance between two points

Format: Personal note

Topic: Explain the mathematical similarities and differences between the Pythagorean Theorem and the Distance Formula.

25. The vertices of $\triangle XYZ$ are $X(-3, -6)$, $Y(21, -6)$, and $Z(21, 4)$. What is the perimeter of the triangle?

26. Use the Distance Formula to show that $\overline{AB} \cong \overline{CD}$.

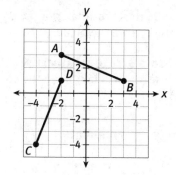

My Notes

ACADEMIC VOCABULARY

The **format** of a piece of writing can refer to its organization or style. For example, personal notes, essays, reports, and printed advertisements are all different formats for writing.

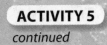
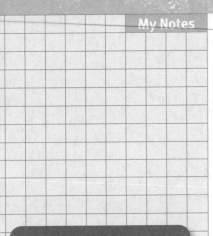

My Notes

MATH TIP

For a segment on a number line, the coordinate of the midpoint is the average of the coordinates of the endpoints.

Learning Targets:
- Use inductive reasoning to determine the Midpoint Formula.
- Use the Midpoint Formula to find the coordinates of the midpoint of a segment on the coordinate plane.

SUGGESTED LEARNING STRATEGIES: Think-Pair-Share, Visualization, Look for a Pattern, Debriefing, Work Backward, Self Revision/Peer Revision, Discussion Groups, Identify a Subtask

In the previous activity, you defined *midpoint* as a point on a segment that divides it into two congruent segments. Follow the steps below to explore the concept of midpoint on the coordinate plane.

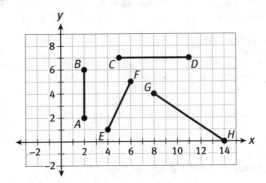

1. In the table below, write the coordinates of the endpoints of each segment shown on the coordinate plane.

   Use appropriate tools strategically. Use a ruler to help you identify the midpoint of each segment. Then write the coordinates of the midpoint in the table.

Segment	Endpoints		Midpoint
$\overline{AB}$	A(____, ____) and B(____, ____)		(____, ____)
$\overline{CD}$	C(____, ____) and D(____, ____)		(____, ____)
$\overline{EF}$	E(____, ____) and F(____, ____)		(____, ____)
$\overline{GH}$	G(____, ____) and H(____, ____)		(____, ____)

2. Use the coordinates in the table in Item 1.
   a. Compare the *x*-coordinates of the endpoints of each segment with the *x*-coordinate of the midpoint of the segment. Describe the pattern you see.

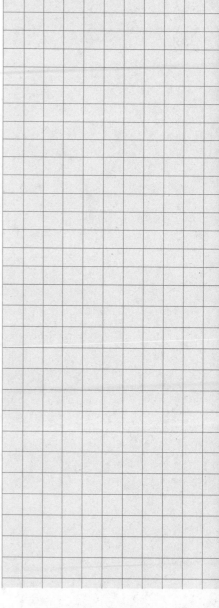

b. **Make use of structure.** Compare the *y*-coordinates of the endpoints of each segment with the *y*-coordinate of the midpoint of the segment. Describe the pattern you see.

3. Use the patterns you described in Item 2 to write a formula for the coordinates of the midpoint *M* of a line segment with endpoints at (x_1, y_1) and (x_2, y_2).

MATH TIP

Your formula for the midpoint should have the form $M = (a, b)$, where *a* is an expression for the *x*-coordinate of the midpoint, and *b* is an expression for the *y*-coordinate of the midpoint.

Look back at the chart in Item 1 to verify the formula you wrote.

4. Use your formula to find the coordinates of the midpoint *M* of $\overline{AC}$ with endpoints *A*(1, 4) and *C*(11, 10). What can you conclude about segments *AM* and *MC*?

Check Your Understanding

5. Explain how you could check that your answer to Item 4 is reasonable.

6. Suppose a segment on the coordinate plane is vertical. Can you use the Midpoint Formula to find the coordinates of its midpoint? Explain.

7. The midpoint *M* of $\overline{ST}$ has coordinates (3, 6). Point *S* has coordinates (1, 2). What are the coordinates of point *T*? Explain how you determined your answer.

8. **Reason quantitatively.** The origin, (0, 0), is the midpoint of a segment. What conclusions can you draw about the coordinates of the endpoints of the segment?

My Notes

LESSON 5-2 PRACTICE

Find the coordinates of the midpoint of each segment with the given endpoints.

9. $Q(-3, 14)$ and $R(7, 5)$

10. $S(13, 7)$ and $T(-2, -7)$

11. $E(4, 11)$ and $F(-11, -5)$

12. $A(-5, 4)$ and $B(-5, 18)$

13. Find and explain the errors that were made in the following calculation of the coordinates of a midpoint. Then fix the errors and determine the correct answer.

Find the coordinates of the midpoint M of the segment with endpoints R(−2, 3) and S(13, −7).

$$M = \left(\frac{-2+3}{2}, \frac{13+(-7)}{2} \right)$$
$$= \left(\frac{1}{2}, \frac{6}{2} \right) = \left(\frac{1}{2}, 3 \right)$$

14. Make sense of problems. $\overline{HJ}$ is graphed on a coordinate plane. Explain how you would determine the coordinates of the point on the segment that is $\frac{1}{4}$ of the distance from H to J.

ACTIVITY 5 PRACTICE
Write your answers on notebook paper.
Show your work.

Lesson 5-1

1. Calculate the distance between the points $A(-4, 2)$ and $B(15, 6)$.

2. Calculate the distance between the points $R(1.5, 7)$ and $S(-2.3, -8)$.

3. Describe how to find the distance between two points on the coordinate plane.

4. To the nearest unit, what is FG?

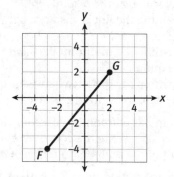

   A. 5 units   **B.** 6 units
   C. 8 units   **D.** 11 units

5. $\overline{JK}$ has endpoints $J(-3, -1)$ and $K(0, 3)$. $\overline{RS}$ has endpoints $R(1, 1)$ and $S(4, 4)$. Is $\overline{JK} \cong \overline{RS}$? Explain how you know.

6. The vertices of $\triangle LMN$ are $L(7, 4)$, $M(7, 16)$, and $N(42, 4)$.
   a. Find the length of each side of the triangle.
   b. What is the perimeter of the triangle?
   c. What is the area of the triangle? Explain how you determined your answer.

7. The distance from the origin to point P is 5 units. Give the coordinates of four possible locations for point P.

8. On a map, a trailhead is located at $(5, 3)$ and a turnaround point is located at $(15, 6)$. Each unit on the map represents 1 km. Ana and Larissa start at the turnaround point and walk directly toward the trailhead. If they walk at an average speed of 4.5 km/h, will they make it to the trailhead in less than 2 hours? Support your answer.

For Items 9–11, determine the length of each segment with the given endpoints.

9. $C(1, 4)$ and $D(11, 28)$

10. $Y(-2, 6)$ and $Z(5, -8)$

11. $P(-7, -7)$ and $Q(9, 5)$

12. Point R has coordinates $(1, 3)$, and point S has coordinates $(6, y)$. If the distance from R to S is 13 units, what are the possible values of y?

13. Use the Distance Formula to show that $\triangle ABC$ is isosceles.

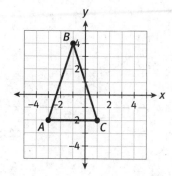

14. Draw a scalene triangle on a coordinate plane, and use the Distance Formula to demonstrate that your triangle is scalene.

Lesson 5-2

15. Determine the coordinates of the midpoint of the segment with endpoints $R(3, 16)$ and $S(7, -6)$.

16. Determine the coordinates of the midpoint of the segment with endpoints $W(-5, 10.2)$ and $X(12, 4.5)$.

17. Point C is the midpoint of $\overline{AB}$. Point A has coordinates $(2, 4)$, and point C has coordinates $(5, 0)$.
   a. What are the coordinates of point B?
   b. What is AB?
   c. What is BC?

18. $\overline{JL}$ has endpoints $J(8, 10)$ and $L(20, 5)$. Point K has coordinates $(13, 9)$.
   a. Is point K the midpoint of $\overline{JL}$? Explain how you know.
   b. How could you check that your answer to part a is reasonable?

19. Find the coordinates of the midpoint of $\overline{DE}$.

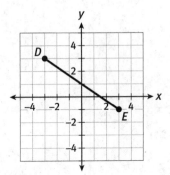

20. What are the coordinates of the midpoint of the segment with endpoints at $(-3, -4)$ and $(5, 8)$?
   A. $(1, 2)$ **B.** $(2, 4)$
   C. $(4, 6)$ **D.** $(8, 12)$

21. A circle on the coordinate plane has a diameter with endpoints at $(6, 8)$ and $(15, 8)$.
   a. What are the coordinates of the center of the circle?
   b. What is the diameter of the circle?
   c. What is the radius of the circle?
   d. Identify the coordinates of another point on the circle. Explain how you found your answer.

22. Two explorers on an expedition to the Arctic Circle have radioed their coordinates to base camp. Explorer A is at coordinates $(-26, -15)$. Explorer B is at coordinates $(13, 21)$. The base camp is located at the origin.
   a. Determine the linear distance between the two explorers.
   b. Determine the midpoint between the two explorers.
   c. Determine the distance between the midpoint of the explorers and the base camp.

23. A segment has endpoints with coordinates $(a, 2b)$ and $(-3a, 4b)$. Write the coordinates of the midpoint of the segment in terms of a and b.

24. Point J is the midpoint of $\overline{FG}$ with endpoints $F(1, 4)$ and $G(5, 12)$. Point K is the midpoint of $\overline{GH}$ with endpoints $G(5, 12)$ and $H(-1, 4)$. What is JK?

MATHEMATICAL PRACTICES
Look for and Express Regularity in Repeated Reasoning

25. Let (x_1, y) and (x_2, y) represent the coordinates of the endpoints of a horizontal segment.
   a. Write and simplify a formula for the distance d between the endpoints of a horizontal segment.
   b. Write and simplify a formula for the coordinates of the midpoint M of a horizontal segment.

Each year, a charity hosts a walk as a fundraising event. The walk starts in Reese Park and then continues along Bell Avenue.

1. The route of the first section of the walk is along an east-west path in the park. The walk starts at point *A*, at marker 32 on the path, and continues to point *B*, at marker 4, as shown in the diagram.

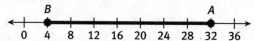

   a. The markers on the path are spaced 200 meters apart. What is the distance in meters between points *A* and *B*?

   b. A water station is located at the midpoint of $\overline{AB}$. At what marker on the path is the water station located?

   c. A first-aid booth is located $\frac{3}{4}$ of the distance from point *A* to point *B*. At what marker on the path is the first-aid booth located?

2. The second section of the walk continues from point *B* along Bell Avenue to the finish line at point *C*, as shown on the map.

   a. Each unit on the map represents 1 kilometer. What is the distance in kilometers from point *B* to point *C*?

   b. What is the total length of the race (from point *A* to point *B* and from point *B* to point *C*) in kilometers?

   c. A water station is located at the midpoint *M* of $\overline{BC}$. Another water station is located at the midpoint *N* of $\overline{MC}$. A race coordinator says that the map coordinates of point *N* are (6, 8). Is the race coordinator correct? Support your answer.

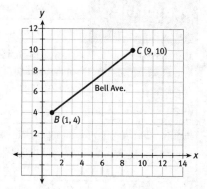

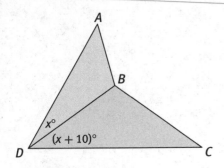

3. An artist is working on the design of a logo for the T-shirts that the participants in the walk will receive. He starts by drawing $\angle ADC$ so that it measures 60°. Next, he draws DB so that $m\angle BDC$ is 10° greater than $m\angle ADB$.

a. What is $m\angle ADB$?

b. What is $m\angle BDC$?

c. What postulate did you make use of to answer parts a and b? How did this postulate help you write an equation that could be solved for x?

Scoring Guide	Exemplary	Proficient	Emerging	Incomplete
	The solution demonstrates these characteristics:			
Mathematics Knowledge and Thinking (Items 1b, 2c, 3)	• Clear and accurate understanding of midpoint and the Angle Addition Postulate	• A functional understanding of midpoint and the Angle Addition Postulate	• Partial understanding of midpoint and the Angle Addition Postulate	• Little or no understanding of midpoint and the Angle Addition Postulate
Problem Solving (Items 1, 2, 3)	• An appropriate and efficient strategy that results in a correct answer	• A strategy that may include unnecessary steps but results in a correct answer	• A strategy that results in some incorrect answers	• No clear strategy when solving problems
Mathematical Modeling / Representations (Item 3)	• Clear and accurate understanding of creating an equation to represent the Angle Addition Postulate	• A functional understanding of creating an equation to represent the Angle Addition Postulate	• Partial understanding of creating an equation to represent the Angle Addition Postulate	• Inaccurate or incomplete understanding of creating an equation to represent the Angle Addition Postulate
Reasoning and Communication (Items 2c, 3c)	• Precise use of the term *midpoint* and other math terms to justify a statement concluding that the given coordinates for point *N* are incorrect • Precise explanation of the Angle Addition Postulate and its relationship to $\angle ADB$, $\angle BDC$, and $\angle ADC$	• Adequate understanding of the term *midpoint* with somewhat correct explanation to justify a statement concluding that the given coordinates for point *N* are incorrect • Adequate explanation of the Angle Addition Postulate and its relationship to $\angle ADB$, $\angle BDC$, and $\angle ADC$	• Misleading or confusing explanation to justify a statement concluding that the given coordinates for point *N* are incorrect • Misleading or confusing explanation of the Angle Addition Postulate and its relationship to $\angle ADB$, $\angle BDC$, and $\angle ADC$	• Incomplete or inaccurate statement to justify whether or not the given coordinates for point *N* are correct • Incomplete or inaccurate explanation of the Angle Addition Postulate and its relationship to $\angle ADB$, $\angle BDC$ and $\angle ADC$

Proofs about Line Segments and Angles

Now I'm Convinced

Lesson 6-1 Justifying Statements

Learning Objectives

● Use definitions, properties, and theorems to justify a statement.

● Write two-column proofs to prove theorems about lines and angles.

Learning Target:

● Use properties, postulates, and definitions to justify statements.

SUGGESTED LEARNING STRATEGIES: Close Reading, Activating Prior Knowledge, Think-Pair-Share, Discussion Groups

A proof is an argument, a justification, or a reason that something is true. A proof is an answer to the question "why?" when the person asking wants an argument that is indisputable.

There are three basic requirements for constructing a good proof.

- Awareness and knowledge of the definitions of the terms related to what you are trying to prove.

- Knowledge and understanding of postulates and previous proven theorems related to what you are trying to prove.

- Knowledge of the basic rules of logic.

To write a proof, you must be able to justify statements. The statements in Example A are based on the diagram to the right in which lines *AC, EG,* and *DF* all intersect at point *B.* Each of the statements is justified using a property, postulate, or definition.

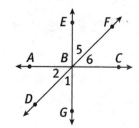

Example A

Name the property, postulate, or definition that justifies each statement.

Statement	Justification
a. If $\angle ABE$ is a right angle, then $m\angle ABE = 90°$.	Definition of right angle
b. If $\angle 2 \cong \angle 1$ and $\angle 1 \cong \angle 5$, then $\angle 2 \cong \angle 5$.	Transitive Property
c. Given: *B* is the midpoint of $\overline{AC}$. Prove: $\overline{AB} \cong \overline{BC}$	Definition of midpoint
d. $m\angle 2 + m\angle ABE = m\angle DBE$	Angle Addition Postulate
e. If $\angle 1$ is supplementary to $\angle FBG$, then $m\angle 1 + m\angle FBG = 180°$.	Definition of supplementary angles

MATH TIP

The Reflexive, Symmetric, and Transitive Properties apply to congruence as well as to equality.

My Notes

Try These A
Using the diagram from the previous page, reproduced here, name the property, postulate, or definition that justifies each statement.

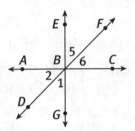

Statement	Justification
a. $EB + BG = EG$	
b. If $\angle 5 \cong \angle 6$, then $\overrightarrow{BF}$ bisects $\angle EBC$.	
c. If $m\angle 1 + m\angle 6 = 90°$, then $\angle 1$ is complementary to $\angle 6$.	
d. If $m\angle 1 + m\angle 5 = m\angle 6 + m\angle 5$, then $m\angle 1 = m\angle 6$.	
e. Given: $\overline{AC} \perp \overline{EG}$ Prove: $\angle ABG$ is a right angle.	

Check Your Understanding

1. Explain why the following statement does not need to be justified.

   The midpoint of a segment is a point on the segment that divides it into two congruent segments.

2. Given: $\overline{RS}$ and $\overline{ST}$ share endpoint S.

   Critique the reasoning of others. Based on this information, Michaela says that the Segment Addition Postulate justifies the statement that $RS + ST = RT$. Is there a flaw in Michaela's reasoning, or is she correct? Explain.

3. **Construct viable arguments.** Write and justify two statements based on the information in the figure.

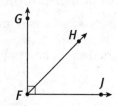

LESSON 6-1 PRACTICE

Lines *CF*, *DH*, and *EA* intersect at point *B*. Use this figure for Items 4–8. Write the definition, postulate, or property that justifies each statement.

4. If $\angle 2$ is supplementary to $\angle CBE$, then $m\angle 2 + m\angle CBE = 180°$.

5. If $\angle 2 \cong \angle 3$, then $\overrightarrow{BF}$ bisects $\angle GBE$.

6. $CB + BF = CF$

7. If $\angle DBF$ is a right angle, then $\overleftrightarrow{HD} \perp \overleftrightarrow{CF}$.

8. If $m\angle 3 = m\angle 6$, then $m\angle 3 + m\angle 2 = m\angle 6 + m\angle 2$.

9. **Reason abstractly.** Write a statement related to the figure above that can be justified by the Angle Addition Postulate.

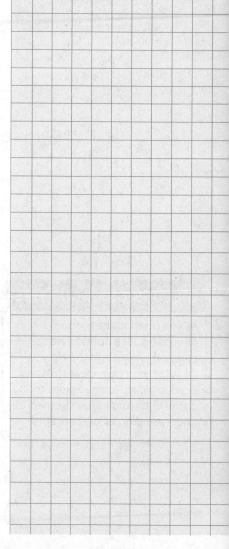

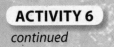

Learning Targets:

- Complete two-column proofs to prove theorems about segments.
- Complete two-column proofs to prove theorems about angles.

SUGGESTED LEARNING STRATEGIES: Vocabulary Organizer, Think-Pair-Share, Close Reading, Discussion Groups, Self Revision/Peer Revision, Group Presentation

Earlier, you wrote two-column proofs to solve algebraic equations. You justified each statement in these proofs by using an algebraic property. Now you will use two-column proofs to prove geometric theorems. You must justify each statement by using a definition, a postulate, a property, or a previously proven theorem.

Recall that *vertical angles* are opposite angles formed by a pair of intersecting lines. In the figure below, $\angle 1$ and $\angle 2$ are vertical angles. The following example illustrates how to prove that vertical angles are congruent.

MATH TERMS

The **Vertical Angles Theorem** states that vertical angles are congruent.

Example A

Theorem: Vertical angles are congruent.

Given: $\angle 1$ and $\angle 2$ are vertical angles.

Prove: $\angle 1 \cong \angle 2$

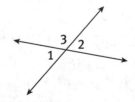

Statements	Reasons
1. $m\angle 1 + m\angle 3 = 180°$	1. Definition of supplementary angles
2. $m\angle 2 + m\angle 3 = 180°$	2. Definition of supplementary angles
3. $m\angle 1 + m\angle 3 = m\angle 2 + m\angle 3$	3. Substitution Property
4. $m\angle 1 = m\angle 2$	4. Subtraction Property of Equality
5. $\angle 1 \cong \angle 2$	5. Definition of congruent angles

Guided Example B

Supply the missing statements and reasons.

Theorem: All right angles are congruent.

Given: $\angle A$ and $\angle B$ are right angles.

Prove: $\angle A \cong \angle B$

Statements	Reasons
1.	1. Given
2. $m\angle A = 90°$; $m\angle B = 90°$	2. Definition of
3. $m\angle A =$	3. Property
4. $\cong \angle B$	4. Definition of

DISCUSSION GROUP TIPS

As you listen to the group discussion, take notes to aid comprehension and to help you describe your own ideas to others in your group. Ask questions to clarify ideas and to gain further understanding of key concepts.

Try These A–B

a. Complete the proof.

Given: Q is the midpoint of $\overline{PR}$.
$\overline{QR} \cong \overline{RS}$

Prove: $\overline{PQ} \cong \overline{RS}$

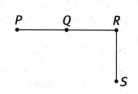

Statements	Reasons
1. Q is the midpoint of $\overline{PR}$.	**1.**
2. $\overline{PQ} \cong \overline{QR}$	**2.**
3. $\overline{QR} \cong \overline{RS}$	**3.**
4. $\overline{PQ} \cong \overline{RS}$	**4.**

MATH TIP

More than one statement in a two-column proof can be given information.

b. Complete the proof.

Given: $\angle 1$ and $\angle 2$ are supplementary.
$m\angle 1 = 68°$

Prove: $m\angle 2 = 112°$

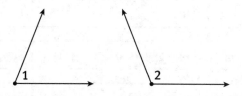

Statements	Reasons
1.	**1.** Given
2.	**2.** Definition of supplementary angles
3.	**3.** Given
4.	**4.** Substitution Property
5.	**5.** Subtraction Property of Equality

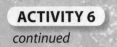

MATH TIP

The theorem stated in Example C is called the Congruent Complements Theorem.

Example C

Arrange the statements and reasons below in a logical order to complete the proof.

Theorem: If two angles are complementary to the same angle, then the two angles are congruent.

Given: $\angle A$ and $\angle B$ are each complementary to $\angle C$.

Prove: $\angle A \cong \angle B$

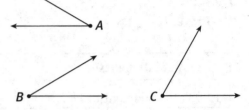

$m\angle A + m\angle C = m\angle B + m\angle C$	Transitive Property

$\angle A$ and $\angle B$ are each complementary to $\angle C$.	Given

$\angle A \cong \angle B$	Definition of congruent segments

$m\angle A = m\angle B$	Subtraction Property of Equality

$m\angle A + m\angle C = 90°$; $m\angle B + m\angle C = 90°$	Definition of complementary angles

Start the proof with the given information. Then decide which statement and reason follow logically from the first statement. Continue until you have proved that $\angle A \cong \angle B$.

Statements	Reasons
1. $\angle A$ and $\angle B$ are each complementary to $\angle C$.	1. Given
2. $m\angle A + m\angle C = 90°$ $m\angle B + m\angle C = 90°$	2. Definition of complementary angles
3. $m\angle A + m\angle C = m\angle B + m\angle C$	3. Transitive Property
4. $m\angle A = m\angle B$	4. Subtraction Property of Equality
5. $\angle A \cong \angle B$	5. Definition of congruent segments

Try These C

a. **Attend to precision.** Arrange the statements and reasons below in a logical order to complete the proof.

Given: $\angle 1$ and $\angle 2$ are vertical angles; $\angle 1 \cong \angle 3$.

Prove: $\angle 2 \cong \angle 3$

$\angle 1 \cong \angle 2$	Vertical angles are congruent.

$\angle 2 \cong \angle 3$	Transitive Property

$\angle 1 \cong \angle 3$	Given

$\angle 1$ and $\angle 2$ are vertical angles.	Given

b. Write a two-column proof of the following theorem.

Theorem: If two angles are supplementary to the same angle, then the two angles are congruent.

Given: $\angle R$ and $\angle S$ are each supplementary to $\angle T$.

Prove: $\angle R \cong \angle S$

Check Your Understanding

1. If you know that $\angle D$ and $\angle F$ are both complementary to $\angle J$, what statement could you prove using the Congruent Complements Theorem?

2. What types of information can you list as reasons in a two-column geometric proof?

3. Kenneth completed this two-column proof. What mistake did he make? How could you correct the mistake?

Given: $\overrightarrow{JL}$ bisects $\angle KJM$; $m\angle KJL = 35°$

Prove: $m\angle LJM = 35°$

Statements	Reasons
1. $\overline{JL}$ bisects $\angle KJM$.	1. Given
2. $\angle KJL \cong \angle LJM$	2. Definition of congruent angles
3. $m\angle KJL = m\angle LJM$	3. Definition of angle bisector
4. $m\angle KJL = 35°$	4. Given
5. $m\angle LJM = 35°$	5. Transitive Property

LESSON 6-2 PRACTICE

4. Supply the missing statements and reasons.

Given: ∠1 is complementary to ∠2; $\overrightarrow{BE}$ bisects ∠DBC.

Prove: ∠1 is complementary to ∠3.

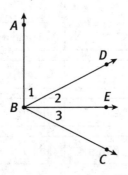

Statements	Reasons
1. $\overrightarrow{BE}$ bisects ∠DBC	1.
2. ∠2 ≅ ∠3	2.
3.	3. Definition of congruent angles
4. ∠1 is complementary to ∠2.	4.
5. $\angle 1 + m\angle 2 = \underline{\quad}$	5.
6. $m\angle 1 + m\angle 3 = 90°$	6.
7.	7. Definition of complementary angles

Construct viable arguments. Write a two-column proof for each of the following.

5. **Given:** M is the midpoint of $\overline{LN}$; $LM = 8$.

   Prove: $LN = 16$

6. **Given:** $\overrightarrow{BD}$ bisects ∠ABC; $m\angle DBC = 90°$.

   Prove: ∠ABC is a straight angle.

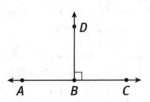

7. **Given:** $\overline{PQ} \cong \overline{QR}$, $QR = 14$, $PR = 14$

   Prove: $\overline{PQ} \cong \overline{PR}$

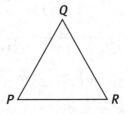

8. **Reason abstractly.** What type of triangle is shown in Item 7? Explain how you know.

ACTIVITY 6 PRACTICE

Write your answers on notebook paper.
Show your work.

Lesson 6-1

Use this diagram to identify the property, postulate, or theorem that justifies each statement in Items 1–4.

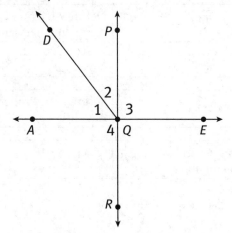

1. $PQ + QR = PR$
   A. Angle Addition Postulate
   B. Addition Property
   C. Definition of congruent segments
   D. Segment Addition Postulate

2. If Q is the midpoint of $\overline{PR}$, then $\overline{PQ} \cong \overline{QR}$.
   A. Definition of midpoint
   B. Definition of congruent segments
   C. Definition of segment bisector
   D. Segment Addition Postulate

3. $\angle 3 \cong \angle 4$
   A. Definition of supplementary
   B. Definition of congruent angles
   C. Vertical angles are congruent
   D. Definition of angle bisector

4. If $\angle 1$ is complementary to $\angle 2$, then $m\angle 1 + m\angle 2 = 90°$.
   A. Angle Addition Postulate
   B. Addition Property
   C. Definition of perpendicular
   D. Definition of complementary

Use this diagram for Items 5–8.

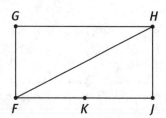

5. Write a statement from the diagram that can be justified by using the Angle Addition Postulate.

6. Write a statement from the diagram that can be justified by using the definition of a right angle.

7. Given that K is the midpoint of $\overline{FJ}$, write a statement that can be justified by using the definition of a midpoint.

8. Given that $\angle GHF \cong \angle JFH$, write a statement that can be justified by using the definition of congruent angles.

Lesson 6-2

9. Complete the proof.

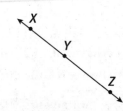

   Given: $XY = 6$, $XZ = 14$
   Prove: $YZ = 8$

Statements		Reasons	
1. $XY = 6$, $XZ = 14$		**1.**	
2. $XY + YZ = XZ$		**2.**	
3. $6 + YZ = 14$		**3.**	
4. $YZ = 8$		**4.**	

10. Based on the given information in Item 9, can you conclude that Y is the midpoint of $\overline{XZ}$? Explain your reasoning.

11. Supply the missing statements and reasons.

Given: $\overrightarrow{PR}$ bisects $\angle QPS$; $\angle QPS$ is a right angle.

Prove: $m\angle RPS = 45°$

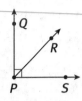

Statements	Reasons
1. $\overrightarrow{PR}$ bisects $\angle QPS$.	**1.** _____
2. $m\angle QPR = m\angle RPS$	**2.** Definition of _____
3. $\angle QPS$ is a right angle.	**3.** _____
4. $m\angle QPS =$ _____	**4.** Definition of _____
5. $m\angle QPR + m\angle RPS =$ $m\angle QPS$	**5.** _____ Postulate
6. $m\angle RPS + m\angle RPS =$ $90°$	**6.** _____ Property
7. $2(m\angle RPS) = 90°$	**7.** Distributive Property
8. $m\angle RPS =$ _____	**8.** _____

12. Complete the proof.

Given: $AC = 2(AB)$

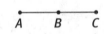

Prove: B is the midpoint of $\overline{AC}$.

Statements	Reasons
1.	**1.** Given
2.	**2.** Segment Addition Postulate
3.	**3.** Transitive Property
4.	**4.** Subtraction Property of Equality
5.	**5.** Definition of congruent segments
6.	**6.** Definition of midpoint

13. Arrange the statements and reasons below in a logical order to complete the proof.

Given: $\angle 1$ and $\angle 2$ are complementary; $m\angle 1 = 28°$.

Prove: $m\angle 2 = 62°$

$28° + m\angle 2 = 90°$	Substitution Property
$m\angle 1 + m\angle 2 = 90°$	Definition of complementary angles
$m\angle 1 = 28°$	Given
$m\angle 2 = 62°$	Subtraction Property of Equality
$\angle 1$ and $\angle 2$ are complementary.	Given

14. Write a two-column proof.

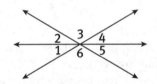

Given: $\angle 1 \cong \angle 2$, $m\angle 4 = 30°$

Prove: $m\angle 2 = 30°$

15. In Item 14, what are the measures of $\angle 3$, $\angle 5$, and $\angle 6$? Explain how you know.

MATHEMATICAL PRACTICES
Construct Viable Arguments and Critique the Reasoning of Others

16. Cara says that the following statement can be justified by the definition of vertical angles. Is her reasoning correct? Explain.

If $\angle G$ and $\angle H$ are vertical angles, then $\angle G \cong \angle H$.

Parallel and Perpendicular Lines

Patios by Madeline
Lesson 7-1 Parallel Lines and Angle Relationships

Learning Targets:

- Make conjectures about the angles formed by a pair of parallel lines and a transversal.
- Prove theorems about these angles.

SUGGESTED LEARNING STRATEGIES: Summarizing, Paraphrasing, Vocabulary Organizer, Interactive Word Wall, Predict and Confirm, Think-Pair-Share, Discussion Groups, Group Presentation, Self Revision/Peer Revision

Matt works for a company called Patios by Madeline. A new customer has asked him to design a patio and walkway. The rows of bricks in the patio will be parallel to the walkway, as shown in the diagram.

So far, Matt has used stakes to tie down two *parallel* strings that he can use to align rows of bricks. He has also used paint to mark the underground gas line to the house so that he can avoid accidents during construction. The string lines and the gas line intersect to form eight angles.

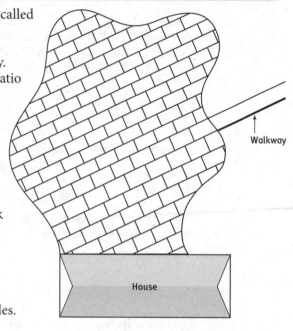

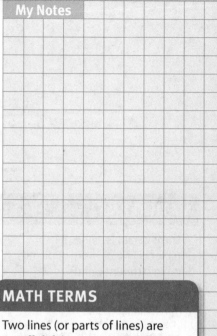

MATH TERMS

Two lines (or parts of lines) are **parallel** if they are coplanar and do not intersect.

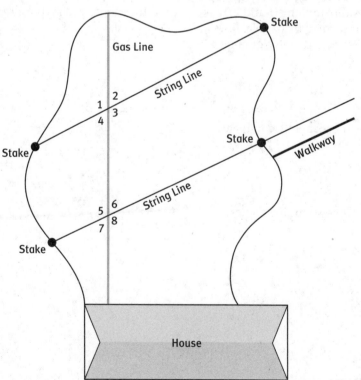

1. **Use appropriate tools strategically.** Use a protractor to measure each of the numbered angles formed by the string lines and the gas line on the previous page.

$m\angle 1 =$ $m\angle 2 =$

$m\angle 3 =$ $m\angle 4 =$

$m\angle 5 =$ $m\angle 6 =$

$m\angle 7 =$ $m\angle 8 =$

2. The gas line is a *transversal* of the string lines. Name the angle pairs formed by these lines that match each description.
   a. Two pairs of *same-side interior angles*

   b. Two pairs of *alternate interior angles*

   c. Four pairs of *corresponding angles*

3. **Express regularity in repeated reasoning.** Based on your answers to Items 1 and 2, make a conjecture about each type of angle pair formed by parallel lines and a transversal.
   a. Same-side interior angles

   b. Alternate interior angles

   c. Corresponding angles

MATH TERMS

A **transversal** is a line that intersects two or more coplanar lines in different points.

When two lines are intersected by a transversal,

- **Same-side interior angles** are a pair of angles that are between the two lines and on the same side of the transversal.
- **Alternate interior angles** are a pair of angles that are between the two lines and on opposite sides of the transversal.
- **Corresponding angles** are a pair of nonadjacent angles such that the angles are on the same side of the transversal and one angle is outside the two lines and one angle is between the two lines.

---

4. The lines below are parallel.
   a. Draw a transversal to the parallel lines.

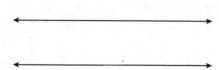

   b. Number the angles formed above and record the measure of each angle.

TECHNOLOGY TIP

You can also use geometry software to draw two parallel lines and a transversal. You can then use the software to measure the angles formed by the intersecting lines.

5. **Construct viable arguments.** Do your answers to Item 4 *confirm* the conjectures you made in Item 3? Explain. Revise your conjectures if needed.

ACADEMIC VOCABULARY

Evidence that *confirms* a conjecture provides support for the conjecture.

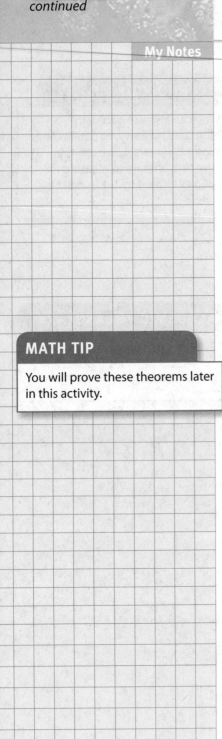

MATH TIP

You will prove these theorems later in this activity.

6. The Same-Side Interior Angles Postulate involves angles formed by two parallel lines cut by a transversal.
   a. Reason abstractly. Based on your earlier conjecture, write the Same-Side Interior Angles Postulate in if-then form.

   b. Do you need to prove that this postulate is true before you can use it as a reason in a proof? Explain.

7. The Alternate Interior Angles Theorem and the Corresponding Angles Theorem also involve angles formed by two parallel lines cut by a transversal.
   a. Based on your earlier conjecture, write the Alternate Interior Angles Theorem in if-then form.

   b. Based on your earlier conjecture, write the Corresponding Angles Theorem in if-then form.

Check Your Understanding

In the diagram, $\ell \parallel m$. Use the diagram for Items 8–10.

8. Explain how you know that $\angle 4$ and $\angle 6$ are same-side interior angles.

9. Are $\angle 2$ and $\angle 3$ corresponding angles? Explain how you know.

10. If $m\angle 5 = 65°$, then what is $m\angle 4$? Support your answer.

11. $\angle BCD$ and $\angle CGE$ are corresponding angles formed by two parallel lines cut by a transversal. Given that $m\angle BCD = 3x + 6$ and $m\angle CGE = x + 24$, complete the following.
    a. What is the value of x?
    b. What is $m\angle BCD$?
    c. Explain how you found your answers.

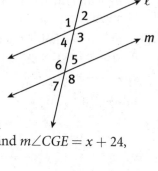

READING MATH

The symbol $\parallel$ means "is parallel to." So, $\ell \parallel m$ means "line ℓ is parallel to line m."

12. **Reason quantitatively.** Complete the following proof of the Corresponding Angles Theorem.

    Given: $m \parallel n$
    Prove: $\angle 1 \cong \angle 5$

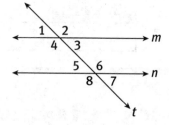

MATH TIP

It is sufficient to prove that one pair of corresponding angles formed by a pair of parallel lines and a transversal are congruent.

Statements	Reasons
1. $m \parallel n$	1.
2. $m\angle 1 + m\angle 4 = 180°$	2. Angle Addition Postulate
3. $\angle 1$ and $\angle 4$ are supplementary.	3.
4. $\angle 4$ and $\angle 5$ are supplementary.	4.
5.	5. Congruent Supplements Theorem

MATH TIP

The Congruent Supplements Theorem states that if two angles are supplementary to the same angle, then they are congruent.

My Notes

MATH TIP

Do not assume that lines in a diagram are parallel just because they appear to be parallel. You can only conclude that lines are parallel if (1) you are given this information in the text or in a diagram, or (2) you prove that the lines are parallel.

Check Your Understanding

13. Look back at your proof in Item 12.
   a. Explain how you know that $\angle 1$ and $\angle 5$ are corresponding angles.
   b. Explain how you know that $\angle 4$ and $\angle 5$ are same-side interior angles.

14. Complete the following proof of the Alternate Interior Angles Theorem.

Given: $m \parallel n$

Prove: $\angle 4 \cong \angle 6$

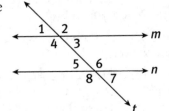

Statements	Reasons
1.	1.
2. $\angle 4 \cong \angle 2$	2.
3. $\angle 2 \cong \angle 6$	3.
4.	4.

LESSON 7-1 PRACTICE

In the diagram, $a \parallel b$. Use the diagram for Items 15–20. Determine whether each statement in Items 15–18 is true or false. Justify your response with the appropriate postulate or theorem.

15. $\angle 2$ is supplementary to $\angle 3$.

16. $\angle 8 \cong \angle 6$

17. $\angle 7$ is supplementary to $\angle 3$.

18. $\angle 6 \cong \angle 4$

19. If $m\angle 2 = 8x - 20$, and $m\angle 3 = 5x + 5$, what is $m\angle 2$? What is $m\angle 3$?

20. **Reason quantitatively.** Based on your answer to Item 19, what are the measures of the other numbered angles in the diagram? Explain your reasoning.

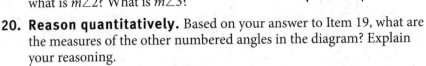

Learning Targets:

- Develop theorems to show that lines are parallel.
- Determine whether lines are parallel.

> **SUGGESTED LEARNING STRATEGIES:** Visualization, Create Representations, Predict and Confirm, Think-Pair-Share, Debriefing, Discussion Groups, Group Presentation

1. **Make use of structure.** State the converse of each postulate or theorem.
   a. Same-Side Interior Angles Postulate

   b. Alternate Interior Angles Theorem

   c. Corresponding Angles Theorem

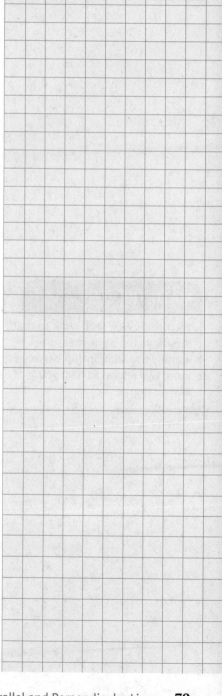

> **MATH TIP**
>
> The converse of the statement "If *p*, then *q*" is "If *q*, then *p*." If a conditional statement is true, the converse of the statement may or may not be true.

With your group, reread the problem scenario as needed. Make notes on the information provided in the problem. Respond to questions about the meaning of key information and organize the information needed to create a reasonable solution.

Matt is working on the blueprint for the new patio, as shown on the next page. Add information to the blueprint as you work through this lesson.

To ensure that the rows of bricks will be parallel to the walkway, Matt extends the string line along the edge of the walkway and labels points, *X*, *A*, and *Y*. He also labels points *B*, *C*, *D*, and *E* where additional string lines will cross the gas line.

2. Follow these steps.
   a. Use a protractor to measure ∠*HAX*.

   b. Locate a stake on the left edge of the patio at point *P* by drawing $\overline{BP}$ so that m∠*HBP* = m∠*HAX*.

   c. Locate a stake on the right edge of the patio at point *J* by extending $\overline{BP}$ in the opposite direction.

ACTIVITY 7
continued

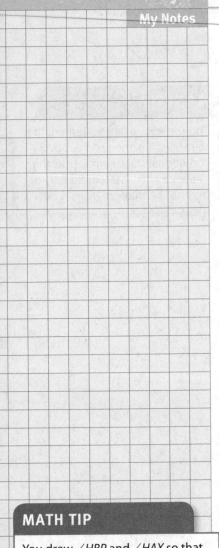

Matt's Blueprint

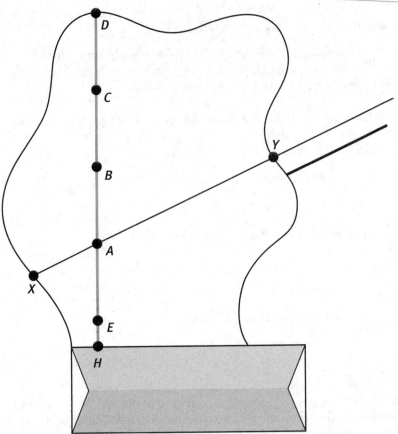

3. For which converse from Item 1 does your drawing from Item 2 provide support? Explain.

MATH TIP

You drew ∠*HBP* and ∠*HAX* so that they have the same measure. Identify the relationship between these two angles to help you answer Item 3.

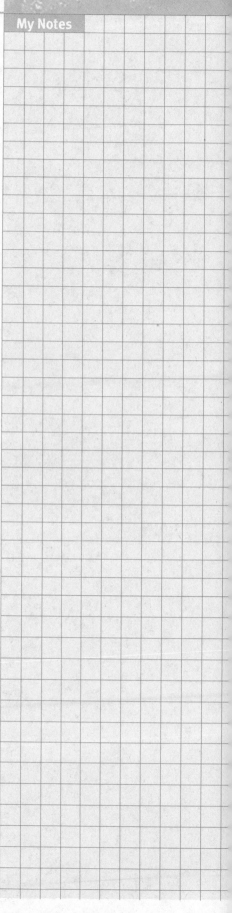

My Notes

4. Matt realizes that he is not limited to using corresponding angles to draw parallel lines. Use a protractor to draw another parallel string through point *C* on the blueprint, using alternate interior angles. Mark the angles that you used to draw this new parallel line.

5. Explain how your drawing from Item 4 provides support for the converse of the Alternate Interior Angles Theorem.

6. **Use appropriate tools strategically.** Use a protractor to draw another parallel string through point *E* on the blueprint, using same-side interior angles. Mark the angles that were used to draw this new parallel line.

7. **Reason abstractly.** Explain how your drawing from Item 6 provides support for the converse of the Same-Side Interior Angles Theorem.

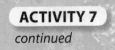
ACTIVITY 7
continued

My Notes

The converses of the Same-Side Interior Angle Postulate, the Alternate Interior Angles Theorem, and the Corresponding Angles Theorem are all true, as indicated by the string lines you drew on the blueprint.

Look back at Item 1 in this lesson to review the converses of these theorems and postulate.

8. **Attend to precision.** Matt's assistant sets up two string lines as shown. Matt finds that $m\angle 2 = 63°$ and $m\angle 6 = 65°$. Explain how Matt can tell that the strings are not parallel.

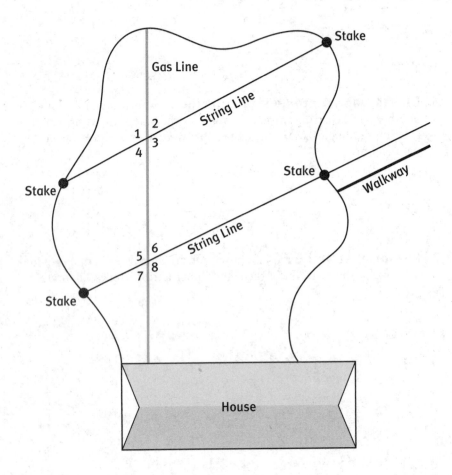

Check Your Understanding

9. Refer back to Item 8. How could Matt adjust the strings so that they are parallel?

10. What is the inverse of the Alternate Interior Angles Theorem? Is the inverse true? Explain how you know.

11. Complete the following proof of the Converse of the Corresponding Angles Theorem.

    Given: $\angle 1 \cong \angle 5$

    Prove: $m \parallel n$

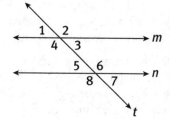

Statements	Reasons
1.	1.
2. $m\angle 1 = m\angle 5$	2.
3. $m\angle 1 + m\angle 4 = 180°$	3. Linear Pair Postulate
4. $m\angle 5 + m\angle 4 = 180°$	4.
5. $\angle 5$ and $\angle 4$ are supplementary.	5.
6.	6. Converse of the Same-Side Interior Angles Postulate

LESSON 7-2 PRACTICE

For Items 12–14, use the diagram to answer each question. Then justify your answer.

12. Given that $m\angle 1 = 52°$ and $m\angle 7 = 52°$, is $m \parallel p$?

13. Given that $m\angle 11 = 52°$ and $m\angle 3 = 56°$, is $m \parallel n$?

14. Given that $m\angle 10 = 124°$ and $m\angle 7 = 52°$, is $n \parallel p$?

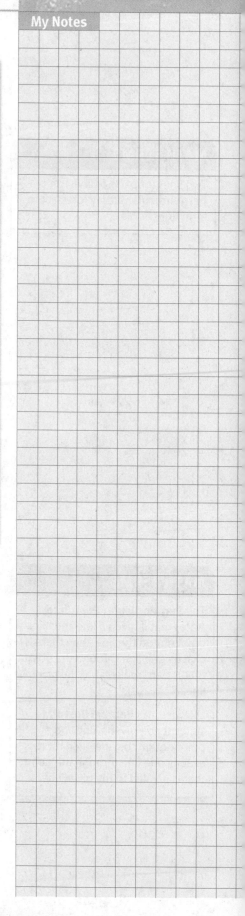

15. **Reason abstractly.** Two lines are cut by a transversal such that a pair of alternate interior angles are right angles. Are the two lines parallel? Explain.

16. **Model with mathematics.** Describe how a stadium worker can determine whether two yard lines painted on a football field are parallel. Assume that the worker has a protractor, string, and two stakes.

My Notes

Learning Targets:
- Develop theorems to show that lines are perpendicular.
- Determine whether lines are perpendicular.

> **SUGGESTED LEARNING STRATEGIES:** Activating Prior Knowledge, Think Aloud, Think-Pair-Share, Create Representations, RAFT

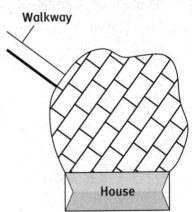

A second customer of Patios by Madeline has hired the company to build a patio with rows of bricks that are *perpendicular* to the walkway, as shown at right.

Matt is planning the design for this patio. So far, he has extended a line along the walkway and labeled points X and Y to mark stakes at the edge of the patio. He has also drawn point W to mark another stake at the edge of the patio, as shown below.

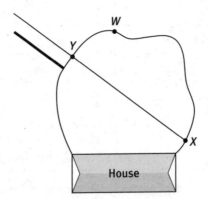

1. Use a protractor to draw the line perpendicular to $\overleftrightarrow{XY}$ that passes through W. Label the point at which the line intersects $\overleftrightarrow{XY}$ point Z.

2. **Use appropriate tools strategically.** Use your protractor and your knowledge of parallel lines to draw a line, across the patio, parallel to $\overleftrightarrow{WZ}$. Explain how you know the lines are parallel.

MATH TERMS

Two lines (or parts of lines) are **perpendicular** if they intersect to form right angles.

MATH TERMS

The **Perpendicular Postulate** states that if given a line and a point not on the line, then there is exactly one line through the point that is perpendicular to the given line.

Likewise, the **Parallel Postulate** states that if given a line and a point not on the line, then there is exactly one line through the point that is parallel to the given line.

3. Describe the relationship between the newly drawn line and $\overleftrightarrow{XY}$.

4. Critique the reasoning of others. Matt reasons that if a transversal is perpendicular to one of two parallel lines, then it is perpendicular to the other line. Show that Matt's conjecture is true. Include a diagram in your answer.

5. Matt draws $\overline{AB}$ on his design of the patio so that $\overleftrightarrow{XY}$ is the ***perpendicular bisector*** of $\overline{AB}$. $\overleftrightarrow{XY}$ intersects $\overline{AB}$ at point M. List three conclusions you can draw from this information.

My Notes

MATH TERMS

The **Perpendicular Transversal Theorem** states that if a transversal is perpendicular to one of two parallel lines, then it is perpendicular to the other line.

MATH TIP

In Item 4, start by drawing line m parallel to line n. Then draw transversal t so that it is perpendicular to m.

You want to show that $t \perp n$ given that $m \parallel n$ and $t \perp m$. Number the angles in your diagram as needed so that you can refer to them in your answer.

MATH TERMS

A **perpendicular bisector** of a segment is a line (or part of a line) that intersects the segment at its midpoint to form right angles.

TECHNOLOGY TIP

An instruction guide often includes diagrams to make the text easier to understand. You can create diagrams for your instruction guide by hand or by using geometry software.

6. Matt's boss Madeline is so impressed with Matt's work that she asks him to write an instruction guide for creating rows of bricks parallel to a patio walkway. Madeline asks that the guide provide enough information so that a bricklayer can use any pair of angles (same-side interior, alternate interior, or corresponding) to determine the location of each pair of stakes. She also requests that Matt include directions for creating rows of bricks that are perpendicular to a walkway. Write Matt's instruction guide, following Madeline's directions.

Check Your Understanding

7. **Reason abstractly.** Lines a, b, and c lie in the same plane. If $a \perp b$ and $b \perp c$, can you conclude that $a \perp c$? Explain. Include a drawing to support your answer.

8. $\overline{RS}$ is the perpendicular bisector of $\overline{JL}$. Can you conclude that point K is the midpoint of $\overline{RS}$? Explain.

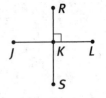

LESSON 7-3 PRACTICE

In the diagram, $\ell \parallel m$, $m\angle 1 = 90°$, and $\angle 5$ is a right angle. Use the diagram for Items 46–48.

9. Explain how you know that $\ell \perp p$.

10. Show that $m\angle 4 = 90°$.

11. **Make use of structure.** Show that $\ell \parallel n$.

12. The perpendicular bisector of $\overline{CD}$ intersects CD at point P. If $CP = 12$, what is CD?

13. An angle formed by the intersection of two lines is obtuse. Could the lines be perpendicular? Explain.

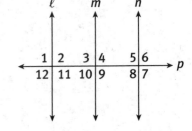

ACTIVITY 7 PRACTICE
Write your answers on notebook paper.
Show your work.

Lesson 7-1

Use this diagram for Items 1–10.

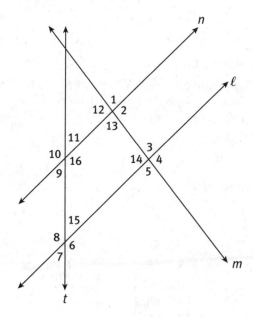

1. List all angles in the diagram that form a corresponding angle pair with ∠5.

2. List all angles in the diagram that form an alternate interior angle pair with ∠14.

3. List all angles in the diagram that form a same side interior angle pair with ∠14.

4. Given $\ell \parallel n$. If $m\angle 6 = 120°$, then $m\angle 16 = \underline{\quad ? \quad}$.

5. Given $\ell \parallel n$. If $m\angle 12 = 5x + 10$ and $m\angle 14 = 6x - 4$, then $x = \underline{\quad ? \quad}$ and $m\angle 4 = \underline{\quad ? \quad}$.

6. Given $\ell \parallel n$. If $m\angle 14 = 75°$, then $m\angle 2 = \underline{\quad ? \quad}$.

7. Given $\ell \parallel n$. If $m\angle 9 = 3x + 12$ and $m\angle 15 = 2x + 27$, then $x = \underline{\quad ? \quad}$ and $m\angle 10 = \underline{\quad ? \quad}$.

8. Given $\ell \parallel n$. If $m\angle 3 = 100°$, then $m\angle 2 = \underline{\quad ? \quad}$.

9. Given $\ell \parallel n$. If $m\angle 16 = 5x + 18$ and $m\angle 15 = 3x + 2$, then $x = \underline{\quad ? \quad}$ and $m\angle 8 = \underline{\quad ? \quad}$.

10. If $m\angle 10 = 135°$, $m\angle 12 = 75°$, and $\ell \parallel n$ determine the measure of each angle. Justify each answer.
    a. $m\angle 16$
    b. $m\angle 15$
    c. $m\angle 8$
    d. $m\angle 14$
    e. $m\angle 3$

11. Supply the missing statements and reasons.

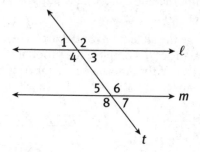

Given: $\ell \parallel m$
Prove: $\angle 1 \cong \angle 7$

Statements	Reasons
1.	1. Given
2. $\angle 1 \cong \angle 5$	2.
3. $\angle 5 \cong \angle 7$	3.
4.	4.

12. Two parallel lines are cut by a transversal. How are the corresponding angles and same-side interior angles alike?
    A. The angles in each pair are congruent.
    B. The angles in each pair are supplementary.
    C. The angles in each pair are between the parallel lines.
    D. The angles in each pair are on the same side of the transversal.

Lesson 7-2

Use this diagram for Items 13–15.

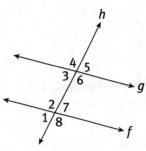

13. If $m\angle 2 = 110°$ and $m\angle 3 = 80°$, is $f \parallel g$? Justify your answer.

14. If $\angle 8 \cong \angle 4$, is $f \parallel g$? Justify your answer.

15. Given that $m\angle 5 = 12x + 4$ and $m\angle 7 = 10x + 16$, what must the value of x be in order for line f to be parallel to line g?

16. If $a \parallel b$ and $b \parallel c$, can you conclude that $a \parallel c$? Explain. Include a drawing to support your answer.

17. Arrange the statements and reasons below in a logical order to complete the proof of the Converse of the Alternate Interior Angles Theorem.

Given: $\angle 4 \cong \angle 6$

Prove: $m \parallel n$

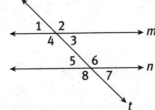

$m\angle 5 + m\angle 6 = 180°$	Linear Pair Postulate
$\angle 4 \cong \angle 6$	Given
$m\angle 5 + m\angle 4 = 180°$	Substitution Property
$\angle 5$ and $\angle 4$ are supplementary.	Definition of supplementary angles
$m\angle 4 = m\angle 6$	Definition of congruent angles
$m \parallel n$	Converse of the Same-Side Interior Angles Postulate

Lesson 7-3

Use this diagram for Items 18–20.

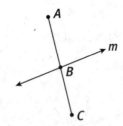

18. What information do you need to know to prove that line m is the perpendicular bisector of $\overline{AC}$?

19. Given that line m is the perpendicular bisector of $\overline{AC}$, $AB = 4x - 1$, and $BC = 2x + 7$, what is the value of x?

20. Based on your answer to Item 19, what is AC?
- **A.** 11
- **B.** 15
- **C.** 22
- **D.** 30

21. How many lines perpendicular to line l can you draw through point P? Explain how you know.

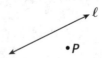

22. Complete the proof.

Theorem: If two lines in the same plane are perpendicular to the same line, then the lines are parallel to each other.

Given: $l \perp n$,
$\qquad m \perp n$

Prove: $l \parallel m$

Statements	Reasons
1.	1. Given
2. $\angle 2$ is a right angle; $\angle 6$ is a right angle	2.
3. $\angle 2 \cong \angle 6$	3.
4.	4.

MATHEMATICAL PRACTICES
Look for and Express Regularity in Repeated Reasoning

23. Suppose you are given the measure of one of the angles formed when a pair of parallel lines is cut by a transversal. Explain how to use this measure to find the measures of the other seven angles.

Equations of Parallel and Perpendicular Lines

Skateboard Geometry
Lesson 8-1 Slopes of Parallel and Perpendicular Lines

Learning Targets:

- Make conjectures about the slopes of parallel and perpendicular lines.
- Use slope to determine whether lines are parallel or perpendicular.

> **SUGGESTED LEARNING STRATEGIES:** Look for a Pattern, Activating Prior Knowledge, Visualization, Debriefing

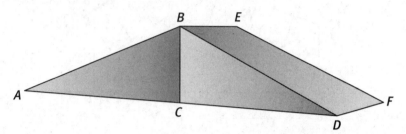

The new ramp at the local skate park is shown above. In addition to the wooden ramp, an aluminum rail (not shown) is mounted to the edge of the ramp. While the image of the ramp may conjure thoughts of kickflips, nollies, and nose grinds, there are mathematical forces at work here as well.

1. Use the diagram of the ramp to complete the chart below:

Describe two parts of the ramp that appear to be parallel.	
Describe two parts of the ramp that appear to be perpendicular.	
Describe two parts of the ramp that appear to be neither parallel nor perpendicular.	

My Notes

My Notes

MATH TIP

The *slope* of a line is the ratio of the rise, or vertical change, to the run, or horizontal change, between two points on the line.

CONNECT **TO** **ALGEBRA**

If (x_1, y_1) and (x_2, y_2) are two points on a line, then the slope m of the line can be calculated as follows.

$$m = \frac{y_2 - y_1}{x_2 - x_1}$$

Recall that the *slope* of a line is the ratio of the vertical change to the horizontal change between two points on the line.

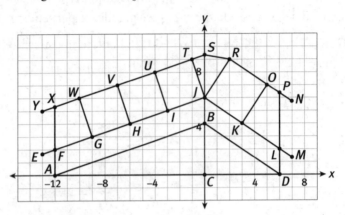

2. The diagram above shows a cross-section of the skate ramp and its railing transposed onto a coordinate grid. Find the slopes of the following segments.

   a. $\overline{AB}$

   b. $\overline{XT}$

   c. $\overline{WG}$

   d. $\overline{TJ}$

   e. $\overline{AD}$

3. **Model with mathematics.** Complete the chart by stating whether each pair of segments appear to be parallel, perpendicular, or neither. Then list the slopes of the segments.

Segments	Parallel, Perpendicular, or Neither?	Slopes
$\overline{AB}$ and $\overline{XT}$		
$\overline{WG}$ and $\overline{TJ}$		
$\overline{XT}$ and $\overline{WG}$		
$\overline{XT}$ and $\overline{TJ}$		
$\overline{AB}$ and $\overline{AD}$	neither	
$\overline{WG}$ and $\overline{AD}$	neither	

4. **Express regularity in repeated reasoning.** Based on the chart in Item 3, make conjectures about the slopes of each type of segments.
   a. Parallel segments

   b. Perpendicular segments

   c. Segments that are neither parallel nor perpendicular

My Notes

Check Your Understanding

5. Do the conjectures you wrote in Item 4 apply to lines as well as segments? Explain.

6. **Reason abstractly.** Are all horizontal lines parallel? Use slope to explain how you know.

7. $\overline{JK}$ has a slope of $\frac{2}{5}$, and $\overline{MN}$ has a slope of $\frac{5}{2}$. Are these segments parallel, perpendicular, or neither? Explain.

LESSON 8-1 PRACTICE

Use slope to support your answers to Items 8–10.

8. Is $\overleftrightarrow{AB} \parallel \overleftrightarrow{DC}$?

9. Is $\overleftrightarrow{AB} \perp \overleftrightarrow{AD}$?

10. Is $\overleftrightarrow{DC} \perp \overleftrightarrow{AD}$?

11. **Reason quantitatively.** Line ℓ passes through the origin and the point (3, 4). What is the slope of a line parallel to line ℓ?

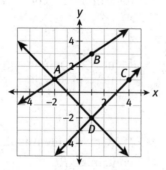

12. $\angle RST$ is a right angle. If $\overline{RS}$ has a slope of 3, what must be the slope of $\overline{ST}$? Explain.

My Notes

Learning Targets:

● Write the equation of a line that is parallel to a given line.
● Write the equation of a line that is perpendicular to a given line.

SUGGESTED LEARNING STRATEGIES: Predict and Confirm, Look for a Pattern, Identify a Subtask, Discussion Groups, Create Representations, Think-Pair-Share, Self Revision/Peer Revision, Visualization, Identify a Subtask

Here again is the diagram of the skate ramp and its railing.

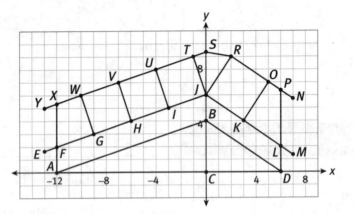

1. The equation of the line containing $\overline{BD}$ is $y = -\frac{2}{3}x + 4$. Identify the slope and the y-intercept of this line.

2. Based on your conjectures in Item 4 in the previous lesson, what would be the slope of the line containing $\overline{JM}$? Use the formula for slope to verify your answer or provide an explanation of the method you used to determine the slope.

3. Identify the y-intercept of the line containing $\overline{JM}$. Use the slope and the y-intercept to write the equation of this line.

4. If $\overline{JM} \perp \overline{RJ}$, identify the slope, y-intercept, and the equation for the line containing $\overline{RJ}$.

5. **Construct viable arguments.** Is $\overline{BD} \perp \overline{RJ}$? Explain your reasoning.

CONNECT TO ALGEBRA

The equation of a line in slope-intercept form is $y = mx + b$, where m represents the slope and b represents the y-intercept of the line.

MATH TIP

The y-intercept of a line is the y-coordinate of the point where the line crosses the y-axis.

The skate park will also have an angled grind rail. A drafter is drawing the grind rail on a coordinate plane.

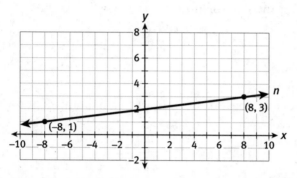

CONNECT TO CAREERS

A drafter creates technical drawings of plans made by engineers and architects. Drafters primarily use computer software to make their drawings. The software positions items such as lines and curves by using a coordinate system.

6. **Make sense of problems.** The drafter has already drawn line n. Next, the drafter needs to draw line p so that it is parallel to line n and passes through point $(-2, 3)$.

   a. What is the slope of line p? How do you know?

   b. What is the equation of line p written in point-slope form?

   c. What is the equation of line p written in slope-intercept form?

CONNECT TO ALGEBRA

The point-slope form of a linear equation is $y - y_1 = m(x - x_1)$, where m is the slope and (x_1, y_1) is a point on the line.

   d. Sketch line p on the drafter's coordinate plane.

My Notes

> **MATH TIP**
>
> If two numbers are opposite reciprocals, then their product is −1.

7. Next, the drafter needs to draw line q so that it is perpendicular to line n and passes through point $(-9, 7)$.

a. What is the slope of line q? How do you know?

b. What is the equation of line q written in point-slope form?

c. What is the equation of line q written in slope-intercept form?

d. Sketch line q on the drafter's coordinate plane.

8. Model with mathematics. Finally, the drafter needs to draw line r so that it is perpendicular to line n and passes through point $(8, 0)$.

a. What is the equation of line r written in point-slope form?

b. What is the equation of line r written in slope-intercept form?

c. Sketch line r on the drafter's coordinate plane.

My Notes

9. **Reason abstractly and quantitatively.** Describe the relationships among the lines n, p, q, and r.

Quadrilaterals can be classified by the presence or absence of parallel lines, and by the presence or absence of perpendicular lines.

10. Which specific quadrilateral is formed by the intersection of the four lines? Explain how you know.

Check Your Understanding

11. What is the slope of a line parallel to the line with equation $y = \frac{4}{5}x - 7$?

12. What is the slope of a line perpendicular to the line with equation $y = -2x + 1$?

13. Consider the lines described below.

    line a: a line with the equation $y = \frac{3}{5}x - 2$

    line b: a line containing the points $(-6, 1)$ and $(3, -14)$

    line c: a line containing the points $(-1, 8)$ and $(4, 11)$

    line d: a line with the equation $-5x + 3y = 6$

    Use the vocabulary from the lesson to write a paragraph that describes the relationships among lines a, b, c, and d.

14. What is the slope of a line parallel to the line with equation $y = -3$? What is the slope of a line perpendicular to the line with equation $y = -3$? Explain your reasoning.

15. **Construct viable arguments.** Suppose you are given the equation of a line and the coordinates of a point not on the line. Explain how to write the equation of a parallel line that passes through the point.

MATH TIP

For Item 13, start by finding the slope of each line.

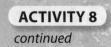

LESSON 8-2 PRACTICE

16. What is the equation of a line parallel to $y = -3x + 5$ that passes through point $(6, 8)$?

17. What is the equation of a line perpendicular to $y = \frac{1}{4}x - 3$ that passes through point $(-2, 4)$?

Use the coordinate plane for Items 24–26.

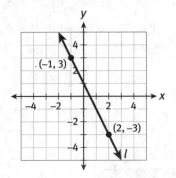

18. What is the equation of the line parallel to line ℓ that passes through point $(3, 3)$?

19. What is the equation of the line perpendicular to line ℓ that passes through point $(3, 3)$?

20. How could you check that your answer to Item 19 is reasonable?

21. Reason abstractly and quantitatively. $\triangle ABC$ has vertices at the points $A(-2, 3)$, $B(7, 4)$, and $C(5, 22)$. What kind of triangle is $\triangle ABC$? Explain your answer.

ACTIVITY 8 PRACTICE
Write your answers on notebook paper.
Show your work.

Lesson 8-1

1. Determine the slope of the line that contains the points with coordinates $(1, 5)$ and $(-2, 7)$.

2. Line m contains the points with coordinates $(-4, 1)$ and $(5, 8)$, and line n contains the points with coordinates $(6, -2)$ and $(10, 7)$. Are the lines parallel, perpendicular, or neither? Justify your answer.

A drafter finished the first stage of a drawing of a metal part. Use the drawing for Items 3–6.

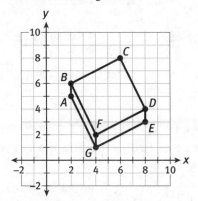

3. The drafter needs to confirm that $\overline{AG} \parallel \overline{CD}$. Are these segments parallel? Explain.

4. The drafter also needs to confirm that $\overline{BF} \perp \overline{FD}$. Are these segments perpendicular? Explain.

5. Which segments in the diagram are perpendicular to $\overline{GE}$?

6. Name a segment that is neither parallel nor perpendicular to $\overline{BC}$.

7. $\overrightarrow{PQ}$ has a slope of $\frac{1}{3}$. What is the slope of a line perpendicular to $\overrightarrow{PQ}$?

   A. -3 **B.** $-\frac{1}{3}$

   C. $\frac{1}{3}$ **D.** 3

8. $\overrightarrow{VW}$ has a slope of 5. What is the slope of a line parallel to $\overrightarrow{VW}$?

   A. -5 **B.** $-\frac{1}{5}$

   C. $\frac{1}{5}$ **D.** 5

Use the diagram for Items 9 and 10.

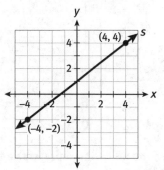

9. What is the slope of a line parallel to line s?

10. What is the slope of a line perpendicular to line s?

Lesson 8-2

11. Which of the following is NOT an equation for a line parallel to $y = \frac{1}{2}x - 6$?

    A. $y = \frac{2}{4}x + 6$ **B.** $y = 0.5x - 3$

    C. $y = \frac{1}{2}x + 1$ **D.** $y = 2x - 4$

12. Determine the slope of a line perpendicular to the line with equation $6x - 4y = 30$.

Use the diagram for Items 13 and 14.

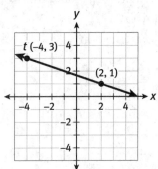

13. Which of the following represents a line parallel to line *t*?

A. $y = -x + 7$ **B.** $y = -\frac{1}{3}x + 5$

C. $y = \frac{1}{3}x - 2$ **D.** $y = x - 4$

14. Which of the following represents a line perpendicular to line *t*?

A. $y = -3x + 4$ **B.** $y = -\frac{1}{3}x - 1$

C. $y = \frac{1}{3}x - 5$ **D.** $y = 3x + 4$

15. Consider the line with equation $y = -2x + 2$.
 a. Can you write the equation of a line through point $(3, -4)$ that is parallel to the given line? Explain.
 b. Can you write the equation of a line through point $(3, -4)$ that is perpendicular to the given line? Explain.

16. Suppose you are given the equation of a line and the coordinates of a point not on the line. Explain how to write the equation of a perpendicular line that passes through the point.

17. What is the equation of a line through point $(0, 5)$ that is parallel to the line with equation $y = x - 7$?

18. What is the equation of a line through point $(-4, 5)$ that is perpendicular to the line with equation $y = -6x + 4$?

Use the diagram for Items 19 and 20.

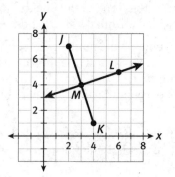

19. Use the Distance Formula to show that $\overline{JM} \cong \overline{MK}$.

20. Is $\overline{LM}$ the perpendicular bisector of $\overline{JK}$? Explain how you know.

MATHEMATICAL PRACTICES
Make Sense of Problems and Persevere in Solving them

21. A drafter is drawing quadrilateral *ABCD* as part of an architectural blueprint. She needs to position point *C* so that $\overline{BC} \parallel \overline{AD}$ and $\overline{CD} \perp \overline{AD}$.

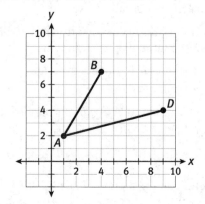

 a. What should be the coordinates of point *C*? Explain how you determined your answer.
 b. Describe how you can check that your answer is reasonable.

Angles, Parallel Lines, and Perpendicular Lines

GRAPH OF STEEL

The first hill of the Steel Dragon 2000 roller coaster in Nagashima, Japan, drops riders from a height of 318 ft. A portion of this first hill has been transposed onto a coordinate plane and is shown to the right.

1. The structure of the supports for the hill consists of steel beams that run parallel and perpendicular to one another. The endpoints of the beam shown by $\overline{BC}$ are (0, 150) and (120, 0). The endpoints of the beam shown by $\overline{AD}$ are (0, 125) and (100, 0).

   a. Verify and explain why the two beams are parallel.
   b. If $\angle DAB = 125°$, what is the measure of $\angle CBA$? Justify your reasoning.

2. Determine the equations of the lines containing the beams from Item 1, and explain how the equations of the lines can help you determine that the beams are parallel.

3. A third support beam is perpendicular to the beam shown by $\overline{BC}$. If marked on the coordinate plane, the line containing this beam would pass through the point (60, 75). What is the equation of the line containing this third beam? Explain how you determined your answer.

The diagram below shows a section of the steel support structure of a roller coaster. Use the diagram for Items 4–6.

4. Given $\overline{JK} \parallel \overline{PL}$, $m\angle JKL = (10x + 5)°$ and $\angle PLK = (12x - 1)°$, what is the measure, in degrees, of $\angle JKL$ and $\angle PLK$? Explain how you determined your answer.

5. Explain how an engineer could determine whether $\overline{PN} \parallel \overline{LM}$ by measuring two angles in the diagram.

6. Write a two-column proof.
   Given: $\overline{JK} \parallel \overline{PL}$, $\angle 1 \cong \angle 2$
   Prove: $\angle 3 \cong \angle 4$

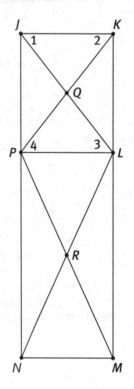

Scoring Guide	Exemplary	Proficient	Emerging	Incomplete
	The solution demonstrates these characteristics:			
Mathematics Knowledge and Thinking (Items 1, 2, 3, 4, 5)	• Clear and accurate understanding of slopes of parallel and perpendicular lines • Clear and accurate understanding of pairs of angles formed by parallel lines cut by a transversal	• A functional understanding of slopes of parallel and perpendicular lines • Adequate understanding of pairs of angles formed by parallel lines cut by a transversal	• Partial understanding of slopes of parallel and perpendicular lines • Partial understanding of pairs of angles formed by parallel lines cut by a transversal	• Little or no understanding of slopes of parallel and perpendicular lines • Little or no understanding of pairs of angles formed by parallel lines cut by a transversal
Problem Solving (Items 1, 2, 3, 4, 6)	• An appropriate and efficient strategy that results in a correct answer	• A strategy that may include unnecessary steps but results in a correct answer	• A strategy that results in some incorrect answers	• No clear strategy when solving problems
Mathematical Modeling / Representations (Items 2, 3, 4)	• Clear and accurate understanding of determining slope and creating an equation to represent a line • Clear and accurate understanding of creating an equation to represent the relationship between a pair of angles formed by parallel lines cut by a transversal	• Mostly correct understanding of determining slope and creating an equation to represent a line • A functional understanding of creating an equation to represent the relationship between a pair of angles formed by parallel lines cut by a transversal	• Partial understanding of determining slope and creating an equation to represent a line • Partially correct understanding of creating an equation to represent the relationship between a pair of angles formed by parallel lines cut by a transversal	• Inaccurate or incomplete understanding of determining slope and creating an equation to represent a line • Little or no understanding of creating an equation to represent the relationship between a pair of angles formed by parallel lines cut by a transversal
Reasoning and Communication (Items 1, 2, 3, 4, 5, 6)	• Precise explanation of the relationships between the slopes of parallel and perpendicular lines • Precise use of appropriate math terms and language to justify the relationships between angles formed by parallel lines cut by a transversal • Clear and accurate proof	• Adequate explanation of the relationships between the slopes of parallel and perpendicular lines • Adequate use of appropriate math terms and language to justify the relationships between angles formed by parallel lines cut by a transversal • Mostly correct proof	• Misleading or confusing characterization of the relationships between the slopes of parallel and perpendicular lines • Misleading or confusing explanation of the relationships between angles formed by parallel lines cut by a transversal • Partially correct proof	• Incomplete or inaccurate characterization of the relationships between the slopes of parallel and perpendicular lines • Incomplete or inaccurate explanation of the relationships between angles formed by parallel lines cut by a transversal • Inaccurate or missing proof

Transformations, Triangles, and Quadrilaterals

Unit Overview

In this unit you will see how transformations are connected to the idea of congruence. Then you will use what you learn about congruence to write proofs involving triangles and quadrilaterals.

Key Terms

As you study this unit, add these and other terms to your math notebook. Include in your notes your prior knowledge of each word, as well as your experiences in using the word in different mathematical examples. If needed, ask for help in pronouncing new words and add information on pronunciation to your math notebook. It is important that you learn new terms and use them correctly in your class discussions and in your problem solutions.

Academic Vocabulary

- criterion
- coincide

Math Terms

- transformation
- pre-image
- image
- rigid motion
- translation
- directed line segment
- rhombus
- reflection
- line of reflection
- reflectional symmetry
- line of symmetry
- rotation
- rotational symmetry
- angle of rotational symmetry
- composition of transformations
- congruent
- corresponding parts
- triangle congruence criteria
- flowchart proof
- Triangle Sum Theorem
- auxiliary line

- interior angle
- exterior angle
- remote interior angle
- Exterior Angle Theorem
- Isosceles Triangle Theorem
- altitude of a triangle
- point of concurrency
- orthocenter
- median
- centroid
- circumcenter
- incenter
- circumscribed circle
- inscribed circle
- kite
- midsegment
- median of a trapezoid
- parallelogram
- corollary
- rectangle
- indirect proof

ESSENTIAL QUESTIONS

 How are transformations related to congruence?

 How does proving theorems extend your understanding of geometry?

EMBEDDED ASSESSMENTS

The four embedded assessments after Activities 10, 12, 14, and 16 in this unit allow you to demonstrate your understanding of transformations, triangles, and quadrilaterals. By using several methods of proof, you will demonstrate your ability to present convincing mathematical arguments.

Getting Ready

Write your answers on notebook paper.

1. Simplify.
   a. $\sqrt{64}$
   b. $\sqrt{98}$

2. Solve the following equations.
   a. $x^2 - 8x + 15 = 0$
   b. $x^2 = 27$

3. If $f(x) = 2x - 5$, find
   a. $f(4)$
   b. $f(-3)$

4. Write the equation of the line shown below.

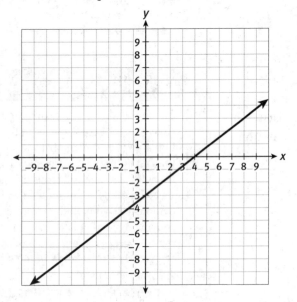

5. Find the slope of a line that passes through $(-2, 5)$ and $(1, 7)$.

6. Write the equation of a line that contains the points $(3, 8)$ and $(-4, -6)$.

7. Find the midpoint and length of a line segment that has endpoints $(3, 5)$ and $(9, -3)$.

8. a. Find the solution of the system of equations:

$$x + 3y = 4$$
$$5x - 2y = 3$$

   b. Explain the method you used to find the solution.

Translations, Reflections, and Rotations

The Marching Cougars
Lesson 9-1 Transformations

Learning Targets:

- Perform transformations on and off the coordinate plane.
- Identify characteristics of transformations that are rigid motions and characteristics of transformations that are non-rigid motions.
- Represent a transformation as a function using coordinates, and show how a figure is transformed by a function.

> **SUGGESTED LEARNING STRATEGIES:** Debriefing, Think-Pair-Share, Predict and Confirm, Self Revision/Peer Revision

Mr. Scott directs the Marching Cougars, the band at Chavez High School. He uses the coordinate plane to represent the football field. For the band's first show, he arranges the band in a rectangle that is 6 marchers wide and 9 marchers deep.

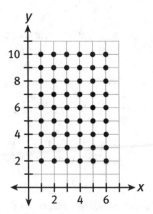

The band begins by marching down the grid in this formation. Then the marchers move apart from each other vertically, while keeping the same distance between marchers within the same row.

The diagrams on the next page show the initial shape of the marchers, and the two *transformations* that they undergo. To describe and classify the transformations, compare the *pre-image* of a transformation to its *image*.

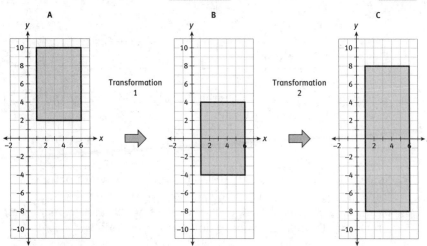

1. Use your own words to describe Transformation 1.

My Notes

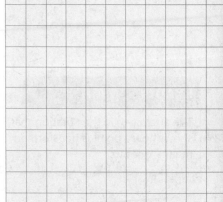

DISCUSSION GROUP TIPS

As you work in groups, read the problem scenario carefully and explore together the information provided. Discuss your understanding of the problem and ask peers or your teacher to clarify any areas that are not clear.

MATH TERMS

A **transformation** is a change in the position, size, or shape of a figure.

The **pre-image** of the transformation is the original figure. The **image** is the figure after the transformation.

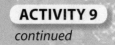

ACTIVITY 9
continued

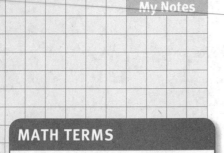

2. Compare Transformation 1 and Transformation 2. How do the two transformations compare?

3. Model with mathematics. Transformation 1 is an example of a *rigid motion*. A rigid motion keeps the same distance between the points that are transformed (in this situation, the marchers of the band); the shape and size of the pre-image and image are the same.
  a. How does Transformation 1 affect the distance between any two marchers in the band?

  b. How does Transformation 2 affect the distance between the marchers? Is Transformation 2 a rigid motion?

4. Review Transformation 1. Each point in the pre-image is mapped to a point in the image. For this reason, the transformation can be expressed as a function.
  a. Complete the table to show the positions of the four corners of the rectangle when Figure A is mapped onto Figure B.

Figure A (pre-image)	Figure B (image)
(1, 10)	(1, 4)
(1, 2)	
(6, 10)	
(6, 2)	

  b. For any given point, how does the transformation change the *x*-coordinate and *y*-coordinate?

  c. You can use the notation $(1, 10) \rightarrow (1, 4)$ to show how a point is transformed. When you use this notation to show how a general point (x, y) is transformed, you are expressing the transformation as a function. Express Transformation 1 as a function.

MATH TERMS

A **rigid motion** is a transformation that preserves size and shape.

TECHNOLOGY TIP

You can also use geometry software to represent transformations, including rigid motions and non-rigid motions.

READING IN MATH

The arrow ($\rightarrow$) in the notation that shows how a point is transformed means "goes to."

5. Review Transformation 2.
   a. Complete the table to show the positions of the four corners of the rectangle when Figure B is mapped onto Figure C.

Figure B (pre-image)	Figure C (image)
(1, 4)	(1, 8)
(1, −4)	

   b. For any given point, how does the transformation change the x-coordinate and y-coordinate?

   c. Can Transformation 2 also be expressed as a function? Explain why or why not. Write the function if it exists.

6. Draw each image on the graph to show how the pre-image is transformed by the function. Then classify the transformation as rigid or non-rigid.
   a. $(x, y) \rightarrow (x + 3, y)$

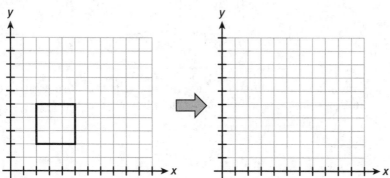

   b. $(x, y) \rightarrow (2x, 2y)$

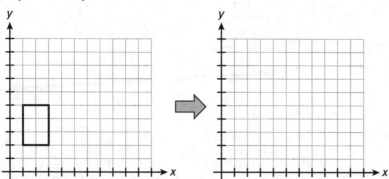

7. Write the numeral "4" in the middle of each pre-image in Item 6. Describe how the numeral should appear in each image.

CONNECT TO ALGEBRA

You've used functions extensively in algebra. Recall that a function is a set of ordered pairs in which each x-value is associated with one, and only one, y-value.

DISCUSSION GROUP TIPS

As you read and discuss the transformations, ask and answer questions to be sure you have a clear understanding of not only all the terminology used, but also the link between the algebraic notation and the graphs.

MATH TIP

A rigid motion can be modeled by sliding, rotating, or flipping a figure. A non-rigid motion often involves stretching or compressing the figure.

Check Your Understanding

Use the text and diagram to answer Items 8 and 9.

The rectangle undergoes the transformation described by the function $(x, y) \rightarrow (x - 2, y + 1)$.

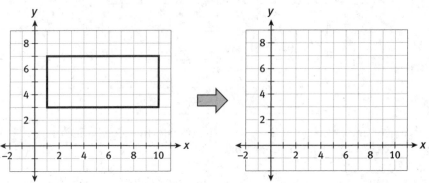

8. Complete the table to show the coordinates of the image and pre-image for the four corners of the rectangle.

Pre-image	Image
(1, 3)	_____
(1, 7)	_____
_____	_____
_____	_____

9. Graph the transformation of the figure. Is the transformation a rigid motion or non-rigid motion? Explain how you know.

10. A rectangle is transformed as shown.

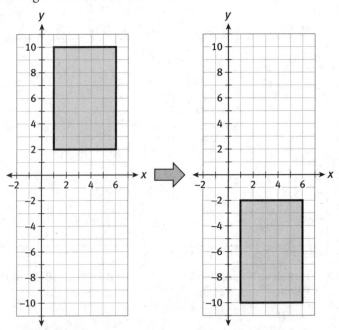

a. Which function describes the transformation?

b. Classify the transformation as rigid or non-rigid. Explain why you classified the transformation that way.

LESSON 9-1 PRACTICE

For Items 11 and 12, consider the following: A rectangle undergoes the transformation described by the function $(x, y) \rightarrow \left(x, \dfrac{y}{2}\right)$.

My Notes

> **MATH TIP**
>
> Many different transformations can transform a pre-image to the same image. Consider sliding, flipping, and turning.

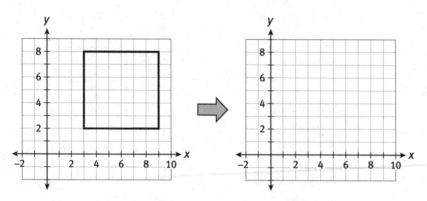

11. Graph the transformation of the figure. Is the transformation a rigid motion? Explain.

12. Reason abstractly. Draw a plus sign (+) in the middle of the image. Describe how the transformation would change the plus sign.

13. Attend to precision. Use the graph of the rectangle to help you classify each of the following transformations.

a. Draw the image of the rectangle under the transformation described by the function $(x, y) \rightarrow \left(\dfrac{x}{2}, y\right)$. Classify the transformation as rigid or non-rigid.

b. Draw the image of the rectangle under the transformation described by the function $(x, y) \rightarrow (x, y + 2)$. Classify the transformation as rigid or non-rigid.

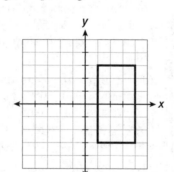

Learning Targets:

● Perform translations on and off the coordinate plane.
● Predict the effect of a translation on a figure.

SUGGESTED LEARNING STRATEGIES: Visualization, Create Representations, Predict and Confirm, Think-Pair-Share

Maria marches with the band. At the start of the halftime show, her position is (2, 4) on the coordinate plane. Then Mr. Scott tells everyone to move 2 yards to the right on the field and 4 yards up the field. The band's transformation is shown in the diagram, and Maria's position is marked with an X.

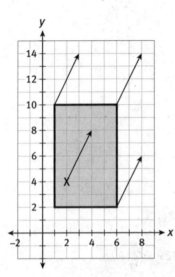 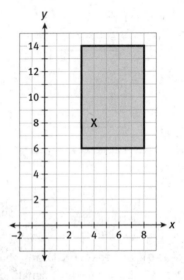

This type of transformation is called a ***translation***. On the coordinate plane, a translation is described by a function of the form $(x, y) \rightarrow (x + a, y + b)$, in which a and b are positive or negative constants. In the example above, $a = 2$ and $b = 4$.

You can think of a translation as a figure sliding up or down, left or right, or diagonally. During the translation, every point of the figure moves the same distance and in the same direction. This distance and direction is called a ***directed line segment***. In the diagram, the directed line segment of the translation is shown by each of the arrows.

1. Complete the table to show how the translation affects four of the Marching Cougars.

Marcher	Pre-image	Image
Maria	(2, 4)	
Joe	(3, 7)	
Alfredo	(1, 8)	
LeJaya		(7, 11)

MATH TERMS

A **translation** is a rigid motion in which every point is moved the same distance and in the same direction.

A **directed line segment** is the distance and direction of the translation.

Mr. Scott arranges the band in a rectangle. Then he directs the band member at (6, 10) to move to (4, 13). The numbers on the coordinate plane show yards of the football field.

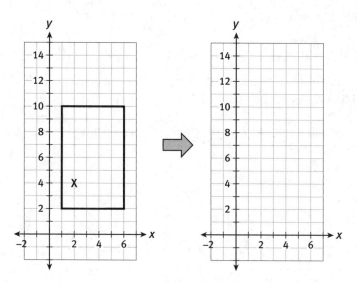

2. For the band to move in a translation, how should each band member move?

3. **Critique the reasoning of others.** Maria was positioned at point (2, 4). Her friend tells her that Maria's new position is described by the function $(x + 3, y - 2)$ since her new position is (7, 0). Is her friend correct? Explain.

Check Your Understanding

Draw the image of the figure under the translation described by the function.

4. $(x, y) \rightarrow (x + 4, y - 4)$

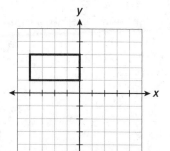

5. $(x, y) \rightarrow (x + 3, y)$

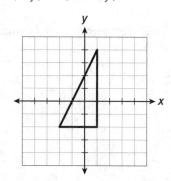

Translations can also be defined without the coordinate plane. For the directed line segment $\overrightarrow{AB}$, a translation maps point P to point P' so that the following statements are true:

- $\overline{PP'}$ is parallel to $\overrightarrow{AB}$
- $PP' = AB$
- $\overrightarrow{PP'}$ is in the same direction as $\overrightarrow{AB}$.

The expression $T_{\overrightarrow{AB}}(P)$ describes the translation of a given point P by the directed line segment $\overrightarrow{AB}$. In the above example, $T_{\overrightarrow{AB}}(P) = P'$.

Items 6 through 8 refer to **rhombus** *ABCD* shown below. Point *P* is in the center of the rhombus.

MATH TERMS

A **rhombus** is a parallelogram with four congruent sides.

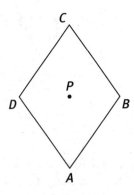

6. Draw the translation of the rhombus described by directed line segment $\overrightarrow{AB'}$. Include $P' = T_{\overrightarrow{AB}}(P)$.

7. Which part of the rhombus maps onto $\overline{BC}$?

8. Identify a translation of the rhombus that would map exactly one point of the rhombus onto another point of the rhombus.

9. Draw the following translations. Show the pre-image and image, and label corresponding points in each.
   a. square *ABCD*, translated four inches to the right
   b. right triangle *ABC*, translated three inches up
   c. right triangle *ABC*, translated by $T_{\overrightarrow{AB}}$

Check Your Understanding

10. Mr. Scott arranges the band in the shape of triangle *ABC*, shown below. Point *P* is in the interior of the triangle. He plans three transformations of the triangle, in which point *P* is mapped onto *P'*, *P''*, and *P'''*, respectively.

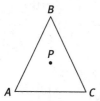

   a. Which of the three transformations are translations? Explain your answer by applying the definition of a translation.
   b. Maria stands at point *P* of triangle *ABC*. To move to point *P'*, her instructions are to move eight steps to the right. Do these instructions apply to all the other band members? Explain.

LESSON 9-2 PRACTICE

The figure shows hexagon *ABCDEF* undergoing a translation to the right.

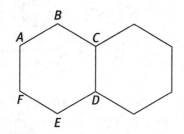

11. Which part of the pre-image is translated onto $\overline{CD}$?

12. Express the translation as a function of two points of the hexagon.

13. **Make use of structure.** By applying this translation many times, you could create a row of hexagons. What additional translation could be repeated to fill the page with hexagons? Is it $T_{\overline{BC}}$, $T_{\overline{BD}}$, or $T_{\overline{BE}}$?

TECHNOLOGY TIP

You can use drawing or painting software to model translations. First draw a figure, then make a copy of it, and then drag the copy of the figure anywhere on the screen. No matter where you place the copy, you have created a translation of the original figure. Try the translation of the hexagon described here.

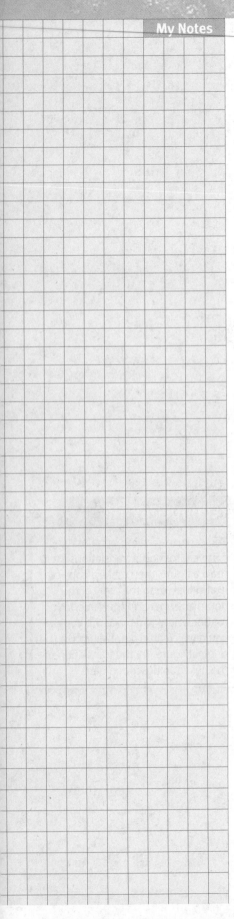

Learning Targets:
- Perform reflections on and off the coordinate plane.
- Identify reflectional symmetry in plane figures.

> **SUGGESTED LEARNING STRATEGIES:** Visualization, Create Representations, Predict and Confirm, Think-Pair-Share

Mr. Scott plans another transformation for the Marching Cougars. The sign of the y-coordinate of each marcher changes from positive to negative. Maria, whose position is shown by the X in the diagram, moves from point $(2, 4)$ to point $(2\ -4)$.

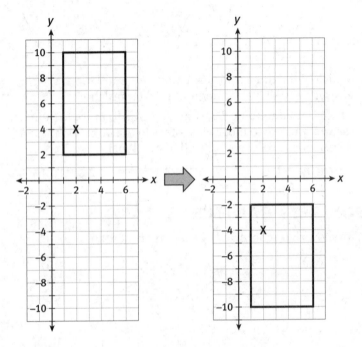

This type of transformation is called a ***reflection***. Reflections are sometimes called flips because the figure is flipped like a pancake. On the coordinate plane, examples of reflections are defined by the functions $(x, y) \rightarrow (-x, y)$, which is a reflection across the y-axis. The example shown above is described by $(x, y) \rightarrow (x, -y)$, which is a reflection across the x-axis. The function $(x, y) \rightarrow (y, x)$ defines a reflection across the line $y = x$.

Every reflection has a ***line of reflection***, which is the line that the reflection maps to itself. In the above diagram, the line of reflection is the x-axis.

1. Complete the table for the two reflections.

Pre-image	Image $(x, y) \rightarrow (x, -y)$	Image $(x, y) \rightarrow (-x, y)$
(1, 10)	(1, −10)	
(6, 10)		
(1, 2)		(−1, 2)
(6, 2)		

My Notes

The figure shows an arrow in the coordinate plane. The tip of the arrow is located at point (4, 10).

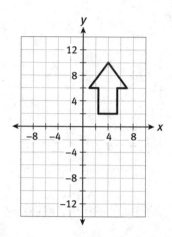

2. Predict the direction of the arrow after these reflections:
   a. across the *x*-axis
   b. across the *y*-axis

3. Draw the two reflections. Were your predictions correct?

4. What reflection maps the arrow to a downward arrow that also has its tip at the point (4, 10)?

5. Could a reflection map the arrow so it points to the right or to the left (i.e., parallel to the *x*-axis)? If yes, describe the line of reflection.

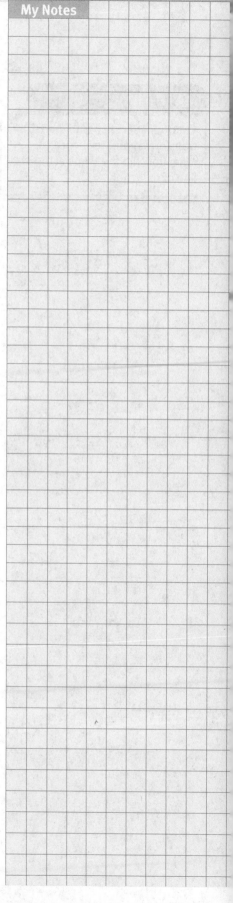

My Notes

MATH TIP

Cut out paper shapes to model transformations. To show a reflection, flip the shape across the line of reflection.

Mr. Scott arranges the tuba players in an arrow formation, shown below. Then the tuba players undergo a reflection that is described by the function $(x, y) \rightarrow (8 - x, y)$.

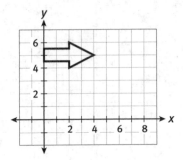

6. Draw the reflection. Identify the line of reflection.

7. Which tuba players travel the longest distance during the reflection? Identify this distance.

8. Which tuba player does not travel any distance during the reflection?

9. Explain why the reflection does not change the distance between any given tuba player and the point (4, 5).

10. **Use appropriate tools strategically.** Use geometry software to explore reflections. First, use the software to draw a pentagon. Then draw a line of reflection that passes through one side of the pentagon. Use the software to reflect the pentagon over this line of reflection.

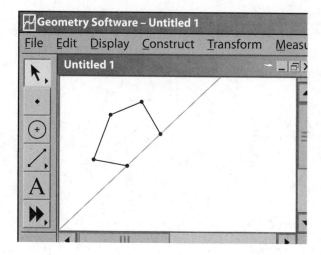 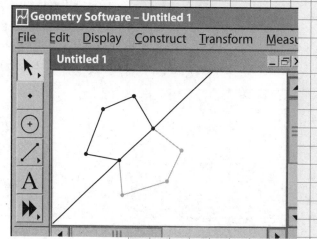

11. What happens under this reflection to points that lie on the line of reflection?

12. Use the software to explore how a point not on the line of reflection is related to its image.
    a. Measure the distance of a point to the line of reflection. Then measure the distance of the point's image to the line of reflection. What do you find?

    b. Draw the segment that connects a point and its image. How is this segment related to the line of reflection?

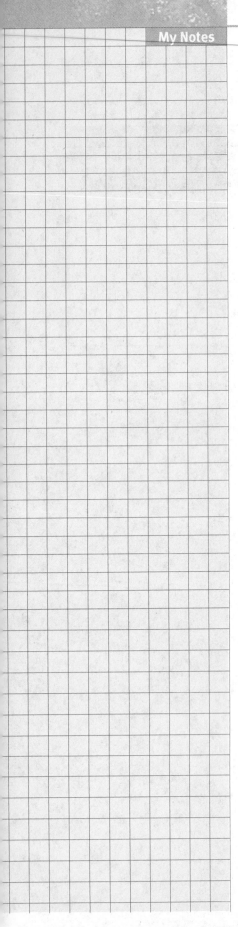

Like other transformations, reflections can be defined independently of the coordinate plane. A **reflection** is a transformation that maps P to P' across line ℓ such that:

- If P is not on ℓ, then ℓ is the perpendicular bisector of $\overline{PP'}$.
- If P is on ℓ, then $P = P'$.

To describe reflections, we will use the notation $r_\ell(P) = P'$, in which r_ℓ is the function that maps point P to point P' across line ℓ, the line of reflection.

13. The diagram shows pentagon $ABCDE$ and the reflection r_ℓ.

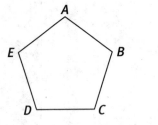
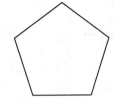

a. Draw line ℓ.

b. Label the points $r_\ell(A) = A'$, $r_\ell(B) = B'$, and so on for the five vertices.

14. Quadrilateral $ABDC$ was constructed by drawing scalene triangle ABC, then drawing its reflection across line BC. Point P is the intersection of $\overline{BC}$ and $\overline{AD}$.

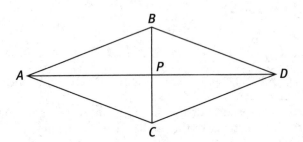

a. Prove that $\overline{BC}$ is perpendicular to $\overline{AD}$.

b. Explain why $AB = BD$.

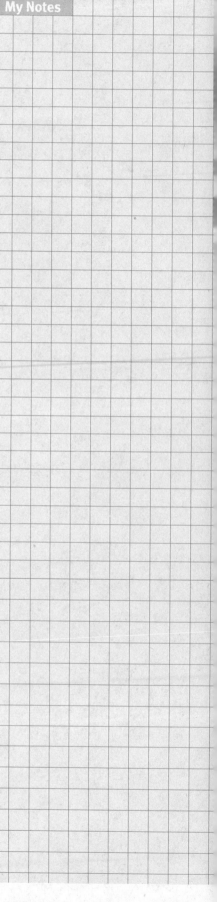

My Notes

Item 15 is related to the Perpendicular Bisector Theorem. The theorem states that if a point is on the perpendicular bisector of a segment, then it is equidistant from the endpoints of the segment. The converse is also true. If a point is equidistant from two points A and B, then it must lie on the perpendicular bisector of $\overline{AB}$.

Look again at quadrilateral $ABDC$. It was constructed by a reflection of a figure, which means that it has **reflectional symmetry**. Line segment BC is the **line of symmetry** of the figure. A line of symmetry can be an actual line in the figure, or it may be imaginary. A figure may have any number of lines of symmetry, including an infinite number.

15. For each figure shown below, draw all of the lines of symmetry.

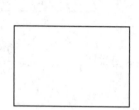
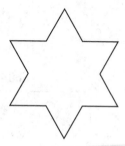

16. Triangle ABC has three lines of symmetry, labeled ℓ_1, ℓ_2, and ℓ_3 in the figure below. What can you conclude about the triangle? Explain.

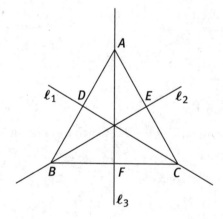

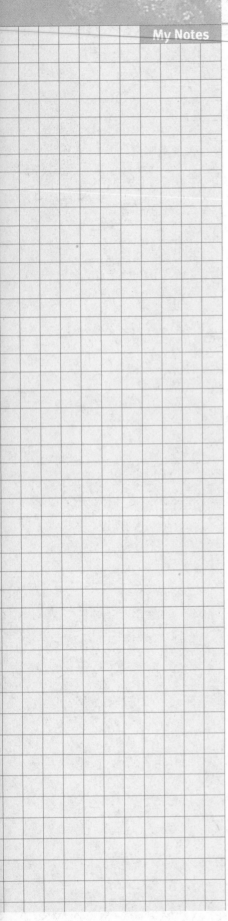

My Notes

Check Your Understanding

17. Match the figures to their number of lines of symmetry.

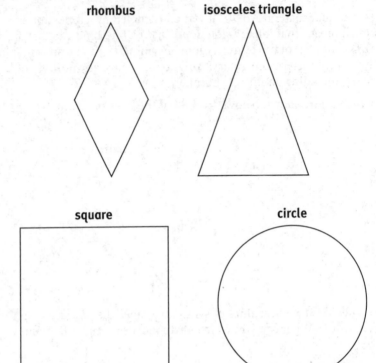

rhombus   isosceles triangle

square   circle

  a. one line
  b. two lines
  c. four lines
  d. infinitely many lines

The figure shows scalene triangle *ABC*, which by definition has three unequal sides. Point *D* is on $\overline{AC}$, and $\overline{BD}$ is perpendicular to $\overline{AC}$.

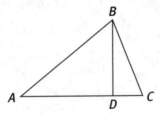

18. Explain why $\overline{BD}$ is not a line of symmetry for the triangle.

19. Does triangle *ABC* have any lines of symmetry? Explain.

LESSON 9-3 PRACTICE

Use the figure for Items 20 and 21.

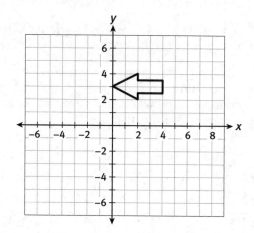

20. Draw the reflection of the arrow described by each of these functions, and identify the line of reflection.
    a. $(x, y) \rightarrow (8 - x, y)$
    b. $(x, y) \rightarrow (-2 - x, y)$
    c. $(x, y) \rightarrow (x, -y)$

21. **Reason abstractly.** Describe a reflection that would map the arrow onto itself.

Irregular pentagon *ABCDE* has exactly one line of symmetry, which passes through point *A*.

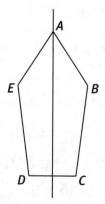

22. What is the image of point *C* under a reflection across the line of symmetry?

23. Does any point remain fixed under a reflection across the line of symmetry? Explain.

24. Which sides of the pentagon must be congruent?

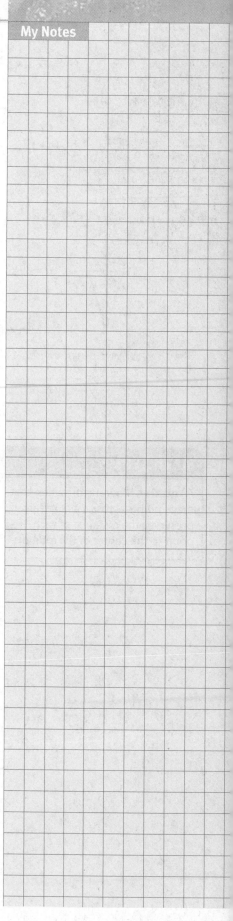

My Notes

Learning Objectives:
- Perform rotations on and off the coordinate plane.
- Identify and distinguish between reflectional and rotational symmetry.

SUGGESTED LEARNING STRATEGIES: Debriefing, Think-Pair-Share, Predict and Confirm, Self Revision/Peer Revision

For the big finish of the Marching Cougars performance, Mr. Scott arranges the band in a triangle formation. Then the triangle appears to rotate clockwise around a point, like a pinwheel. The center of the rotation is the vertex located at (0, 0) on the coordinate plane.

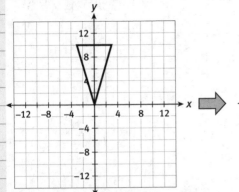
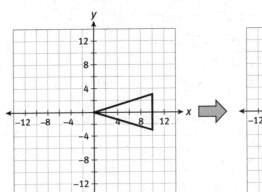
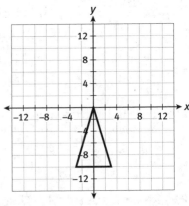

MATH TERMS

A **rotation** is a transformation that maps points across a circular arc. It preserves the distance of each point to the center of the rotation.

This spinning type of transformation is called a ***rotation***. It is defined by the center of the rotation, which is mapped to itself, and the angle of the rotation.

The center of rotation may be part of the figure being rotated, as is the case shown above. Or it may be a point outside the figure.

Functions that describe rotations include $(x, y) \rightarrow (y, -x)$, which is a clockwise rotation of 90°. Repeat the function twice to produce $(x, y) \rightarrow (-x, -y)$, which is a rotation of 180°. The function $(x, y) \rightarrow (-y, x)$ is a clockwise rotation of 270°, or 90° counterclockwise.

1. Complete the table for the two rotations shown above.

Pre-image	Image $(x, y) \rightarrow (y, -x)$	Image $(x, y) \rightarrow (-x, -y)$
(3, 10)	(10, −3)	
(−3, 10)		
(0, 0)		

Use the figure for Items 2 and 3.

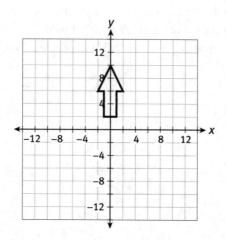

2. Predict the direction of the arrow after these rotations. The center of each rotation is (0, 0).

   a. 90 degrees clockwise

   b. 180 degrees

   c. 90 degrees counterclockwise

3. Draw the three rotations. Were your predictions correct?

4. Describe the rotation that maps figure *A* onto figure *B*. (*Hint*: First identify the center of rotation.)

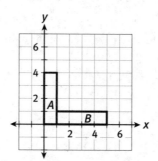

a.

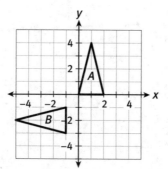

b.

My Notes

The angle of rotation can be used to describe the image of every point of the figure. Consider the rotation shown below. Rectangle $ABCO$ is rotated $90°$ clockwise, and maps onto rectangle $A'B'C'O$. From the diagram, it appears that $\overline{AO} \perp \overline{A'O}$ and that $\overline{CO} \perp \overline{C'O}$. If you measure $\angle BOB'$, you will find that it, too, equals $90°$.

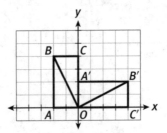

The following figure is a square that is centered around the origin O. Point A is one vertex of the square.

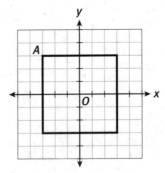

5. Draw a rotation of the square $45°$ clockwise about the origin. Label the point A' that is the image of point A.

6. What is the measure of $\angle AOA'$?

7. **Use appropriate tools strategically.** Use geometry software to explore rotations. First, use the software to draw a quadrilateral. Then plot a point *P* that will serve as the center of rotation. Use the software to rotate the quadrilateral 120° counterclockwise around point *P*.

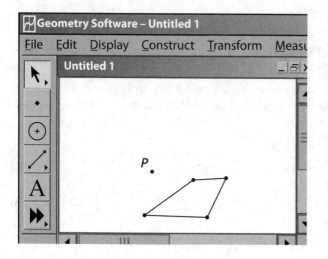
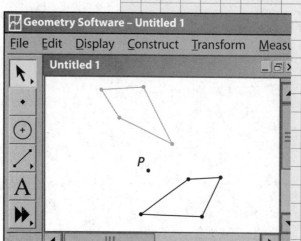

8. Choose a point of the pre-image and the corresponding point of the image. Use the software to measure the distance of each point from point *P*. What do you find?

9. Use the software to measure the angle formed by a point, its image, and point *P*, with point *P* as the vertex of the angle. What do you notice about this measure?

10. Use the software to change the shape of the quadrilateral by dragging one or more of the points that form the quadrilateral. Do the results from Items 8 and 9 remain true no matter the shape of the quadrilateral? Explain.

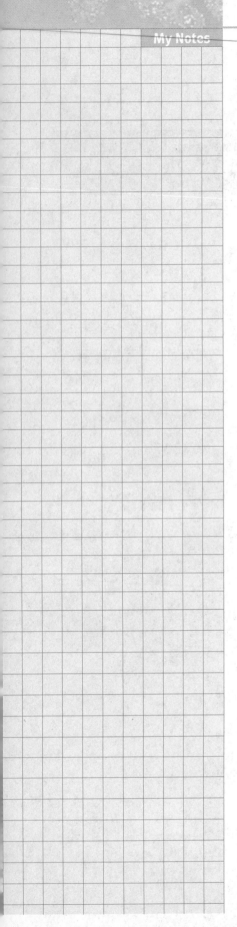

Like translations and reflections, rotations can be defined independently of the coordinate plane. A **rotation** that maps P to P' and Q to Q' has the following properties. Let point O be the center of rotation.

- $PO = P'O$, and $QO = Q'O$
- $\angle POP' \cong \angle QOQ'$

To describe rotations, we will use the notation $R_{O,m^\circ}(P) = P'$, in which R_{O,m° is the function that maps point P to point P' with center of rotation at point O and through an angle of m°.

11. The diagram shows isosceles triangle ABC, and point O inside it. Draw the following rotations. Label the images of the three vertices.

  a. $R_{O,-90^\circ}$

  b. $R_{C,90^\circ}$

  c. $R_{A,90^\circ}$

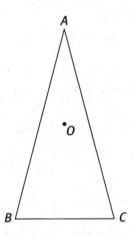

12. Describe three rotations that each map a square onto itself.

Review your answer to Item 12. Figures such as squares have ***rotational symmetry***, meaning that a rotation of less than 360° can map the shape onto itself. The smallest such angle is the ***angle of rotational symmetry***.

13. Identify whether these figures have rotational symmetry, reflectional symmetry, or both. Also identify the angles of rotational symmetry and lines of reflectional symmetry.

    a. isosceles triangle

    b. equilateral triangle

    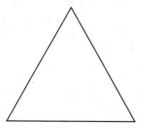

    c. rhombus

    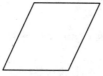

    d. regular hexagon

    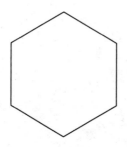

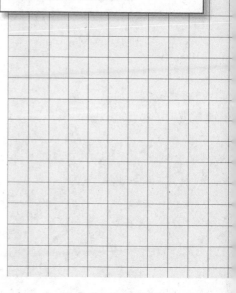

MATH TIP

Each side of a regular polygon has the same measure, and each angle has the same measure.

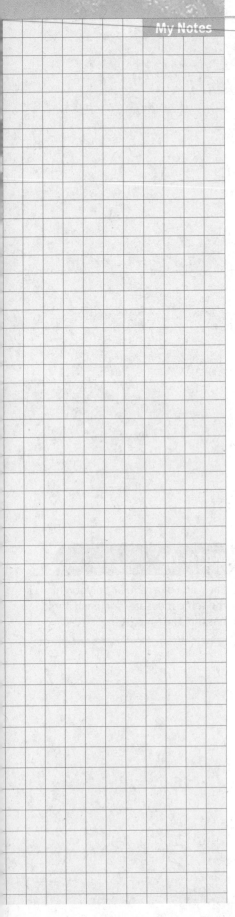

My Notes

Check Your Understanding

14. The figure shows parallelogram *ABCD* (shaded) and its rotation.
    a. Name the rotation.
    b. Label the vertices *A′*, *B′*, and *C′* of the rotated figure.
    c. If ∠*ADC* = 30°, find ∠*A′DC*.

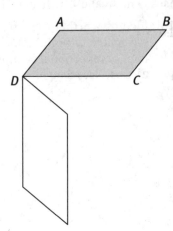

15. Identify an example of a figure that meets these sets of properties.
    a. rotational symmetry with angle of rotational symmetry of 90°
    b. rotational symmetry with angles of rotational symmetry of 72°
    c. rotational symmetry with angle of rotational symmetry of 180°, two lines of reflectional symmetry
    d. rotational symmetry with angle of rotational symmetry of 180°, no lines of reflectional symmetry

LESSON 9-4 PRACTICE

16. Describe the rotation that would move the arrow to these positions.
    a. pointing up, with the tip at (4, 7)
    b. pointing down, with the tip at (0, 3)
    c. pointing up, with the tip at (3, 0)

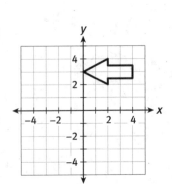

17. Identify the direction of the arrow and the position of the tip after these rotations.
    a. 90° counterclockwise about (4, 3)
    b. 180° about (2, 3)
    c. 90° clockwise about (2, 0)

18. Describe a figure that has an angle of rotational symmetry of 10°.

19. **Construct viable arguments.** Do you think it is possible for a figure to have an angle of rotational symmetry of 37°? If so, describe the figure. If not, explain why not.

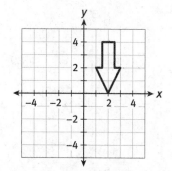

ACTIVITY 9 PRACTICE
Write your answers on notebook paper.
Show your work.

Lesson 9-1

For Items 1–4, a square is drawn in the coordinate plane, with vertices as shown in the diagram. Then the square undergoes a rigid motion.

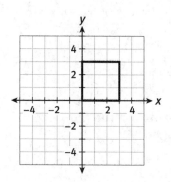

1. The function that describes the rigid motion could be $(x, y) \rightarrow$
   A. $(2x, y)$.
   B. $(x - 3, y)$.
   C. $(y, -2x)$.
   D. $(x, 3)$.

2. If the point $(0, 3)$ is mapped to $(0, 0)$, what could be the image of $(3, 0)$?
   A. $(0, 0)$
   B. $(0, 3)$
   C. $(3, -3)$
   D. $(-3, 3)$

3. The length of the diagonal of the square is $2\sqrt{3}$. Can you determine the length of the diagonal of the image of the square? Explain.

4. Draw the transformations of the square described by these functions. Classify each as rigid or non-rigid.
   a. $(x, y + 2)$
   b. $(x + 3, y - 3)$
   c. $\left(2x, \frac{1}{2}y\right)$

Lesson 9-2

For Items 5 and 6, a down arrow is drawn with its tip at $(2, 0)$. Then it undergoes a translation described by the directed line segment $(-3, 1)$.

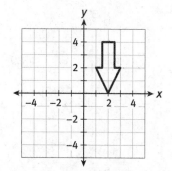

5. The image of the tip of the arrow is at point
   A. $(2, 1)$.
   B. $(-1, 1)$.
   C. $(2, -3)$.
   D. $(-3, 2)$.

6. The image of the arrow points in which direction?
   A. down
   B. left
   C. right
   D. diagonal

7. The diagram shows regular pentagon $ABCDE$.

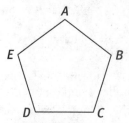

   a. Draw the translation $T_{\overline{EB}}$. Label the images of each vertex.
   b. Is it possible for a translation to map more than one point of the pentagon onto another point of the pentagon? Explain.

Lesson 9-3

For Items 8–10, a square is drawn in the coordinate plane, with vertices as shown in the diagram. Then the square is reflected across the *x*-axis.

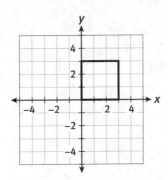

8. The function that describes the reflection is $(x, y) \rightarrow$

   A. $(x, y - 3)$.   **B.** $(x, y - 6)$.

   C. $(-x, y)$.   **D.** $(x, -y)$.

9. An up-pointing arrow is drawn inside the square. In the image, the arrow points in which direction?
   A. up   **B.** down
   C. left   **D.** right

10. Describe a reflection of the square that would map it onto itself.

11. Right triangle *ABC* is reflected across line ℓ, which is parallel to but distinct from $\overline{AB}$, one of the legs of the triangle. Prove that points B, C, B', and C' are collinear.

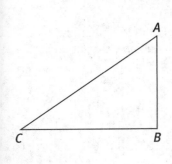
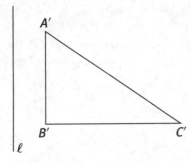

Lesson 9-4

For Items 12 and 13, a down arrow is drawn with its tip at (2, 0). Then it undergoes a clockwise rotation of 90°.

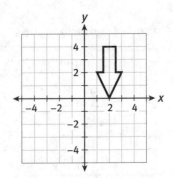

12. If the tip of the arrow moves to (0, 2), what is the center of rotation?
    A. (2, 2)   **B.** (2, 4)
    C. (0, 2)   **D.** (0, 0)

13. How many possible centers of rotation will produce an image of a left-pointing arrow?
    A. zero   **B.** one
    C. two   **D.** infinite

14. Describe the rotational and reflectional symmetry of these shapes.

   a. ellipse   **b.** right isosceles triangle

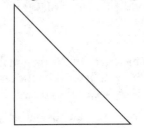

   c. letter S   **d.** plus sign

MATHEMATICAL PRACTICES
Construct Viable Arguments and Critique the Reasoning of Others

15. Figure A is a square that is centered at the origin O. A student claims that the reflection $r_{(y=0)}$ and the rotation $R_{O,180°}$ transform the square in the same way. Critique this claim.

Compositions and Congruence

More Rigid Motions
Lesson 10-1 Compositions of Transformations

Learning Targets:
- Find the image of a figure under a composition of rigid motions.
- Find the pre-image of a figure under a composition of rigid motions.

> **SUGGESTED LEARNING STRATEGIES:** Close Reading, Think-Pair-Share, Predict and Confirm, Self Revision/Peer Revision

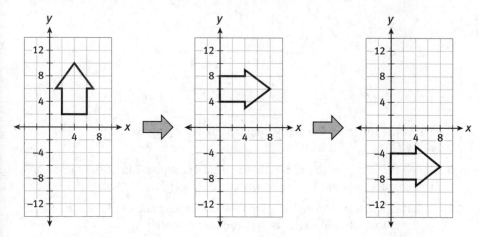

Consider the series of transformations shown in the figures above. The first is $R_{(6,4),90°}$, or a clockwise rotation of $90°$ about the point $(4, 6)$. The second transformation is $r_{y=0}$, or a reflection across the x-axis. Together they are a *composition of transformations*, which is two or more transformations performed in sequence.

The notation for a composition of transformations is similar to the way you express the composition of functions. The composition pictured above is described as $r_{y=0}(R_{(6,4),90°})$. If a reflection across the x-axis were added as the third transformation of the sequence, then the notation would be $r_{x=0}(r_{y=0}(R_{(6,4),90°}))$. Notice that the transformation that occurs first in the series is in the interior of the notation, and subsequent transformations are written outside of it.

1. **Attend to precision.** Write the notations for these compositions of transformations. Use the points $A(0, 0)$, $B(1, 1)$, and $C(0, -1)$.
   a. a clockwise rotation of $60°$ about the origin, followed by a translation by directed line segment $\overline{AB}$

   b. a reflection about the line $x = 1$, followed by a reflection about the line $x = 2$

   c. three translations, each of directed line segment $\overline{AC}$

MATH TERMS

A **composition of transformations** is a series of two or more transformations performed on a figure one after another.

DISCUSSION GROUP TIP

As needed, refer to the Glossary to review meanings of key terms. Incorporate your understanding into group discussions to confirm your knowledge and use of key mathematical language.

MATH TIP

Use cut-out shapes to model each transformation in the composition. Remember that the notation shows the transformations in order from *right to left*.

The figure shows an arrow that points from a short horizontal line through (4, 2) to its tip at (4, 10).

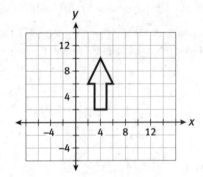

2. Draw the image of the arrow mapped by the composition $r_{(x=4)}(R_{(4,0),90°})$. Label it A.

3. Draw the image of the arrow mapped by a composition of the same transformations in the reverse order: $R_{(4,0),90°}(r_{(x=4)})$. Label it B.

4. What single transformation maps the arrow to image A? Write the name of the transformation and its symbolic representation.

5. What single transformation maps the arrow to image B?

As demonstrated by Items 2 and 3, the order of transformations in a composition can affect the position and orientation of the image. And as shown by Items 4 and 5, a composition can produce the same image as a single translation, reflection, or rotation.

6. For each of these compositions, predict the single transformation that produces the same image.
    a. $T_{(1,1)}(T_{(0,1)}(T_{(1,0)}))$

    b. $R_{O,90°}(R_{O,90°})$

    c. $r_{(x=0)}(r_{(y=0)})$

My Notes

Use the figure for Items 7–9.

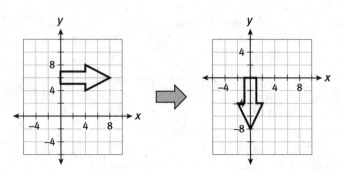

7. Identify a composition of transformations that could map the arrow on the left to the image of the arrow on the right.

8. Consider the composition you identified in Item 7 but with the transformations in reverse order. Does it still map the arrow to the same image?

9. Identify a composition that undoes the mapping, meaning it maps the image of the arrow on the right to the pre-image on the left.

You can also find combinations of transformations away from the coordinate plane.

10. Points A, B, C, and D are points on the right-pointing arrow shown here. Predict the direction of the arrow after it is mapped by these combinations.

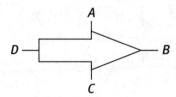

a. $T_{\overline{DB}}(T_{\overline{AC}})$

b. $r_{\overline{D'B'}}(R_{D,90°})$

c. $R_{A,180°}(r_{\overline{AC}})$

My Notes

Like many functions, transformations have inverses, which are transformations that map the image back to the pre-image. The inverse of transformation T is designated T^{-1}, and it has the property $T^{-1}(T(P)) = P$ for all points P. The table lists the general formulas for the inverses of translations, rotations, and reflections.

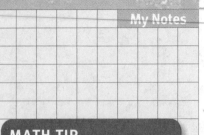

MATH TIP

You can think of an inverse transformation as a "reversing" or "undoing" of the transformation. It maps the image to the pre-image.

Function	Notation	Inverse
Translation by directed line segment AB	$T_{\overline{AB}}$	$(T_{\overline{AB}})^{-1} = T_{\overline{BA}}$
Reflection about line l	r_l	$(r_l)^{-1} = r_l$
Rotation of m degrees about point O	R_{O,m°	$(R_{O,m^\circ})^{-1} = R_{O,-m^\circ}$

Example A

Isosceles triangle $A'B'C'$ is shown in the diagram. It is the image of the combination $T_{\overline{BC}}(R_{O,90^\circ})$, in which point O is the center of the triangle.

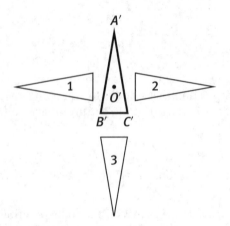

Is the pre-image shown by triangle 1, 2, or 3?

Step 1: Find the inverse combination.

$$(R_{O,90^\circ})^{-1} = (R_{O',-90^\circ}), \text{ and } (T_{\overline{BC}})^{-1} = T_{\overline{C'B'}}$$

So, the inverse combination is $R_{O,-90^\circ}(T_{\overline{CB}})$.

Step 2: Determine the result of the translation and rotation.

When the pre-image is translated by the directed line segment $\overline{C'B'}$, and then rotated $90°$ counterclockwise about its center, the result is triangle 1.

Try These A

a. Find a composition that maps triangle 2 to triangle $A'B'C'$.
b. Find a composition that maps triangle 3 to triangle $A'B'C'$.

Check Your Understanding

An isosceles triangle has vertices at $(-3, 0)$, $(0, 1)$, and $(3, 0)$.

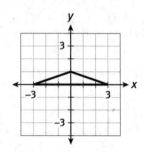

11. Draw the image of the triangle after the combination $T_{(0,2)}(R_{O,180°})$.

12. Identify the inverse transformation.

13. Compare the mapping of the triangle produced by $T_{(0,2)}(R_{O,180°})$ with the mapping produced by $r_{(y=1)}$.

LESSON 10-1 PRACTICE

14. Construct viable arguments. Give examples of a combination of rotation $R_{O,m°}$ $(0 < m < 360)$ and transformation T that is commutative (i.e., for all points P, $T(R_{O,m°}(P)) = R_{O,m°}(T(P))$ and that is not commutative (i.e., for at least one point P, $T(R_{O,m°}(P)) \neq R_{O,m°}(T(P))$).

15. The tail of an arrow is placed at $(0, 0)$ and its tip at $(3, 0)$, and it serves as the pre-image for four compositions. Complete the table to show the compositions and images.

Composition	Image (position of tip, direction of arrow)
$T_{(3,-3)} R_{0,90°}$	
$r_{(x=3)}(R_{(3,0),180°})$	
	$(0, 6)$; left
	$(-3, 0)$; down

MATH TIP

If a transformation is commutative, the order in which the transformations are performed does not matter—the resulting image will be the same.

My Notes

Learning Targets:

● Determine whether given figures are congruent.
● Specify a sequence of rigid motions that will carry a given figure to a congruent figure.

SUGGESTED LEARNING STRATEGIES: Visualization, Close Reading, Think-Pair-Share, Predict and Confirm

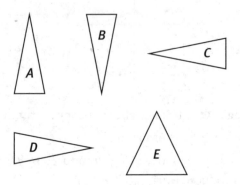

MATH TERMS

Two figures are **congruent** if and only if a composition of rigid motions maps one to the other.

Consider the five labeled triangles shown here. Isosceles triangles *A*, *B*, *C*, and *D* are **congruent** because a series of rigid motions—translations, rotations, or reflections—can map any of the triangles onto another. The series could involve a rotation of 90° or 180°, followed by a translation. However, no such combination can map either of the four triangles onto equilateral triangle *E*, nor does the inverse combination exist that would map triangle *E* onto triangle *A*, *B*, *C*, or *D*. Therefore, triangle *E* is not congruent to the other triangles.

The definition of congruent figures applies both on and off the coordinate plane. It also agrees with an intuitive understanding of the concept of congruency. For example, if you trace a figure, then rotate or reflect the tracing, the tracing will fit exactly over any congruent figures and will not fit over noncongruent figures.

1. Shade all of the figures that appear to be congruent to figure *A*.

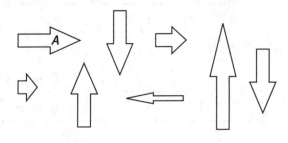

Lesson 10-2
Congruence

To prove that two figures are congruent, a specific combination of rigid motions must be found that maps each point *P* of one figure to corresponding point *P'* of the other figure.

2. **Make use of structure.** Predict whether the two triangles shown in the figure are congruent. Explain your prediction.

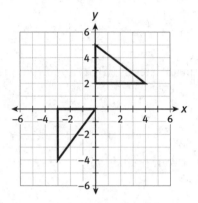

3. How can your prediction be confirmed?

4. Could a single translation, reflection, or rotation map one of the triangles onto the other? Explain.

5. How could a rotation followed by a translation map one triangle onto another?

6. Propose a composition of rotation and translation to map the triangle in the first quadrant onto the triangle in the third quadrant. Then complete the table to test your proposal.

Pre-image:	Rotation: _____	Translation: _____
(0, 2)		(−3, 0)
(0, 5)		(0, 0)
(4, 0)		(−5, −4)

7. Was your prediction correct? Explain.

My Notes

Use the figure for Items 8–10.

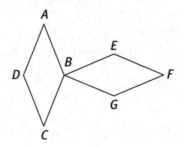

8. Predict whether quadrilaterals *ABCD* and *BEFG* are congruent.

9. How could you test your prediction?

10. Follow your plan to test your prediction. Identify the rigid motions that you applied.

Check Your Understanding

11. An arrow is placed with its base at the origin and its tip at the point $(0, 2)$. For each arrow listed below, find the rigid motion or composition that shows the two arrows are congruent.
  a. base at $(3, 3)$, tip at $(3, 5)$
  b. base at $(-2, 2)$, tip at $(-2, 0)$
  c. base at $(4, 0)$, tip at $(6, 0)$

12. Consider the right triangles shown below.

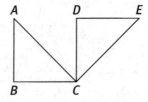

  a. Identify a composition of reflections that shows that these two triangles are congruent.
  b. Identify a rotation that shows that these two triangles are congruent.

In Activity 4, you learned another definition of congruent figures. This definition involves the measurements of sides and angles of a figure. For example, if two triangles each have sides of lengths a, b, and c, then the triangles are congruent. Congruency can also be shown when two triangles each have two sides of lengths a and b, and the angle between the two sides is the same in both triangles.

If two figures are congruent by one of the two definitions, are they congruent by the other definition as well? As you will see, the answer is yes.

Line A connects points $(2, 3)$ and $(5, 3)$. Line B connects points $(1, 0)$ and $(1, -6)$.

My Notes

> **MATH TIP**
>
> Two triangles are congruent by SAS (side-angle-side).

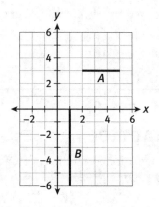

13. Find a composition of two rigid motions that maps line B to a line B' that overlaps line A.

14. What pair of points does line B' connect?

15. Can you add a third rigid motion to the composition that maps B'? Explain why or why not.

16. In the composition you identified, what subsection of line B maps onto line A exactly? What is the length of this subsection?

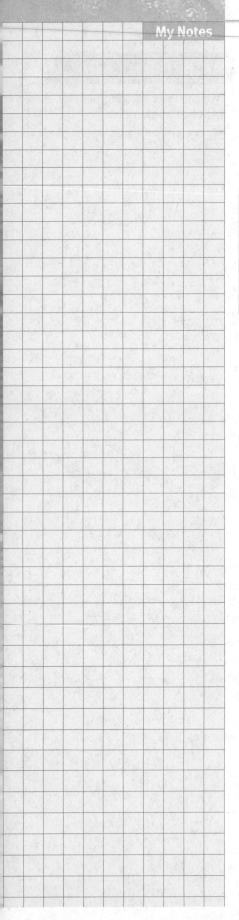

As you've seen in this lesson, two congruent figures have corresponding sides of equal length and corresponding angles of equal measure. Congruence also has the following properties:

- reflexive (Every figure is congruent to itself.)
- symmetric (If *A* is congruent to *B*, then *B* is congruent to *A*.)
- transitive (If *A* is congruent to *B* and *B* is congruent to *C*, then *A* is congruent to *C*.)

Check Your Understanding

17. Explain why a circle of radius 1 is not congruent to a circle of radius 2.

18. Figure *A* is transformed by a series of *n* rigid motions, in which *n* is a positive integer. Explain why figure *A* is congruent to its image after this series.

LESSON 10-2 PRACTICE

Rectangles *F*, *G*, and *H* are positioned on the coordinate plane as shown in the figure. Use the figure for Items 19–21.

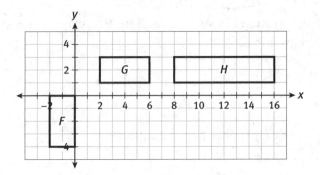

19. Explain why figure *F* is congruent to figure *G*.

20. Explain why figure *G* is not congruent to figure *H*.

21. Use the answers to Items 19 and 20 to explain why figure *F* is not congruent to figure *H*.

22. **Make sense of problems.** The endpoints of $\overline{AB}$ are $A(-2, -1)$ and $B(1, 3)$. Suppose you know that $\overline{CD} \cong \overline{AB}$ and that the coordinates of *C* are $C(1, 0)$. What are possible coordinates for point *D*? Is there more than one answer? Explain.

ACTIVITY 10 PRACTICE
Write your answers on notebook paper.
Show your work.

Lesson 10-1

1. Write the notations for these compositions of transformations.
   a. a translation of directed line segment from the origin to $(0, -3)$, followed by a reflection around the line $y = x$
   b. a reflection about the line $y = 1$, followed by a clockwise rotation of 90 degrees about the origin

2. An arrow is placed with its base at $(1, 1)$ and its tip at $(1, 5)$. Identify the positions of the base and tip of the images of these compositions.
   a. $r_{(x=0)}(R_{(1,0),90°})$
   b. $T_{(1,1)}((R_{O,-90°})T_{(-1,-1)})$
   c. $R_{(3,3),-90°}(R_{(1,3),90°})$

3. For any given figure A, does $r_{(x=0)}(R_{(2,0),90°}(A))$ equal $R_{(2,0),90°}(r_{(x=0)}(A))$? Use an example to explain your answer.

4. Identify the inverses of these transformations and compositions.
   a. $r_{(y=0)}$
   b. $T_{(1,3)}$
   c. $R_{O,-90°}(T_{(0,-1)})$
   d. $r_{x=2}(T_{(1,2)}(r_{x=0}))$

5. An up-pointing arrow is defined by points A, B, C, and D, as shown below. Identify the direction of the arrow after these compositions.

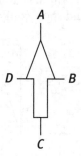

   a. $r_{\overline{BD}}(r_{\overline{AC}})$
   b. $T_{\overline{BD}}(R_{A,-90°})$
   c. $R_{D,90°}(R_{A,180°})$

6. For each of these compositions, identify the single rigid motion that performs the same mapping.
   a. $T_{(1,-6)}(T_{(-1,8)})$
   b. $r_{(x=0)}(r_{(y=0)})$
   c. $R_{(2,0),90°}(R_{(2,0),180°})$

7. A right isosceles triangle is placed with vertices at $(0, 0)$, $(4, 0)$, and $(0, 4)$.

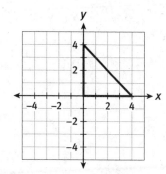

   Compare the images of the triangle produced by $r_{y=0}(R_{O,180°})$, $r_{y=x}(R_{O,90°})$ and by $r_{x=0}(r_{y=x})$.

   Hint: For any given point P, exactly two of the combinations map P to the same point.

Lesson 10-2

8. Identify the congruent triangles to triangle *ABC*. For the congruent triangles, identify the specific rotation or reflection that, along with a translation, would show congruence.

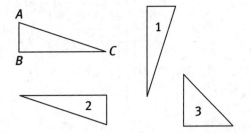

9. Which combination shows that triangles *A* and *B* are congruent?

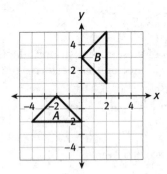

A. $T_{(2,3)}(R_{(-2,0),-90°}(A))$

B. $R_{(O,90°)}(r_{(y=1.5)}(A))$

C. $r_{(x=0)}(r_{(y=1.5)}(A))$

D. $T_{(0,5)}(R_{(0,-2),-60°}(A))$

10. Arrow *A* is placed with its base at the origin and its tip at the point (2, 2). For each arrow listed below, identify whether it is congruent or not congruent to arrow *A*. For the congruent arrows, find the rigid motion or composition that shows the congruency.
    a. base at (2, 2), tip at (0, 0)
    b. base at (−2, 2), tip at (−4, 0)
    c. base at (4, 0), tip at the origin
    d. base at (1, 1), tip at (−1, −1)

MATHEMATICAL PRACTICES
Look for and Make Use of Structure

11. Isosceles right triangles *ABC* and *A′B′C′* are ____ positioned so that point *B* is the midpoint of $\overline{A'B'}$ and point *B′* is the midpoint of $\overline{BC}$.

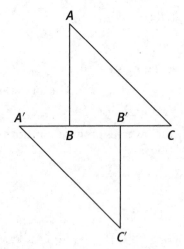

a. Find a composition of rigid motions that shows the two triangles are congruent.
b. Is there more than one composition that shows congruence? If yes, identify another composition.
c. Could triangle *ABA′* be congruent to triangle *ABC*? Explain why or why not.

City planner Regina Kane is designing a new plaza for the city. Her plan is organized on a coordinate plane, as shown and described below.

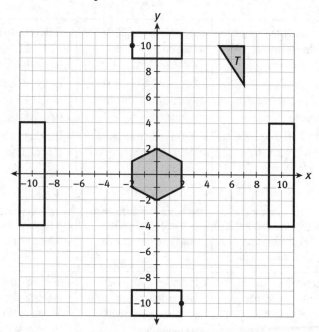

Hexagonal fountain: centered at (0, 0), all sides of length 2 units
Short rectangular benches: centered at (0, 10) and (0, −10), length 4 units
Long rectangular benches: centered at (10, 0) and (−10, 0), length 8 units
Triangular statue *T*: vertices at (5, 10), (7, 10), (7, 7)
Flagpoles (shown as dots): at (−2, 10) and (2, −10), next to short benches

1. Why could a single translation map one of the long rectangular benches onto the other long rectangular bench, but not map one short rectangular bench and flagpole onto the other short rectangular bench and flagpole?

2. Describe a rigid motion or composition of rigid motions that maps the rectangular bench at (0, 10) and the adjacent flagpole onto the other short rectangular bench and flagpole.

3. Regina wants to know if it is possible for a composition of rigid motions to map one of the short rectangular benches onto a long rectangular bench. Write a short explanation that you could send to Regina in an email.

4. Which of the polygonal shapes in the plan has the greatest number of lines of symmetry? How many lines of symmetry does this polygon have? Describe them.

5. A landscape architect recommends installing a triangular statue with vertices at (10, −10), (10, −8), and (7, −10).
   a. Is the triangle congruent to triangle *T*? Justify your answer.
   b. Propose a series of rigid motions that justifies your answer to part a.

6. Another landscape architect recommends installing a triangular statue with vertices at (−5, 10), (−5, 8), and (−7, 8).
   a. Is the triangle congruent to triangle *T*? Justify your answer.
   b. Propose a series of rigid motions that justifies your answer to part a.

Scoring Guide	Exemplary	Proficient	Emerging	Incomplete
	The solution demonstrates these characteristics:			
Mathematics Knowledge and Thinking (Items 1, 2, 3, 4, 5, 6)	• Clear and accurate understanding of different types of rigid transformations • Clear and accurate understanding of rigid transformations and congruence • Clear and accurate understanding of lines of symmetry	• A functional understanding of different types of rigid transformations • A functional understanding of rigid transformations and congruence • A functional understanding of lines of symmetry	• Partial understanding of different types of rigid transformations • Partial understanding of rigid transformations and congruence • Partial understanding of lines of symmetry	• Little or no understanding of different types of rigid transformations • Little or no understanding of rigid transformations and congruence • Little or no understanding of lines of symmetry
Problem Solving (Items 4, 5a, 6a)	• An appropriate and efficient strategy that results in a correct answer	• A strategy that may include unnecessary steps but results in a correct answer	• A strategy that results in some incorrect answers	• No clear strategy when solving problems
Mathematical Modeling / Representations (Items 5, 6)	• Effective understanding of how to determine triangle congruence using rigid transformations	• Largely correct understanding of how to determine triangle congruence using rigid transformations	• Partial understanding of how to determine triangle congruence using rigid transformations	• Inaccurate or incomplete understanding of how to determine triangle congruence using rigid transformations
Reasoning and Communication (Items 1, 2, 3, 4, 5b, 6b)	• Clear, complete, and accurate explanation of why a single translation will not map the short bench and flagpole onto its image, while a single translation will map the long bench onto its image • Clear and accurate description of a rigid motion or composition of rigid motions that maps one shape onto another • Precise use of appropriate math terms and language to justify whether or not rigid motions will map one shape onto another	• Adequate explanation of why a single translation will not map the short bench and flagpole onto its image, while a single translation will map the long bench onto its image • Adequate description of a rigid motion or composition of rigid motions that maps one shape onto another • Adequate use of appropriate math terms and language to justify whether or not rigid motions will map one shape onto another	• Misleading or confusing explanation of why a single translation will not map the short bench and flagpole onto its image, while a single translation will map the long bench onto its image • Misleading or confusing description of a rigid motion or composition of rigid motions that maps one shape onto another • Partially correct justification of whether or not rigid motions will map one shape onto another	• Incomplete or inaccurate explanation of why a single translation will not map the short bench and flagpole onto its image, while a single translation will map the long bench onto its image • Incomplete or inaccurate description of a rigid motion or composition of rigid motions that maps one shape onto another • Incomplete or inaccurate use of appropriate math terms and language to justify whether or not rigid motions will map one shape onto another

Congruence Transformations and Triangle Congruence

Truss Your Judgment
Lesson 11-1 Congruent Triangles

Learning Targets:

- Use the fact that congruent triangles have congruent corresponding parts.
- Determine unknown angle measures or side lengths in congruent triangles.

> **SUGGESTED LEARNING STRATEGIES:** Visualization, Discussion Groups, Debriefing, Use Manipulatives, Think-Pair-Share

Greg Carpenter works for the Greene Construction Company. The company is building a new recreation hall, and the roof of the hall will be supported by triangular trusses, like the ones shown below.

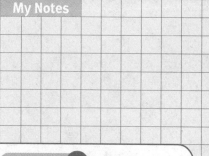

CONNECT TO CAREERS

Triangles are often used in construction for roof and floor trusses because of their strength and rigidity. Each angle of a triangle is held solidly in place by its opposite side. That means the angles will not change when pressure is applied—unlike other shapes.

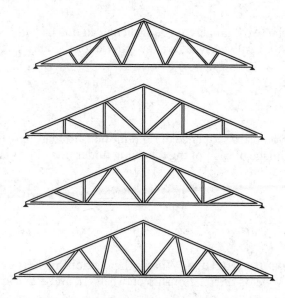

Each of the trusses contains pairs of congruent triangles. Greg's boss tells him that his first job will be to determine the side lengths and angle measures in the triangles that make up one of the trusses.

MATH TIP

Congruent triangles are triangles that have the same size and shape. More precisely, you have seen that two triangles are congruent if and only if one can be obtained from the other by a sequence of rigid motions.

My Notes

Greg wonders, "If I know that two triangles are congruent, and I know the side lengths and angle measures in one triangle, do I have to measure all the sides and angles in the other triangle?"

Greg begins by examining two triangles from a truss. According to the manufacturer, the two triangles are congruent.

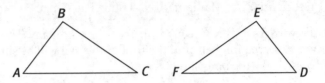

1. Because the two triangles are congruent, can one triangle be mapped onto the other? If yes, what are the criteria for the mapping?

2. Suppose you use a sequence of rigid motions to map △ABC to △DEF. Find the image of each of the following under this sequence of transformations.

   $\overline{AB} \rightarrow$ _____ $\overline{BC} \rightarrow$ _____ $\overline{AC} \rightarrow$ _____

   $\angle A \rightarrow$ _____ $\angle B \rightarrow$ _____ $\angle C \rightarrow$ _____

3. **Make use of structure.** What is the relationship between $\overline{AB}$ and $\overline{DE}$? What is the relationship between $\angle B$ and $\angle E$? How do you know?

MATH TERMS

Corresponding parts result from a one-to-one matching of sides and angles from one figure to another. Congruent triangles have three pairs of congruent sides and three pairs of congruent angles.

The triangles from the truss that Greg examined illustrate an important point about congruent triangles. In congruent triangles, corresponding pairs of sides are congruent and corresponding pairs of angles are congruent. These are *corresponding parts*.

When you write a congruence statement like △ABC ≅ △DEF, you write the vertices so that corresponding parts are in the same order. So, you can conclude from this statement that $\overline{AB} \cong \overline{DE}$, $\overline{BC} \cong \overline{EF}$, $\overline{AC} \cong \overline{DF}$, $\angle A \cong \angle D$, $\angle B \cong \angle E$, and $\angle C \cong \angle F$.

My Notes

Example A

For the truss shown below, Greg knows that $\triangle JKL \cong \triangle MNP$.

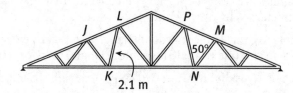

Greg wants to know if there are any additional lengths or angle measures that he can determine.

Since $\triangle JKL \cong \triangle MNP$, $\overline{KL} \cong \overline{NP}$. This means $KL = NP$, so $NP = 2.1\,\text{m}$.

Also, since $\triangle JKL \cong \triangle MNP$, $\angle K \cong \angle N$. This means $m\angle K = m\angle N$, so $m\angle K = 50°$.

Try These A

In the figure, $\triangle RST \cong \triangle XYZ$. Find each of the following, if possible.

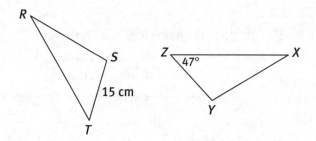

a. $m\angle X$

b. YZ

c. $m\angle T$

d. XZ

e. Both $\triangle JKL$ and $\triangle MNP$ are equilateral triangles in which the measure of each angle is 60°. Can you tell whether or not $\triangle JKL \cong \triangle MNP$? Explain.

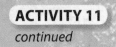

My Notes

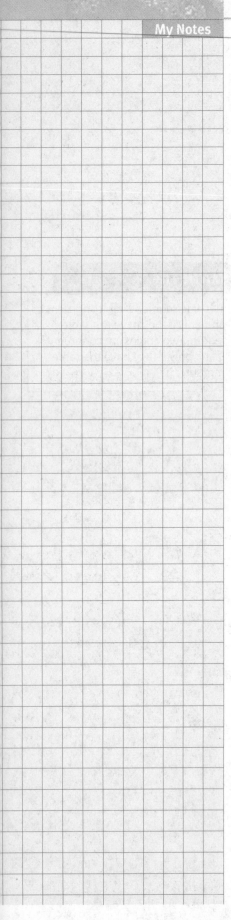

Check Your Understanding

4. If two triangles are congruent, can you conclude that they have the same perimeter? Why or why not?

5. Is it possible to draw two congruent triangles so that one triangle is an acute triangle and one triangle is a right triangle? Why or why not?

6. Rectangle *ABCD* is divided into two congruent right triangles by diagonal $\overline{AC}$.

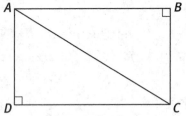

Fill in the blanks to show the congruent sides and angles.

   a. $\overline{AB} \cong$ _____
   b. $\overline{BC} \cong$ _____
   c. $\angle BAC \cong$ _____
   d. $\angle ACB \cong$ _____

7. $\triangle PQR \cong \triangle GHJ$. Complete the following.

   a. $\overline{QR} \cong$ _____
   b. $\overline{GJ} \cong$ _____
   c. $\angle R \cong$ _____
   d. $\angle G \cong$ _____

LESSON 11-1 PRACTICE

In the figure, $\triangle ABC \cong \triangle DFE$.

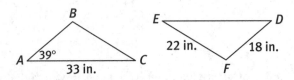

8. Find the length of $\overline{AB}$.

9. Find the measure of all angles in $\triangle DEF$ that it is possible to find.

10. What is the perimeter of $\triangle DEF$? Explain how you know.

11. **Construct viable arguments.** Suppose $\triangle XYZ \cong \triangle TUV$ and that $\overline{XY}$ is the longest side of $\triangle XYZ$. Is it possible to determine which side of $\triangle TUV$ is the longest? Explain.

Learning Targets:

- Develop criteria for proving triangle congruence.
- Determine which congruence criteria can be used to show that two triangles are congruent.

SUGGESTED LEARNING STRATEGIES: Visualization, Discussion Groups, Use Manipulatives, Think-Pair-Share

As you have seen, congruent triangles have six pairs of congruent corresponding parts. The converse of this statement is also true. That is, if two triangles have three pairs of congruent corresponding sides and three pairs of congruent corresponding angles, the triangles are congruent.

Greg's boss asks him to check that two triangles in a truss are congruent. Greg wonders, "Must I measure and compare all six parts of both triangles?" He decides that a shortcut will allow him to conclude that two triangles are congruent without checking all six pairs of corresponding parts.

1. Greg begins by checking just one pair of corresponding parts of the two triangles.

   a. In your group, each student should draw a triangle that has a side that is 2 inches long. The other two sides can be any measure. Draw the triangles on acetate or tracing paper.

   b. To check whether two triangles are congruent, place the sheets of acetate on the desk. If the triangles are congruent, you can use a sequence of translations, reflections, and rotations to map one triangle onto the other.

   Are all of the triangles congruent to each other? Why or why not?

   c. Cite your results from part b to prove or disprove this statement: "If one part of a triangle is congruent to a corresponding part of another triangle, then the triangles must be congruent."

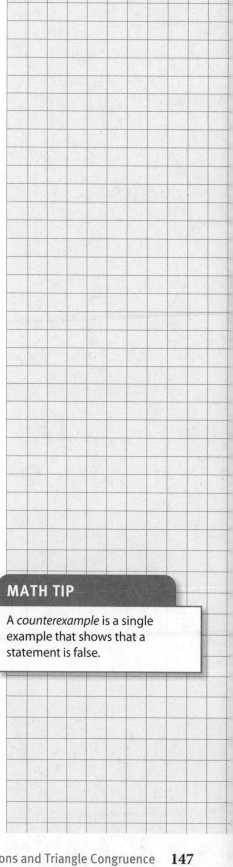

My Notes

MATH TIP

A *counterexample* is a single example that shows that a statement is false.

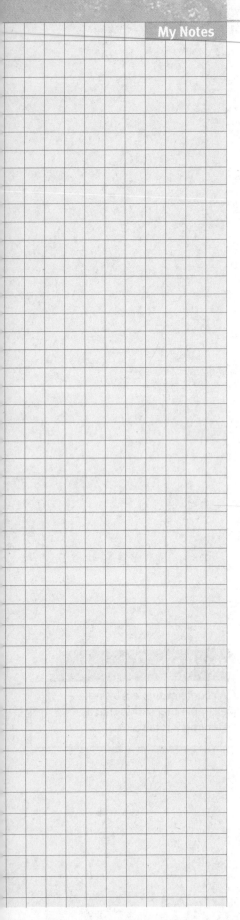

My Notes

Now Greg wonders if checking two pairs of corresponding parts suffices to show that two triangles are congruent.

2. Greg starts by considering △ABC below.

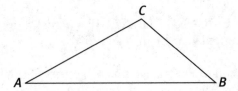

a. Draw triangles that each have one side congruent to $\overline{AB}$ and another side congruent to $\overline{AC}$. Use transformations to check whether every triangle is congruent to △ABC. Explain your findings.

b. Draw triangles that each have an angle congruent to ∠A and an adjacent side congruent to $\overline{AB}$. Is every such triangle congruent to △ABC? Explain.

c. Draw triangles that each have an angle congruent to ∠A and an opposite side congruent to $\overline{CB}$. Is every such triangle congruent to △ABC? Explain.

d. Draw triangles that each have an angle congruent to ∠A and an angle congruent to ∠B. Is every such triangle congruent to △ABC? Explain.

e. Consider the statement: "If two parts of one triangle are congruent to the corresponding parts in a second triangle, then the triangles must be congruent." Prove or disprove this statement. Cite the triangles you constructed.

Greg decides that he must have at least three pairs of congruent parts in order to conclude that two triangles are congruent. In order to work more efficiently, he decides to make a list of all possible combinations of three congruent parts.

3. Greg uses *A* as an abbreviation to represent angles and *S* to represent sides. For example, if Greg writes *SAS*, it represents two sides and the included angle, as shown in the first triangle below. Here are the combinations in Greg's list: SAS, SSA, ASA, AAS, SSS, and AAA.

   a. Mark each triangle below to illustrate the combinations in Greg's list.

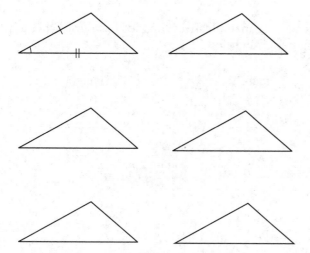

   b. Are there any other combinations of three parts of a triangle? If so, is it necessary for Greg to add these to his list? Explain.

My Notes

Now Greg wants to find out *which* pairs of congruent corresponding parts guarantee congruent triangles.

4. Three segments congruent to the sides of △ABC and three angles congruent to the angles of △ABC are given in Figures 1–6, shown below.

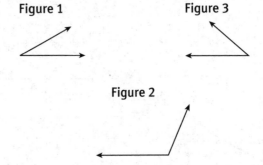

a. If needed, use manipulatives supplied by your teacher to recreate the six figures given below.

Figure 1   **Figure 3**

Figure 2

Figure 4 _____

Figure 5 _____

Figure 6 _____

b. Identify which of the figures in part a is congruent to each of the parts of △ABC.

∠A: _____   ∠B: _____

∠C: _____ $\overline{AB}$: _____

$\overline{CB}$: _____ $\overline{AC}$: _____

5. For each combination in Greg's list in Item 3, choose three appropriate triangle parts from Item 4. Each student should create a triangle using these parts. Then use transformations to check whether every such triangle is congruent to △ABC. Use the table to organize your results.

Combination	Name the Three Figures Used by Listing the Figure Numbers	Is Every Such Triangle Congruent to △ABC?

6. **Express regularity in repeated reasoning.** Compare your results from Item 5 with those of students in other groups. Then list the different combinations that seem to guarantee a triangle congruent to △ABC. These combinations are called *triangle congruence criteria*.

7. Do you think there is an AAA triangle congruence *criterion*? Why or why not?

ACADEMIC VOCABULARY

A *criterion* (plural: *criteria*) is a standard or rule on which a judgment can be based. Criteria exist in every subject area. For example, a scientist might use a set of criteria to determine whether a sample of water is safe for human consumption.

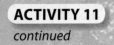

My Notes

Greg realizes that it is not necessary to check all six pairs of corresponding parts to determine if two triangles are congruent. The triangle congruence criteria can be used as "shortcuts" to show that two triangles are congruent.

Example A

For each pair of triangles, write the triangle congruence criterion, if any, that can be used to show the triangles are congruent.

a.

Since three pairs of corresponding sides are congruent, the triangles are congruent by SSS.

b.

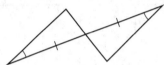

Although they are not marked as such, the vertical angles in the figure are congruent. The triangles are congruent by ASA.

Try These A

For each pair of triangles, write the triangle congruence criterion, if any, that can be used to show the triangles are congruent.

a.

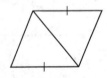

b.

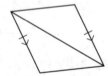

MATH TIP

You can use theorems about vertical angles, midpoints, bisectors, and parallel lines that are cut by a transversal to identify additional congruent parts that may not be marked in the figure.

Check Your Understanding

8. Two triangles each have two sides that are 8 feet long and an included angle of 50°. Must the two triangles be congruent? Why or why not?

9. Two equilateral triangles each have a side that is 5 cm long. Is it possible to conclude whether or not the triangles are congruent? Explain.

10. The figure shows a circle and two triangles. For both triangles, two vertices are points on the circle and the other vertex is the center of the circle. What information would you need in order to prove that the triangles are congruent?

LESSON 11-2 PRACTICE

For each pair of triangles, write the congruence criterion, if any, that can be used to show the triangles are congruent.

11.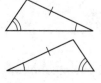

12.

13.

14.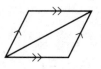

CONNECT **TO** **AP**

The free-response items on the AP Calculus exam will often ask you to *justify* your answer. Such justifications should follow the same rules of deductive reasoning as the proofs in this geometry course.

15. **Make sense of problems.** What one additional piece of information do you need, if any, in order to conclude that △ABD ≅ △CBD? Is there more than one set of possible information? Explain.

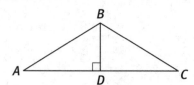

My Notes

Learning Targets:
● Prove that congruence criteria follow from the definition of congruence.
● Use the congruence criteria in simple proofs.

SUGGESTED LEARNING STRATEGIES: Close Reading, Marking the Text, Think Aloud, Discussion Groups, Visualization

You can use the SSS, SAS, or ASA congruence criteria as shortcuts to show that two triangles are congruent. In order to prove *why* these criteria work, you must show that they follow from the definition of congruence in terms of rigid motions.

1. To justify the SSS congruence criterion, consider the two triangles below.

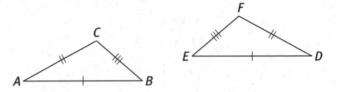

a. What given information is marked in the figure?

b. Based on the definition of congruence, what do you need to do in order to show that $\triangle ABC \cong \triangle DEF$?

c. It is given that $\overline{AB} \cong \overline{DE}$. What does this tell you?

d. Draw a figure to show the result of the sequence of rigid motions that maps $\overline{AB}$ to $\overline{DE}$. Assume that this sequence of rigid motions does *not* map point C to point F.

> **MATH TIP**
>
> You are asked to assume that the sequence of rigid motions that maps $\overline{AB}$ to $\overline{DE}$ does not map C to F. If it did map C to F, you would have found a sequence of rigid motions that maps $\triangle ABC$ to $\triangle DEF$ and the proof would be complete!

e. Which points coincide in your drawing? Which segments coincide?

f. Mark the line segments that you know are congruent in the figure below.

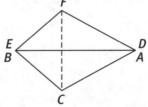

g. Based on the figure, how is $\overline{ED}$ related to $\overline{FC}$? Why?

h. Consider the reflection of △*ABC* across $\overline{ED}$. What is the image of △*ABC*? How do you know?

MATH TIP

The Perpendicular Bisector Theorem states that a point lies on the perpendicular bisector of a line segment if and only if it is equidistant from the endpoints of the segment.

The argument in Item 1 shows that a sequence of rigid motions maps △*ABC* to △*DEF*. Specifically, the sequence of rigid motions is a rotation that maps $\overline{AB}$ to $\overline{DE}$, followed by a reflection across $\overline{ED}$. By the definition of congruence, △*ABC* ≅ △*DEF*.

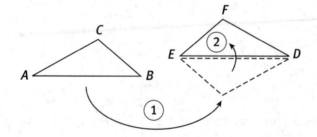

2. In the proof, is it important to know exactly which rigid motions map $\overline{AB}$ to $\overline{DE}$? Explain.

3. **Attend to precision.** How is the definition of a reflection used in the proof?

My Notes

4. To justify the SAS congruence criterion, consider the two triangles below.

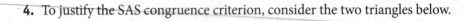
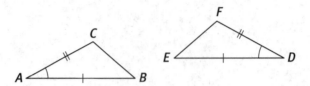

a. What given information is marked in the figure?

b. The proof begins in the same way as in Item 1. Since $\overline{AB} \cong \overline{DE}$, there is a sequence of rigid motions that maps $\overline{AB}$ to $\overline{DE}$. Draw a figure at the right to show the result of this sequence of rigid motions. Assume that this sequence of rigid motions does *not* map point C to point F.

c. Mark the line segments and angles that you know are congruent in your figure.

d. Suppose you reflect $\triangle ABC$ across $\overline{ED}$. What is the image of $\overline{AC}$? Why?

e. When you reflect $\triangle ABC$ across $\overline{ED}$, can you conclude that the image of point C is point F? Explain.

The argument in Item 4 shows that there is a sequence of rigid motions that maps $\triangle ABC$ to $\triangle DEF$. Specifically, the sequence of rigid motions that maps $\overline{AB}$ to $\overline{DE}$, followed by the reflection across $\overline{ED}$, maps $\triangle ABC$ to $\triangle DEF$. By the definition of congruence, $\triangle ABC \cong \triangle DEF$.

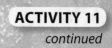
My Notes

5. To justify the ASA congruence criterion, consider the two triangles below.

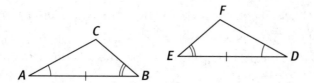

a. What given information is marked in the figure?

b. The proof begins in the same way as in Item 1. Since $\overline{AB} \cong \overline{DE}$, there is a sequence of rigid motions that maps $\overline{AB}$ to $\overline{DE}$. Draw a figure at the left to show the result of this sequence of rigid motions. Assume that this sequence of rigid motions does *not* map point C to point F.

c. Mark the line segments and angles that you know are congruent in your figure.

d. Suppose you reflect $\triangle ABC$ across $\overline{ED}$. What is the image of $\overline{AC}$? What is the image of $\overline{BC}$? Why?

e. When you reflect $\triangle ABC$ across $\overline{ED}$, can you conclude that the image of point C is point F? Explain.

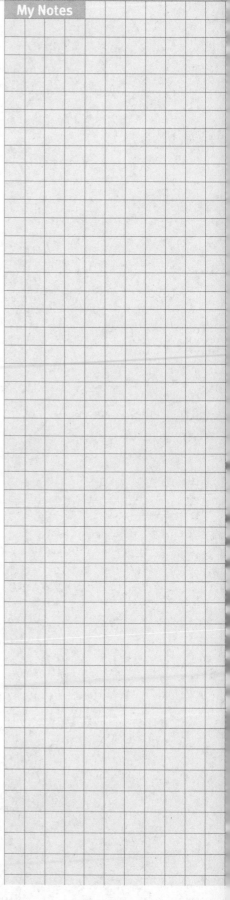

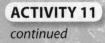

My Notes

The argument in Item 5 shows that there is a sequence of rigid motions that maps △ABC to △DEF. Specifically, the sequence of rigid motions that maps $\overline{AB}$ to $\overline{DE}$, followed by the reflection across $\overline{ED}$, maps △ABC to △DEF. By the definition of congruence, △ABC ≅ △DEF.

Now you can use the SSS, SAS, and ASA congruence criteria to prove that triangles are congruent.

Example A

Greg knows that point X is the midpoint of $\overline{JK}$ in the truss shown below. He also makes measurements and finds that $\overline{JL} \cong \overline{KL}$. He must prove to his boss that △JXL is congruent to △KXL.

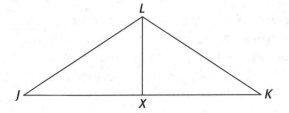

Given: X is the midpoint of $\overline{JK}$; $\overline{JL} \cong \overline{KL}$.
Prove: △JXL ≅ △KXL

Statements	Reasons
1. X is the midpoint of $\overline{JK}$.	1. Given
2. $\overline{JX} \cong \overline{KX}$	2. Definition of midpoint
3. $\overline{JL} \cong \overline{KL}$	3. Given
4. $\overline{LX} \cong \overline{LX}$	4. Congruence is reflexive.
5. △JXL ≅ △KXL	5. SSS

Try These A

a. Suppose that Greg knew instead that $\overline{LX}$ was perpendicular to $\overline{JK}$ and suppose he made measurements to find that $\overline{JX} \cong \overline{KX}$. Could he prove to his boss that △JXL is congruent to △KXL? If so, write the proof. If not, explain why not.

b. Suppose that Greg knew instead that $\overline{LX}$ bisects ∠JLK. Could he prove to his boss that △JXL is congruent to △KXL? If so, write the proof. If not, explain why not.

Check Your Understanding

6. In the Example, can Greg conclude that ∠J ≅ ∠K? Why or why not?

7. Draw a figure that contains two triangles. Provide given information that would allow you to prove that the triangles are congruent by the ASA congruence criterion.

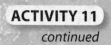
LESSON 11-3 PRACTICE

For Items 8–10, write each proof as a two-column proof.

8. **Given:** $\overline{AD} \cong \overline{CD}$;

   $\angle ADB \cong \angle CDB$

   Prove: $\triangle ADB \cong \triangle CDB$

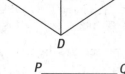

9. **Given:** $\overline{PQ} \cong \overline{QR} \cong \overline{RS} \cong \overline{SP}$

   Prove: $\triangle PQR \cong \triangle RSP$

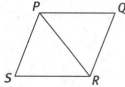

10. **Given:** $\angle K \cong \angle L$;

    $\overline{KH} \cong \overline{LH}$

    Prove: $\triangle GKH \cong \triangle JLH$

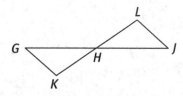

11. **Critique the reasoning of others.** A student wrote the proof shown below. Critique the student's work and correct any errors he or she may have made.

    Given: $\overline{WX} \cong \overline{YZ}$;

    $\overline{ZW} \cong \overline{XY}$

    Prove: $\triangle ZWX \cong \triangle XYZ$

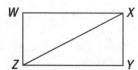

Statements	Reasons
1. $\overline{WX} \cong \overline{YZ}$	1. Given
2. $\overline{ZW} \cong \overline{XY}$	2. Given
3. $\angle W$ and $\angle Y$ are right angles.	3. Given
4. $\angle W \cong \angle Y$	4. All right angles are congruent.
5. $\triangle ZWX \cong \triangle XYZ$	5. SAS

12. **Model with mathematics.** A graphic designer made a logo for an airline, as shown below. The designer made sure that $\overline{AB}$ bisects $\angle CAD$ and that $\overline{AC} \cong \overline{AD}$. Can the designer prove that $\triangle ABC \cong \triangle ABD$? Why or why not?

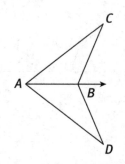

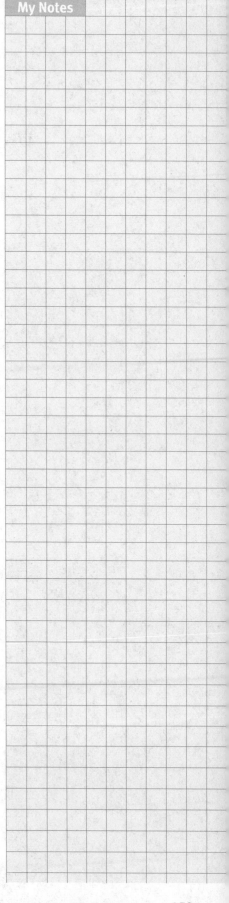

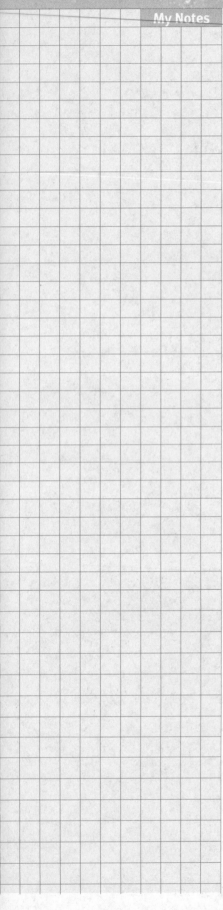

Learning Targets:

- Apply congruence criteria to figures on the coordinate plane.
- Prove the AAS criterion and develop the HL criterion.

SUGGESTED LEARNING STRATEGIES: Visualization, Discussion Groups, Debriefing

You can use the triangle congruence criteria on the coordinate plane.

1. **Reason quantitatively.** Greg's boss hands him a piece of graph paper that shows the plans for a truss. Greg's boss asks him if he can prove that $\triangle DBE$ is congruent to $\triangle FCE$.

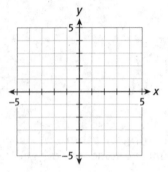

   a. Use the distance formula to find each length.

   $BD =$ _____ $CF =$ _____

   $DE =$ _____ $FE =$ _____

   $BE =$ _____ $CE =$ _____

   b. Can Greg use this information to prove that $\triangle DBE \cong \triangle FCE$? Explain.

2. In Item 5 of Lesson 11-2, you discovered that SSS, SAS, and ASA are not the only criteria for proving two triangles are congruent. You also discovered that there is an AAS congruence criterion. What does the AAS congruence criterion state? Mark the triangles below to illustrate the statement.

Lesson 11-4
Extending the Congruence Criteria

3. The proof of the AAS congruence criterion follows from the other congruence criteria. Complete the statements in the proof of the AAS congruence criterion below.

Given: $\triangle MNO$ and $\triangle PQR$ with $\angle N \cong \angle Q$, $\angle O \cong \angle R$, and $\overline{MO} \cong \overline{PR}$

Prove: $\triangle MNO \cong \triangle PQR$

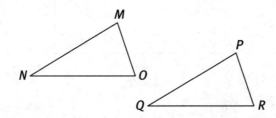

Statements	Reasons
1. $\triangle MNO$ and $\triangle PQR$	1.
2. $m\angle M + m\angle N + m\angle O = 180°$, $m\angle P + m\angle Q + m\angle R = 180°$	2.
3. $m\angle M + m\angle N + m\angle O = m\angle P + m\angle Q + m\angle R$	3.
4. $\angle N \cong \angle Q$; $\angle O \cong \angle R$	4.
5. $m\angle N = m\angle Q$; $m\angle O = m\angle R$	5.
6. $m\angle M + m\angle N + m\angle O = m\angle P + m\angle N + m\angle O$	6.
7. $m\angle M = m\angle P$	7.
8. $\angle M \cong \angle P$	8.
9. $\overline{MO} \cong \overline{PR}$	9.
10. $\triangle MNO \cong \triangle PQR$	10.

My Notes

4. Below are pairs of triangles in which congruent parts are marked. For each pair of triangles, name the angle and side combination that is marked and tell whether the triangles *appear* to be congruent.

   a.

   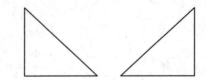

   b.

   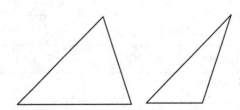

   c.

   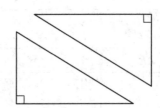

   d.

   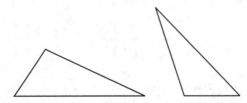

5. We know that in general SSA does not always determine congruence of triangles. However, for two of the cases in Item 4 the triangles appear to be congruent. What do the congruent pairs of triangles have in common?

My Notes

6. In a right triangle, we refer to the correspondence SSA shown in Items 4a and 4c as *hypotenuse-leg* (HL). Write a convincing argument in the space below to prove that HL will ensure that right triangles are congruent.

Check Your Understanding

7. Is it possible to prove that $\triangle LKM \cong \triangle JKM$ using the HL congruence criterion? If not, what additional information do you need?

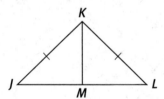

8. Do you think there is a leg-leg congruence criterion for right triangles? If so, what does the criterion say? If not, why not? Review your answers. Be sure to check that you have described the situation with specific details, included the correct mathematical terms to support your reasoning, and that your sentences are complete and grammatically correct.

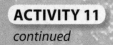
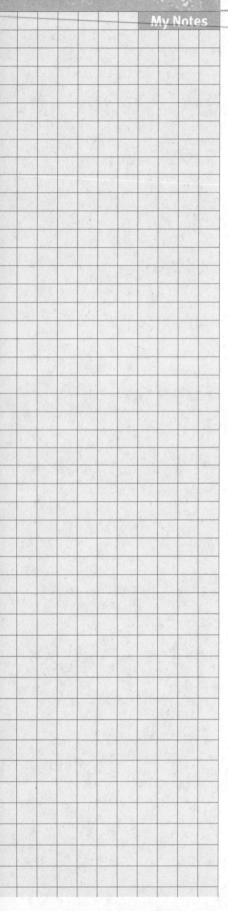

My Notes

LESSON 11-4 PRACTICE

9. **Construct viable arguments.** On a coordinate plane, plot triangles *ABC* and *DEF* with vertices *A*(−3, −1), *B*(−1, 2), *C*(1, 1), *D*(3, −4), *E*(1, −1), and *F*(−1, −2). Then prove △*ABC* ≅ △*DEF*.

For each pair of triangles, write the congruence criterion, if any, that can be used to show the triangles are congruent.

10.

11.
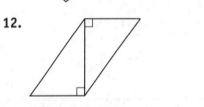

12.
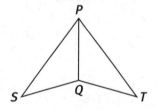

13. $\overline{PQ}$ bisects ∠*SPT*.

ACTIVITY 11 PRACTICE

Write your answers on notebook paper.
Show your work.

1. $\triangle FLX \cong \triangle TOP$. Complete the following.
   a. Name three pairs of corresponding vertices.
   b. Name three pairs of corresponding sides.
   c. Name three pairs of corresponding angles.
   d. Is it correct to say that $\triangle POT \cong \triangle XIF$? Why or why not?
   e. Is it correct to say that $\triangle IFX \cong \triangle PTO$? Why or why not?

In the figure, $\triangle MNP \cong \triangle UVW$. Use the figure for Items 2–4.

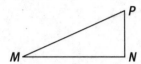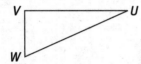

2. Write six congruence statements about line segments and angles in the figure.

3. Suppose $MN = 14$ cm and $m\angle U = 24°$. What other side lengths or angle measures can you determine? Why?

4. Suppose $MN = 2PN$ and $VW = 8$ in. Find MP.

5. If $\triangle MAP \cong \triangle TON$, $m\angle M = 80°$, and $m\angle N = 50°$, name four congruent angles.

6. $\triangle ABC \cong \triangle DEF$, $AB = 15$, $BC = 20$, $AC = 25$, and $FE = 3x - 7$. Find x.

7. $\triangle MNO \cong \triangle PQR$, $m\angle N = 57°$, $m\angle P = 64°$ and $m\angle O = 5x + 4$. Find x and $m\angle R$.

For each pair of triangles, write the congruence criterion, if any, that can be used to show the triangles are congruent.

8.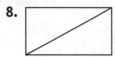

9. M bisects $\overline{AB}$ and $\overline{CD}$.

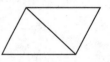

10.

11.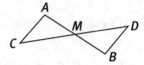

In Items 12–15, write each proof as a two-column proof.

12. Given: $\overline{EF}$ bisects $\angle GEH$;

$\overline{EF}$ bisects $\angle GFH$.

Prove: $\triangle EGF \cong \triangle EHF$

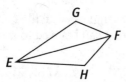

13. Given: $\overline{PQ}$ is parallel to $\overline{SR}$;

$\overline{PQ} \cong \overline{SR}$.

Prove: $\triangle PQS \cong \triangle RSQ$

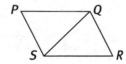

14. Given: M is the midpoint of $\overline{AB}$;

M is the midpoint of $\overline{CD}$.

Prove: $\triangle AMD \cong \triangle BMC$

15. Given: $\overline{UV}$ is parallel to $\overline{WX}$;

$\overline{UV} \cong \overline{WX}$.

Prove: $\triangle UVY \cong \triangle XWY$

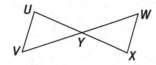

16. Draw a figure that includes two triangles. Provide given information that would allow you to prove that the triangles are congruent by the AAS Congruence Postulate.

17. a. Explain why $\triangle ABD \cong \triangle CDB$.

   b. Can you conclude that $\angle A \cong \angle C$? Why or why not?

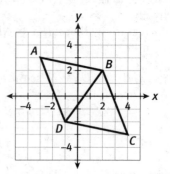

18. a. Explain why $\overline{RS}$ and $\overline{PQ}$ are perpendicular to $\overline{QS}$.

   b. Explain how to use the SAS Congruence Postulate to show that $\triangle PQT \cong \triangle RST$.

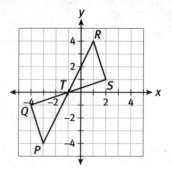

MATHEMATICAL PRACTICES
Look For and Make Use of Structure

19. The opposite sides of a rectangle are congruent. Describe three different ways you could show that a diagonal divides a rectangle into two congruent triangles.

Flowchart Proofs

Go with the Flow
Lesson 12-1 Flowchart Proofs

Learning Targets:
- Write a simple flowchart proof as a two-column proof.
- Write a flowchart proof.

> **SUGGESTED LEARNING STRATEGIES:** Marking the Text, Think-Pair-Share, Create Representations, Identify a Subtask

You know how to write two-column and paragraph proofs. In this activity you will use your knowledge of congruent triangles to explore flowchart proofs. You will also see how the three types of proofs are related.

Example A
Rewrite the two-column proof as a flowchart proof.

Given: $\overrightarrow{DB}$ bisects $\overline{AC}$; $\overline{DA} \cong \overline{DC}$

Prove: $\triangle ADB \cong \triangle CDB$

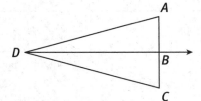

Statements	Reasons
1. $\overrightarrow{DB}$ bisects $\overline{AC}$.	1. Given
2. $\overline{AB} \cong \overline{CB}$	2. Definition of bisect
3. $\overline{DA} \cong \overline{DC}$	3. Given
4. $\overline{DB} \cong \overline{DB}$	4. Congruence is reflexive.
5. $\triangle ADB \cong \triangle CDB$	5. SSS Congruence Postulate

Step 1: Write a *statement* and then write the *reason* below the statement.

Step 2: Use arrows to show the flow of logical arguments.

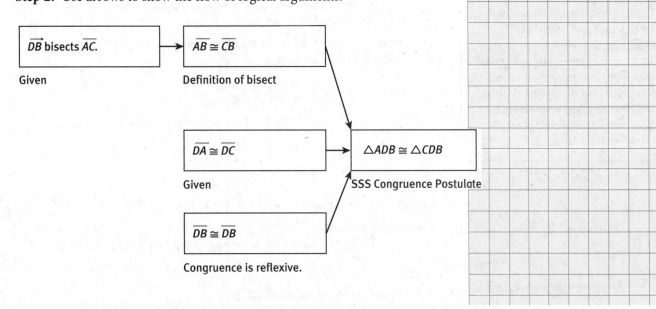

1. Why does it make sense that there are three arrows pointing to the box on the far right-hand side of the proof?

Try These A

Rewrite the following flowchart proof as a two-column proof.

Given: $\overline{PQ} \parallel \overline{SR}; \overline{PS} \parallel \overline{QR}$

Prove: $\triangle PSR \cong \triangle RQP$

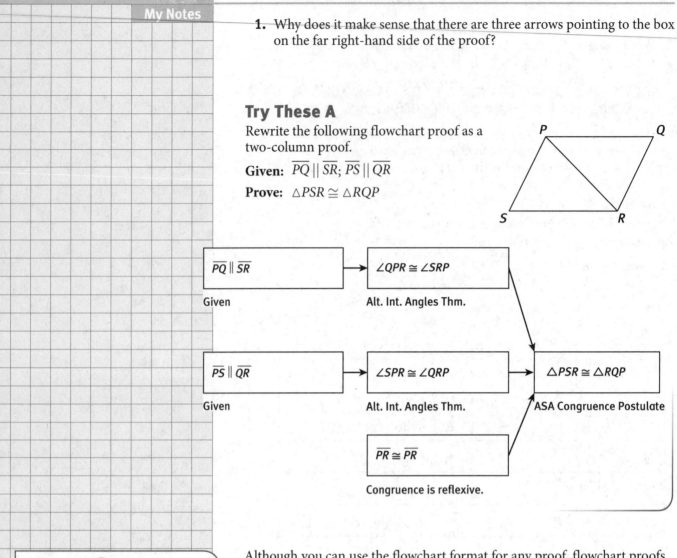

Although you can use the flowchart format for any proof, flowchart proofs are usually most useful in longer proofs because they show how steps are logically interconnected. The following sequence of steps will help you plan and write your own flowchart proof.

You will use the diagram and statements below to prove that the *opposite sides* in the diagram are parallel.

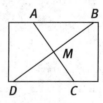

Given: M is the midpoint of $\overline{BD}$; M is the midpoint of $\overline{AC}$.

Prove: $\overline{AB} \parallel \overline{DC}$

CONNECT TO AP

The free-response portions of the AP Calculus and Statistics examinations require you to justify your work. Learning to use logical reasoning in geometry through flowchart and paragraph proofs will help develop your ability to document and explain your thinking in future courses.

2. **Make sense of problems.** A paragraph proof can serve as a plan or "pathway" for writing a flowchart proof. Use what you know about congruent triangles to write a paragraph proof to justify that the opposite sides in the diagram are parallel.

One way to organize your thoughts into a logical sequence is to use a *flowchart proof*. A significant difference between paragraph and flowchart proofs is justification. Many times, in paragraph proofs, justifications that are expected to be clear are omitted. However, in a flowchart proof, each statement must be justified. The categories of valid *reasons* in a proof are:

- Algebraic properties
- Definitions
- Given
- Postulates
- Theorems

A flowchart proof can begin with *statements* based on given information or information that can be assumed from the diagram. Flowchart proofs will end with the statement you are trying to prove is true.

3. Use the diagram on the previous page and the prove statements to prove that the opposite sides in the diagram are parallel. Begin with the statement you are trying to prove. Write that statement below and in box #8 on page 171 for the proof.

4. Start your flowchart for this proof with the *given* information.
   a. Write your statements below and in boxes #1 and #2 on page 171 for the proof.

   b. Remember that in a flowchart proof, each statement must be justified. Write *Given* on the line under the boxes in #1 and #2 on page 171.

> **MATH TERMS**
>
> A **flowchart** is a concept map showing a procedure. The boxes represent specific actions, and the arrows connect actions to show the flow of the logic.

> **CONNECT TO CAREERS**
>
> Computer programmers and game designers use flowcharts to describe an algorithm, or plan, for the logic in a program.

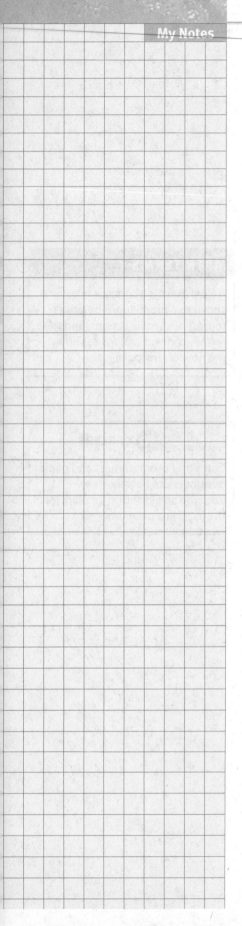

My Notes

5. Once a statement has been placed on the flowchart proof and has been justified, that statement can be used to support other statements.

   a. Use mathematical notation to write a statement about $\overline{BM}$ and $\overline{DM}$ that can be supported with the given statement "M is the midpoint of $\overline{BD}$." Write your statement in box #3 of the flowchart on page 171.

   b. Mark the information on your diagram using appropriate symbols.

6. Write the reason that justifies the statement in box #3 on the line below the box on page 171.

7. An argument similar to the one in Items 4 and 5 can be made concerning point M and $\overline{AC}$. Use this argument to fill in box #4 on page 171 and supply the reason that justifies the statement in the box on the line below the box. Mark the information on your diagram using appropriate symbols.

8. a. Is there more information that can be assumed from the diagram? If so, what is it?

   b. Mark the information on your diagram using appropriate symbols.

   c. Use appropriate mathematical notation to add the information pertaining to △AMB and △DMC to box #5 of your flowchart on page 171.

   d. Include a valid reason for your statement on the line below the box.

1.

3.

2.

4.

6.

5.

7.

8.

My Notes

9. There is no arrow from any prior statement to box #5. Why is it unnecessary to draw an arrow from any prior statement to the statement in box #5?

10. There are two triangles in the diagram that appear to be congruent.
   a. Is there enough information in your diagram and flowchart to prove conclusively that the two triangles are indeed congruent? Explain your answer.

   b. Justify your answer in part a by naming the appropriate congruent triangle method.

   c. Record the congruence statement in box #6 of your flowchart. Include the reason on the line below the box.

   d. There are three arrows connecting box #6 to previous boxes. Explain why the three arrows are necessary.

11. There is some information that can be concluded based on the fact that $\triangle CMD \cong \triangle AMB$.
   a. Write this information below, using mathematical statements.

   b. What valid mathematical reason supports all of the statements listed in part a?

   c. Because the triangles are congruent, the corresponding parts are congruent. This is often referred to as CPCTC (corresponding parts of congruent triangles are congruent) in proofs. Since these statements have a valid reason, mark them on your diagram.

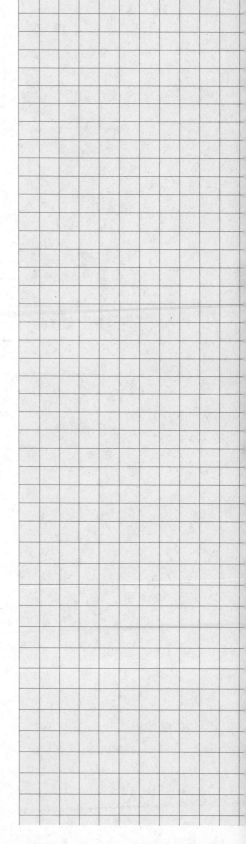

d. Which of the congruence statements from part a can be used to prove the fact that $\overline{AB} \parallel \overline{DC}$? Explain your answer.

e. Record the relevant statement from part a in box #7 on your flowchart. Include the reason given in part b on the line below the box.

12. Based on your knowledge of parallel line postulates and theorems, add a reason on the line below the prove statement written in box #8 on your flowchart. Explain your reasoning in the space below this item.

Remember that a *two-column proof* lists the statements in the left column and the corresponding reasons that justify each statement in the right column.

13. Refer to the flowchart proof that you wrote on page 171.
   a. Record the diagram you drew with the relevant information indicated, the given information, and the statement to be proven.

   b. List the statements and the reasons for each box on your *flowchart proof* to create a *two-column proof*.

Statements	Reasons
1.	1.
2.	2.
3.	3.
4.	4.
5.	5.
6.	6.
7.	7.
8.	8.

My Notes

Check Your Understanding

14. In the flowchart proof on page 171, does it matter whether you write "M is the midpoint of $\overline{AC}$" in box #1 or box #2? Are there any other boxes in which this statement could be written?

15. How is the two-column proof similar to the flowchart proof that you wrote on page 171?

LESSON 12-1 PRACTICE

16. Supply the missing statements and/or reasons for the following proof.

Given: $\overline{AD} \parallel \overline{BC}$; $\overline{AD} \cong \overline{BC}$

Prove: $\triangle ABD \cong \triangle CDB$

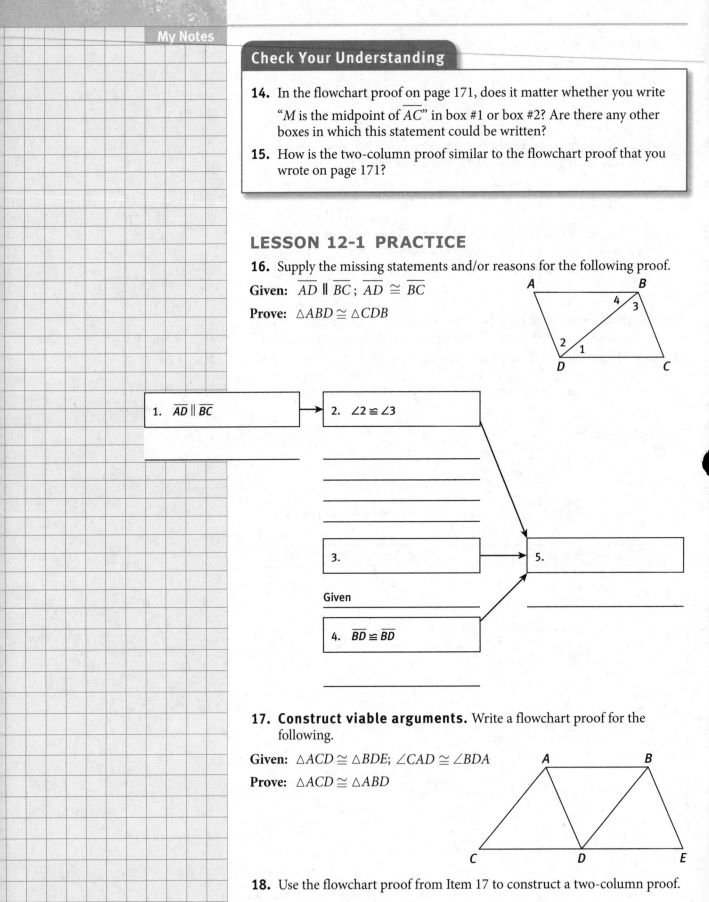

1. $\overline{AD} \parallel \overline{BC}$

2. $\angle 2 \cong \angle 3$

3. _____
   Given

4. $\overline{BD} \cong \overline{BD}$

5. _____

17. Construct viable arguments. Write a flowchart proof for the following.

Given: $\triangle ACD \cong \triangle BDE$; $\angle CAD \cong \angle BDA$

Prove: $\triangle ACD \cong \triangle ABD$

18. Use the flowchart proof from Item 17 to construct a two-column proof.

Learning Targets:

- Write a proof in three different formats.
- Write proofs using the fact that corresponding parts of congruent triangles are congruent.

SUGGESTED LEARNING STRATEGIES: Self Revision/Peer Revision, Quickwrite, Think-Pair-Share

Writing your flowchart proof involved several steps. First, the diagram, given information, and prove statement were added to the flowchart. Next, information that could be justified using a valid reason was added to the proof in a logical sequence. Finally, the statement to be proved true was validated.

Now you will write a proof using the three formats you have learned.

1. Write a paragraph proof for the following.

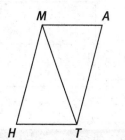

Given: $\overline{MA} \parallel \overline{HT}$; $\angle MAT \cong \angle THM$
Prove: $\overline{MH} \cong \overline{AT}$

2. **Attend to precision.** Write a flowchart proof for the proof in Item 1.

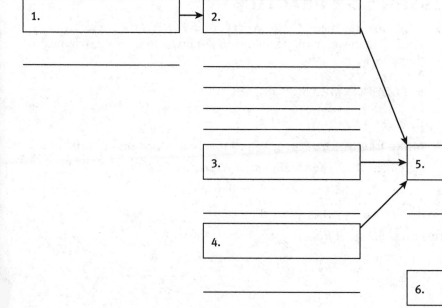
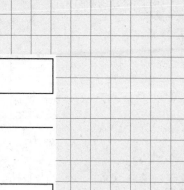

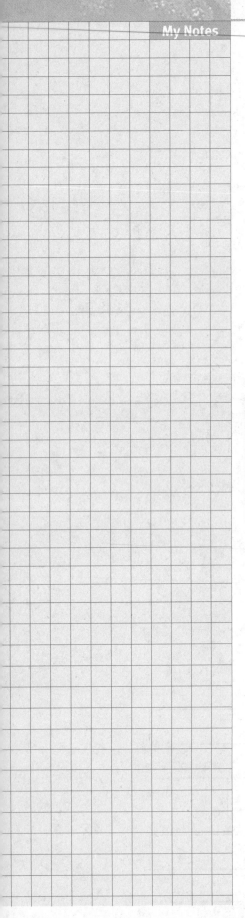

3. Write a two-column proof for the proof in Item 1.

Statements	Reasons

Check Your Understanding

4. Why might it make sense to write a paragraph proof before writing a flowchart proof or a two-column proof?

5. What are some of the advantages and disadvantages of each of the three types of proofs you have learned?

LESSON 12-2 PRACTICE

6. If the first statement in a flowchart proof is "$\overrightarrow{BX}$ *is the bisector of* $\angle ABC$," then which of the following should be the second statement in the proof?
   A. $\angle ABC \cong \angle XBC$
   B. $m\angle ABX + m\angle XBC = m\angle ABC$
   C. $\angle ABX \cong \angle CBX$
   D. $\angle ABC \cong \angle CBX$

7. Make use of structure. Which theorem or definition justifies the statement "If E is the midpoint of $\overline{AF}$, then $\overline{AE} \cong \overline{EF}$"?

8. Write a flowchart proof for the following.

Given: $\overline{CD}$ bisects $\overline{AB}$; $\angle A \cong \angle B$

Prove: $\triangle AED \cong \triangle BEC$

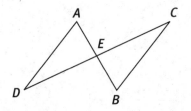

ACTIVITY 12 PRACTICE

Lesson 12-1

1. Rewrite the following flowchart proof as a two-column proof.

   Given: $\overline{MN} \perp \overline{PQ}$; $\overline{MP} \cong \overline{MQ}$

   Prove: $\triangle PMN \cong \triangle QMN$

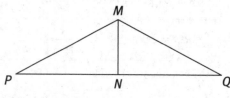

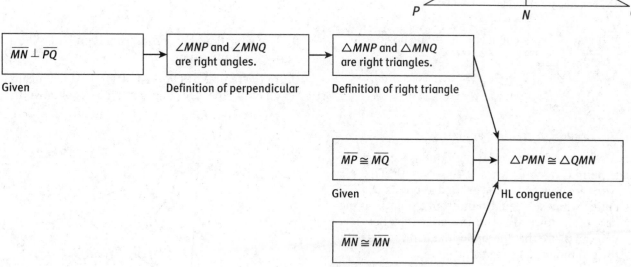

2. **a.** What reason should be written in the final step of the flowchart proof in part b?
   b. Rewrite the following flowchart proof as a two-column proof.

   Given: $\overrightarrow{AB}$ bisects $\angle CAD$; $\overrightarrow{BA}$ bisects $\angle CBD$.

   Prove: $\overline{AC} \cong \overline{AD}$

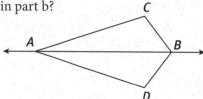

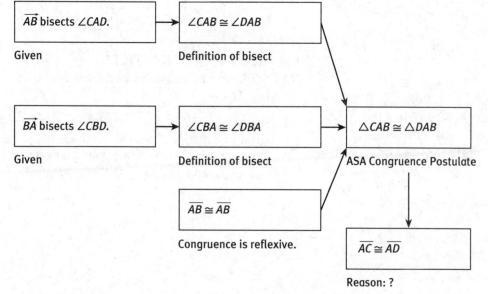

Lesson 12-2

3. DeShawn is writing a flowchart proof. Part of his flowchart proof is shown below.

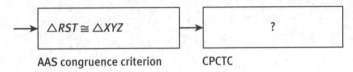

$\triangle RST \cong \triangle XYZ$

AAS congruence criterion

?

CPCTC

Which statement could appear in the box on the right?

A. $\overline{ST} \cong \overline{XY}$

B. $\angle T \cong \angle Z$

C. $\overline{RS} \parallel \overline{XY}$

D. $\angle S$ and $\angle Y$ are right angles.

4. A cell phone tower on level ground is supported at point Q by three wires of equal length. The wires are attached to the ground at points D, E, and F, which are equidistant from a point T at the base of the tower. Explain in a paragraph how you can prove that the angles the wires make with the ground are all congruent.

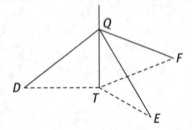

5. Which of the following would *not* be a valid reason for a statement in a flowchart proof?

A. Vertical angles are congruent.

B. Definition of segment bisector

C. Given

D. Prove

6. If "M is the midpoint of $\overline{LP}$" is the first statement in a flowchart proof, which of the following should be the second statement?

A. $\overline{LP} \cong \overline{PM}$ **B.** $\overline{LM} \cong \overline{MP}$

C. $\overline{PL} \cong \overline{LM}$ **D.** $LP = \frac{1}{2}PM$

7. $\angle A \cong \angle C$

$\angle ADB \cong \angle CDB$

Is $\overline{AD} \cong \overline{CD}$?

Why or why not? Explain your answer in paragraph form.

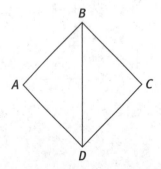

8. Write a flowchart proof for the following.

Given: $\overline{DA} \parallel \overline{YN}$; $\overline{DA} \cong \overline{YN}$

Prove: $\angle ANY \cong \angle YDA$

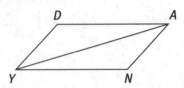

9. Use your flowchart proof from Item 8 to write a two-column proof.

10. In the figure, $\triangle PQR$ is equilateral, which means all of its sides are congruent. It is also known that $\overline{RS}$ bisects $\angle PRQ$.

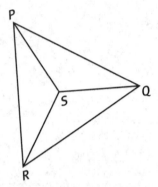

If you write a flowchart proof to show $\triangle PRS \cong \triangle QRS$, what will be the last reason in your proof?

A. AAS Congruence Postulate

B. SSS Congruence Postulate

C. ASA Congruence Postulate

D. SAS Congruence Postulate

MATHEMATICAL PRACTICES
Make Sense of Problems and Persevere in Solving Them

11. Suppose $\overline{AB} \perp \overline{BC}$, $\overline{BC} \perp \overline{CD}$, and $\overline{AB} \cong \overline{CD}$. Draw and mark a diagram with the given information. Then write a paragraph explaining how you could prove that $\overline{AC} \cong \overline{DB}$.

Congruence, Triangles, and Proof
BUILDING A FITNESS CENTER

The Booster Club at Euclid High School is building a new fitness center/ weight room. The fitness center will be divided into four triangular regions, as shown below. It will have cardio equipment, free weights, resistance machines, and mats for warm-up/cool-down. Each type of equipment will be located in a separate triangular region. The Booster Club would like to make sure that an equal amount of space is allotted for cardio equipment and free weights.

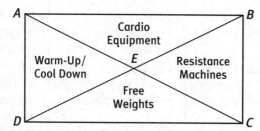

1. If E is the midpoint of $\overline{DB}$ and the walls of the fitness center, $\overline{AB}$ and $\overline{CD}$, are parallel, will the cardio equipment and the free weights have an equal amount of space?

   Prepare a report that indicates whether the cardio equipment and the free weights will have the same amount of space. Include the following in your report:
   - Mark the diagram with the given information and any other important facts.
   - Write a congruence statement for the two triangles you would like to show are congruent. State the congruence method you will use to show that the triangles are congruent.
   - Justify, using a paragraph proof, why these two triangles are congruent.

2. Write a flowchart proof to support your congruence statement.

3. Write a two-column proof to show that E is also the midpoint of $\overline{AC}$.

4. Assume that the walls of the fitness center form a rectangle, that $\overline{DE} \cong \overline{CE}$, and that the measure of $\angle EDC$ is 32°. List the measure of all other angles in the diagram. Justify each answer.

Scoring Guide	Exemplary	Proficient	Emerging	Incomplete
	The solution demonstrates these characteristics:			
Mathematics Knowledge and Thinking (Items 1, 2, 3, 4)	• Clear and accurate understanding of theorems and postulates related to congruent triangle methods • Accuracy in writing the paragraph, flowchart, and two-column proofs • Clear and accurate understanding of relationships between angle measures in rectangles	• A functional understanding of theorems and postulates related to congruent triangle methods • Mostly correct paragraph, flowchart, and two-column proofs • Adequate understanding of relationships between angle measures in rectangles	• Partial understanding of theorems and postulates related to congruent triangle methods • Somewhat correct paragraph, flowchart, and two-column proofs • Partial understanding of relationships between angle measures in rectangles	• Little or no understanding of theorems and postulates related to congruent triangle methods • Incorrect or incomplete paragraph, flowchart, and two-column proofs • Little or no understanding of relationships between angle measures in rectangles
Problem Solving (Items 1, 3, 4)	• An appropriate and efficient strategy that results in a correct answer	• A strategy that may include unnecessary steps but results in a correct answer	• A strategy that results in some incorrect answers	• No clear strategy when solving problems
Mathematical Modeling / Representations (Item 1)	• Effective understanding of how to mark a diagram using given information	• Largely correct understanding of how to mark a diagram using given information	• Partial understanding of how to mark a diagram using given information	• Inaccurate or incomplete understanding of how to mark a diagram using given information
Reasoning and Communication (Items 1, 2, 3, 4)	• Clear, complete, and accurate proofs • Precise use of appropriate math terms and language to justify angle measures in a rectangle	• Mostly correct proofs • Adequate use of appropriate math terms and language to justify angle measures in a rectangle	• Partially correct proofs • Misleading or confusing geometric vocabulary to justify angle measures in a rectangle	• Incomplete or inaccurate proofs • Incomplete or inaccurate geometric vocabulary to justify angle measures in a rectangle

Properties of Triangles

Best Two Out of Three
Lesson 13-1 Angle Relationships in Triangles

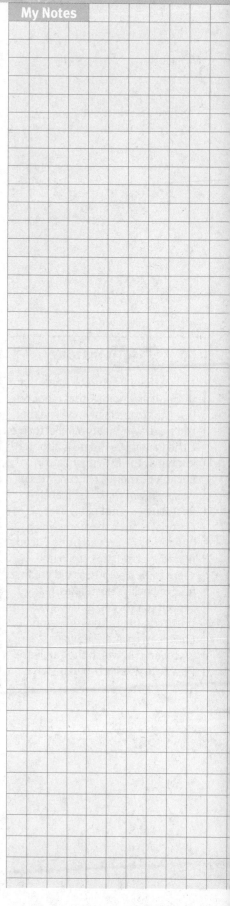

Learning Targets:

- Prove theorems about angle measures in triangles.
- Apply theorems about angle measures in triangles.

> **SUGGESTED LEARNING STRATEGIES:** Think-Pair-Share, Use Manipulatives, Look for a Pattern, Quickwrite, Self Revision/Peer Revision

The architectural design of the Rock and Roll Hall of Fame in Cleveland, Ohio, includes triangles. Some of the glass panels on the façade need to be replaced. To cut the glass correctly, angle measures of some of the triangles will need to be determined.

Jason owns a glass company and he will be cutting the glass for the repairs. One of the tools he will use to determine angle measures of the triangles is the Parallel Postulate. Jason cannot remember the sum of the measures of the angles of a triangle. He begins by drawing one of the triangles of glass he needs to replace.

1. Draw or trace the triangle below.

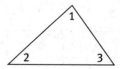

2. Tear off each corner of the triangle.

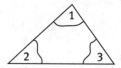

3. Arrange the corners so they are adjacent. What is formed?

4. What appears to be true about the sum of the measures of the angles of a triangle? Write a conjecture. This is known as the ***Triangle Sum Theorem***.

My Notes

You have just made a conjecture about the sum of the measures of the angles of a triangle, but the conjecture is not proven. Jason wants to prove the relationship to be absolutely certain he is correct.

5. **Make use of structure.** When you are given a figure for a proof, you cannot change anything in the figure. But you can add a line to a figure to help you complete the proof. A line used in this manner is called an *auxiliary line*. The proof of the Triangle Sum Theorem begins by drawing an auxiliary line D that intersects point A and is parallel to $\overline{BC}$. Line D forms angles 4 and 5. Explain why you can draw line D.

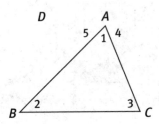

6. Complete the proof of the Triangle Sum Theorem.

   Theorem: The sum of the angles of a triangle is 180°.

   Given: $\triangle ABC$
   Prove: $m\angle 2 + m\angle 1 + m\angle 3 = 180°$

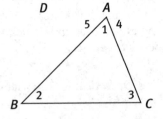

Statements	Reasons
1. Through point A, draw $\overrightarrow{AD}$, so that $\overrightarrow{AD} \parallel \overrightarrow{BC}$.	1.
2. $m\angle 5 + m\angle 1 + m\angle 4 = 180°$	2.
3.	3. If parallel lines are cut by a transversal, then alternate interior angles are congruent.
4.	4. Definition of congruent angles
5.	5. Substitution Property

CONNECT TO HISTORY

The **Parallel Postulate** states that through any point P that is not on line l, there is exactly one line that can be drawn that is parallel to line l. The Parallel Postulate is also known as the fifth postulate in Euclid's Elements. For centuries it was believed that the Parallel Postulate was not really a postulate, but a theorem, which needed to be proved using Euclid's first four postulates. It did not seem to be obvious, as did the first four of Euclid's postulates. Many set out to prove it, but always unsuccessfully. Ultimately, non-Euclidean geometries were discovered in which the Parallel Postulate was shown to be false.

Check Your Understanding

7. In the proof of the Triangle Sum Theorem, could auxiliary line D have been drawn through vertex B or vertex C instead of vertex A? Explain.

8. How can you use the Triangle Sum Theorem to show that the measure of each angle of an equiangular triangle is 60°?

9. How can you use the Triangle Sum Theorem to show that the measures of the acute angles of a right triangle are complementary?

My Notes

An *interior angle* of a triangle is formed by two sides of the triangle. An *exterior angle* of a triangle is formed by one side of the triangle and the extension of an adjacent side. A *remote interior angle* of a triangle is an interior angle that is not adjacent to a given exterior angle.

Sometimes Jason will only know the measure of an exterior angle of a triangle in the façade. He needs to be able to determine the interior angles of a triangle if he knows an exterior angle measure.

10. Label each angle of the triangle using one of the following terms: interior angle, exterior angle, remote interior angle.

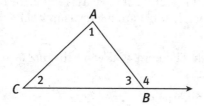

11. Use a protractor to measure angles 1, 2, and 4. What are their measures?

12. What appears to be true about the measure of an exterior angle of a triangle in relationship to the measures of its two remote interior angles? Write a conjecture. This is known as the *Exterior Angle Theorem*. It is a corollary to the Triangle Sum Theorem.

13. Complete the proof of the Exterior Angle Theorem. You will use the Triangle Sum Theorem to help you prove it.

Theorem: The measure of an exterior angle of a triangle is equal to the sum of the measures of its two remote interior angles.

Given: $\triangle ABC$

Prove: $m\angle 4 = m\angle 1 + m\angle 2$

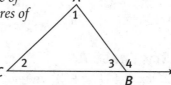

Statements	Reasons
1. $\triangle ABC$ with exterior angle 4	**1.**
2.	**2.** Triangle Sum Theorem
3. $m\angle 3 + m\angle 4 = 180°$	**3.**
4. $m\angle 4 = 180° - m\angle 3$	**4.**
5.	**5.**
6.	**6.**

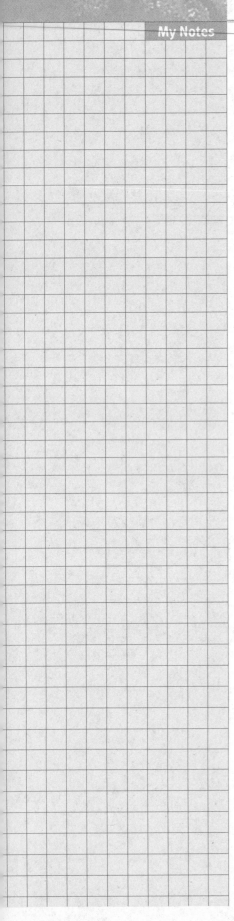

My Notes

Example A

The shaded piece of glass shown below is one of the triangles Jason needs to replace.

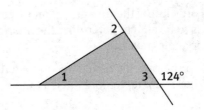

Jason knows that in this section of the glass façade, the measure of ∠2 is three times the measure of ∠1. What are the measures of all the angles in the piece of glass?

By the Exterior Angle Theorem, you know that $m\angle 1 + m\angle 2 = 124°$. You also know $m\angle 2 = 3(m\angle 1)$.

Use substitution to find the measure of ∠1.

$$m\angle 1 + m\angle 2 = 124°$$
$$m\angle 1 + 3(m\angle 1) = 124°$$
$$4(m\angle 1) = 124°$$
$$m\angle 1 = 31°$$

Now you can find the measure of ∠2.

$$m\angle 1 + m\angle 2 = 124°$$
$$31° + m\angle 2 = 124°$$
$$m\angle 2 = 93°$$

One way to find the measure of ∠3 is to use the Triangle Sum Theorem.

$$m\angle 1 + m\angle 2 + m\angle 3 = 180°$$
$$31° + 93° + m\angle 3 = 180°$$
$$m\angle 3 = 56°$$

Try These A

If $m\angle 2 = (10x + 2)°$ and $m\angle 1 = (11x - 11)°$, complete the following.

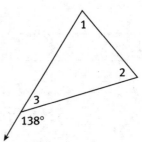

a. $m\angle 1 = $ _____

b. $m\angle 2 = $ _____

c. $m\angle 3 = $ _____

Check Your Understanding

14. In an equiangular triangle, are all the measures of the exterior angles of the triangle equal? Explain.

15. Is it possible for the measure of an exterior angle of a triangle to be equal to the measure of a remote interior angle? Explain.

16. If the measures of two angles of a triangle are equal to the measures of two angles of another triangle, what can you conclude about the measures of the third angles of the triangles?

LESSON 13-1 PRACTICE

Use the figure below to find each measure.

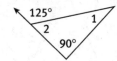

125°

2

1

90°

17. $m\angle 1 =$ _____

18. $m\angle 2 =$ _____

19. Reason abstractly. Two remote interior angles of a triangle measure 37° and 62°. What is the measure of the exterior angle associated with the remote interior angles? What is the measure of the third angle of the triangle?

Use the figure below to find each measure.

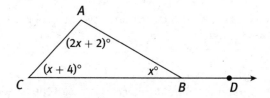

A

$(2x + 2)°$

$(x + 4)°$

$x°$

C

B

D

20. $m\angle A =$ _____

21. $m\angle C =$ _____

22. $m\angle ABC =$ _____

23. $m\angle ABD =$ _____

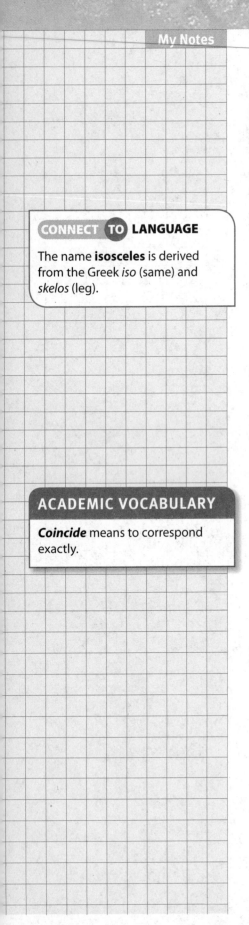

CONNECT TO LANGUAGE

The name **isosceles** is derived from the Greek *iso* (same) and *skelos* (leg).

ACADEMIC VOCABULARY

Coincide means to correspond exactly.

Learning Targets:
- Develop theorems about isosceles triangles.
- Prove theorems about isosceles triangles.

SUGGESTED LEARNING STRATEGIES: Quickwrite, Self Revision/ Peer Revision, Think-Pair-Share, Group Presentation, Use Manipulatives, Look for a Pattern

Some of the triangles Jason needs to replace are isosceles triangles. Again, he thinks he knows what an isosceles triangle is, but wants to be sure he is correct.

1. **Attend to precision.** Define isosceles triangle. On the triangle below, classify and appropriately label each side and angle using the terms vertex angle, base angle, leg, base.

2. Draw and cut out an isosceles triangle.

3. Fold your triangle so that the two legs *coincide*.

4. List the conjectures about the relationships you observe in the angles of your isosceles triangle.

5. What appears to be true about the base angles of the isosceles triangle? Write a conjecture in if-then form. This is known as the **Isosceles Triangle Theorem**.

6. The proof of the Isosceles Triangle Theorem begins by drawing the bisector of the vertex angle. On the diagram below, draw in the bisector of the vertex angle and write a paragraph proof of the theorem.

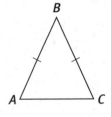

7. The measure of the vertex angle of an isosceles triangle is 80°. What is the measure of a base angle?

8. The measure of one base angle of an isosceles triangle is 25°. What is the measure of the vertex angle?

9. Solve for *x*.

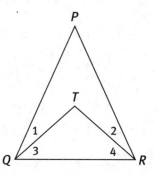

10. Using the figure below, $\overline{PQ} \cong \overline{PR}$ and $\overline{TQ} \cong \overline{TR}$.
    Explain why $\angle 1 \cong \angle 2$.

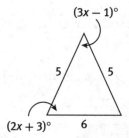

11. Use the Isosceles Triangle Theorem to explain why an equilateral triangle must be equiangular.

CONNECT TO HISTORY

Euclid's proof of the Isosceles Triangle Theorem, given as the fifth proposition in Euclid's first book of *The Elements*, is somewhat subtle and has been given the nickname *Pons asinorum*, Latin for "Bridge of Asses." The two reasons why this proposition earned its name are: (1) Euclid's diagram for this theorem looked like a bridge, and (2) this was the first proposition that tested students' ability to understand more advanced concepts in Euclidean geometry. Therefore, this proposition served as a bridge from the trivial portion of Euclidean geometry to the nontrivial portion, and the people who could not cross this bridge were considered to be unintelligent.

12. Carlie said that "if an isosceles triangle is obtuse, then the obtuse angle must be the vertex." Is she correct? If so, justify her statement. If not, give a counterexample.

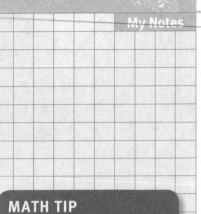

My Notes

13. Write the converse of the Isosceles Triangle Theorem and determine whether it will always be true. If yes, explain. If not, give a counterexample.

14. In $\triangle ABC$, $\angle A \cong \angle C$. If $AB = 4x + 25$, $BC = 2x + 45$, and $AC = 3x - 15$, determine the lengths of the three sides.

15. Look at the fold in your cutout triangle.

 a. What appears to be true about the segment determined by the fold?

 b. What geometric term(s) can be used to classify this segment?

MATH TIP

Create an organized summary of the properties of triangles.

Check Your Understanding

16. $\overline{AB} \cong \overline{BC}$ and $\angle 4 \cong \angle 2$. Explain why $\triangle ADC$ must be isosceles.

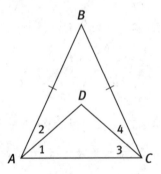

17. An isosceles triangle can be defined as a triangle with at least two congruent sides. Using this definition, what other type of triangle could be described as isosceles? Explain.

LESSON 13-2 PRACTICE

18. $\triangle ABC$ is an isosceles triangle with vertex angle B, $AB = 5x - 28$, $AC = x + 5$, and $BC = 2x + 11$. Determine the length of the base of the triangle.

19. The measure of the vertex angle of an isosceles triangle is $120°$. What is the measure of a base angle?

20. Given $\triangle ABC$, $m\angle A = (x + 14)°$, $m\angle B = (4x + 6)°$, and $m\angle C = (15x + 40)°$.
 a. Find the value of x.
 b. Determine the measure of each of the three angles.
 c. Classify $\triangle ABC$ by side length and angle measure.

21. **Critique the reasoning of others.** Juan said that he drew a triangle with angles of measure $118°$, $30°$, and $y°$. He said that by choosing the correct value of y he could make the triangle an isosceles triangle. Do you agree or disagree? Why?

ACTIVITY 13 PRACTICE
Write your answers on notebook paper.
Show your work.

Lesson 13-1

Use the figure for Items 1–3. The measure of $\angle 1$ is equal to the measure of $\angle 2$. Find the measure of the interior angle of the triangle.

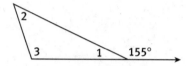

1. $m\angle 1 =$ _____
2. $m\angle 2 =$ _____
3. $m\angle 3 =$ _____

For each triangle, find the indicated angle measure.

4.

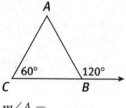

$m\angle A =$ _____

5.

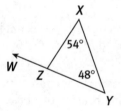

$m\angle WZX =$ _____

6.

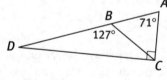

$m\angle BCD =$ _____

7. The measure of an exterior angle of a triangle is 125°. The measure of one of its remote interior angles is 65°. What is the measure of the other remote interior angle?

8. The measure of an exterior angle of a triangle is 84°. The measure of one of its remote interior angles is 22°. What are the measures of the other two interior angles of the triangle?

9. Prove the Third Angles Theorem by completing the two-column proof.

Third Angles Theorem: If the measures of two angles of one triangle are equal to the measures of two angles of another triangle, then the measures of the third angles are equal.

Given: $\triangle ABC$ and $\triangle DEF$

$$m\angle 1 = m\angle 4 \text{ and } m\angle 2 = m\angle 5$$

Prove: $m\angle 3 = m\angle 6$

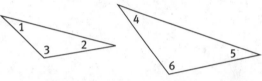

Statements	Reasons
1.	1. Given
2. $m\angle 1 + m\angle 2 + m\angle 3 =$ _____	2. Triangle Sum Theorem
3. $m\angle 3 =$ _____	3. Subtraction Property of Equality
4. _____	4. Triangle Sum Theorem
5. $m\angle 6 =$ _____	5. _____
6. $m\angle 6 =$ _____	6. _____
7. _____	7. _____

For each triangle, find the value of *x*. Then find the measure of each interior angle.

10.

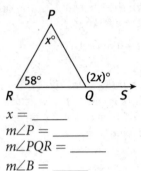

$x =$ _____
$m\angle P =$ _____
$m\angle PQR =$ _____
$m\angle B =$ _____

11.

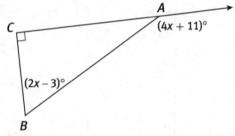

$x =$ _____

$m\angle C =$ _____

$m\angle CAB =$ _____

Lesson 13-2

12.

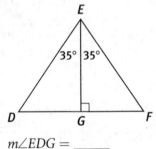

$m\angle EDG =$ _____

Find the measure of the base angles for each isosceles triangle.

13.

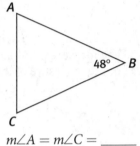

$m\angle A = m\angle C =$ _____

14.

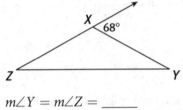

$m\angle Y = m\angle Z =$ _____

15. The measure of each of the base angles of an isosceles triangle is 47°. What is the measure of the third angle?

16. The measure of the vertex angle of an isosceles triangle is 64°. What is the measure of each base angle?

17. What are the interior angle measures of a right isosceles triangle?

18. $\triangle ABC$ is an isosceles triangle with vertex angle B, $AB = 2x + 10$, $AC = 2x$, and $BC = 4x - 16$. Determine the length of the base of the triangle.

19. The measure of the vertex angle of an isosceles triangle is 98°. What is the measure of a base angle?

MATHEMATICAL PRACTICES
Look For and Make Use of Structure

20. You know the measure of the exterior angle of an isosceles triangle which forms a linear pair with the vertex angle. Describe two ways you can find measures of the interior angles of the triangle.

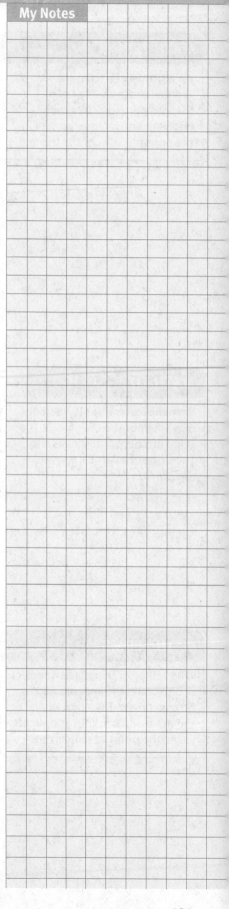

Concurrent Segments in Triangles

What's the Point?

Lesson 14-1 Altitudes of a Triangle

Learning Targets:

- Determine the point of concurrency of the altitudes of a triangle.
- Use the point of concurrency of the altitudes of a triangle to solve problems.

> **SUGGESTED LEARNING STRATEGIES:** Summarizing, Paraphrasing, Interactive Word Wall, Vocabulary Organizer, Create Representations, Identify a Subtask, Use Manipulatives

Lucky Leon was an old gold miner whose hobby was mathematics. In his will, Leon left a parcel of land to be used as a nature preserve. The will included a map and the following clue to help find a buried treasure.

> *At the point on this map where two altitudes cross,*
> *In a hole in the ground some treasure was tossed.*
> *Stand at the place where two medians meet,*
> *And the rest of the treasure will be under your feet.*
> *Each locked in chests where they will stay*
> *Until the time someone finds a way*
> *To open each lock with a combination,*
> *Using digits of the coordinates of each location.*

Al Gebra, Geoff Metry, and Cal Lucas will design the layout of the nature preserve. They use the map to help with the design. The parcel is shaped like a triangle, with two rivers and a lake bordering the three sides.

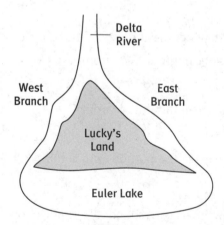

In order to preserve the natural surroundings, Al, Geoff, and Cal want to build as few structures as possible. They decide that the design of the nature preserve will include:

- a visitor center at each of the three vertices of the triangle;
- a power station that is equidistant from the three visitor centers;
- a primitive campground inland, equidistant from each shoreline.

They also want to find Lucky Leon's buried treasure.

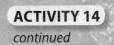

My Notes

MATH TERMS

An **altitude of a triangle** is a segment from a vertex of the triangle, perpendicular to the opposite side (or line containing the opposite side) of the triangle.

Al, Geoff, and Cal decide that their first priority is to find the treasure. They begin with the first clue from Leon's poem.

> At the point on this map where two altitudes cross,
> In a hole in the ground some treasure was tossed.

Since they do not know which two **altitudes** Leon meant, Geoff decides to place a grid over the map and draw all three altitudes to find the coordinates of any points of intersection.

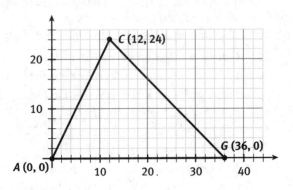

1. Determine the slopes of the three sides of △*AGC*.

2. Determine the slopes of the altitudes of the triangle.

MATH TIP

Perpendicular lines have slopes that are opposite reciprocals. The slope of a horizontal line is *zero*. The slope of a vertical line is *undefined*.

   a. What is the slope of the altitude from *A* to $\overline{CG}$? Justify your answer.

   b. What is the slope of the altitude from *C* to $\overline{AG}$? Justify your answer.

   c. What is the slope of the altitude from *G* to $\overline{AC}$? Justify your answer.

3. Use each vertex with its corresponding altitude's slope to graph the three altitudes of the triangle on the grid in Item 1.

MATH TERMS

When three or more lines intersect at one point, the lines are said to be **concurrent**. The point where the three or more lines intersect is called the **point of concurrency**.

4. After drawing the altitudes, Geoff is surprised to see that all three altitudes meet at one point. State the coordinates of the *point of concurrency*.

Al is not convinced that the altitudes of the triangle are concurrent and wants to use algebra to determine the coordinates of the points of intersection of the altitudes.

5. To use algebra to find the point where the altitudes meet, we need to know the equations of the altitudes.
   a. State the coordinates of one point on the altitude from A to $\overline{CG}$.

   b. Write the equation of the altitude from A to $\overline{CG}$.

   c. Write the equation of the altitude from C to $\overline{AG}$.

   d. Write the equation of the altitude from G to $\overline{AC}$.

> **MATH TIP**
>
> Recall that the **point-slope form** for the equation of a line is $y - y_1 = m(x - x_1)$, where m is the slope and (x_1, y_1) is any point on the line.
>
> The equation of a horizontal line is in the form $y = k$.
>
> The equation of a vertical line is in the form $x = h$.

6. Use the equations for the altitude from point A and the altitude from point C to determine the point of intersection. Show your work.

7. Verify that the point of intersection from Item 6 is also on the altitude from point G.

> **MATH TIP**
>
> There are several methods to solve a **system of equations** including the *substitution method* and the *elimination method* (also called linear combinations).

8. Explain why the algebra from Items 6 and 7 demonstrates that the three altitudes are concurrent.

Al reviews the first clue to the treasure in the poem:

> *At the point on this map where two altitudes cross,*
> *In a hole in the ground some treasure was tossed.*

9. **Use appropriate tools strategically.** Al is also not convinced that the altitudes are concurrent for every triangle. Use geometry software to draw a triangle and its three altitudes. Then drag the vertices to change the shape of the triangle.
   a. Do the altitudes remain concurrent?

   b. Is the point of concurrency always inside the triangle?

> **MATH TERMS**
>
> The point of concurrency of the altitudes of a triangle is called the **orthocenter**.

10. The first part of the buried treasure is located at the ***orthocenter*** of the triangle. What are the coordinates of the location of the first part of the treasure?

My Notes

Check Your Understanding

11. Explain why two of the altitudes of a right triangle are its legs.

12. If one altitude of a triangle lies in the triangle's exterior and one lies in the triangle's interior, what is true about the location of the third altitude?

LESSON 14-1 PRACTICE

13. Graph the altitudes and the orthocenter of the triangle.

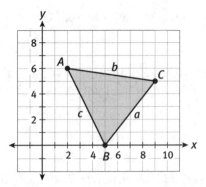

14. **Attend to precision.** Graph the altitudes and the orthocenter of the triangle.

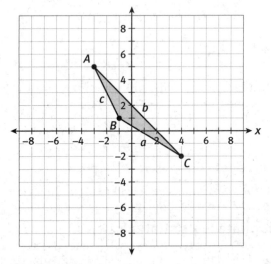

Find the coordinates of the orthocenter of the triangle with the given vertices.

15. $A(-1, 2)$, $B(9, 2)$, $C(-1, -3)$

16. $X(0, 4)$, $Y(2, 2)$, $Z(0, -5)$

17. $D(-4, 9)$, $E(5, 6)$, $F(-2, 0)$

18. $A(8, 10)$, $B(5, -10)$, $C(0, 0)$

Learning Targets:

- Determine the point of concurrency of the medians of a triangle.
- Use the point of concurrency of the medians of a triangle to solve problems.

SUGGESTED LEARNING STRATEGIES: Summarizing, Paraphrasing, Interactive Word Wall, Vocabulary Organizer, Create Representations, Identify a Subtask, Use Manipulatives

The next two lines of the poem give the next clue:

Stand at the place where two medians meet,
And the rest of the treasure will be under your feet.

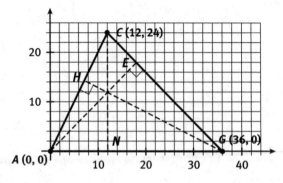

1. Carefully draw all three *medians* on △*AGC*. Name the coordinates of the point(s) where the medians appear to cross. Do they appear to be concurrent?

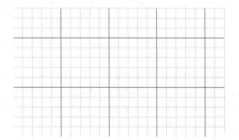

> **MATH TERMS**
>
> A **median** of a triangle is a segment from a vertex of the triangle to the midpoint of the opposite side of the triangle.

Use concepts from algebra in Items 2–7 to prove or disprove your answer to Item 1.

2. Write the coordinates of the midpoints of each side of △*AGC*. Label the midpoints as follows:

   H is the midpoint of $\overline{AC}$.

   N is the midpoint of $\overline{AG}$.

   E is the midpoint of $\overline{CG}$.

3. Determine the equation of median $\overline{AE}$. Show your work.

My Notes

4. Determine the equation of median $\overline{GH}$. Show your work.

5. Determine the equation of median $\overline{CN}$. Show your work.

6. Determine the coordinates of the intersection of $\overline{AE}$ and $\overline{CN}$. Show your work.

7. Verify that the point of intersection from Item 6 is also on $\overline{GH}$.

8. Explain how the algebra demonstrates that the three medians are concurrent.

9. **Use appropriate tools strategically.** Al wants to be certain that the medians are concurrent for every triangle. Use geometry software to draw a triangle and its three medians. Then drag the vertices to change the shape of the triangle.
   a. Do the medians remain concurrent?

   b. Is the point of concurrency always inside the triangle?

The second part of the buried treasure is located at the ***centroid*** of the triangle.

10. What are the coordinates of the location of the second part of the treasure? Label the centroid R in the diagram provided in Item 1.

The centroid's location has a special property related to segment lengths.

11. Use geometry software to draw the triangle and its medians shown in Item 1.

12. Use geometry software to find each length.
   a. CR **b.** RN **c.** AR
   d. RE **e.** GR **f.** RH

MATH TERMS

The point of concurrency of the medians of a triangle is called the **centroid** of the triangle.

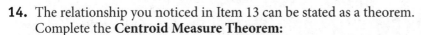

13. Compare the lengths of the collinear segments. What relationship do you notice between the distance from the vertex to the centroid and the distance from the centroid to the midpoint of the opposite side?

14. The relationship you noticed in Item 13 can be stated as a theorem. Complete the **Centroid Measure Theorem:**

The centroid of a triangle divides each median into two parts so that the distance from the vertex to the centroid is _____ the distance from the centroid to the midpoint of the opposite side.

The centroid is also the center of mass (balance point) of any triangle.

15. Create any triangle on construction paper. Locate the centroid. Cut out the triangle and balance the triangle on a pencil point placed under the centroid.

Check Your Understanding

16. Can an altitude of a triangle also be a median of the triangle? Explain.

Tell whether each statement is *always*, *sometimes*, or *never* true. Draw a sketch to support your answer.

17. The medians of a triangle bisect each of the angles of the triangle.

18. The centroid of a triangle lies in the interior of the triangle.

19. The centroid of an equilateral triangle is equidistant from each of the vertices.

LESSON 14-2 PRACTICE

Given: △*BAY* with centroid *U*. Complete the following.

20. If *EU* = 8 cm, then

  UY = _____ and *YE* = _____.

21. If *BS* = 12 cm, then

  BU = _____ and *US* = _____.

22. Reason abstractly. If *TU* = 10*x* cm, then

  AU = _____ and *AT* = _____.

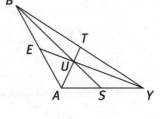

Find the coordinates of the centroid of the triangle with the given vertices.

23. $A(0, -4)$, $B(1, 1)$, $C(-2, 6)$ **24.** $X(6, 0)$, $Y(2, 8)$, $Z(-2, -2)$

25. $D(-4, -2)$, $E(1, 0)$, $F(9, 5)$ **26.** $A(8, 6)$, $B(3, -1)$, $C(0, 7)$

My Notes

Learning Targets:

- Determine the points of concurrency of the perpendicular bisectors and the angle bisectors of a triangle.
- Use the points of concurrency of the perpendicular bisectors and the angle bisectors of a triangle to solve problems.

SUGGESTED LEARNING STRATEGIES: Summarizing, Paraphrasing, Interactive Word Wall, Vocabulary Organizer, Create Representations, Identify a Subtask, Use Manipulatives

The third part of the poem tells how to determine the combination of the lock:

> *Each locked in chests where they will stay*
> *Until the time someone finds a way*
> *To open each lock with a combination,*
> *Using digits of the coordinates of each location.*

1. *. . . the coordinates of each location* refers to the coordinates of the orthocenter and the centroid you found in the previous lessons. If the combination consists of three numbers that are digits of the coordinates of the location of the treasure, list some possible combinations for the lock on the second treasure chest.

MATH TERMS

The perpendicular bisectors of the sides of a triangle are concurrent. This point of concurrency is called the **circumcenter**.

Al, Geoff, and Cal found the treasure by locating the point of concurrency of the altitudes of a triangle, called the orthocenter, and the point of concurrency of the medians of a triangle, called the centroid. Cal tells Al and Geoff to learn about two more types of concurrent points, called the **circumcenter** and the **incenter**, before they design the nature preserve. They start by locating the coordinates of the circumcenter of △*AGC*.

MATH TERMS

The angle bisectors of the angles of a triangle are concurrent, and this point of concurrency is called the **incenter** of the triangle.

2. Al took an algebraic approach similar to the manner in which he found the orthocenter and centroid of the triangle. He calculated the circumcenter to be (18, 6). Geoff decided to carefully sketch the *perpendicular bisector* of each side of the triangle. Carefully draw the perpendicular bisector of each side of the triangle and label the point of concurrency *Q*.

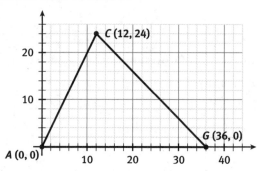

Does your drawing verify that Al is correct?

The circumcenter of a triangle has a special property.

3. Use the distance formula to complete the following table.

Distance from *Q* to *A*	
Distance from *Q* to *C*	
Distance from *Q* to *G*	

4. The distances suggest that the circumcenter of a triangle is equidistant from the three vertices of the triangle. Write a convincing argument that this special property applies to all triangles.

5. Sketch the ***circumscribed circle*** on the grid in Item 2.

Cal located the incenter of △*AGC*. He estimated that the coordinates of the incenter are approximately (14.446, 8.928).

6. On the grid below, carefully draw the three bisectors of the angles of △*AGC*. Label the point of concurrency *I*. Does your drawing support Cal's results?

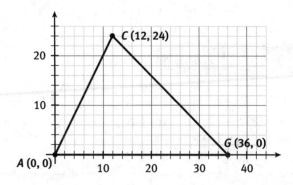

To explore a special property of the incenter, Cal needs to calculate the distances from the incenter to each of the three sides.

7. **a.** Draw a perpendicular segment from *I* to $\overline{AC}$ on the triangle in Item 6. Label the point of intersection *L*.
   b. Cal estimated the coordinates of *L* to be (6.177, 12.353). Find the length *IL*.

8. **a.** Draw a perpendicular segment from *I* to $\overline{AG}$ on the triangle in Item 6. Label the point of intersection *M*.
   b. Estimate the coordinates of *M*.

   c. Find the length *IM*.

9. **a.** Draw a perpendicular segment from *I* to $\overline{CG}$ on the triangle in Item 6. Label the point of intersection *B*.
   b. Estimate the coordinates of *B*.

   c. Find the length *IB*.

The distances suggest that the incenter of a triangle is equidistant to the three sides of the triangle.

10. Sketch the ***inscribed circle*** on the triangle in Item 6.

MATH TERMS

A **circumscribed circle** is a circle that contains all the vertices of a polygon.

MATH TIP

Since the circumcenter is equidistant from the three vertices of the triangle, it is the center of the circle with radius equal to the distance from the circumcenter to any of the vertices.

MATH TIP

The distance from a point to a line (or segment) is the length of the perpendicular segment from the point to the line.

MATH TERMS

Since the **incenter** is equidistant to the three sides of the triangle, it is the center of the circle with radius equal to the distance from the incenter to any of the sides. This is called the **inscribed circle**.

11. Reason quantitatively. Refer back to the description of the nature preserve at the beginning of this Activity. On the map below, locate and label the three visitor centers, the power station, and the campground. Explain why you chose each location.

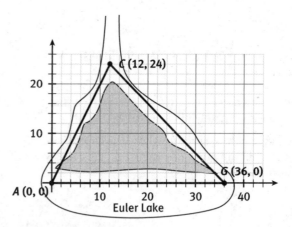

Check Your Understanding

12. Can the incenter of a triangle lie outside the triangle? Explain.

13. Draw three sketches showing the circumcenter lying inside, outside, and on the triangle. Make a conjecture about the location of a circumcenter and the type of triangle.

LESSON 14-3 PRACTICE

Given: $\triangle XYZ$ with circumcenter P.

Complete the following.

14. If $PX = 18$ mm, then

$PY = \underline{\hphantom{xxx}}$ and $PZ = \underline{\hphantom{xxx}}$.

15. If $WX = 12$ cm, then $XY = \underline{\hphantom{xxx}}$.

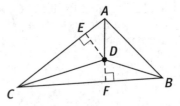

Given: $\triangle ABC$ with incenter D. Complete the following.

16. If $DE = 3$ cm, then $DF = \underline{\hphantom{xxx}}$.

17. Make sense of problems. If and $m\angle CAB = 90°$ and $m\angle CBA = 25°$, $m\angle ACB = \underline{\hphantom{xxx}}$ and $m\angle ACD = \underline{\hphantom{xxx}}$.

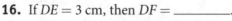

Find the coordinates of the circumcenter of the triangle with the given vertices.

18. $A(-3, 0)$, $B(0, 0)$, $C(0, 20)$ **19.** $X(2, 1)$, $Y(-5, -3)$, $Z(0, 7)$

ACTIVITY 14 PRACTICE
Write your answers on notebook paper.
Show your work.

Lesson 14-1

Graph the altitudes and find the orthocenter of each triangle.

1.

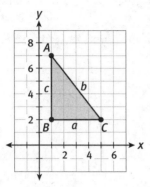

2.

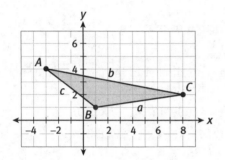

Find the coordinates of the orthocenter of the triangle with the given vertices.

3. $A(-1, 2)$, $B(9, 2)$, $C(-1, -3)$

4. $X(0, 8)$, $Y(3, 5)$, $Z(2, -2)$

5. $D(-4, 9)$, $E(5, 6)$, $F(-2, 0)$

6. $A(1, 1)$, $B(4, -1)$, $C(0, 2)$

7. Are the altitudes of an equilateral triangle also its lines of symmetry? Explain.

Lesson 14-2

8. Draw the centroid of $\triangle HOP$ and name its coordinates.

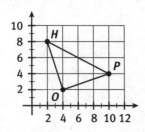

For Items 9 and 10, use $\triangle DTG$ with centroid I.

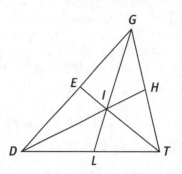

9. If $GI = 24$ cm, then $LI =$ _____ and $LG =$ _____.

10. If $DH = (4x + 10)$ in. and $HI = (2x - 4)$ in., then $x =$ _____, $HI =$ _____, and $ID =$ _____.

Graph the medians and find the centroid of each triangle.

11.

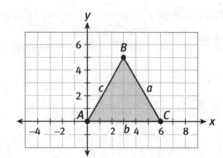

12.

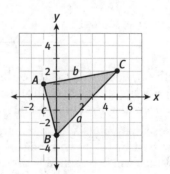

Find the coordinates of the centroid of the triangle with the given vertices.

13. $A(8, 10)$, $B(4, -10)$, $C(0, 0)$

14. $X(0, 5)$, $Y(3, 12)$, $Z(1, -5)$

15. $D(-4, 9)$, $E(5, 6)$, $F(-1, 0)$

16. $A(8, 10)$, $B(1, -10)$, $C(3, 3)$

17. Use geometry software to draw an equilateral triangle. Draw the altitudes and the medians of the triangle. Make a conjecture about the orthocenter and centroid of an equilateral triangle. Write a two-column proof to prove your conjecture or find a counterexample to show it is false.

If _____,

then _____.

Given: Equilateral △ABC with _____

Prove: _____

Lesson 14-3

Points A, B, C, and D represent different points of concurrency of segments associated with △XYZ. The coordinates are $X(0, 0)$, $Z(9, 0)$, and $Y(3, 9)$.

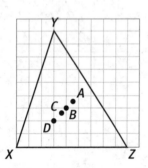

18. Identify A, B, C, and D as the orthocenter, centroid, circumcenter, or incenter of the triangle. Explain your reasoning.

19. Suppose that points X, Y, and Z are the locations of three rustic cabins with no running water. If the cabins will be supplied with water from a single well, where would you locate the well? Explain your reasoning.

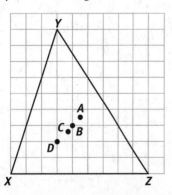

20. Three sidewalks cross near the middle of City Park, forming a triangular region. Levi donated money to the city to create a fountain in memory of his father. He wants the fountain to be located at a place that is equidistant from the three sidewalks. At which point of concurrency should it be located?

A. orthocenter   **B.** centroid
C. circumcenter   **D.** incenter

21. Which of the points of concurrency is illustrated?

A. orthocenter
B. centroid
C. circumcenter
D. incenter

Find the coordinates of the circumcenter of the triangle with the given vertices.

22. $A(-3, -1)$, $B(-4, -5)$, $C(0, -1)$

23. $X(7, 4)$, $Y(-2, -7)$, $Z(1, 2)$

MATHEMATICAL PRACTICES
Reason Abstractly and Quantitatively

24. a. Which point(s) of concurrency could lie outside of a triangle?
    b. What type(s) of triangle would cause that to happen?
    c. Sketch the incenter of △NET.

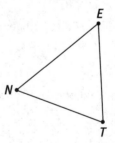

The city council is planning a new city park on a triangular plot of land formed by three intersecting streets.

The designer placed the triangle on a grid to determine the side lengths and angle measures needed for the purchase and placement of a fence surrounding the park. Each unit on the grid is one inch, which represents 20 feet of actual length.

The measure of angle CAB in the designer's diagram is $(5x + 1)°$, and the measure of angle ACB is $(3x + 12.5)°$.

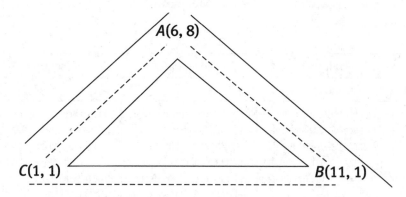

1. **Persevere in solving problems.** Create a report that provides a detailed description of the park. Include the following in your report:
   - the actual side lengths of the triangular plot of land
   - the type of triangle formed by the intersection of the three streets
   - the amount of fencing needed to surround the city park
   - the actual measure of each angle of the triangle

2. The centroid of a triangle is the triangle's center of gravity.

A fountain will be placed at the centroid of the park. The designer wants to place a stone path from the fountain to the midpoint of each side.

a. Reproduce the diagram in Item 1 showing the location of the fountain and the stone paths. Mark congruent segments on your diagram.

b. What are the coordinates of the location of the fountain?

c. What is the actual distance from the fountain to each vertex?

d. Find the actual length of each stone path.

Scoring Guide	Exemplary	Proficient	Emerging	Incomplete
	The solution demonstrates these characteristics:			
Mathematics Knowledge and Thinking (Items 1, 2)	• Accurate use of the distance formula and scale factor to determine the lengths of the sides and the perimeter of the triangular plot • Clear and accurate understanding of isosceles triangles and their angle measures • Clear and accurate understanding of the centroid of a triangle	• Mostly correct use of the distance formula and scale factor to determine the lengths of the sides and the perimeter of the triangular plot • A functional understanding of isosceles triangles and their angle measures • Adequate understanding of the centroid of a triangle	• Correct use of the distance formula to determine the lengths of the sides and the perimeter of the triangular plot while omitting the use of scale to determine actual length • Partial understanding of isosceles triangles and their angle measures • Partial understanding of the centroid of a triangle	• Incorrect or incomplete use of the distance formula and scale factor to determine the lengths of the sides and the perimeter of the triangular plot • Little or no understanding of isosceles triangles and their angle measures • Little or no understanding of the centroid of a triangle
Problem Solving (Items 1, 2b, 2c, 2d)	• An appropriate and efficient strategy that results in a correct answer	• A strategy that may include unnecessary steps but results in a correct answer	• A strategy that results in some incorrect answers	• No clear strategy when solving problems
Mathematical Modeling / Representations (Item 2a)	• Clear and accurate drawing of the triangle showing locations of the fountain (centroid) and stone paths (segments from the centroid to the midpoints of the sides) and identifying congruent segments	• Largely correct drawing of the triangle showing locations of the fountain (centroid) and stone paths (segments from the centroid to the midpoints of the sides) and identifying congruent segments	• Partially correct drawing of the triangle showing locations of the fountain (centroid) and stone paths (segments from the centroid to the midpoints of the sides) and identifying congruent segments	• Inaccurate or incomplete drawing of the triangle showing locations of the fountain (centroid) and stone paths (segments from the centroid to the midpoints of the sides) and identifying congruent segments
Reasoning and Communication (Item 1)	• Precise use of appropriate math terms and language to justify side lengths and angle measures in an isosceles triangle	• Adequate use of appropriate math terms and language to justify side lengths and angle measures in an isosceles triangle	• Misleading or confusing use of math terms and language to justify side lengths and angle measures in an isosceles triangle	• Incomplete or inaccurate use of math terms and language to justify side lengths and angle measures in an isosceles triangle

Quadrilaterals and Their Properties

A 4-gon Hypothesis
Lesson 15-1 Kites and Triangle Midsegments

Learning Targets:
- Develop properties of kites.
- Prove the Triangle Midsegment Theorem.

SUGGESTED LEARNING STRATEGIES: Discussion Groups, Shared Reading, Create Representations, Think-Pair-Share, Interactive Word Wall, Group Presentations

Mr. Cortez, the owner of a tile store, wants to create a database of all of the tiles he sells in his store. All of his tiles are quadrilaterals, but he needs to learn the properties of different quadrilaterals so he can correctly classify the tiles in his database.

Mr. Cortez begins by exploring convex quadrilaterals. The term *quadrilateral* can be abbreviated "quad."

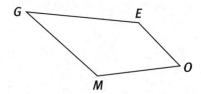

1. Given quad *GEOM*.
   a. List all pairs of opposite sides.

   b. List all pairs of consecutive sides.

   c. List all pairs of opposite angles.

   d. List all pairs of consecutive angles.

   e. Draw the diagonals, and list them.

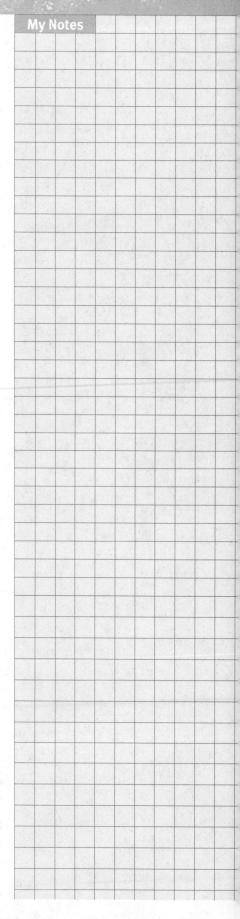

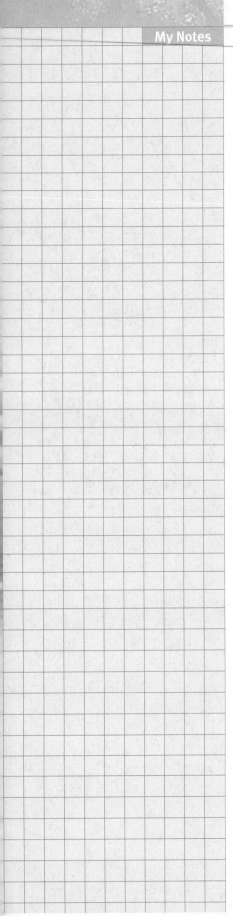

A *kite* is a quadrilateral with exactly two distinct pairs of congruent consecutive sides.

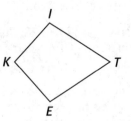

2. Given quad *KITE* with $\overline{KI} \cong \overline{KE}$ and $\overline{IT} \cong \overline{ET}$.

    a. One of the diagonals divides the kite into two congruent triangles. Draw that diagonal and list the two congruent triangles. Explain how you know the triangles are congruent.

    b. Draw the other diagonal. Explain how you know the diagonals are perpendicular.

    c. Complete the following list of properties of a kite. Think about the angles of a kite as well as the segments.

      1. Exactly two pairs of consecutive sides are congruent.
      2. One diagonal divides a kite into two congruent triangles.
      3. The diagonals of a kite are perpendicular.
      4.
      5.
      6.

3. Critique the reasoning of others. Mr. Cortez says that the diagonals of a kite bisect each other. Is Mr. Cortez correct? Support your answer with a valid argument.

Check Your Understanding

4. Why is a square not considered a kite?

5. Suppose $\overline{AC}$ and $\overline{BD}$ are the diagonals of a kite. What is a formula for the area of the kite in terms of the diagonals?

The segment whose endpoints are the midpoints of two sides of a triangle is called a ***midsegment***.

Triangle Midsegment Theorem The midsegment of a triangle is parallel to the third side, and its length is one-half the length of the third side.

6. Use the figure and coordinates below to complete the coordinate proof for the Triangle Midsegment Theorem.

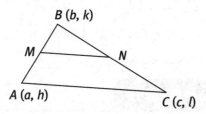

a. Complete the hypothesis and conclusion for the Triangle Midsegment Theorem.

Hypothesis: M is the midpoint of _____.

N is the midpoint of _____.

Conclusion: $\overline{MN} \parallel$ _____

$MN =$ _____

b. Find the coordinates of midpoints M and N in terms of a, b, c, h, k, and l.

c. Find the slope of $\overline{AC}$ and $\overline{MN}$.

d. Simplify your response to part c and explain how your answers to part c show $\overline{MN} \parallel \overline{AC}$.

MATH TIP

Given $A(x_1, y_1)$ and $B(x_2, y_2)$.

Midpoint Formula:

$M = \left(\dfrac{x_1 + x_2}{2}, \dfrac{y_1 + y_2}{2} \right)$

Slope of $\overline{AB}$: $m = \dfrac{(y_2 - y_1)}{(x_2 - x_1)}$

Distance Formula:

$AB = \sqrt{(x_2 - x_1)^2 + (y_2 - y_1)^2}$

My Notes

e. Find AC and MN.

f. Simplify your response to part e and explain how your answers to part e show that $MN = \frac{1}{2}AC$.

Check Your Understanding

7. Are the midsegments of an isosceles triangle congruent? Explain.
8. Given $\overline{DE} \parallel \overline{AC}$. Is $\overline{DE}$ a midsegment of triangle ABC? Explain.

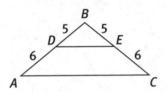

LESSON 15-1 PRACTICE

9. $\overline{XY}$ is a midsegment of triangle DEF. Find each measure.

   $XY = $ _____

   $DX = $ _____

   $YF = $ _____

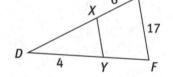

10. $\overline{QR}$ is a midsegment of triangle WYZ. Find each measure.

    $x = $ _____

    $WZ = $ _____

    $QR = $ _____

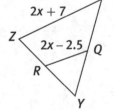

11. **Make sense of problems.** Figure $ABCD$ is a kite with diagonals $\overline{BD}$ and $\overline{AC}$. Complete each statement.

    $\overline{BD} \perp$ _____

    $\triangle ABC \cong \triangle$ _____

    $\angle ABC \cong \angle$ _____

    $\overline{AB} \cong$ _____

    $\angle BAC \cong \angle$ _____

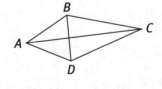

Learning Targets:
- Develop properties of trapezoids.
- Prove properties of trapezoids.

> **SUGGESTED LEARNING STRATEGIES:** Visualization, Shared Reading, Create Representations, Think-Pair-Share, Interactive Word Wall

A **trapezoid** is a quadrilateral with exactly one pair of parallel sides. The parallel sides of a trapezoid are called **bases**, and the nonparallel sides are called **legs**. The pairs of consecutive angles that include each of the bases are called **base angles**.

1. Sketch a trapezoid and label the vertices T, R, A, and P. Identify the bases, legs, and both pairs of base angles.

The **median of a trapezoid** is the segment with endpoints at the midpoint of each leg of the trapezoid.

Trapezoid Median Theorem The median of a trapezoid is parallel to the bases and its length is the average of the lengths of the bases.

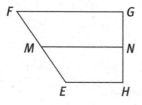

Given: Trapezoid $EFGH$

$\overline{MN}$ is a median.

Prove: $\overline{MN} \parallel \overline{FG}$ and $\overline{MN} \parallel \overline{EH}$

$MN = \frac{1}{2}(FG + EH)$

2. Draw one diagonal in trapezoid $EFGH$. Label the intersection of the diagonal with $\overline{MN}$ as X and explain below how the Triangle Midsegment Theorem can be used to justify the Trapezoid Median Theorem.

> **CONNECT TO LANGUAGE**
>
> The British use the term *trapezium* for a quadrilateral with exactly one pair of parallel sides and the term *trapezoid* for a quadrilateral with no parallel sides. They drive on a different side of the road, too.

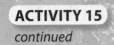

My Notes

3. Given trapezoid *EFGH* and $\overline{MN}$ is a median. Use the figure in Item 2, properties of trapezoids, and/or the Trapezoid Median Theorem for each of the following.
   a. If $m\angle GFE = 42°$, then $m\angle NME =$ _____ and $m\angle MEH =$ _____.
   b. Write an equation and solve for *x* if $FG = 4x + 4$, $EH = x + 5$, and $MN = 22$.

   c. Find *FG* if $MN = 19$ and $EH = 12$.

4. **Make use of structure.** What property or postulate allowed you to draw the auxiliary line in Item 2?

Check Your Understanding

5. How does a trapezoid differ from a kite?

6. Can a trapezoid have bases that are congruent? Explain.

An *isosceles trapezoid* is a trapezoid with congruent legs.

7. Given $\triangle ABC$ is isosceles with $AB = CB$ and $AD = CE$.

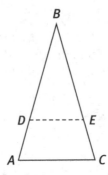

   a. $\angle A \cong$ _____. Explain.

   b. Explain why $\triangle BDE$ is isosceles.

   c. $\overline{AC} \parallel$ _____. Explain.

   d. Explain why quad *ADEC* is an isosceles trapezoid.

   e. $\angle ADE \cong$ _____. Explain.

My Notes

f. Complete the theorem.

The base angles of an isosceles trapezoid are _____.

8. On grid paper, plot quad *COLD* with coordinates $C(1, 0)$, $O(2, 2)$, $L(5, 3)$, and $D(7, 2)$.

a. Show that quad *COLD* is a trapezoid.

b. Show that quad *COLD* is isosceles.

c. Identify and find the length of each diagonal.

d. Based on the results in part c, complete the theorem.

The diagonals of an isosceles trapezoid are _____.

9. At this point, the theorem in Item 8 is simply a conjecture based on one example. Given the figure below, write the key steps for a proof of the theorem. Hint: You may want to use a pair of overlapping triangles and the theorem from Item 8 as part of your argument.

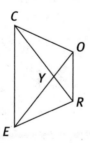

Hypothesis:	*CORE* is a trapezoid.
	$\overline{CO} \cong \overline{ER}$
Conclusion:	$\overline{CR} \cong \overline{EO}$

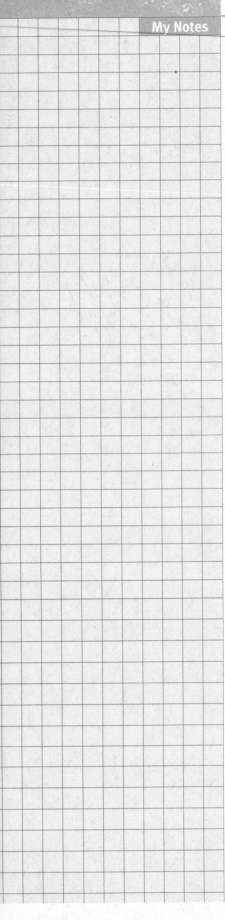
Check Your Understanding

10. Given quad *PLAN* is an isosceles trapezoid, use the diagram below and the properties of isosceles trapezoids to find each of the following.

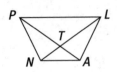

a. $\angle LPN \cong$ _____

b. If $m\angle PLA = 70°$, then $m\angle LPN =$ _____ and $m\angle PNA =$ _____.

c. Write an equation and solve for x if $AP = x$ and $NL = 3x - 8$.

LESSON 15-2 PRACTICE

11. $\overline{UV}$ is a midsegment of trapezoid *QRST*. Find each measure.

$QU =$ _____

$VS =$ _____

$UV =$ _____

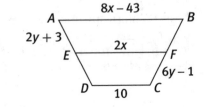

12. Reason abstractly. $\overline{EF}$ is a midsegment of isosceles trapezoid *ABCD*. Find each measure.

$x =$ _____

$y =$ _____

$AE =$ _____

$ED =$ _____

$BF =$ _____

$FC =$ _____

$AB =$ _____

$EF =$ _____

Learning Targets:

- Develop properties of parallelograms.
- Prove properties of parallelograms.

> **SUGGESTED LEARNING STRATEGIES:** Visualization, Create Representations, Think-Pair-Share, Interactive Word Wall, Discussion Groups

A ***parallelogram*** is a quadrilateral with both pairs of opposite sides parallel. For the sake of brevity, the symbol ▱ can be used for parallelogram.

1. Given ▱*KATY* as shown.
   a. Which angles are consecutive to ∠*K*?

   b. Use what you know about parallel lines to complete the theorem.

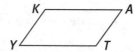

   Consecutive angles of a parallelogram are _____.

2. **Express regularity in repeated reasoning.** Use three index cards and draw three different parallelograms. Then cut out each parallelogram. For each parallelogram, draw a diagonal and cut along the diagonal to form two triangles. What do you notice about each pair of triangles?

3. Based upon the exploration in Item 2, complete the theorem.

   Each diagonal of a parallelogram divides that parallelogram into _____.

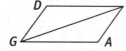

4. Given parallelogram *DIAG* as shown above. Complete the theorems.
   a. Opposite sides of a parallelogram are _____.

   b. Opposite angles of a parallelogram are _____.

   c. Prove the theorem you completed in part a. Use the figure in Item 3.

   d. Prove the theorem you completed in part b. Use the figure in Item 3.

MATH TERMS

A **corollary** is a statement that results directly from a theorem.

5. Explain why the theorems in Item 4 can be considered as *corollaries* to the theorem in Item 3.

6. Given ▱*LUCK*, use the figure and the theorems in Items 1, 3, and 4 to find the following.

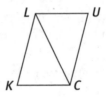

 a. △*KCL* ≅ _____

 b. Solve for x if $m\angle KCU = 10x - 15$ and $m\angle K = 6x + 3$.

 c. Solve for x and y if $KL = 2x + y$, $LU = 7$, $UC = 14$, and $KC = 5y - 4x$.

Theorem: The diagonals of a parallelogram bisect each other.

7. a. Rewrite the above theorem in "if-then" form.

 b. Draw a figure for the theorem, including the diagonals. Label the vertices and the point of intersection for the diagonals. Identify the information that is "given" and what is to be proved.

 Given:

 Prove:

 c. Write a two-column proof for the theorem.

CONNECT TO AP

Theorems are key to the development of many branches of mathematics. In calculus, two theorems that are frequently used are the Mean Value Theorem and the Fundamental Theorem of Calculus.

Check Your Understanding

8. Why are trapezoids and kites not parallelograms?

9. The measure of one angle of a parallelogram is 68°. What are the measures of the other three angles of the parallelogram?

10. The lengths of two sides of a parallelogram are 12 in. and 18 in. What are the lengths of the other two sides?

LESSON 15-3 PRACTICE

11. $\overline{AC}$ and $\overline{DB}$ are diagonals of parallelogram *ABCD*. Find each measure.

$AE =$ _____

$EC =$ _____

$DE =$ _____

$EB =$ _____

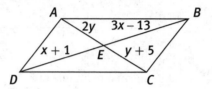

12. **Make sense of problems.** One of the floor tiles that Mr. Cortez sells is shaped like a parallelogram. Find each measure of the floor tile.

$m\angle W =$ _____

$m\angle X =$ _____

$m\angle Y =$ _____

$m\angle Z =$ _____

$WZ =$ _____

$XY =$ _____

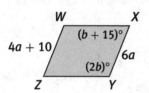

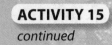

My Notes

Learning Targets:
- Develop properties of rectangles, rhombuses, and squares.
- Prove properties of rectangles, rhombuses, and squares.

> **SUGGESTED LEARNING STRATEGIES:** Visualization, Create Representations, Think-Pair-Share, Interactive Word Wall, Discussion Groups

A *rectangle* is a parallelogram with four right angles.

1. Given quad *RECT* is a rectangle. List all right triangles in the figure. Explain how you know the triangles are congruent.

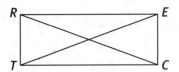

2. Complete the theorem.

   The diagonals of a rectangle are _____.

3. Explain how you know the theorem in Item 2 is true.

4. List all of the properties of a rectangle. Begin with the properties of a parallelogram.

5. Given quad *PINK* is a rectangle with coordinates $P(3,0)$, $I(0,6)$, and $N(8,10)$. Find the coordinates of point K.

6. Given quad *TGIF* is a rectangle. Use the properties of a rectangle and the figure at right to find the following.

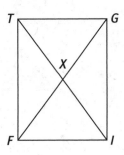

   a. If $TX = 13$, then $TI = $ _____ and $FG = $ _____.

   b. Solve for x if $TX = 4x + 4$ and $FX = 7x - 23$.

   c. Solve for x if $m\angle XFT = 6x - 4$ and $m\angle XTG = 10x - 2$.

My Notes

Indirect proofs can be useful when the conclusion is a negative statement.

Example of an Indirect Proof

Given: $m\angle SCR \neq m\angle CSI$
Prove: $\square RISC$ is not a rectangle.

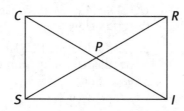

Statements	Reasons
1. $\square RISC$ is a rectangle.	1. Assumption
2. $m\angle SCR = m\angle CSI = 90°$	2. Definition of a rectangle
3. $m\angle SCR \neq m\angle CSI$	3. Given
4. $\square RISC$ is not a rectangle.	4. The assumption led to a contradiction between statements 2 and 3.

7. Complete the missing reasons in this indirect proof.

Given: $WT \neq TS$
Prove: Quad *WISH* is not a $\square$.

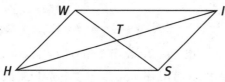

Statements	Reasons
1. $\square WISH$	1.
2. $\overline{WS}$ and $\overline{HI}$ bisect each other.	2.
3. $WT = TS$ and $HT = TI$	3.
4. $WT \neq TS$	4.
5. Quad *WISH* is not a $\square$.	5.

MATH TIP

An indirect proof begins by assuming the opposite of the conclusion. The assumption is used as if it were given until a contradiction is reached. Once the assumption leads to a contradiction, the opposite of the assumption (the original conclusion) must be true.

Check Your Understanding

8. What do rectangles, trapezoids, and kites have in common? How do they differ?

9. Tell whether each of the following statements is true or false.
   a. All rectangles are parallelograms.
   b. Some rectangles are trapezoids.
   c. All parallelograms are rectangles.
   d. All rectangles are quadrilaterals.

A ***rhombus*** is a parallelogram with four congruent sides.

10. Graph quad *USMC* with coordinates *U*(1, 1), *S*(4, 5), *M*(9, 5), and *C*(6, 1) on the grid below.

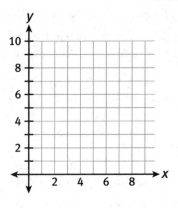

    a. Verify that quad *USMC* is a parallelogram by finding the slope of each side.

    b. Verify that ▱*USMC* is a rhombus by finding the length of each side.

    c. Find the slopes of the diagonals, $\overline{MU}$ and $\overline{SC}$.

    d. Use the results in part c to complete the theorem.

        The diagonals of a rhombus are _____.

11. Given quad *EFGH* is a rhombus.

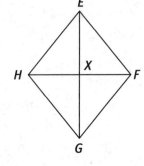

    a. List the three triangles that are congruent to △*HXE*.

    b. Explain why ∠*EFX* ≅ ∠*GFX* and ∠*HGX* ≅ ∠*FGX*.

    c. Complete the theorem.

        Each diagonal of a rhombus _____.

A formal proof for the theorem in Item 11 is left as an exercise.

12. List all of the properties of a rhombus. Begin with the properties of a parallelogram.

13. Given quad *UTAH* is a rhombus. Use the properties of a rhombus and the figure at right to find each of the following.

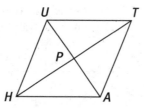

   a. Solve for *x* if $m\angle UPT = 4x + 18$.

   b. Solve for *x* and *y* if
   $UT = 5x + 4$,
   $TA = 2x + y$,
   $HA = 2y - 8$, and
   $UH = 24$.

   c. Solve for *x* if $m\angle PAH = 8x + 2$ and $m\angle PAT = 10x - 10$.

A *square* is a parallelogram with four right angles and four congruent sides.

14. Alternate definitions for a square.

   a. A square is a rectangle with

   _____.

   b. A square is a rhombus with

   _____.

15. List all of the properties of a square.

16. Match each region in the Venn diagram below with the correct term in the list.

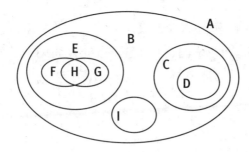

kites	isosceles trapezoids	parallelograms
polygons	quadrilaterals	rectangles
rhombi	squares	trapezoids

My Notes

17. Model with mathematics. Mr. Cortez uses the table below to organize his findings before he enters information in the database. Place a check mark if the polygon has the given property.

	4 Sides	Opposite Sides Parallel	Opposite Sides Congruent	Opposite Angles Congruent	Diagonals Bisect Each Other	Consecutive Angles Supplementary	Diagonals Perpendicular	4 Right Angles	4 Congruent Sides	Exactly One Pair of Opposite Sides Parallel
Quadrilateral										
Kite										
Trapezoid										
Parallelogram										
Rectangle										
Rhombus										
Square										

Check Your Understanding

18. Tell whether each statement is true or false.
   a. All squares are rectangles.
   b. All rhombuses are squares.
   c. All squares are parallelograms.
   d. Some squares are kites.
   e. No rhombuses are trapezoids.

19. What do all rectangles, squares, and rhombuses have in common?

LESSON 15-4 PRACTICE

20. $\overline{AC}$ and $\overline{DB}$ are diagonals of rectangle *ABCD*. Find each measure.

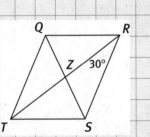

   $m\angle DAB = $ _____ $m\angle AEB = $ _____

   $m\angle ADC = $ _____ $m\angle BEC = $ _____

   $m\angle BDC = $ _____ $m\angle BCE = $ _____

   $m\angle BDA = $ _____

21. $\overline{QS}$ and $\overline{RT}$ are diagonals of rhombus *QRST*. Find each measure.

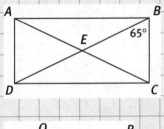

   $m\angle QSR = $ _____ $m\angle QZR = $ _____

   $m\angle QST = $ _____ $m\angle QTR = $ _____

   $m\angle QTS = $ _____ $m\angle RZS = $ _____

22. Make sense of problems. A diagonal of a square tile is 10 mm. What is the area of the tile?

ACTIVITY 15 PRACTICE

Write your answers on notebook paper.
Show your work.

Lesson 15-1

1. Tell whether each statement about kites is *always*, *sometimes*, or *never* true.
   a. Exactly two pairs of consecutive sides are congruent.
   b. The diagonals divide the kite into four congruent triangles.
   c. The diagonals are perpendicular.
   d. A kite is a parallelogram.
   e. One diagonal bisects a pair of opposite angles.
   f. A kite is a rhombus.

Lesson 15-2

2. Make a true statement by filling in each blank with *always*, *sometimes*, or *never*.
   a. A trapezoid is _____ isosceles.
   b. A trapezoid is _____ a quadrilateral.
   c. The length of the median of a trapezoid is _____ equal to the sum of the lengths of the bases.
   d. Trapezoids _____ have a pair of parallel sides.
   e. Trapezoids _____ have two pairs of supplementary consecutive angles.

3. Given quad *GHJK* is a trapezoid. $\overline{PQ}$ is the median.

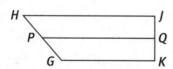

   a. If *HJ* = 40 and *PQ* = 28, find *GK*.
   b. If *HJ* = 5*x*, *PQ* = 5*x* − 9, and *GK* = 3*x* + 2, then solve for *x*.

4. Given quad *JONE* is a trapezoid.

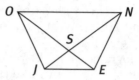

   a. ∠*ONJ* ≅ _____
   b. If $\overline{OJ} \cong \overline{NE}$, then $\overline{OE} \cong$ _____.
   c. If $\overline{OJ} \cong \overline{NE}$, then ∠*NEJ* ≅ _____.

Lesson 15-3

5. Quadrilateral *XENA* is a parallelogram. *T* is the point of intersection of the diagonals. For each situation, write an equation and solve for *y*.

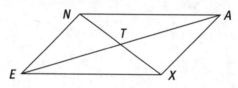

   a. *EN* = 5*y* + 1 and *AX* = 8*y* − 5
   b. *m*∠*ANX* = 3*y* − 1 and *m*∠*NXE* = 2*y* + 1
   c. *ET* = *y* − 1 and *EA* = 3*y* − 10
   d. *m*∠*ANE* = 7*y* − 5 and *m*∠*NEX* = 3*y* + 5

6. *M* is the fourth vertex of a parallelogram. The coordinates of the other vertices are (6, 4), (8, 1), and (2, 0). *M* can have any of the following coordinates except:
   A. (6, −2)   **B.** (12, 5)
   C. (4, −3)   **D.** (0, 3)

7. Given quad *QRST* with coordinates *Q*(0, 0), *R*(2, 6), *S*(12, 6), and *T*(12, 0).
   a. What is the best name for quad *QRST*? Explain.
   b. Find the coordinates of the midpoint for each side of quad *QRST* and label them *M, N, O,* and *P*. What is the best name for quad *MNOP*? Explain.

Lesson 15-4

8. Given quad *WHAT* with vertices $W(2, 4)$, $H(5, 8)$, $A(9, 5)$, and $T(6, 1)$. What is the best name for this quadrilateral?

    A. parallelogram   **B.** rhombus

    C. rectangle   **D.** square

9. Given quad *ABCD* is a rhombus and $m\angle ABD = 32°$. Find the measure of each numbered angle.

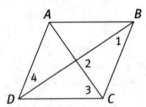

10. Given quad *RIGH* is a rectangle.

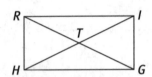

    a. If $RT = 18$, then $RG =$ _____.

    b. If $RG = 4x + 12$ and $HI = 10x - 15$, then $x =$ _____.

11. Given: Parallelogram *PQRS* with diagonal *PR*.
Prove: $\triangle PQR \cong \triangle RSP$

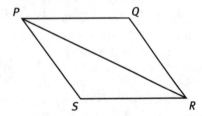

12. Write an indirect proof.
Given: $\triangle WIN$ is not isosceles.
Prove: Quad *WIND* is not a rhombus.

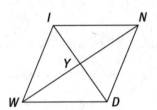

MATHEMATICAL PRACTICES
Reason Abstractly and Quantitatively

13. Ginger noticed that no matter the height of the adjustable stand for her electric piano, the keyboard remains level and centered over the stand. What has to be true about the legs of the stand? Explain.

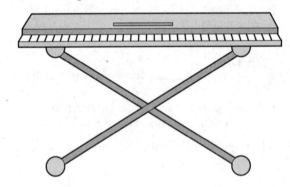

More About Quadrilaterals
A 4-gon Conclusion
Lesson 16-1 Proving a Quadrilateral Is a Parallelogram

Learning Targets:

- Develop criteria for showing that a quadrilateral is a parallelogram.
- Prove that a quadrilateral is a parallelogram.

> **SUGGESTED LEARNING STRATEGIES:** Think-Pair-Share, Group Presentation, Discussion Groups, Visualization

In a previous activity, the definition of a parallelogram was used to verify that a quadrilateral is a parallelogram by showing that both pairs of opposite sides are parallel.

1. Given quadrilateral *CHIA*:
   a. Find the slope of each side.

   b. Use the slopes to explain how you know quadrilateral *CHIA* is a parallelogram.

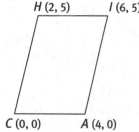

H (2, 5)   *I* (6, 5)

C (0, 0)   *A* (4, 0)

MATH TIP

Slope Formula

Given $A(x_1, y_1)$ and $B(x_2, y_2)$

Slope of $\overline{AB}$: $m = \dfrac{(y_2 - y_1)}{(x_2 - x_1)}$

2. Given quadrilateral *SKIP* with $SK = IP$ and $KI = SP$.
   a. $\triangle PSI \cong$ _____. Explain.

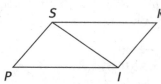

S   *K*

P   *I*

MATH TIP

Once a theorem has been proven, it can be used to justify other steps or statements in proofs.

   b. $\angle SIP \cong$ _____ and $\angle PSI \cong$ _____. Explain.

   c. $\overline{SK} \parallel \overline{IP}$ and $\overline{KI} \parallel \overline{SP}$ because _____.

   d. Complete the theorem.

   Theorem If both pairs of opposite sides of a quadrilateral are congruent, then the quadrilateral is a _____.

3. Given quadrilateral *WALK* with coordinates $W(8, 7)$, $A(11, 3)$, $L(4, 1)$, and $K(1, 5)$. Use the theorem in Item 2 to show that $\square WALK$ is a parallelogram.

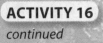

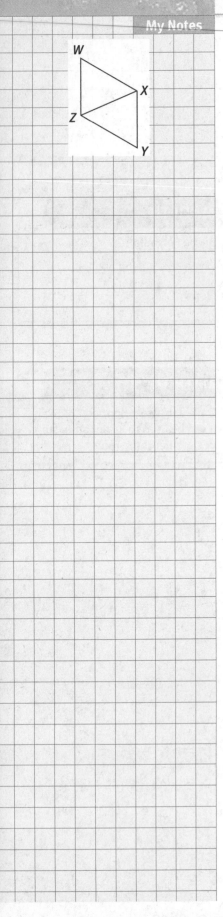

My Notes

4. Given □*WXYZ* with $\overline{WX} \parallel \overline{ZY}$ and $\overline{WX} \cong \overline{ZY}$.

   a. △*WZX* ≅ ____. Explain.

   b. **Construct viable arguments.** Explain why $\overline{WZ} \parallel \overline{XY}$.

   c. Complete the theorem.

   Theorem If one pair of opposite sides of a quadrilateral are congruent and parallel, then the quadrilateral is a _____.

5. Given □*GOLD* with coordinates *G*(−1, 0), *O*(5, 4), *L*(9, 2), and *D*(3, −2). Use the theorem in Item 4 to show that □*GOLD* is a parallelogram.

Now you can prove a theorem that can be used to show that a given quadrilateral is a parallelogram.

Example A

Theorem *If both pairs of opposite angles of a quadrilateral are congruent, then the quadrilateral is a parallelogram.*

Given: □*POLY* with ∠*P* ≅ ∠*L* and ∠*O* ≅ ∠*Y*

Prove: □*POLY* is a parallelogram.

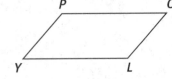

Statements	Reasons
1. □*POLY* with ∠*P* ≅ ∠*L* and ∠*O* ≅ ∠*Y*	1. Given
2. $m\angle P = m\angle L$ and $m\angle O = m\angle Y$	2. Def. of congruent angles
3. $m\angle P + m\angle O + m\angle L + m\angle Y = 360°$	3. The sum of the measures of the interior angles of a quadrilateral is 360°.
4. $m\angle P + m\angle O + m\angle P + m\angle O = 360°$	4. Substitution Property
5. $2m\angle P + 2m\angle O = 360°$	5. Simplify.
6. $m\angle P + m\angle O = 180°$	6. Division Property of Equality
7. $m\angle P + m\angle Y + m\angle P + m\angle Y = 360°$	7. Substitution Property
8. $2m\angle P + 2m\angle Y = 360°$	8. Simplify.

Statements	Reasons
9. $m\angle P + m\angle Y = 180°$	**9.** Division Property of Equality
10. $\overline{PY} \parallel \overline{OL}$ and $\overline{PO} \parallel \overline{YL}$	**10.** If two lines are intersected by a transversal and a pair of consecutive interior angles are supplementary, then the lines are parallel.
11. ▱*POLY* is a parallelogram.	**11.** Def. of a parallelogram

Try These A

Write a proof using the theorem in Example 1 as the last reason.

Given: $\overline{RT} \cong \overline{RK}$
$\angle RKT \cong \angle U$
$\angle 1 \cong \angle 2$

Prove: ▱*TRUC*

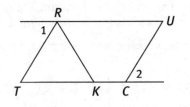

6. Given ▱*PLAN* whose diagonals, $\overline{PA}$ and $\overline{LN}$, bisect each other.

Complete the statements.
a. $\triangle LEP \cong$ _____ and $\triangle LEA \cong$ _____. Explain.

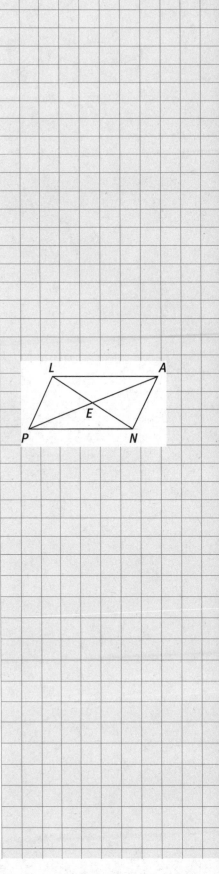

b. $\angle ALE \cong$ _____ and $\angle ELP \cong$ _____. Explain.

c. Explain how the information in part b can be used to prove that ▱*PLAN* is a parallelogram.

d. Complete the theorem.

Theorem If the diagonals of a quadrilateral _____, then the quadrilateral is a _____.

7. Given ▱*THIN* with coordinates $T(3, 3)$, $H(5, 9)$, $I(6, 5)$, and $N(4, -1)$.
a. Find the coordinates for the midpoint of each diagonal.

b. Do the diagonals bisect each other? Explain.

c. The best name for this quadrilateral is:
  A. quadrilateral   **B.** kite   **C.** trapezoid   **D.** parallelogram

8. Summarize this part of the activity by making a list of the five ways to prove that a quadrilateral is a parallelogram.

Check Your Understanding

9. Explain why showing that only one pair of opposite sides of a quadrilateral are parallel is not sufficient for proving it is a parallelogram.

10. Three of the interior angle measures of a quadrilateral are 48°, 130°, and 48°. Is the quadrilateral a parallelogram? Explain.

LESSON 16-1 PRACTICE

Make use of structure. Tell what theorem can be used to prove the quadrilateral is a parallelogram. If there is not enough information to prove it is a parallelogram, write "not enough information."

11.

12.

13.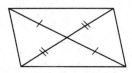

14.

Three vertices of a parallelogram are given. Find the coordinates of the fourth vertex.

15. (1, 5), (3, 3), (8, 3)

16. (−5, 0), (−2, −4), (3, 0)

Find the values of *x* and *y* that make the quadrilateral a parallelogram.

17.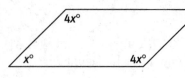

18.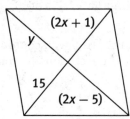

Learning Targets:
- Develop criteria for showing that a quadrilateral is a rectangle.
- Prove that a quadrilateral is a rectangle.

> **SUGGESTED LEARNING STRATEGIES:** Think-Pair-Share, Create Representations, Group Presentation, Discussion Groups

1. Complete the following definition.

   A rectangle is a parallelogram with _____.

2. **a.** Complete the theorem.

   > **Theorem** If a parallelogram has one right angle, then it has _____ right angles, and it is a _____.

   b. Use one or more properties of a parallelogram and the definition of a rectangle to explain why the theorem in Item 1 is true.

3. Given □ *WXYZ*.
   a. If □ *WXYZ* is equiangular, then find the measure of each angle.

   b. Complete the theorem.

   > **Theorem** If a quadrilateral is equiangular, then it is a _____.

   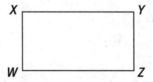

4. **Make sense of problems.** Identify the hypothesis and the conclusion of the theorem in Item 3. Use the figure in Item 3.

   Hypothesis:

   Conclusion:

5. Write a proof for the theorem in Item 3.

My Notes

6. Given $\square OKAY$ with congruent diagonals, $\overline{OA}$ and $\overline{KY}$.

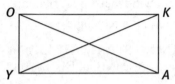

a. List the three triangles that are congruent to $\triangle OYA$, and the reason for the congruence.

b. List the three angles that are corresponding parts of congruent triangles and congruent to $\angle OYA$.

c. Find the measure of each of the angles in part b.

d. Complete the theorem.

> **Theorem** If the diagonals of a parallelogram are _____, then the parallelogram is a _____.

7. Given $\square ABCD$ with coordinates $A(1, 0)$, $B(0, 3)$, $C(6, 5)$, and $D(7, 2)$.
a. Show that $\square ABCD$ is a parallelogram.
b. Use the theorem in Item 6 to show that $\square ABCD$ is a rectangle.

8. Write a two-column proof using the theorem in Item 6 as the last reason.

Given: $\square GRAM$

$\triangle GRM \cong \triangle RGA$

Prove: $\square GRAM$ is a rectangle.

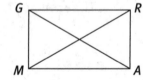

9. Summarize this part of the activity by making a list of the ways to prove that a quadrilateral (or parallelogram) is a rectangle.

My Notes

Check Your Understanding

10. Jamie says a quadrilateral with one right angle is a rectangle. Find a counterexample to show that Jamie is incorrect.

11. Do the diagonals of a rectangle bisect each other? Justify your answer.

LESSON 16-2 PRACTICE

Three vertices of a rectangle are given. Find the coordinates of the fourth vertex.

12. $(-3, 2), (-3, -1), (3, -1)$

13. $(-12, 2), (-6, -6), (4, 2)$

14. $(4, 5), (-3, -4), (6, -1)$

Find the value of x that makes the parallelogram a rectangle.

15.
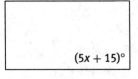
$(5x + 15)°$

16.
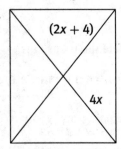
$(2x + 4)$
$4x$

17. **Model with mathematics.** Jill is building a new gate for her yard as shown. How can she use the diagonals of the gate to determine if the gate is a rectangle?

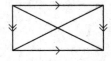

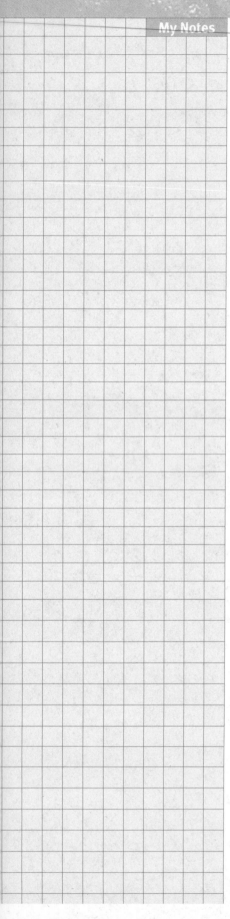

My Notes

Learning Targets:

● Develop criteria for showing that a quadrilateral is a rhombus.
● Prove that a quadrilateral is a rhombus.

SUGGESTED LEARNING STRATEGIES: Think-Pair-Share, Create Representations, Group Presentation, Discussion Groups

1. Complete the following definition.

   A rhombus is a parallelogram with _____.

2. **a.** Complete the theorem.

   Theorem If a parallelogram has two consecutive congruent sides, then it has _____ congruent sides, and it is a _____.

   b. Use one or more properties of a parallelogram and the definition of a rhombus to explain why the theorem in Item 2a is true.

3. Complete the theorem.

   Theorem If a quadrilateral is equilateral, then it is a _____.

4. Write a paragraph proof to explain why the theorem in Item 3 is true.

5. Given □*KIND* with $\overline{KN} \perp \overline{ID}$.

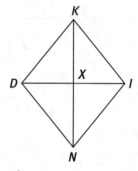

   a. List the three triangles that are congruent to △*KXD*, and give the reason for the congruence.

   b. List all segments congruent to $\overline{KD}$ and explain why.

   c. Complete the theorem.

   Theorem If the diagonals of a parallelogram are _____, then the parallelogram is a _____.

My Notes

6. Given □*BIRD* with coordinates $B(-2, -3)$, $I(1, 1)$, $R(6, 1)$, and $D(3, -3)$.
   a. Show that □*BIRD* is a parallelogram.

   b. Use the theorem in Item 5 to show □*BIRD* is a rhombus.

7. Given □*WEST* with $\overline{TE}$ that bisects $\angle WES$ and $\angle WTS$.

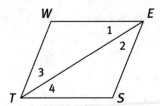

   a. List all angles congruent to $\angle 1$ and explain why.

   b. In $\triangle WET$, $\overline{WT} \cong$ _____. In $\triangle SET$, $\overline{ST} \cong$ _____. Explain.

   c. Complete the theorem.
   Theorem If a diagonal bisects _____ in a parallelogram, then the parallelogram is a _____.

8. **Construct viable arguments.** Write a proof that uses the theorem in Item 7 as the last reason.

   Given: □*BLUE*

   $\triangle BLE \cong \triangle ULE$

   Prove: □*BLUE* is a rhombus.

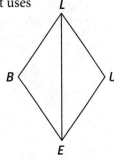

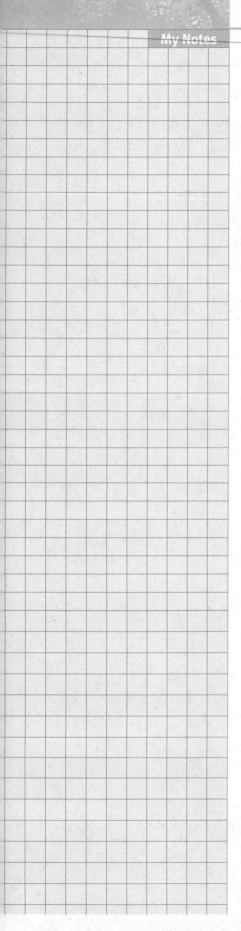
My Notes

9. Summarize this part of the activity by making a list of the ways to prove that a quadrilateral is a rhombus.

Check Your Understanding

10. Can a rectangle ever be classified as a rhombus as well? Explain.

LESSON 16-3 PRACTICE

Three vertices of a rhombus are given. Find the coordinates of the fourth vertex.

11. $(-2, -8), (3, -3), (-9, -7)$

12. $(-1, 2), (-1, -1), (2, 1)$

13. $(1, 1), (-1, -2), (1, -5)$

14. Find the value of x that makes the parallelogram a rhombus.

a.
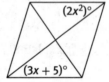
$(2x^2)°$
$(3x + 5)°$

b.
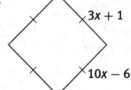
$3x + 1$
$10x - 6$

15. **Reason quantitatively.** LaToya is using a coordinate plane to design a new pendant for a necklace. She wants the pendant to be a rhombus. Three of the vertices of the rhombus are $(3, 1), (-1, -1)$, and $(1, -2)$. Assuming each unit of the coordinate plane represents one centimeter, what is the perimeter of the pendant? Round your answer to the nearest tenth.

Learning Targets:

● Develop criteria for showing that a quadrilateral is a square.
● Prove that a quadrilateral is a square.

> **SUGGESTED LEARNING STRATEGIES:** Think-Pair-Share, Create Representations, Group Presentation, Discussion Groups

1. Given □*JKLM*.
   a. What information is needed to prove that □*JKLM* is a square?

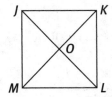

   b. What additional information is needed to prove that □*JKLM* is a square? Explain.

   c. What additional information is needed to prove that rectangle *JKLM* is a square? Explain.

   d. What additional information is needed to prove that rhombus *JKLM* is a square? Explain.

2. Given □*DAVE* with coordinates *D*(−1, 1), *A*(0, 7), *V*(6, 6), and *E*(5, 0). Show that □*DAVE* is a square.

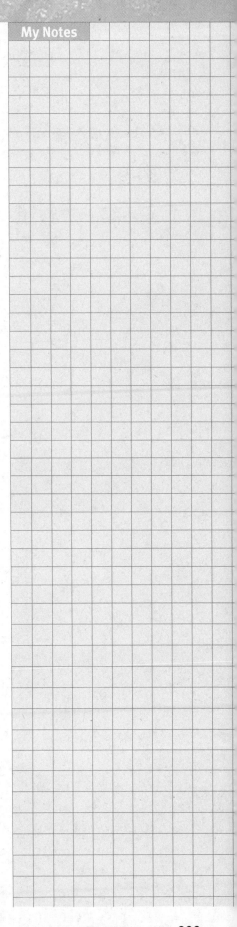

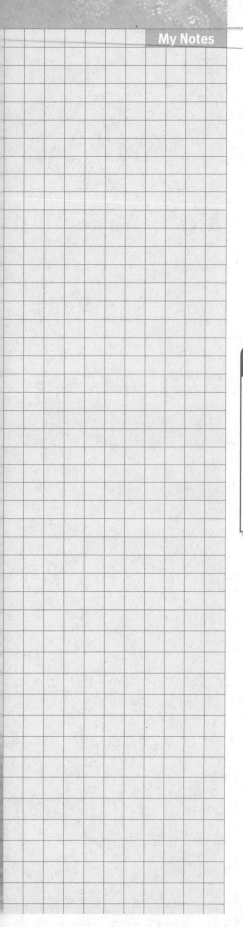

My Notes

3. **Critique the reasoning of others.** Several students in a class made the following statements. Decide whether you agree with each statement. If you disagree, change the statement to make it correct.
   a. A quadrilateral with congruent diagonals must be a rectangle.

   b. A parallelogram with two right angles must be a square.

   c. A quadrilateral with a pair of opposite parallel sides is always a parallelogram.

   d. A rhombus with four congruent angles is a square.

Check Your Understanding

4. Elena has a garden with congruent sides, as shown below. Describe two different ways to show the garden is square.

LESSON 16-4 PRACTICE

The coordinates of a parallelogram are given. Determine whether the figure is a square.

5. $(-2, 3)$, $(3, 3)$, $(3, 0)$, $(-2, 0)$

6. $(0, 1)$, $(-1, 3)$, $(1, 4)$, $(2, 2)$

7. $(3, 6)$, $(6, 2)$, $(-2, 3)$, $(-5, 7)$

8. $(3, 8)$, $(-1, 6)$, $(1, 2)$, $(5, 4)$

9. **Express regularity in repeated reasoning.** Find the length of the diagonal of a square with three of its vertices at $(1, 0)$, $(0, 0)$, and $(0, 1)$. Then find the length of the diagonal of a square with three of its vertices at $(2, 0)$, $(0, 0)$, and $(0, 2)$. Finally, find the length of the diagonal of a square with three of its vertices at $(3, 0)$, $(0, 0)$, and $(0, 3)$. Use your findings to make a conjecture about the length of the diagonal of a square with three of its vertices at $(s, 0)$, $(0, 0)$, and $(0, s)$.

ACTIVITY 16 PRACTICE
Write your answers on notebook paper.
Show your work.

Lesson 16-1

1. Given ▱*RSTU* with coordinates *R*(0, 0), *S*(−2, 2), *T*(6, 6), and *U*(8, 4).
   a. Show that ▱*RSTU* is a parallelogram by finding the slope of each side.
   b. Show that ▱*RSTU* is a parallelogram by finding the length of each side.
   c. Show that ▱*RSTU* is a parallelogram by showing that the diagonals bisect each other.

2. Write a proof using the theorem in Item 2 of Lesson 16-1 as the last reason.

   Given: △*ABC* ≅ △*FED*

   $\overline{CD} \cong \overline{CG}$

   $\overline{CG} \cong \overline{AF}$

   Prove: ▱*ACDF*

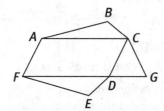

3. Write a proof using the theorem in Item 4 of Lesson 16-1 as the last reason.

   Given: ▱*JKLM*

   X is midpt of $\overline{JK}$.

   Y is midpt of $\overline{ML}$.

   Prove: ▱*JXLY*

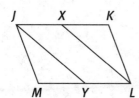

4. Which of the following is not a sufficient condition to prove a quadrilateral is a parallelogram?
   A. The diagonals bisect each other.
   B. One pair of opposite sides are parallel.
   C. Both pairs of opposite sides are congruent.
   D. Both pairs of opposite angles are congruent.

5. Show that the quadrilateral with vertices (−2, 3), (−2, −1), (1, 1), and (1, 5) is a parallelogram.

6. Which of the following additional pieces of information would allow you to prove that *ABCD* is a parallelogram?

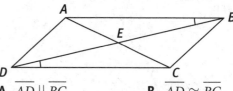

   A. $\overline{AD} \parallel \overline{BC}$ **B.** $\overline{AD} \cong \overline{BC}$
   C. $\overline{AB} \parallel \overline{DC}$ **D.** $\overline{AB} \cong \overline{DC}$

Lesson 16-2

7. Each of the following sets of given information is sufficient to prove that ▱*SPAR* is a rectangle *except*:

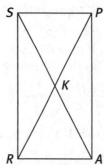

   A. ▱*SPAR* and ∠*SPA* ≅ ∠*PAR*
   B. *SK* = *KA* = *RK* = *KP*
   C. ▱*SPAR* and ∠*SKP* ≅ ∠*PKA*
   D. ∠*RSP* ≅ ∠*SPA* ≅ ∠*PAR* ≅ ∠*ARS*

8. Given ▱*FOUR* with coordinates *F*(0, 6), *O*(10, 8), *U*(13, 3), and *R*(3, 0). Show that ▱*FOUR* is not a rectangle.

9. Write an indirect proof.

   Given: *CE* ≠ *DF*

   Prove: ▱*CDEF* is not a rectangle.

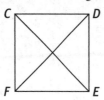

10. What is the best name for a quadrilateral if the diagonals are congruent and bisect each other?
   A. parallelogram   **B.** rectangle
   C. kite   **D.** trapezoid

11. Three vertices of a rectangle are (−4, −3), (8, 3), and (5, 6). Show that the diagonals are congruent.

Lesson 16-3

12. Each of the following sets of given information is sufficient to prove that $\square HOPE$ is a rhombus *except*:

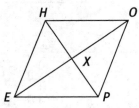

   A. $HX = XP = XE = XO$
   B. $OH = OP = PE = HE$
   C. $\square HOPE$ and $\angle HXO \cong \angle OXP$
   D. $\square HOPE$ and $HE = PE$

13. Given $\square DRUM$ with coordinates $D(-2, -2)$, $R(-3, 3)$, $U(2, 5)$, and $M(3, 0)$. Show that $\square DRUM$ is not a rhombus.

14. Write a proof using the theorem in Item 5 of Lesson 16-3 as the last reason.

   Given: $\square NIGH$

   $\triangle NTI \cong \triangle NTH$

   Prove: $\square NIGH$ is a rhombus.

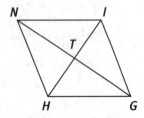

Lesson 16-4

15. Write a proof.

   Given: $\square PEAR$, $\overline{PE} \perp \overline{EA}$;

   $\overline{PE} \cong \overline{AE}$

   Prove: $\square PEAR$ is a square.

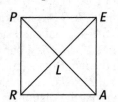

16. Given $\square SOPH$ with coordinates $S(-8, 0)$, $O(0, 6)$, $P(10, 6)$, and $H(2, 0)$. What is the best name for this quadrilateral?
   A. parallelogram   **B.** rectangle
   C. rhombus   **D.** square

17. What is the best name for an equilateral quadrilateral whose diagonals are congruent?
   A. parallelogram   **B.** rectangle
   C. rhombus   **D.** square

MATHEMATICAL PRACTICES
Look For and Make Use of Structure

18. Why is every rhombus a parallelogram but not every parallelogram a rhombus? Why is every square a rectangle but not every rectangle a square? Why is every square a rhombus but not every rhombus a square?

Lucy Latimer acquired a new company in a hostile takeover. This new company, Math Manipulatives, needed a new logo. Ms. Latimer's husband teaches geometry, and his class submitted a logo and the following instructions for reproducing the logo.

- Begin with a large isosceles trapezoid, and locate the midpoint of each side.
- Use these midpoints as the vertices of a new quadrilateral to be formed inside the first quadrilateral.
- Locate the midpoint of each side of the second quadrilateral, and use these midpoints as vertices to form a third quadrilateral.
- Repeat this process with each new quadrilateral until the newest quadrilateral is too small to be seen.

Suppose you were one of Ms. Latimer's employees, and she assigned you the task of investigating this design proposal. Write a report to be sent to Ms. Latimer. In your report, you should include:

1. a reproduction of this design on a piece of graph paper. (You must show at least six quadrilaterals, including the first.)

2. how you know that your first quadrilateral is an isosceles trapezoid.

3. the best name (trapezoid, parallelogram, rectangle, rhombus, or square) for each subsequent quadrilateral and a convincing argument that supports the name you chose.

4. a description of any patterns that you may find in the sequence of the shapes.

5. definitions, postulates, and theorems from geometry to support your claims.

Scoring Guide	Exemplary	Proficient	Emerging	Incomplete
	The solution demonstrates these characteristics:			
Mathematics Knowledge and Thinking (Items 2, 3, 5)	• Clear and accurate understanding of isosceles trapezoids, rectangles, and rhombi	• A functional understanding of isosceles trapezoids, rectangles, and rhombi	• Partially correct understanding of isosceles trapezoids, rectangles, and rhombi	• Little or no understanding of isosceles trapezoids, rectangles, and rhombi
Problem Solving (Items 2, 3, 4)	• An appropriate and efficient strategy that results in a correct answer	• A strategy that may include unnecessary steps but results in a correct answer	• A strategy that results in some incorrect answers	• No clear strategy when solving problems
Mathematical Modeling / Representations (Item 1)	• Clear and accurate drawing of the logo showing at least six quadrilaterals	• Largely correct drawing of the logo showing at least six quadrilaterals	• Partially correct drawing of the logo showing at least six quadrilaterals	• Inaccurate or incomplete drawing of the logo showing at least six quadrilaterals
Reasoning and Communication (Items 2, 3, 5)	• Precise use of appropriate math terms and language to justify that the first quadrilateral is an isosceles trapezoid, the second quadrilateral is a rhombus, the third is a rectangle, and so on	• Adequate use of appropriate math terms and language to justify that the first quadrilateral is an isosceles trapezoid, the second quadrilateral is a rhombus, the third is a rectangle, and so on	• Misleading or confusing use of math terms and language to justify that the first quadrilateral is an isosceles trapezoid, the second quadrilateral is a rhombus, the third is a rectangle, and so on	• Incomplete or inaccurate use of math terms and language to justify that the first quadrilateral is an isosceles trapezoid, the second quadrilateral is a rhombus, the third is a rectangle, and so on

Similarity and Trigonometry

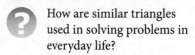

3

Unit Overview

In this unit, you will study special right triangles and right triangle trigonometry. You will also study similarity transformations and similarity in polygons.

Key Terms

As you study this unit, add these and other terms to your math notebook. Include in your notes your prior knowledge of each word, as well as your experiences in using the word in different mathematical examples. If needed, ask for help in pronouncing new words and add information on pronunciation to your math notebook. It is important that you learn new terms and use them correctly in your class discussions and in your problem solutions.

Academic Vocabulary
- triangulation

Math Terms
- dilation
- center of dilation
- similarity transformation
- similar
- indirect measurement
- Triangle Proportionality Theorem
- Parallel Proportionality Theorem
- Right Angle Altitude Theorem
- geometric mean
- Pythagorean Theorem
- Pythagorean triple
- opposite leg
- adjacent leg
- trigonometric ratio
- sine
- cosine
- tangent
- inverse trigonometric function
- Law of Sines
- Law of Cosines

ESSENTIAL QUESTIONS

? How are similar triangles used in solving problems in everyday life?

? What mathematical tools do I have to solve right triangles?

EMBEDDED ASSESSMENTS

These embedded assessments, following Activities 18, 21, and 23, allow you to demonstrate your understanding of similarity, proportionality, special right triangles, and right angle trigonometry.

Embedded Assessment 1:	
Similarity in Polygons	p. 273
Embedded Assessment 2:	
Right Triangles	p. 301
Embedded Assessment 3:	
Trigonometry	p. 331

Write your answers on notebook paper.
Show your work.

1. Draw a graph to show how the figure is transformed by the function. Then classify the transformation as rigid or nonrigid.

    a. $(x, y) \rightarrow (x - 2, y + 1)$

    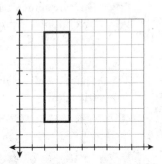

    b. $(x, y) \rightarrow (0.5x, 0.5y)$

    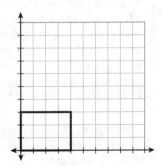

2. Simplify.

    a. $\sqrt{72}$

    b. $\dfrac{7}{\sqrt{5}}$

3. Solve the following for x.

    a. $5 = \dfrac{2}{x}$

    b. $x^2 + 3x + 2 = 0$

    c. $\dfrac{\sqrt{2}}{\sqrt{7}} = \dfrac{x}{\sqrt{14}}$

4. Find the distance between $(3, 5)$ and $(7, -1)$.

5. Find the lengths AB and BD if $AD = 29$ units.

    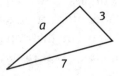

6. Solve the following equation for a.
    $$\frac{2a + b}{c} = d$$

7. Evaluate $4\sqrt{2} + 2\left(\sqrt{36} - \sqrt{8}\right)$.

8. Find the length of side a in the right triangle pictured.

    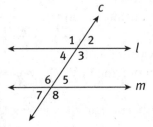

9. In the figure below, c is a transversal cutting parallel lines l and m. List at least four geometric relationships that exist among angles 4, 5, and/or 8.

Dilations and Similarity Transformations

Scaling Up/Scaling Down
Lesson 17-1 Dilations

Learning Targets:

- Perform dilations on and off the coordinate plane.
- Describe dilations.

> **SUGGESTED LEARNING STRATEGIES:** Create Representations, Visualization, Summarizing

Graphic artists create visual information for electronic and print media. They use graphic design software in their daily work. For example, a graphic artist can use computer software to design a brochure. The text and art for the pages of the brochure can be moved around or scaled up and down before the actual brochure is printed.

Kate is a graphic artist. She wants to create two different layouts of a brochure for her client to review.

The art for the layouts is shown.

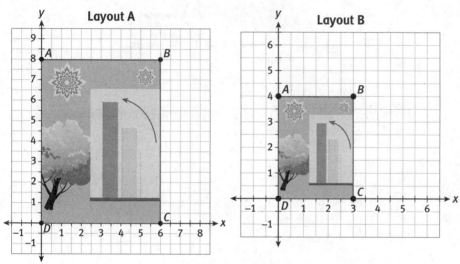

1. What are the coordinates of the vertices of the pre-image shown in Layout A?

2. What are the coordinates of the vertices of the image shown in Layout B?

3. What relationship do you notice between the coordinates for Layout A and the coordinates for Layout B?

4. Express the transformation in Item 3 as a function.

> ### DISCUSSION GROUP TIPS
>
> Use your group discussions to clarify the meaning of mathematical concepts and other language used to describe problem information. With your group or your teacher, review background information that will be useful in applying concepts.

My Notes

5. Kate created a third layout for the client to review. What are the coordinates of the vertices of the image shown in Layout C?

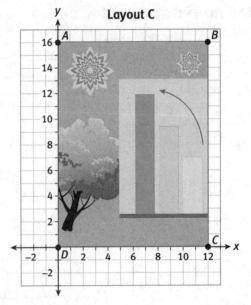

Layout C

6. What relationship do you notice between the coordinates for Layout A and the coordinates for Layout C?

7. Express the relationship in Item 6 as a function.

A **dilation** is a transformation that changes the size of a figure, but not its shape, by a scale factor k. The scale factor determines whether the transformation is a reduction or an enlargement.

8. a. What is the scale factor for the transformation of Layout A to Layout B?

   b. Is Layout B a reduction or an enlargement of Layout A?

   c. What is the scale factor for the transformation of Layout A to Layout C?

   d. Is Layout C a reduction or an enlargement of Layout A?

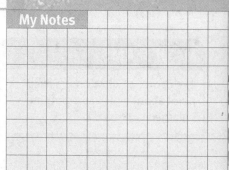

My Notes

9. In general, for what values of scale factor k is a dilation a reduction?

10. In general, for what values of scale factor k is a dilation an enlargement?

11. **Express regularity in repeated reasoning.** How can you find the coordinates of an image point after a dilation with scale factor k if the corresponding pre-image point has the coordinates (a, b)?

12. Express the relationship in Item 11 as a function.

Check Your Understanding

13. Triangle $R(0, 0)$, $S(0, 4)$, $T(3, 0)$ is mapped onto $\triangle R'S'T'$ by a dilation.
    a. If $\frac{RS}{R'S'} = \frac{5}{2}$, is $\triangle R'S'T'$ a reduction or an enlargement? Explain.
    b. The coordinates of $\angle R'$ are $(0, 0)$. What are the coordinates of $\angle S'$?
14. Describe a dilation with a scale factor of 1.

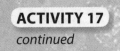

My Notes

MATH TERMS

The **center of dilation** is a fixed point about which all points are enlarged or reduced.

MATH TIP

Alternatively, when the center of a dilation is not the origin, you can also do the following:

- Translate the center of dilation to the origin and find the image of the vertices.
- Perform the dilation and record the coordinates of the second image.
- Translate the second image back so that the center of dilation is in its original position.

In each of Kate's layouts above, the ***center of dilation*** was the origin. Now she considers some dilations where the center is not the origin.

Kate wants to dilate triangle *ABC* with a scale factor of 2 and center of dilation $(-2, 4)$.

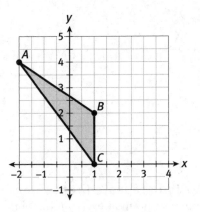

When the origin is not the center of a dilation, you need to subtract the coordinates of the center of dilation from the coordinates of the pre-image, multiply this difference by the scale factor, and then add the coordinates of the center of dilation.

If the point (x, y) lies on the pre-image and the figure is dilated with a scale factor of k with (a, b) as the center of dilation, the corresponding point on the image is $(a + k(x - a), b + k(y - b))$.

15. What are the coordinates of the vertices of the pre-image?

16. What are the coordinates of the vertices of the image?

17. Graph the pre-image and image of the dilation below.

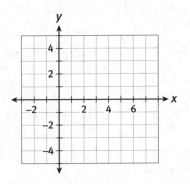

Check Your Understanding

18. Triangle $T(6, 4)$, $U(-4, 2)$, $V(2, -3)$ is mapped onto $\triangle T'U'V'$ by a dilation with a scale factor of $\frac{1}{2}$ and center $(2, -3)$. What are the coordinates of $\triangle T'U'V'$?

19. A point (x, y) is dilated by a scale factor of 4 with center $(-2, 1)$. What are the coordinates of the image?

You can use geometry software to explore dilations.

20. To perform a dilation, first plot a point for the center of dilation.
   a. Draw triangle ABC and dilate it using a scale factor of 2.

   b. Compare and contrast the pre-image and the image.

> **MATH TIP**
>
> A rigid transformation keeps the same distance between the points that are transformed; the shape and size of the pre-image and image are the same.

21. Perform dilations on triangle ABC using different scale factors. Use $k > 1$, $k = 1$, and $0 < k < 1$.
   a. Describe how, in general, a dilation transforms a figure.

   b. Do dilations preserve angle measures? Justify your answer using your drawing.

   c. Is a dilation a rigid transformation? Explain.

My Notes

Dilations don't have to be performed on the coordinate plane or with the use of software. Here is a more general definition of a dilation.

Given a point O and a positive real number k, the dilation with center of dilation O and scale factor k maps point P to P', where P' is the point on $\overrightarrow{OP}$ such that $OP' = k \cdot OP$.

A dilation centered at point O with scale factor k can be written in function notation as $D_{O,k}(P) = P'$.

The figure shows a dilation with a scale factor of 3 because $OP' = 3 \cdot OP$.

22. How would you write the dilation above in function notation?

Check Your Understanding

23. $\triangle XYZ$ is an isosceles triangle with a base angle of $65°$. The triangle is dilated by a factor of $\frac{2}{3}$. What are the measures of the angles of $\triangle X'Y'Z'$? Explain your reasoning.

24. A dilation is centered at point O with a scale factor of $\frac{1}{4}$, such that $OP' = \frac{1}{4}OP$. Write the dilation in function notation.

LESSON 17-1 PRACTICE

25. Given a triangle and its image under a dilation, explain how you can use a ruler to determine the scale factor.

26. A graphic artist has enlarged a rectangular photograph using a scale factor of 4. The perimeter of the enlargement is 144 in. What is the perimeter of the original photograph?

27. A photographer enlarged a picture. If the width of the image is 5 inches and the width of the pre-image was x, what is the scale factor for the dilation in terms of x?

28. Sketch the pre-image with the given vertices, and sketch the image with the given scale factor and center of dilation at the origin.

    $A(2, 4)$, $B(-3, -1)$, $C(0, 1)$; scale factor of 3

29. Sketch the pre-image with the given vertices, and sketch the image with the given scale factor and center of dilation at the origin.

    $A(-2, 3)$, $B(2, 3)$, $C(2, -1)$, $D(-2, -1)$; scale factor of $\frac{1}{4}$

30. Sketch the image of a line segment with endpoints $A(-2, -5)$ and $B(1, -1)$ under a dilation centered at the origin with a scale factor of 1.5.

31. Sketch the image of a line segment with endpoints $A(0, 0)$ and $B(5, 4)$ under a dilation centered at the origin with a scale factor of $\frac{1}{2}$.

32. **Reason abstractly.** A dilation maps each point (x, y) of the pre-image to $\left(-5 + \frac{1}{2}(x + 5), 8 + \frac{1}{2}(y - 8)\right)$. What are the scale factor and center of dilation for the transformation?

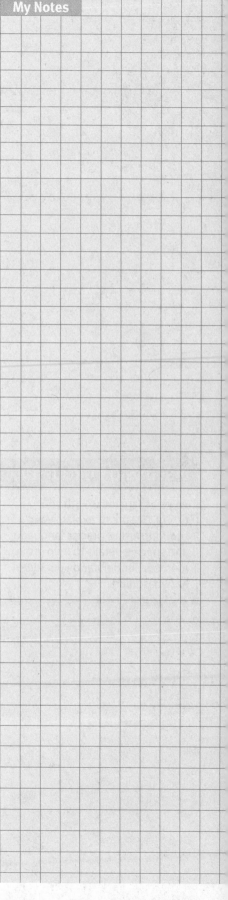

Learning Targets:

● Understand the meaning of similarity transformations.
● Use similarity transformations to determine whether figures are similar.

> **SUGGESTED LEARNING STRATEGIES:** Create Representations, Graphic Organizer, Predict and Confirm, Visualization, Think-Pair-Share

Another of Kate's clients has decided he wants the picture shown in Layout A enlarged and repositioned so that it looks like Layout B. Kate needs to transform the picture in Layout A to Layout B.

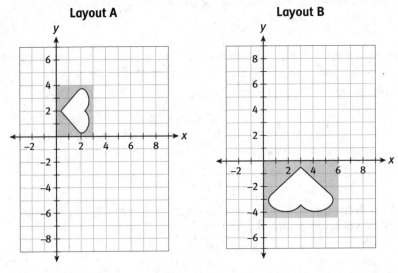

DISCUSSION GROUP TIP

As you share ideas with your group, be sure to explain your thoughts using precise language and specific details to help group members understand your ideas and reasoning.

1. Can a single dilation centered at the origin transform Layout A to Layout D? Explain.

2. Can a single rigid motion transform Layout A to Layout D? Explain.

3. Describe in words a composition that would map Layout A to Layout B.

4. Describe the composition you used in Item 3 in function notation.

My Notes

5. Perform the following compositions of transformations on the pre-image, $\triangle ABC$. Draw the pre-image and image on the grids.

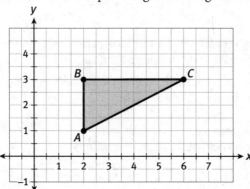

a. $D_{O,2}(r_{(y=1)})$

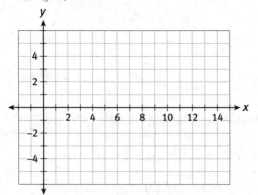

b. $R_{O,90°}\left(D_{O,\frac{1}{4}}\right)$

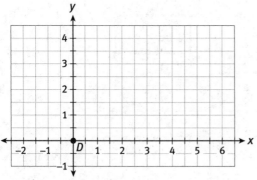

c. $D_{O,4}\left(T_{(2,-2)}\left(D_{O,\frac{1}{2}}\right)\right)$

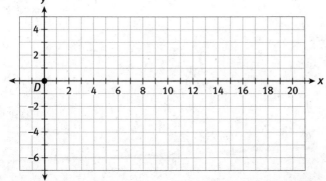

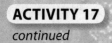

My Notes

6. What can you conclude about the pre-image and image of each of the figures in Item 5?

A *similarity transformation* is a transformation which results in the pre-image and image having the same shape.

7. Model with mathematics. Complete the Venn diagram using each of the transformations on the right.

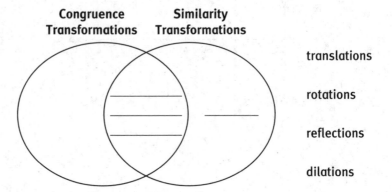

Two figures are **similar** if and only if one figure can be transformed from the other figure using one or more similarity transformations.

8. Kate wants to make sure the two figures below are similar. Use transformations to justify that the two figures are similar. Describe the transformations using words and function notation.

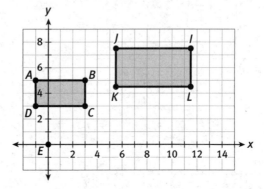

My Notes

Check Your Understanding

9. What single dilation produces the same image as the composition of dilations $D_{O,6} (D_{O,\frac{1}{2}} (D_{O,2.5}))$?

10. Explain why rigid motions are similarity transformations.

LESSON 17-2 PRACTICE

11. Use geometry software or grid paper to perform the following compositions of transformations on the pre-image.

    a. $D_{O,3} (r_{(x = y)})$

    pre-image:

    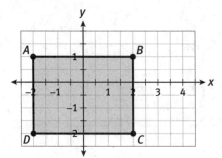

    b. $R_{O, 90°} (D_{O,\frac{1}{4}})$

    pre-image:

    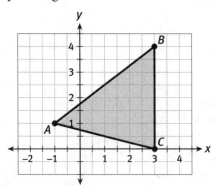

12. **Make sense of problems.** Determine whether the figures are similar. If they are, describe in words two sequences of similarity transformations that could be used to map the pre-image to the image.

    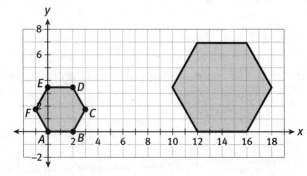

My Notes

Learning Targets:
- Identify properties of similar figures.
- Apply properties of similar figures.

SUGGESTED LEARNING STRATEGIES: Create Representations, Predict and Confirm, Visualization, Create a Plan, Look for a Pattern

1. The two figures shown below are similar. The symbol for similarity is $\sim$. So you can write the similarity statement $ABCD \sim A'B'C'D'$.

   Rectangle $ABCD$ has coordinates $(-1, 0)$, $(-1, 3)$, $(5, 3)$, and $(5, 0)$.

   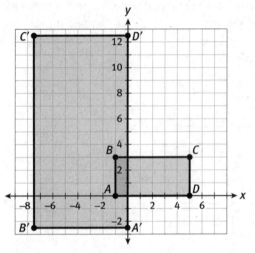

   a. Describe a sequence of similarity transformations that maps $ABCD$ to $A'B'C'D'$.

   b. Do you get the same image if you perform the similarity transformations in a different order?

2. Each similarity transformation described in Item 1 preserves angle measures, so corresponding angles of similar figures are _____.

3. Write the ratios of the corresponding side lengths of the pre-image and image. What do you notice about the ratios?

4. Kate is about to meet with her final client of the day. She needs to create a wall mural. She can measure the length of the wall but not the height. She has a prototype picture and knows that the wall and the picture are similar rectangles. Kate needs to find the area of the wall.

Wall

14 ft

Prototype

18 in.

31.5 in.

a. Which sides of the two rectangles are corresponding?

b. Write two different proportions that can be used to find the height of the wall.

c. **Reason abstractly and quantitatively.** Can the proportion $\frac{x}{18} = \frac{31.5}{168}$ be used to find the height of the wall? Explain why or why not.

d. What is the height of the wall? Show your work.

e. What is the area of the wall? Show your work.

> **MATH TIP**
>
> Equality provides an example of a relationship that is reflexive, symmetric, and transitive.
>
> Equality is reflexive ($a = a$).
>
> Equality is symmetric (if $a = b$, then $b = a$).
>
> Equality is transitive (if $a = b$ and $b = c$, then $a = c$).

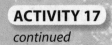
My Notes

Check Your Understanding

5. Rectangle *DEFG* ~ rectangle *WXYZ*. Which side lengths must be proportional? Write the appropriate proportions.

6. If the two rectangles are similar, what is the value of *x*?

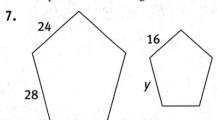

LESSON 17-3 PRACTICE

For each pair of similar figures, find the missing side length.

7.

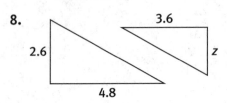

8.

9. $\triangle ABC \sim \triangle DEF$, $m\angle A = 45°$, and $m\angle C = 90°$. Classify $\triangle DEF$ as precisely as possible.

10. Explain how the scale factor in Item 1a relates to the similarity ratio in Item 3.

11. **Critique the reasoning of others.** Mario's teacher wrote the statement $\triangle PQR \sim \triangle STU$ on the board. She asked him to write a proportion that must be true. Mario wrote $\dfrac{PQ}{QR} = \dfrac{ST}{TU}$. Do you agree with Mario's proportion? Justify your answer.

ACTIVITY 17 PRACTICE

Write your answers on notebook paper.
Show your work.

Lesson 17-1

1. Sketch the image of each figure with the given vertices and scale factor and center of dilation at the origin.
   a. $A(0, 1)$, $B(4.5, 0)$, $C(2, 2)$; scale factor of 2
   b. $B(10, 6)$, $C(8, 5)$, $D(-7, 9)$; scale factor of $\frac{1}{2}$
   c. $B(-4, 6)$, $C(6, 6)$, $D(6, 3)$, $E(-4, 3)$; scale factor of $\frac{1}{5}$

2. Sketch the image of a line segment with endpoints $A(-1, 4)$ and $B(2, 3)$ under a dilation centered at the origin with a scale factor of $\frac{1}{2}$.

3. Sketch the image of a triangle with vertices $(-3, 2)$, $(0, 0)$, and $(2, 1)$ under a dilation centered at $(2, 1)$ with a scale factor of 3.

4. What is the scale factor of the dilation centered at the origin that maps ABC to $A'B'C'$?

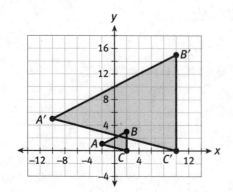

   A. $\frac{1}{6}$ **B.** $\frac{1}{5}$

   C. 5   **D.** 6

5. A graphic artist has reduced a rectangular photograph using a scale factor of $\frac{1}{6}$. The perimeter of the original photograph is 165 in. What is the perimeter of the reduced photograph?

6. What are the coordinates of A after the figure undergoes a dilation with a scale factor of 1.2 centered at the origin?

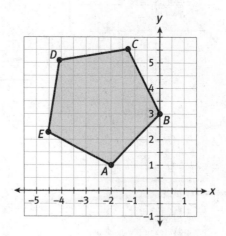

Lesson 17-2

7. What single dilation produces the same image as the composition of dilations $D_{O,\frac{2}{3}}(D_{O,9}(D_{O,2}))$?

   A. $D_{O,12}$ **B.** $D_{O,6}$

   C. $D_{O,2}$ **D.** $D_{O,\frac{2}{9}}$

8. Use geometry software to perform the following compositions of transformations on the pre-image.

a. $D_{O,2}(r_{(y=0)})$

pre-image:

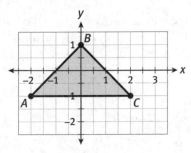

b. $T_{(1,2)}\left(D_{O,\frac{1}{2}}(R_{O,90°})\right)$

pre-image:

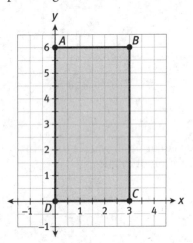

9. Determine whether the figures are similar. If they are, write, in function notation, the sequence of similarity transformations that maps the pre-image to the image.

a.

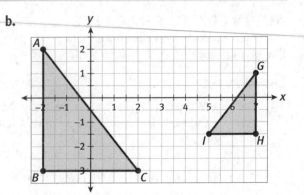

b.

Lesson 17-3

10. Find the indicated measurement for each pair of similar figures.

a.

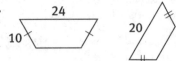

b.

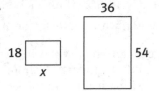

MATHEMATICAL PRACTICES
Attend to Precision

11. The vertices of a quadrilateral have the coordinates $A(-3, 0)$, $B(-8, -6)$, $C(8, 4)$, and $D(2, 4)$. After a dilation with a scale factor of 5, the vertices are translated $T(1, -3)$. What are the coordinates of the vertices of the final image?

Similar Triangles

Measuring Up
Lesson 18-1 Similarity Criteria

Learning Targets:

- Develop criteria for triangle similarity.
- Prove the AA similarity criterion.

> **LEARNING STRATEGIES:** Close Reading, Marking the Text, Questioning the Text, Think-Pair-Share, Create Representations, Visualization

A land boundary dispute exists between a national park and a bordering landowner. Surveyors have been hired to determine land boundaries and help settle the dispute. The surveyors will use similar triangles to find measurements.

You learned in Unit 2 that it is not always necessary to use the definition of congruence to determine if triangles are congruent, because there are congruence criteria you used to show two triangles are congruent. In a similar way, you can look for criteria for showing triangles are similar.

1. Recall that two figures are similar if and only if their corresponding angles are congruent and their corresponding side lengths are proportional.

   a. **Use appropriate tools strategically.** Use a ruler and protractor to draw two noncongruent triangles, $\triangle ABC$ and $\triangle DEF$, with angle measures 45°, 60°, and 75°. Then complete the table.

$\triangle ABC$	$\triangle DEF$	Ratios of Lengths of Corresponding Sides
$AB = $ _____ $BC = $ _____ $CA = $ _____	$DE = $ _____ $EF = $ _____ $FD = $ _____	$\dfrac{AB}{DE} = \dfrac{\square}{\square}$, $\dfrac{BC}{EF} = \dfrac{\square}{\square}$, $\dfrac{CA}{FD} = \dfrac{\square}{\square}$

   b. Do you think three pairs of congruent angles guarantee triangle similarity? Justify your response.

   c. Use a ruler and protractor to draw two noncongruent triangles, $\triangle QRS$ and $\triangle XYZ$, with angle measures of 45° and 60°. Then complete the table.

$\triangle QRS$	$\triangle XYZ$	Ratios of Lengths of Corresponding Sides
$QR = $ _____ $RS = $ _____ $SQ = $ _____	$XY = $ _____ $YZ = $ _____ $ZX = $ _____	$\dfrac{QR}{XY} = \dfrac{\square}{\square}$, $\dfrac{RS}{YZ} = \dfrac{\square}{\square}$, $\dfrac{SQ}{ZX} = \dfrac{\square}{\square}$

   d. **Look for and express regularity in repeated reasoning.** Without measuring, could you have predicted that the triangles in Item 1c would be similar? Justify your response.

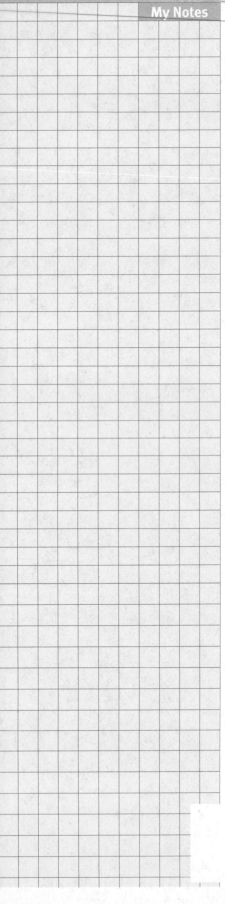

e. Do you think two pairs of congruent angles guarantee triangle similarity? Explain.

2. The investigation you did in Item 1 suggests the AA Similarity Postulate for triangles. State the postulate.

Check Your Understanding

3. Write whether AA similarity can be used to show that the pair of triangles are similar. Explain your answer.

a.

45°
110°
30°
110°

b.

35°
55°

You can use the AA Similarity Postulate to show that two triangles are similar. In order to prove *why* this criterion works, you must show that it follows from the definition of similarity in terms of rigid motions.

4. To justify the AA Similarity Postulate, consider the two triangles below.

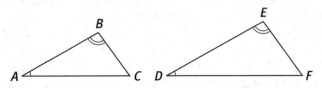

a. What given information is marked in the figure?

b. Based on the definition of similarity, explain whether transformations can show that $ABC \sim DEF$.

c. Draw a figure to show the result of a dilation that maps $\triangle ABC$ to $\triangle A'B'C'$ using the scale factor $k = \dfrac{DE}{AB}$.

My Notes

d. By the definition of similarity transformations, complete the following statements.

$\angle A' \cong \boxed{}$ $\angle B' \cong \boxed{}$ $\angle A'B' = k \bullet AB = \boxed{}$

e. By the Transitive Property of Congruence, $\angle A' \cong \angle D$ and _____.

f. How are $\triangle A'B'C'$ and $\triangle DEF$ related? How do you know?

The argument in Items 4d through 4f shows that a sequence of rigid motions maps $\triangle A'B'C'$ to $\triangle DEF$. The dilation in Item 4c followed by the sequence of rigid motions shows that there is a sequence of similarity transformations that maps $\triangle ABC$ to $\triangle DEF$. So, by the definition of similarity, $\triangle ABC \sim \triangle DEF$.

You learned there were six criteria for showing that triangles are congruent, so it seems logical that there may be other criteria for showing that triangles are similar.

5. First investigate whether there is an SAS similarity criterion.
   a. How do you think the SAS similarity criterion differs from the SAS congruence criterion?

   b. State what you think the SAS criterion would say.

   c. Use geometry software to construct the following triangles with the given measurements.

$\triangle ABC$	$\triangle DEF$
$AB = 4$	$DE = 2$
$BC = 6$	$EF = 3$
$m\angle B = 47°$	$m\angle E = 47°$

   d. Use the software to determine the remaining side and angle measures for each triangle.

   e. Are the triangles similar? Explain why or why not.

   f. Based on your answers above, state the SAS Similarity Theorem.

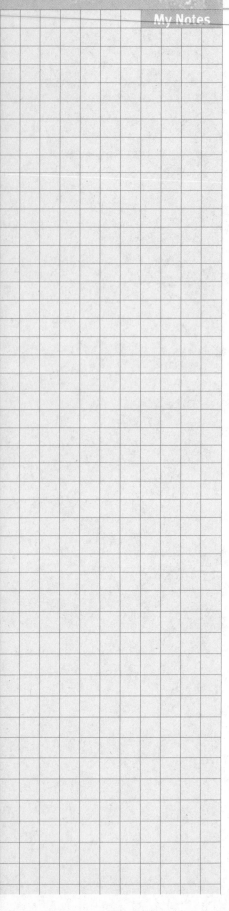

My Notes

6. Now investigate whether there is an SSS similarity criterion.
  a. How do you think the SSS similarity criterion differs from the SSS congruence criterion?

  b. State what you think the SSS criterion would say.

  c. Use geometry software to construct the following triangles with the given measurements.

△*ABC*	△*DEF*
AB = 6	*DE* = 9
BC = 8	*EF* = 12
CA = 10	*FD* = 15

  d. What are the angle measures of each triangle?

  e. Are the triangles similar? Explain why or why not.

  f. Based on your answers above, state the SSS Similarity Theorem.

7. For each pair of triangles, write the similarity criterion, if any, that can be used to show the triangles are similar.

  a.

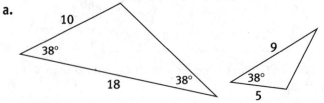

  b.   **c.**

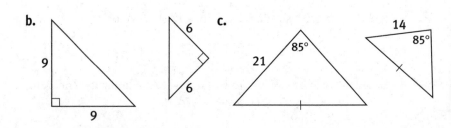

My Notes

Check Your Understanding

8. Are all right isosceles triangles similar? Explain.

9. Are all equilateral triangles similar? Explain.

LESSON 18-1 PRACTICE

For each pair of triangles, write which similarity criterion, if any, can be used to show the triangles are similar. Remember to use complete sentences and words such as *and, or, since, for example, therefore, because of, by the,* to make connections between your thoughts.

10.

11.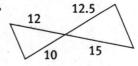

12.

13.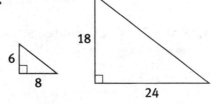

14. Make use of structure. What additional information do you need, if any, in order to conclude that △ACD ~ △BCD? Is there more than one set of information that would work? Explain.

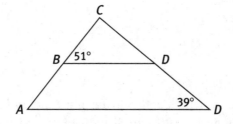

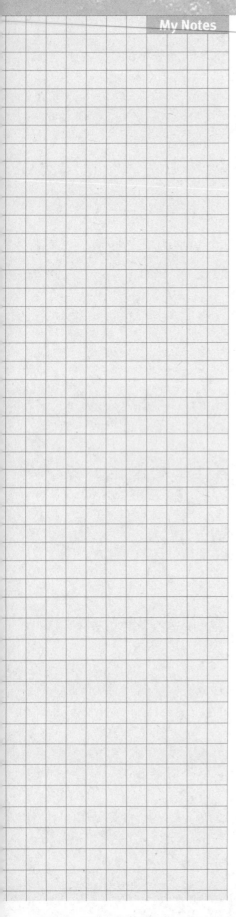

My Notes

Learning Targets:

- Show triangles are similar.
- Use similar triangles to solve problems.

> **SUGGESTED LEARNING STRATEGIES:** Close Reading, Graphic Organizer, Marking the Text, Questioning the Text, Think-Pair-Share, Create Representations, Identify a Subtask, Note Taking, Quickwrite

Clarissa is one of the surveyors hired to help determine land boundaries. She needs to find the distance across a ravine. She thinks she can use properties of similar triangles to find the distance. She locates points *A*, *B*, *C*, *D*, and *E* and takes the measurements shown.

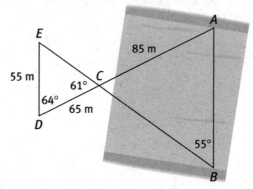

1. **Make sense of problems.** Which similarity criterion, if any, can be used to show $\triangle ABC \sim \triangle DEC$? Explain.

2. The triangles are similar, so the corresponding sides are proportional. Complete and solve the proportion to find the distance *AB*.

$$\frac{65}{\boxed{}} = \frac{\boxed{}}{AB}$$

Clarissa measured the length of the ravine indirectly. ***Indirect measurement*** is a technique that does not use a measurement tool, such as a ruler, to measure an unknown length. Indirect measurement is used to measure distances that cannot be measured directly, such as the height of a tree or the distance across a lake or a ravine. Triangle similarity is often used to make indirect measurements.

Example A

Clarissa needs to find the width of a rock formation in the national park. She locates points A, B, C, D, and E and takes the measurements shown. Find the width of the rock formation, AB.

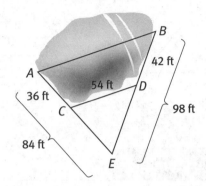

Step 1: Show $\triangle DEC \sim \triangle BEA$.

Find CE and DE.

$CE = 84 \text{ ft} - 36 \text{ ft} = 48 \text{ ft}$

$DE = 98 \text{ ft} - 42 \text{ ft} = 56 \text{ ft}$

Write a proportion to determine whether corresponding sides are proportional.

$$\frac{CE}{AE} \overset{?}{=} \frac{DE}{BE}$$

$$\frac{48}{84} \overset{?}{=} \frac{56}{98}$$

$$48 \cdot 98 \overset{?}{=} 56 \cdot 84$$

$$4704 = 4704 \ \checkmark$$

By the Reflexive Property, $\angle E \cong \angle E$. So by SAS similarity, $\triangle DEC \sim \triangle BEA$.

Step 2: Write and solve a proportion to find AB.

$$\frac{CE}{AE} = \frac{CD}{AB}$$

$$\frac{48}{84} = \frac{54}{AB}$$

$$48 \cdot AB = 54 \cdot 84$$

$$AB = 94.5$$

Solution: The width of the rock formation is 94.5 feet.

My Notes

Try These A

a. Find *CB*.

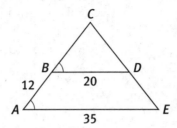

b. Find *XY*.

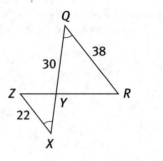

Check Your Understanding

3. Jorge found *DA* by writing and solving the proportion shown, but he is incorrect. What mistake did Jorge make?

$$\frac{10}{12} = \frac{12}{DA}$$
$$10 \cdot DA = 12 \cdot 12$$
$$DA = 14.4$$

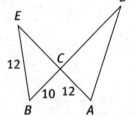

LESSON 18-2 PRACTICE

4. Determine whether each pair of triangles is similar. If so, write the similarity criterion that can be used to show they are similar and find the unknown measure.

a.

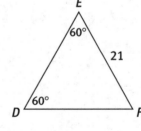

ED = _____
DF = _____

b.

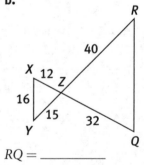

RQ = _____

5. Critique the reasoning of others. $\triangle ABC \sim \triangle DEC$. Clarissa wants to measure another ravine and wrote the following proportion to find *EC*. Is she correct? If not, explain why and correct her work. Then find *EC*.

$$\frac{9}{10} = \frac{EC}{8.75}$$

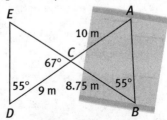

Learning Targets:

- Prove the Triangle Proportionality Theorem and its converse.
- Apply the Triangle Proportionality Theorem and its converse.

> **SUGGESTED LEARNING STRATEGIES:** Close Reading, Marking the Text, Questioning the Text, Think-Pair-Share, Create Representations, Identify a Subtask, Work Backward

Clarissa needs to find the distance across a lake in the national park. She locates points A, B, C, D, and E and takes the measurements shown. She thinks she can use similar triangles to find the distance.

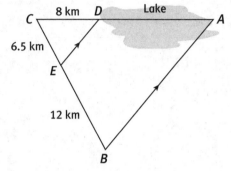

1. If $\overleftrightarrow{MR} \parallel \overline{ST}$ in the figure below, explain why $\triangle MAR \sim \triangle SAT$.

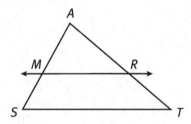

2. Knowing that corresponding sides of similar triangles are proportional, complete this proportion:

$$\frac{AM}{AS} = \frac{AR}{?}$$

3. If $AM = 12$ cm, $MS = 9$ cm, and $AR = 15$ cm, determine RT. Show your work.

4. If $MS = 8$ cm, $AR = 25$ cm, and $RT = 10$ cm, determine AM. Show your work.

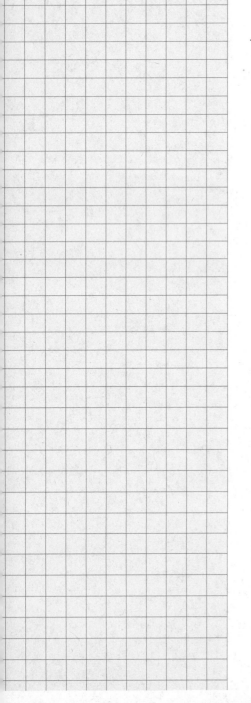

MATH TERMS

Triangle Proportionality Theorem
If a line parallel to a side of a triangle intersects the other two sides, then it divides them proportionally.

5. Complete the proof of the *Triangle Proportionality Theorem*.

Given: _____

Prove: $\dfrac{b}{a} = \dfrac{c}{d}$

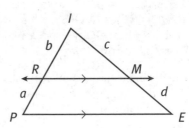

Statements	Reasons
1. $\triangle PIE$ and $\triangle RIM$ with ___ $\|$ ___	**1.** Given
2.	**2.** If two parallel lines are cut by a transversal, the corresponding angles are congruent.
3.	**3.**
4. $\triangle$ _____ $\sim \triangle PIE$	**4.**
5. $\dfrac{b}{b+a} = \dfrac{c}{c+d}$	**5.**
6. $\dfrac{b(b+a)(c+d)}{(b+a)} = \dfrac{(b+a)(c+d)c}{(c+d)}$	**6.** Multiplication Property of Equality
7. $b(c+d) = (b+a)c$	**7.** Property of the Multiplicative Identity
8.	**8.** Distributive Property
9. $bd = ac$	**9.**
10. $\dfrac{bd}{ad} = \dfrac{ac}{ad}$	**10.**
11.	**11.**

My Notes

Now you can use the theorem to solve the problem from the beginning of the lesson.

6. Clarissa needs to find the distance across the lake shown. The known measurements are shown. What is the distance *DA*?

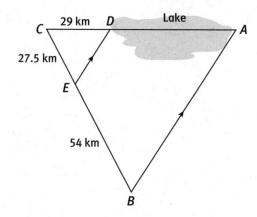

7. State the converse of the Triangle Proportionality Theorem.

8. Construct viable arguments. Write a convincing argument about why the converse of the Triangle Proportionality Theorem is true.

Check Your Understanding

Consider △*SAT*.

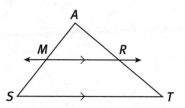

9. Determine if each statement is true or false.

a. $\dfrac{AM}{MS} = \dfrac{AR}{RT}$

b. $\dfrac{AM}{AS} = \dfrac{AR}{RT}$

10. If *AM* = 8 in., *AR* = 12 in., and *RT* = 5 in., what is *MS*?

MATH TERMS

Parallel Proportionality Theorem
If two or more lines parallel to a side of a triangle intersect the other two sides of the triangle, then they divide them proportionally.

MATH TIP

The Parallel Proportionality Theorem is a *corollary* of the Triangle Proportionality Theorem because it is proven directly from it.

11. Given: $\overline{RE} \parallel \overline{AT} \parallel \overline{IO} \parallel \overline{NS}$. Determine each length. Show your work.

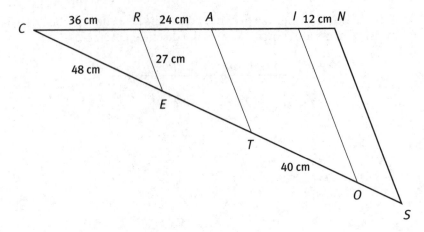

a. *ET*

b. *AI*

c. *AT*

d. *OS*

e. *IO*

f. *NS*

12. **Attend to precision.** A land developer is using a surveyor to measure distances to ensure that the streets in the new community are parallel.

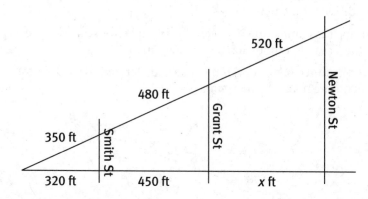

a. If Grant Street and Newton Street are parallel, what is the value of *x*? Support your answer.

b. Are Smith Street and Grant Street parallel? Support your answer.

Check Your Understanding

13. Given the diagram with $\overline{LD} \parallel \overline{AE} \parallel \overline{NT}$ and segment measures as shown, determine the following measures. Show your work.

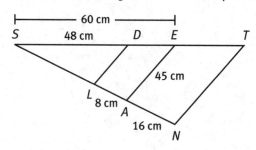

a. *SL*   b. *LD*   c. *ET*   d. *NT*

LESSON 18-3 PRACTICE

14. State the Triangle Proportionality Theorem and its converse as a biconditional statement.

15. Describe the connection between the Triangle Midsegment Theorem and the Triangle Proportionality Theorem.

16. Reason abstractly. Given the diagram, determine whether the segments are parallel. Show your work.

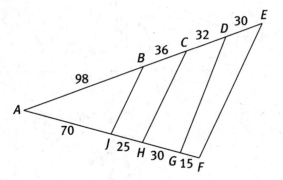

a. $\overline{BJ}$ and $\overline{CH}$

b. $\overline{BJ}$ and $\overline{EF}$

c. $\overline{DG}$ and $\overline{EF}$

d. $\overline{BJ}$ and $\overline{DG}$

ACTIVITY 18 PRACTICE
Write your answers on notebook paper.
Show your work.

Lesson 18-1

1. For each pair of triangles, write which similarity criterion, if any, can be used to show the triangles are similar.

a.

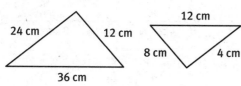

b.

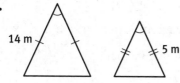

c.

The arrows indicate parallel lines.

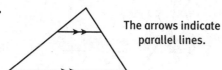

d.

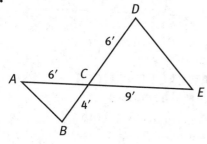

e.

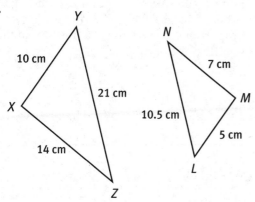

Lesson 18-2

2. Solve for x in the following figure.

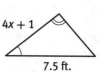

22 ft. 18 ft. $4x + 1$ 7.5 ft.

3. The following triangles are similar. Determine the values of x, y, and z.

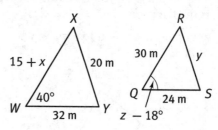

4. $\triangle CLU \sim \triangle ELU$. Given $\triangle CEL$ with measures as shown, determine x. Show your work.

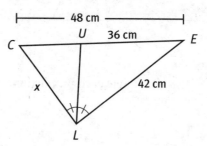

5. Explain why the following triangles are similar to each other.

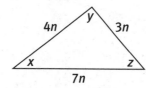
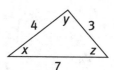

6. The lengths of the corresponding sides of two similar triangles are 10, 15, and 20 and 15, 22.5, and x. What is the value of x?

   A. 20
   B. 25
   C. 30
   D. 40

7. Standing 8 feet from a puddle of water on the ground, Gretchen, whose eye height is 5 feet 2 inches, can see the reflection of the top of a flagpole. The puddle is 20 feet from the flagpole. How tall is the flagpole?

8. Write a convincing argument to explain why $\triangle TUV \sim \triangle RSV$.

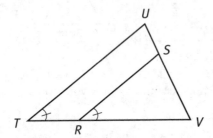

Lesson 18-3

Given: $\overrightarrow{AT} \mid \overrightarrow{EY} \parallel \overrightarrow{SB}$. Complete each proportion with the appropriate measure.

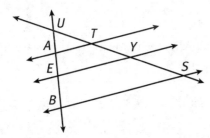

9. $\dfrac{EA}{BE} = \dfrac{TY}{?}$ 10. $\dfrac{AT}{?} = \dfrac{UA}{UB}$

11. $\dfrac{AB}{UA} = \dfrac{?}{TU}$

Given the diagram with $\overline{TH} \parallel \overline{IN} \parallel \overline{KE}$ and segment measures as shown.

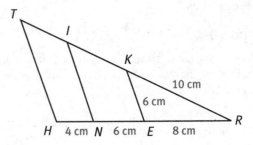

Determine the following measures. Show your work.

12. IK 13. IN

14. IT 15. TH

16. Given the diagram with $\overleftrightarrow{BI} \parallel \overleftrightarrow{ST} \parallel \overleftrightarrow{EN}$, explain how to demonstrate that $\dfrac{ES}{SB} = \dfrac{NT}{TI}$.

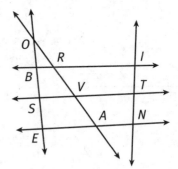

MATHEMATICAL PRACTICES
Model with Mathematics

17. If you sketched triangle MPR and drew a line parallel to side RP that intersected side MR at point X and side MP at point Z, name a pair of similar triangles formed. Write two different proportions to show the relationships of the line segments in your figure.

Phaedra has finally saved up enough money from her after-school job to buy a new computer monitor. She wants to buy a monitor that is similar to her current monitor. She does an online search and decides to compare the three models shown to her current monitor.

Current monitor:

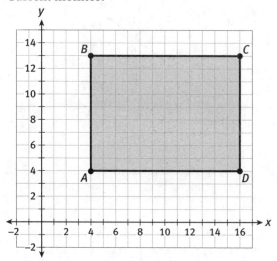

New models:
Model 1: 20-inch monitor

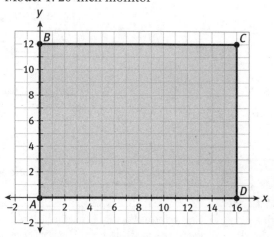

1. a. Which of the new models, if any, are similar to Phaedra's current monitor? Justify your response.

b. For those that are similar to her current monitor, describe the scale factor that maps her current monitor to the new model.

2. Phaedra wants to mount her new monitor in a different position on her wall.

Model 2: 26-inch monitor

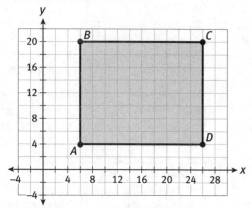

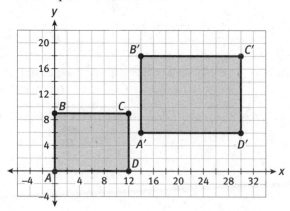

Describe the similarity transformations that map her current monitor to her new one.

Model 3: 21-inch monitor

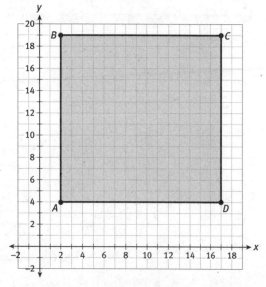

3. Phaedra decides to buy the 20-inch model, which replaces her old 15-inch monitor. She knows that screen size is measured diagonally, so the measurements would be as follows:

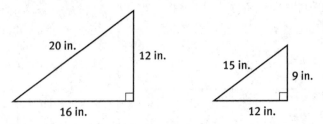

Write a convincing argument using similarity criteria that explains why the triangles are similar to each other.

Scoring Guide	Exemplary	Proficient	Emerging	Incomplete
	The solution demonstrates these characteristics:			
Mathematics Knowledge and Thinking (Items 1, 2, 3)	• Clear and accurate understanding of similar figures, scale factor, and transformations	• Adequate understanding of similar figures, scale factor, and transformations	• Partial understanding of similar figures, scale factor, and transformations	• Little or no understanding of similar figures, scale factor, and transformations
Problem Solving (Items 1, 2)	• An appropriate and efficient strategy that results in a correct answer	• A strategy that may include unnecessary steps but results in a correct answer	• A strategy that results in some incorrect answers	• No clear strategy when solving problems
Mathematical Modeling / Representations (Item 2)	• Clear and accurate understanding of representations of similarity transformations	• A functional understanding of representations of similarity transformations	• Partial understanding of representations of similarity transformations	• Little or no understanding of representations of similarity transformations
Reasoning and Communication (Items 1a, 3)	• Precise use of appropriate math terms and language to justify whether or not figures are similar	• Mostly correct use of appropriate math terms and language to justify whether or not figures are similar	• Misleading or confusing use of appropriate math terms and language to justify whether or not figures are similar	• Incomplete or inaccurate use of appropriate math terms and language to justify whether or not figures are similar

Geometric Mean

Do You Mean It?
Lesson 19-1 The Right Triangle Altitude Theorem

Learning Targets:

- Identify the relationships that exist when an altitude is drawn to the hypotenuse of a right triangle.
- Prove the Right Triangle Altitude Theorem.

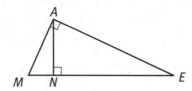

SUGGESTED LEARNING STRATEGIES: Close Reading, Marking the Text, Questioning the Text, Think-Pair-Share, Create Representations, Visualization

You have investigated properties and relationships of sides and angles in similar triangles. In this section, you examine a special characteristic of right triangles.

Given the figure with right triangle MAE, $\overline{AN} \perp \overline{ME}$, $m\angle M = 70°$.

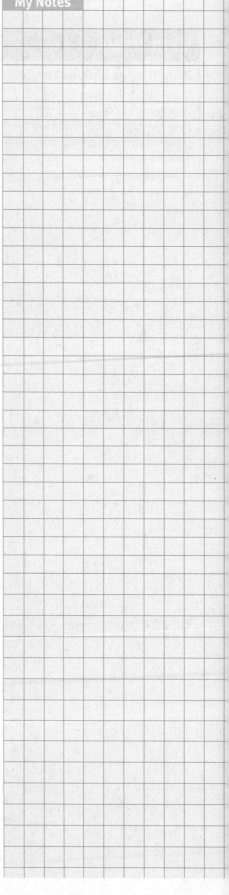

1. Determine these angle measures.

   $m\angle MAN =$ $m\angle EAN =$ $m\angle E =$

2. Justify that $\triangle MAN \sim \triangle AEN$.

3. The large triangle is also similar to the two smaller triangles. Complete the similarity statement, naming the large triangle appropriately.

   $\triangle MAN \sim$ _____

4. Name the type of special segment AN is in relation to $\triangle MAE$.

5. Given $AN = 9$ in. and $NE = 12$ in. Use the Pythagorean Theorem and the properties of similar triangles to determine these segment lengths. Show your work.

   $AE =$ $MA =$ $MN =$

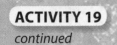

My Notes

MATH TERMS

Right Triangle Altitude Theorem
If an altitude is drawn to the hypotenuse of a right triangle, then the two triangles formed are similar to the original right triangle and to each other.

6. **Construct viable arguments.** Complete the proof of the *Right Triangle Altitude Theorem*.

Given: $\triangle YEA$ with right angle EAY and altitude AS

Prove: $\triangle YEA \sim \triangle YAS \sim \triangle AES$

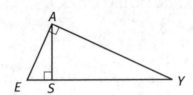

Statements	Reasons
1.	1. Given
2. $\angle ESA$ and $\angle ASY$ are right angles.	2.
3. $\angle ESA \cong \angle ASY \cong \angle EAY$	3.
4. $\angle Y \cong \angle Y$	4.
5. $\triangle \quad \sim \triangle$	5.
6. $\angle E \cong \angle E$	6.
7. $\triangle \quad \sim \triangle$	7.
8. $\triangle YEA \sim \triangle YAS \sim \triangle AES$	8.

My Notes

Check Your Understanding

7. There are three right triangles in the figure below. Draw each triangle with the right angle in the lower left position.

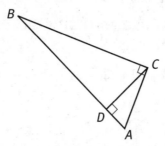

LESSON 19-1 PRACTICE

8. In the figure, $\triangle XYZ$ is a right triangle and $\overline{YW}$ is an altitude to the hypotenuse. Suppose you know that $m\angle X = 62°$. What other angle in the figure must also measure $62°$? Why?

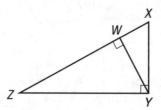

9. Given the figure with right triangle DEF, $\overline{FG} \perp \overline{DE}$, $m\angle E = 25°$, $DF = 8$, $DE = 17$.
   Complete the similarity statement.

   $\triangle DEF \sim \triangle$ _____ $\sim \triangle$ _____

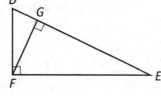

10. Use the figure in Item 9 to find each of the following measures.

    a. $m\angle D =$ _____   **b.** $m\angle DFG =$ _____
    c. $m\angle GFE =$ _____ **d.** $FE =$ _____
    e. $FG =$ _____

11. **Make use of structure.** Triangle HIJ is an isosceles right triangle. Make a conjecture about the two triangles formed by drawing the altitude to the hypotenuse. Write a paragraph proof to prove your conjecture.

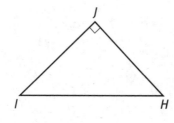

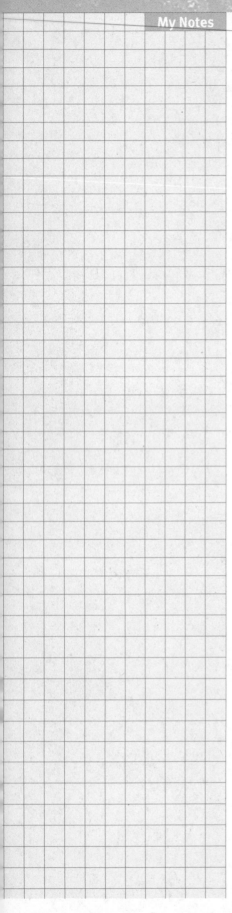

My Notes

Learning Targets:

- Identify the relationships that exist when an altitude is drawn to the hypotenuse of a right triangle.
- Apply the relationships that exist when an altitude is drawn to the hypotenuse of a right triangle.

SUGGESTED LEARNING STRATEGIES: Close Reading, Think-Pair-Share, Create Representations, Self Revision/Peer Revision, Visualization

1. Which two similar triangles allow us to show $\frac{x}{t} = \frac{t}{z}$?

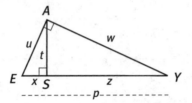

2. Which two similar triangles allow us to show $\frac{x}{u} = \frac{u}{p}$?

The answers to Items 1 and 2 indicate two corollaries of the Right Triangle Altitude Theorem.

> Corollary 1: When the altitude is drawn to the hypotenuse of a right triangle, the length of the altitude is the **geometric mean** between the segments of the hypotenuse.

> Corollary 2: When the altitude is drawn to the hypotenuse of a right triangle, each leg is the *geometric mean* between the hypotenuse and the part of the hypotenuse that is adjacent to the leg.

3. In Item 2 we used properties of similar triangles to justify that $\frac{x}{u} = \frac{u}{p}$. Solve the proportion for u. Show your work.

4. Attend to precision. Write and solve the proportion that can be written from corollary 2. Use w.

Example A

Given $\triangle DEF$ with altitude $\overline{FG}$. Determine x, if $y = 9$ and $z = 36$.

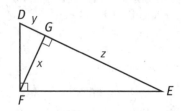

Step 1. Use the corollary above to determine the relationships.

The altitude is drawn to the hypotenuse of the right triangle. So, the altitude, x, is the geometric mean between the segments of the hypotenuse, y and z.

Step 2. Write an equation and simplify.

$\dfrac{y}{x} = \dfrac{x}{z}$ Definition of geometric mean

$x^2 = yz$ Multiply.

$x^2 = 9 \cdot 36$ Substitute 9 for y and 36 for z.

$x^2 = 324$ Multiply.

$\sqrt{x^2} = \sqrt{324}$ Take the square root of both sides.

$x = 18$ Simplify.

Try These A

Use the figure in Example A and the corollary above to answer Items a and b.

a. If $y = 2$ and $x = 16$, determine z. Show your work.

b. If $x = 18$ and $z = 45$, determine y. Show your work.

MATH TERMS

The **geometric mean** of two positive numbers a and b is the positive number x such that $\dfrac{a}{x} = \dfrac{x}{b}$. When solving, $x = \sqrt{ab}$.

Example:
6 is the geometric mean of 4 and 9 since $\dfrac{4}{x} = \dfrac{x}{9}$, so that $x^2 = 4(9)$ or $x = \sqrt{4(9)} = 6$.

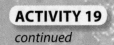

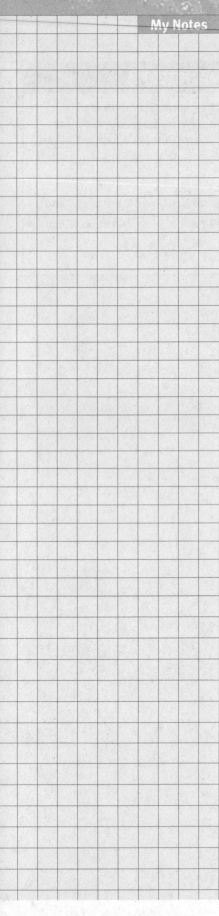

My Notes

Check Your Understanding

5. Explain how to use the corollary on the first page of this lesson to find *JM*. Then find *JM*.

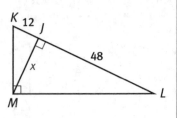

6. Given $\triangle AYE$ with altitude $\overline{AS}$ (not to scale) as shown, solve the following. Show your work.
   a. $x = 4$ cm, $z = 9$ cm. Determine t.
   b. $x = 6$ cm, $t = 12$ cm. Determine z.
   c. $z = 18$ cm, $t = 32$ cm. Determine x.

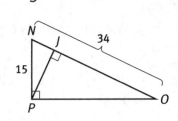

7. Explain how to use the two corollaries you learned in this lesson to find *PJ*. Then find *PJ*.

LESSON 19-2 PRACTICE

8. Find the geometric mean of each set of numbers. Write in radical form.
   a. 25 and 4
   b. 3 and 60
   c. 2.5 and 9.1

9. Given right triangle *XYZ*, with altitude $\overline{WZ}$, find each length.
   a. If $XW = 3$ and $WY = 12$, determine WZ.
   b. If $WZ = 4$ and $XW = 2$, determine WY.
   c. If $XY = 22$ and $XW = 9$, determine WZ.
   d. If $XZ = 10$ and $XW = 4$, determine XY.
   e. If $WZ = 18$ and $XW = 9$, determine XZ.
   f. If $WZ = 4$, $XW = x$, and $XY = 10$, determine ZY.

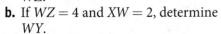

10. **Make sense of problems.** Explain how the corollaries in this lesson can help you find the area of $\triangle PQR$. What is the area of $\triangle PQR$?

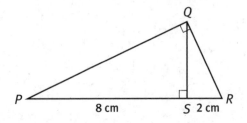

ACTIVITY 19 PRACTICE
Write your answers on notebook paper.
Show your work.

Lesson 19-1

1. Given right triangle ABC with altitude $\overline{CE}$. By the Right Triangle Altitude Theorem, which similarity statement is true?

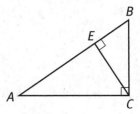

   A. $\triangle ABC \sim \triangle EBC$
   B. $\triangle ABC \sim \triangle CBE$
   C. $\triangle ABC \sim \triangle AEC$
   D. $\triangle ABC \sim \triangle BCE$

2. Write a similarity statement comparing the three triangles in each figure.

   a.

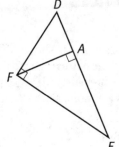

   b.

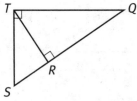

   c.

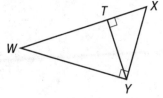

Lesson 19-2

3. Determine the geometric mean of 21 and 84.

4. Determine the geometric mean of 15 and 100.

5. The figure below shows a side view of a garage. The roof hangs over the base portion by 2 feet in the back. Determine each of the following.
   a. x **b.** z **c.** y

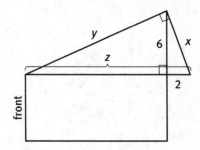

6. Given △*KID* as shown.
   a. Determine *ND*.
   b. Determine *KD*.
   c. Determine *KI*.

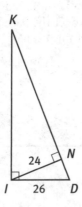

7. Given the kite with diagonal measures as shown.
   a. Determine the length of the short diagonal.
   b. Determine the side lengths.

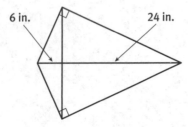

8. Carly is 5 feet tall. She wants to know the height of a tree in her yard. She stands so that her lines of sight to the top of the tree and the bottom of the tree form a 90° angle, as shown in the diagram below. How tall is the tree?

9. Juan built the birdhouse as shown. How tall is the roof of the birdhouse?

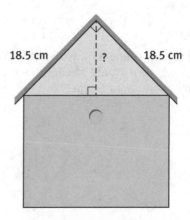

10. The altitude to the hypotenuse of a right triangle divides the hypotenuse into two segments. One segment is three times as long as the other. If the altitude is 12 mm long, what are the lengths of the two segments?

MATHEMATICAL PRACTICES
Reason Abstractly and Quantitatively

11. Given △*YEA* with altitude $\overline{AS}$ as shown; if given any two of the variable measures, is it possible to determine all the other measures? If so, explain how. If it is not always possible, state when it is and when it is not.

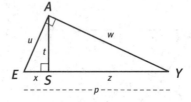

The Pythagorean Theorem and Its Converse

Is That Right?
Lesson 20-1 Pythagorean Theorem

Learning Targets:

- Use similar triangles to prove the Pythagorean Theorem.
- Apply the Pythagorean Theorem to solve problems.

> **SUGGESTED LEARNING STRATEGIES:** Marking the Text, Summarizing, Paraphrasing, Think-Pair-Share, Create Representations

Sara owns an online company that manufactures custom kites. Her customers go to her website and design their own kites. Then Sara's company builds them. Many of her customers don't know the correct names for the parts of a kite. Sara is creating a Web page to educate them so they can communicate better with Sara and her staff.

Because many kites include right triangles, the **Pythagorean Theorem** is useful in analyzing the dimensions of a kite.

1. **Model with mathematics.** The simplest kite is the diamond kite shown. When the sides of this type of kite meet at a right angle, you can use the Pythagorean Theorem to find the length of the spine.

   a. Which side of triangle *XYZ* is the hypotenuse? Which sides are the legs?

   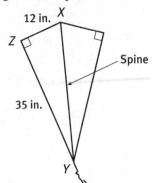

   b. What is the length of the spine? Show your work.

> ### MATH TERMS
>
> **Pythagorean Theorem**
>
> In any right triangle, the square of the length of the hypotenuse is equal to the sum of the squares of the lengths of the legs.
>
> If *a* and *b* are the lengths of the legs and *c* is the length of the hypotenuse, then, $c^2 = a^2 + b^2$.

> ### CONNECT TO HISTORY
>
> Although many applications of the **Pythagorean Theorem** were known and used by the Babylonians, Chinese, Hindus, and Egyptians well before Pythagoras was born (about 570 B.C.E.), he is given credit for being the first to formally prove the theorem. Many others since Pythagoras's time, including a young man named James Garfield who would go on to be president of the United States, have also offered formal proofs of the well-known theorem.

One way to prove the Pythagorean Theorem is by using similar triangles. In right triangle *ABC* below, an altitude is drawn to hypotenuse $\overline{AB}$, forming two right triangles that are similar to triangle *ABC*.

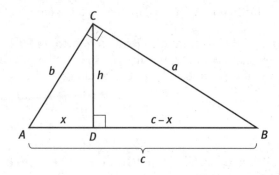

2. Write a similarity statement for the three similar triangles.

My Notes

3. The corresponding sides of similar triangles are proportional, so you can write proportions involving sides of the triangles from Item 2. Complete each proportion. Then find the cross products.

$$\frac{b}{x} = \frac{\square}{b}$$

$$\frac{a}{\square} = \frac{c}{a}$$

4. Use the equations from Item 3 and algebra to prove $a^2 + b^2 = c^2$.

Check Your Understanding

5. A ***Pythagorean triple*** is a set of three nonzero whole numbers that satisfy the Pythagorean Theorem. Explain why the numbers 3, 4, and 6 do not form a Pythagorean triple.

6. Explain why the Pythagorean Theorem relationship, $a^2 + b^2 = c^2$, is only true if c is greater than both a and b.

One of Sara's customers designed the rhombus-shaped kite shown.

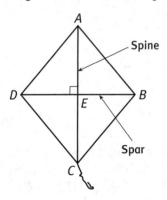

7. The length of the spine, AC, is 28 inches, and the length of the spar, DB, is 24 inches.
   a. **Construct viable arguments.** Explain how to find the perimeter of a kite if the lengths of the spine and the spar are known. Include the properties of a rhombus in your explanation.

   b. Use the Pythagorean Theorem to find AD. Then find the perimeter of the kite.

DISCUSSION GROUP TIPS

If you do not understand something in group discussions, ask for help or raise your hand for help. Describe your questions as clearly as possible, using synonyms or other words when you do not know the precise words to use.

My Notes

Check Your Understanding

8. Use the Pythagorean Theorem to show the diagonals of a square with side length s are congruent.

9. How high up a vertical wall will a 24-foot ladder reach if the foot of the ladder is placed 10 feet from the wall? Show your work.

LESSON 20-1 PRACTICE

10. Find each unknown length. Simplify your answer in radical form.

   a.

   27
   38
   b

   $b =$ _____

   b.

   35
   14
   x

   $x =$ _____

11. **Reason quantitatively.** Find the area of a rectangular rug if the width of the rug is 13 feet and the diagonal measures 20 feet.

12. Which of the following is a Pythagorean triple?
   A. 3, 4, 6
   B. 7, 25, 26
   C. 15, 21, 25
   D. 9, 40, 41

13. One of the diagonals of a rectangle measures 15 cm. The width of the rectangle is 6 cm. Determine the perimeter of the rectangle.

14. The longer diagonal of a rhombus is 16 cm. Determine the length of the shorter diagonal, if the perimeter of the rhombus is 40 cm.

15. **Construct viable arguments.** To store his art supplies, Kyle buys a cube-shaped box with 8-inch sides. His longest paintbrush is 13.5 inches long. Explain how Kyle determined that the 13.5-inch paintbrush could fit in the box.

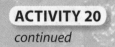

My Notes

Learning Targets:

- Use the converse of the Pythagorean Theorem to solve problems.
- Develop and apply Pythagorean inequalities.

> **SUGGESTED LEARNING STRATEGIES:** Use Manipulatives, Look for a Pattern, Create Representations, Activating Prior Knowledge, Think-Pair-Share

One of Sara's customers designed the kite shown. The customer claims that $\triangle QRS$ is a right triangle.

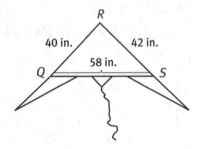

1. a. Write the Pythagorean Theorem in if-then form.

b. The converse of the Pythagorean Theorem is also true. Write the converse of the Pythagorean Theorem in if-then form.

c. Use the converse of the Pythagorean Theorem to determine whether $\triangle QRS$ is a right triangle.

2. Construct viable arguments. Write an algebraic proof to show that if a, b, and c form a Pythagorean triple, then any positive whole-number multiple of the numbers is also a Pythagorean triple.

Given: Positive whole numbers a, b, and c with $a^2 + b^2 = c^2$

Prove: For any positive whole number x, $(xa)^2 + (xb)^2 = (xc)^2$.

MATH TIP

To create a triangle, the sum of the lengths of any two sides must be greater than the length of the third side.

3. Use each of the following sets of triangle side lengths to build triangles using the manipulatives (straws) provided by your teacher.

   Step 1: Cut straws into 5 cm, 6 cm, 12 cm, 13 cm, and 15 cm lengths.

   Step 2: Build each triangle on centimeter grid paper.

   Step 3: Identify each triangle as right, acute, or obtuse.

   Step 4: Complete the table.

Triangle Side Lengths	Type of Triangle	Square of Longest Segment	Sum of the Squares of the Two Shorter Sides
5, 12, 13			
6, 6, 12			
5, 6, 12			
5, 12, 15			
5, 12, 12			
6, 12, 13			
6, 12, 15			

4. **Express regularity in repeated reasoning.** If a and b represent the legs and c represents the hypotenuse, what do the results in Item 3 suggest about how $a^2 + b^2$ compares to c^2 for the different types of triangles?

5. Use the converse of the Pythagorean Theorem to determine whether each of the following sets of side lengths forms a right triangle. If a right triangle is not possible, tell whether an acute or obtuse triangle can be formed. Show the method you use to determine your answers.

   a. 12, 34, 37

   b. $\dfrac{6}{7}, \dfrac{8}{7}, \dfrac{10}{7}$

   c. 20, $\sqrt{42}$, 21

6. Sara's best customer wants to design a kite in the shape of a triangle with side lengths 27 inches, 34 inches, and 45 inches. Classify the triangle.

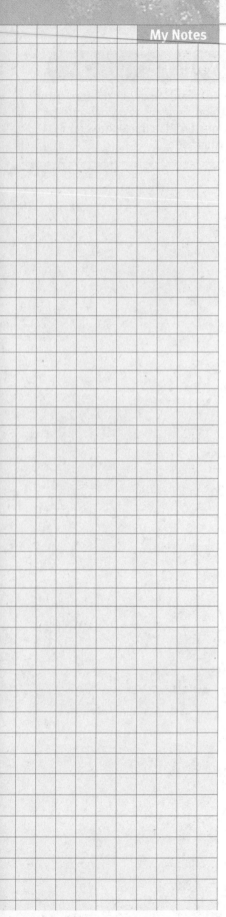

Check Your Understanding

7. Determine whether the triangle below is right, acute, or obtuse. Justify your reasoning.

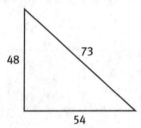

8. The numbers 11, 60, and 61 form a Pythagorean triple. Use this fact to write two additional Pythagorean triples.

LESSON 20-2 PRACTICE

9. Tell whether each triangle is a right triangle. Justify your reasoning.

   a.

   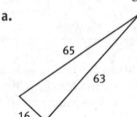

   b.

10. Tell whether a triangle having the following side lengths can be formed. If a triangle can be formed, tell whether it is right, acute, or obtuse.
    a. 36, 77, 85
    b. 22, 18, 3
    c. 33, 56, 68
    d. 6, 11, 12

11. **Use appropriate tools strategically.** Shauntay is making a picture frame. Explain how Shauntay can use a ruler and the converse of the Pythagorean Theorem to determine whether the sides meet at right angles.

ACTIVITY 20 PRACTICE

Write your answers on notebook paper or on grid paper. Show your work.

Lesson 20-1

1. Find the length of the hypotenuse of each right triangle with the given leg lengths. Express the answer as a simplified radical.
   a. legs: 11 ft and 60 ft
   b. legs: 7 mm and 8 mm
   c. legs: 40 cm and 41 cm
   d. legs: 20 in. and 99 in.
   e. legs: 16 ft and 23 ft

2. Find each unknown length. Express the length in radical form.
   a.
   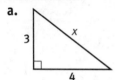

   $x =$ _____

   b.
   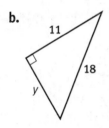

   $y =$ _____

   c.
   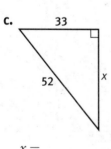

   $x =$ _____

3. Find the area of parallelogram $ABCD$.

   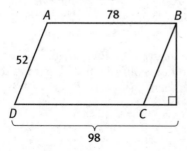

4. If a flat-screen television is a rectangle with a 53-inch diagonal and a width of 45 inches, what is the height of the screen?

5. A standard baseball diamond is a square 90 feet on each side. Find the distance of a throw made from the catcher 3 feet behind home plate in an attempt to throw out a runner trying to steal second base. Round to the nearest whole number.
   A. 93 ft   B. 124 ft
   C. 130 ft   D. 183 ft

6. Which best approximates the lengths of the legs of a right triangle if the hypotenuse is 125 mm and the shorter leg is one-half the length of the longer leg?
   A. 25 mm and 55 mm
   B. 56 mm and 112 mm
   C. 5 mm and 10 mm
   D. 63 mm and 63 mm

7. A kite is shaped like an isosceles triangle.

   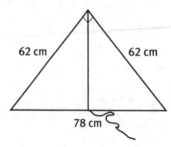

   To the nearest tenth, what is the length of the spine?

8. Find the length of the hypotenuse of an isosceles right triangle with leg length 5 centimeters. Give the exact answer.

9. Find the length of the altitude drawn from the vertex of an isosceles triangle with side lengths 13 in., 13 in., and 24 in.

10. An isosceles trapezoid has bases that are 7 inches and 13 inches long. The height of the trapezoid is 4 inches. Find the perimeter of the trapezoid.

Lesson 20-2

11. Tell whether each triangle is a right triangle.

a.

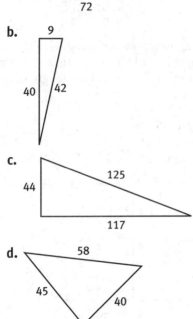

b.

c.

d.

12. Tell whether a triangle having the following side lengths can be formed. If a triangle can be formed, tell whether it is right, acute, or obtuse.

a. 9, 40, 41   **b.** 4, 5, 6

c. 5, 12, 18   **d.** 9, 9, 13

e. 27, 36, 45   **f.** $\sqrt{8}, \sqrt{8}, \sqrt{16}$

13. Use the given vertices to determine whether $\triangle ABC$ is a right triangle. Explain your reasoning and show the calculations that led to your answer. $A(2, 7)$, $B(3, 6)$, $C(-4, -1)$.

14. A triangle has side lengths of x, $2x$, and 45. If the length of the longest side is 45, what values of x make the triangle acute? right? obtuse?

15. Which of the following cannot be the side lengths of a triangle?

A. 10, 12, 18   **B.** 9, 9, 10
C. 3, 11, 15   **D.** 10, 15, 20

16. Complete the following proof.

Given: $\triangle ABC$, $c^2 > a^2 + b^2$, where c is the length of the longest side of the triangle, and right $\triangle ABX$ with side lengths a, b, and x, where x is the length of the hypotenuse.

Prove: $\triangle ABC$ is obtuse.

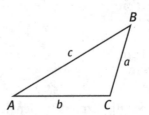 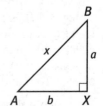

Statements	Reasons
1. $\triangle ABC$, $c^2 > a^2 + b^2$, where c is the length of the longest side of the triangle, and right $\triangle ABX$ with side lengths a, b, and x, where x is the length of the hypotenuse.	1.
2. $x^2 = a^2 + b^2$	2.
3. $c^2 >$ _____	3.
4. $c >$ _____	4. Property of square roots
5. $m\angle X = 90°$	5.
6. $m\angle C > m$_____	6.
7.	7.
8. C is _____	8.
9. $\triangle ABC$ is _____	9.

MATHEMATICAL PRACTICES
Look For and Make Use of Structure

17. The Pythagorean Theorem was thought of by the early Greeks as the following: *The area of the square on the hypotenuse of a right triangle is equal to the sum of the areas of the squares on the legs.*

Draw a diagram to illustrate this statement. Explain how your diagram illustrates the Pythagorean Theorem.

Special Right Triangles
The Community Quilting Project
Lesson 21-1 45°-45°-90° Triangles

Learning Targets:

- Describe the relationships among the side lengths of 45°-45°-90° triangles.
- Apply relationships in special right triangles to solve problems.

SUGGESTED LEARNING STRATEGIES: Marking the Text, Summarizing, Paraphrasing, Create Representations, Use Manipulatives, Predict and Confirm, Look for a Pattern, Quickwrite

The Community Hospital wants to make its rooms more cheerful. The hospital asked volunteers to sew quilts for patient rooms and to decorate the common areas. The Hoover High Student Council wants to participate in the project. Ms. Jones, a geometry teacher, decides to have her classes investigate the mathematical patterns found in quilts.

Quilt blocks are often squares made up of smaller fabric pieces sewn together to create a pattern. There are many different quilt block designs. Often these designs are named. A quilt block design made up of nine small squares, called the "Friendship Star," is shown.

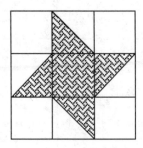

1. The Friendship Star quilt block contains five small squares and eight triangles.
   a. Identify congruent figures in the quilt block and explain why they are congruent.

   b. Classify the triangles in the quilt block by their angle measures.

   c. Classify the triangles in the quilt block by their side lengths.

My Notes

Some sample quilt block designs are shown below.

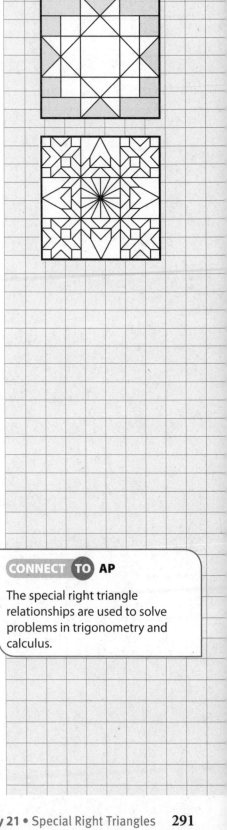

CONNECT TO AP

The special right triangle relationships are used to solve problems in trigonometry and calculus.

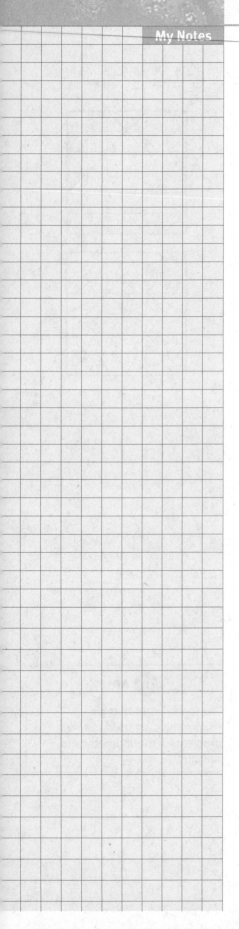

My Notes

d. What are the measures of the acute angles in each of the triangles? Explain your reasoning.

The Hoover High Student Council decided to make Friendship Star quilts of various sizes with different-sized quilt blocks.

2. Work with your group and use the Pythagorean Theorem to find the exact values of the missing dimensions and ratios in the table below.

Dimensions of Quilt Block	Length of Triangle Leg (in inches)	Length of Hypotenuse (in inches)	Ratio of Hypotenuse to Leg
9 in. × 9 in.			
15 in. × 15 in.			
	1		
	1.5		
	2		
		$6\sqrt{2}$	
		4	

3. What patterns do you notice in the table in Item 2?

4. Suppose that you are only given the length of one leg of an isosceles right triangle (45°-45°-90°).
   a. Write a verbal rule for finding the lengths of the other two sides.

   b. Let l be the length of the leg of any isosceles right triangle (45°-45°-90°). Use the Pythagorean Theorem to derive an algebraic rule for finding the length of the hypotenuse, h, in terms of l.

My Notes

Check Your Understanding

For each 45°-45°-90° triangle, find the unknown length, x.

5.

x 17

6.
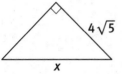
$4\sqrt{5}$
x

7.

x
$5\sqrt{12}$

8. Ms. Jones designed a variation on the Friendship Star quilt block, called the "Twisted Star." Using the rules you derived in Item 4, what are the dimensions of the smallest triangle on the 12 in. × 12 in. quilt block shown below? Explain how you found your answer.

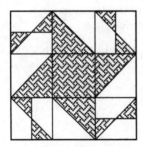

9. The perimeter of a square picture frame is 40 cm. Find the length of a diagonal of the frame.

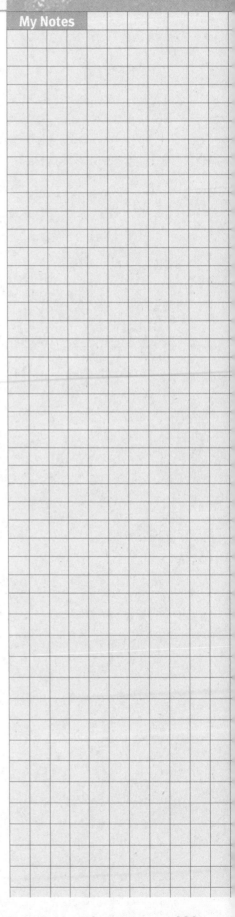

My Notes

LESSON 21-1 PRACTICE

Unless otherwise indicated, write all answers in simplest radical form.

10. For each 45°-45°-90° triangle, find *a* and *b*.

a.

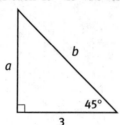

b.

c.

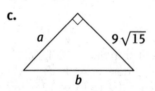

11. The length of each leg of an isosceles right triangle is 5.
a. Find the perimeter of the triangle.
b. Find the area of the triangle.

12. Attend to precision. Find the perimeter of a square, as a simplified radical, if the length of its diagonal is 14 inches.

My Notes

Learning Targets:

● Describe the relationships among the side lengths of 30°-60°-90° triangles.
● Apply relationships in special right triangles to solve problems.

> **SUGGESTED LEARNING STRATEGIES:** Marking the Text, Create Representations, Quickwrite, Think-Pair-Share, Look for a Pattern

Ms. Jones introduces her class to a quilt block in the shape of a hexagon. This block is formed from six equilateral triangles, divided in half along their altitudes. Ms. Jones's students know that if an altitude is drawn in an equilateral triangle, two congruent triangles are formed. The resulting hexagonal quilt block is shown below.

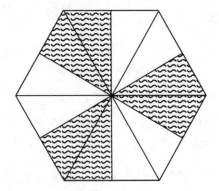

1. What is the measure of each of the angles in any equilateral triangle?

2. What are the measures of each of the angles in the smallest triangles in the hexagonal quilt block shown above? Explain your answer.

3. The smallest triangles are special scalene right triangles. They are often called 30°-60°-90° right triangles.
   a. How can you determine which leg is shorter and which leg is longer using the angles of the triangle?

   b. If each of the sides of the hexagonal quilt block is 4 inches, how long is the shorter leg in the 30°-60°-90° right triangle? Explain your answer.

   c. What is the relationship between the length of the hypotenuse and the length of the shorter leg in a 30°-60°-90° triangle? Explain your answer.

My Notes

4. Look for patterns between the longer leg of the 30°-60°-90° right triangle and the other sides, by completing the table below using the Pythagorean Theorem. Write each ratio in simplest radical form.

Length of Hypotenuse (in inches)	Length of Shorter Leg (in inches)	Length of Longer Leg (in inches)	Ratio of Length of Longer Leg to Length of Shorter Leg
6			
8			
4			
	3.5		
	1		

5. **Express regularity in repeated reasoning.** What patterns do you notice in the table in Item 4?

6. Write a verbal rule for finding the length of the longer leg of a 30°-60°-90° right triangle if you are given the length of the shorter leg.

7. Write a verbal rule for finding the length of the hypotenuse of a 30°-60°-90° right triangle if you are given the length of the shorter leg.

8. Let *s* be the length of the shorter leg of any 30°-60°-90° right triangle. Use the Pythagorean Theorem to derive an algebraic rule for finding the length of the longer leg, *l*, in terms of *s*.

9. One of the students in Ms. Jones's class wrote the proportion shown to find the unknown leg length *x* in the quilt patch. Did the student correctly find the length? If not, explain why and correct the error.

$$\frac{x}{5} = \frac{\sqrt{3}}{1}$$
$$x = 5\sqrt{3}$$

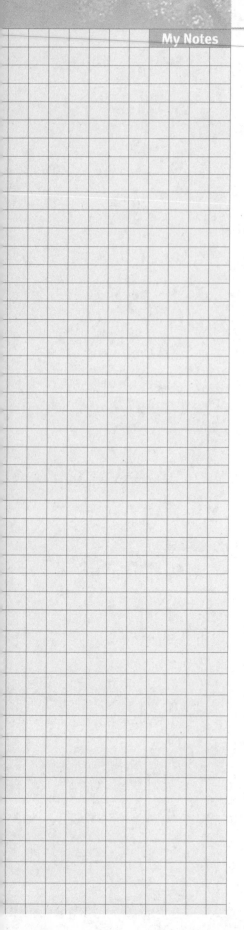

Check Your Understanding

10. In a 30°-60°-90° triangle, the length of the shorter leg is 6 in.
    a. What is the length of the longer leg?
    b. What is the length of the hypotenuse?

11. In a 30°-60°-90° triangle, the length of the hypotenuse is 10 cm.
    a. What is the length of the shorter leg?
    b. What is the length of the longer leg?

LESSON 21-2 PRACTICE

Unless otherwise indicated, write all answers in simplest radical form.

12. Model with mathematics. Use your work from Items 4–7 to determine the height of the hexagon block shown below, whose sides are 4 inches, if the height is measured from the midpoint of one side to the midpoint of the opposite side. Explain how you found your answer.

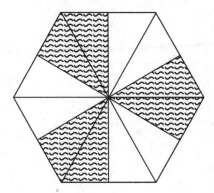

13. Find d and e.

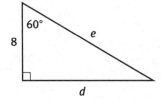

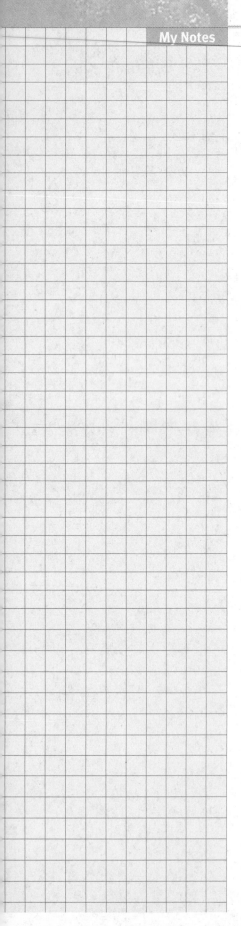

My Notes

14. The longer leg of a 30°-60°-90° triangle is 6 inches. What is the length of the hypotenuse?

15. The length of an altitude of an equilateral triangle is $2\sqrt{3}$ inches. Find the length of a side of the triangle.

16. One side of an equilateral triangle is 8 cm. Find the length of the altitude.

17. The perimeter of an equilateral triangle is 36 inches. Find the length of an altitude.

18. Find the perimeter of the trapezoid.

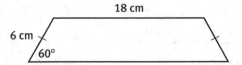

19. Find the perimeter of $\triangle PQR$.

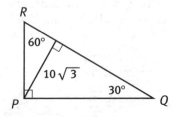

ACTIVITY 21 PRACTICE
Write your answers on notebook paper.
Show your work.

Unless otherwise indicated, write all answers in simplest radical form.

Lesson 21-1

1. In a 45°-45°-90° triangle, if the length of a leg is 6 cm, the length of the hypotenuse is:
   A. 12 cm
   B. $6\sqrt{3}$ cm
   C. $6\sqrt{5}$ cm
   D. $6\sqrt{2}$ cm

2. For each 45°-45°-90° triangle, find a and b.
   a.

   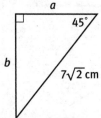

   b.

   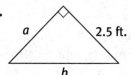

   c.

3. Square *MNOP* has a diagonal of 12 inches. Find the length of each side of the square.

4. The length of the hypotenuse of an isosceles right triangle is 8.
   a. Find the perimeter of the triangle.
   b. Find the area of the triangle.

5. Find the perimeter of a square, as a simplified radical, if the length of its diagonal is $4\sqrt{10}$ inches.

6. Which of the following statements is true?

   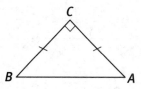

   A. $BC = \sqrt{2}BA$
   B. $BA = BC$
   C. $BA = \sqrt{2}BC$
   D. $BC = 2BA$

Lesson 21-2

7. Find *a* and *b*.

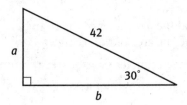

8. Find *a* and *c*.

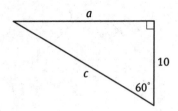

9. Find *m*.

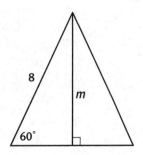

A. 4

B. $4\sqrt{2}$

C. $4\sqrt{3}$

D. $8\sqrt{3}$

10. A ladder leaning against a house makes an angle of 60° with the ground. The foot of the ladder is 7 feet from the house. How long is the ladder?

11. An equilateral triangle has a side length of 4 ft. What is the area of the triangle?

A. 12 ft²

B. $4\sqrt{3}$ ft²

C. 6 ft²

D. $2\sqrt{3}$ ft²

12. What is the area of the quilt patch, as a simplified radical?

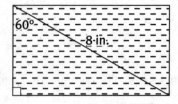

13. Find *a* and *b*.

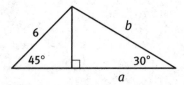

MATHEMATICAL PRACTICES
Construct Viable Arguments and Critique the Reasoning of Others

14. Brayden's teacher asked him to draw a 30°-60°-90° right triangle. He drew the figure shown. Tell why it is not possible for Brayden's triangle to exist.

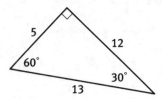

Yoshio owns a farm that uses wind turbines to produce wind power. Wind power, also known as wind energy, uses the power of the wind to generate electrical or mechanical power.

1. One of the wind turbines that Yoshio owns is shown in the figure below. He needs to know the height of the turbine. Yoshio is 5 feet 6 inches tall. If he stands 12 feet from the turbine, his line of sight forms a 90° angle with the top and bottom of the turbine.

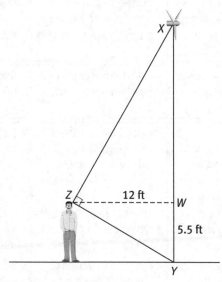

a. What special segment is $\overline{ZW}$? Explain.
b. Write a similarity statement to show the relationship among triangle *XYZ* and the two triangles formed by drawing $\overline{ZW}$.
c. What is the height of the turbine?

2. Another wind turbine that Yoshio owns uses guy wires for support. In the figure, $AC = 15$ ft, $m\angle ABC = 60°$, $m\angle ADC = 45°$, and $m\angle AEC = 30°$.

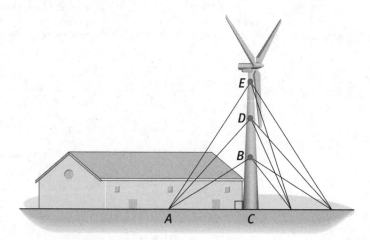

Find each of the following measures.
a. $AB =$ _____
b. $AD =$ _____
c. $AE =$ _____
d. What is the height of the turbine, *EC*?

3. Use the converse of the Pythagorean Theorem to prove that triangle *AEC* is a right triangle.

Scoring Guide	Exemplary	Proficient	Emerging	Incomplete
	The solution demonstrates these characteristics:			
Mathematics Knowledge and Thinking (Items 1, 2, 3)	• Clear and accurate understanding of similar figures created by an altitude drawn to the hypotenuse of a right triangle, special right triangles, and the Converse of the Pythagorean Theorem	• Adequate understanding of similar figures created by an altitude drawn to the hypotenuse of a right triangle, special right triangles, and the Converse of the Pythagorean Theorem	• Partial understanding of similar figures created by an altitude drawn to the hypotenuse of a right triangle, special right triangles, and the Converse of the Pythagorean Theorem	• Little or no understanding of similar figures created by an altitude drawn to the hypotenuse of a right triangle, special right triangles, and the Converse of the Pythagorean Theorem
Problem Solving (Items 1, 2)	• An appropriate and efficient strategy that results in correct answers	• A strategy that may include unnecessary steps but results in correct answers	• A strategy that results in some incorrect answers	• No clear strategy when solving problems
Mathematical Modeling / Representations (Items 1b, 1c)	• Clear and accurate understanding of writing a similarity statement to show the relationship among similar triangles created by drawing an altitude to the hypotenuse of a right triangle • Clear and accurate understanding of creating a proportion to determine missing lengths in similar triangles	• Mostly accurate understanding of writing a similarity statement to show the relationship among similar triangles created by drawing an altitude to the hypotenuse of a right triangle • A functional understanding of creating a proportion to determine missing lengths in similar triangles	• Partial understanding of writing a similarity statement to show the relationship among similar triangles created by drawing an altitude to the hypotenuse of a right triangle • Partial understanding of creating a proportion to determine missing lengths in similar triangles	• Little or no understanding of writing a similarity statement to show the relationship among similar triangles created by drawing an altitude to the hypotenuse of a right triangle • Little or no understanding of creating a proportion to determine missing lengths in similar triangles
Reasoning and Communication (Item 3)	• Precise use of appropriate mathematics and language to justify whether or not triangle *AEC* is a right triangle	• Mostly correct use of appropriate mathematics and language to justify whether or not triangle *AEC* is a right triangle	• Misleading or confusing use of appropriate mathematics and language to justify whether or not triangle *AEC* is a right triangle	• Incomplete or inaccurate use of appropriate mathematics and language to justify whether or not triangle *AEC* is a right triangle

Basic Trigonometric Relationships

The Sine of Things to Come
Lesson 22-1 Similar Right Triangles

Learning Targets:

- Find ratios of side lengths in similar right triangles.
- Given an acute angle of a right triangle, identify the opposite leg and adjacent leg.

> **SUGGESTED LEARNING STRATEGIES:** Graphic Organizer, Marking the Text, Create Representations, Close Reading, Interactive Word Wall, Think-Pair-Share

Tricia is a commercial artist working for The Right Angle Company. The company specializes in small business public relations. Tricia creates appealing logos for client companies. In fact, she helped create the logo for her company. The Right Angle Company will use its logo in different sizes for stationery letterhead, business cards, and magazine advertisements. The advertisement and stationery letterhead-size logos are shown below.

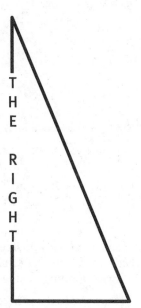

Magazine Advertising-Size Logo

Stationery Letterhead-Size Logo

1. **Use appropriate tools strategically.** Measure the two acute angles and the lengths of the sides of each logo above. Measure the angles to the nearest degree and the sides to the nearest tenth of a centimeter. Be as accurate as possible. Record the results in the table below.

Logo Size	Hypotenuse	Longer Leg	Shorter Leg	Larger Acute Angle	Smaller Acute Angle
Advertisement					
Letterhead					

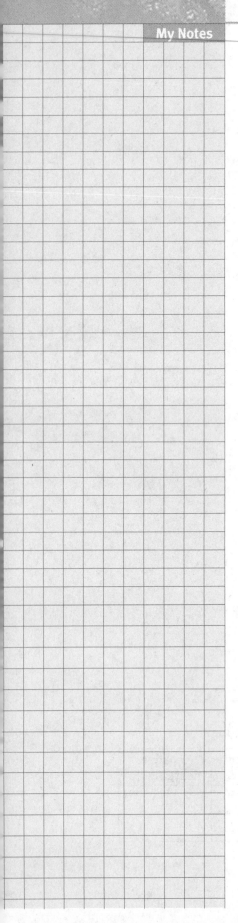

My Notes

2. Although the measurements can never be exact, the lengths of the sides of any right triangle satisfy the Pythagorean Theorem. Confirm that the Pythagorean Theorem is satisfied by the measurements of the two right triangular logos on the preceding page. Show your work and results but allow for some error due to measurement limitations.

3. The logos are similar triangles. Justify this statement. Then give the scale factor of advertising logo lengths to corresponding letterhead logo lengths.

4. The triangular logo used on The Right Angle Company business cards is also similar to the logos used for advertisements and letterheads. The scale factor of letterhead logo lengths to corresponding business card logo lengths is 2.3:1.
   a. Determine the length of each side of the business card logo.

   b. Use a ruler to draw the business card logo to scale in the space below.

Tricia tries to incorporate a right triangle into many of the logos she designs for her clients. As she does, Tricia becomes aware of a relationship that exists between the measures of the acute angles and the ratios of the lengths of the sides of the right triangles.

5. Use each grid below to draw a right triangle that has a longer vertical leg of L units and a shorter horizontal leg of S units. The first triangle is drawn for you. Use the Pythagorean Theorem to find the length H of the resulting hypotenuse to the nearest tenth. Record its length in the appropriate place at the bottom of each grid.

Grid A	Grid B	Grid C
$L = 8, S = 6$	$L = 5, S = 4$	$L = 4, S = 3$
$H =$	$H =$	$H =$

Grid D	Grid E	Grid F
$L = 10, S = 8$	$L = 12, S = 9$	$L = 6, S = 3$
$H =$	$H =$	$H =$

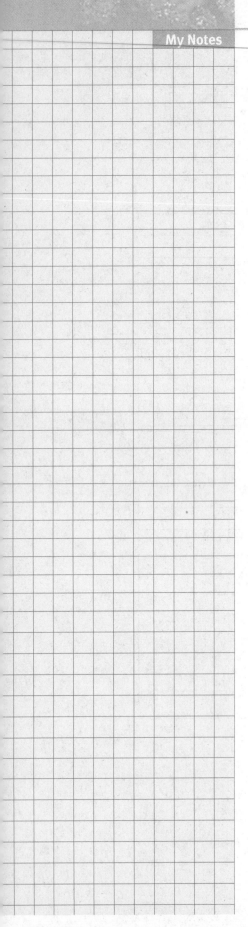

My Notes

6. Some of the triangles in Grids A–F are similar to each other. Identify the groups of similar triangles using the grid letter and explain below how you know they are similar. You should find a group of three similar triangles and a group of two similar triangles.

In any right triangle, the hypotenuse is opposite the right angle. For each acute angle, one of the right triangle's legs is known as that angle's *opposite leg* and the remaining leg is known as that angle's *adjacent leg*. In △*CAR* below, the hypotenuse is $\overline{AC}$. For acute ∠*C*, side $\overline{AR}$ is its opposite leg and side $\overline{RC}$ is its adjacent leg. For acute ∠*A*, side $\overline{RC}$ is its opposite leg and side $\overline{AR}$ is its adjacent leg.

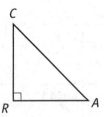

7. In right △*BUS*, identify the opposite leg and the adjacent leg for ∠*U*.

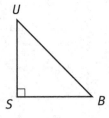

Check Your Understanding

8. Are all isosceles right triangles similar? Explain.

9. Two right triangles are similar with a scale factor of 3:4.5. The triangle with the shorter hypotenuse has leg lengths of 6 and 8. What is the length of the longer hypotenuse?

LESSON 22-1 PRACTICE

10. Use △QRS to find the following.
   a. the leg opposite ∠Q

   b. the leg adjacent to ∠Q

   c. the leg opposite ∠R

   d. the leg adjacent to ∠R

   e. the hypotenuse

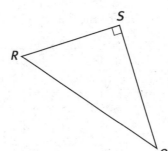

11. Make sense of problems. Find the scale factor and the unknown side lengths for each pair of similar triangles.

   a. △ABC ~ △DEF

   Scale factor _____

   AC = _____

   AB = _____

   DE = _____

 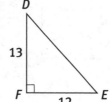

   b. △TUV ~ △XYZ

   Scale factor _____

   UT = _____

   YZ = _____

   XY = _____

 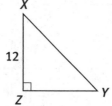

   c. △LMN ~ △GHI

   Scale factor _____

   NL = _____

   HI = _____

   GI = _____

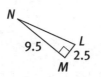 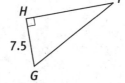

My Notes

Learning Targets:

- Understand the definitions of sine, cosine, and tangent ratios.
- Calculate the trigonometric ratios in a right triangle.
- Describe the relationship between the sine and cosine of complementary angles.

SUGGESTED LEARNING STRATEGIES: Create Representations, Graphic Organizer, Look for a Pattern, Quickwrite, Interactive Word Wall

1. One group of similar triangles, identified in Item 5 of the previous lesson, is shown on the grids below. For each right triangle, the vertex opposite the longer leg has been named with the same letter as the grid. Determine the ratios in the table and write the ratios in lowest terms.

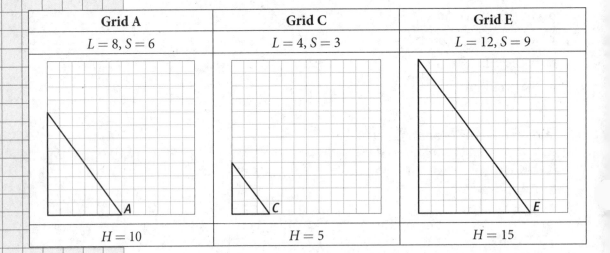

Grid A	Grid C	Grid E
$L = 8, S = 6$	$L = 4, S = 3$	$L = 12, S = 9$
$H = 10$	$H = 5$	$H = 15$

	$\dfrac{\text{Length of Opposite Leg}}{\text{Length of Hypotenuse}}$	$\dfrac{\text{Length of Adjacent Leg}}{\text{Length of Hypotenuse}}$	$\dfrac{\text{Length of Opposite Leg}}{\text{Length of Adjacent Leg}}$
$\angle A$			
$\angle C$			
$\angle E$			

My Notes

2. For each of the triangles in Item 1, use your protractor to find the measure of the larger acute angle.

	∠A	∠C	∠E
Measure of Larger Acute Angle			

3. In Item 2, you found that the measures of each of the three angles are the same. If, in another right triangle, the measure of the larger acute angle was the same as the measures of ∠A, ∠C, and ∠E, what would you expect the following ratios to be?

   a. $\dfrac{\text{length of opposite leg}}{\text{length of hypotenuse}} =$

   b. $\dfrac{\text{length of adjacent leg}}{\text{length of hypotenuse}} =$

   c. $\dfrac{\text{length of opposite leg}}{\text{length of adjacent leg}} =$

4. Explain how you reached your conclusions in Item 3.

The ratio of the lengths of two sides of a right triangle is a *trigonometric ratio*. The three basic trigonometric ratios are *sine*, *cosine*, and *tangent*, which are abbreviated **sin**, **cos**, and **tan**.

5. **Use appropriate tools strategically.** Use a scientific or graphing calculator to evaluate each of the following to the nearest tenth. Make sure your calculator is in DEGREE mode.

   a. $\sin 53° =$

   b. $\cos 53° =$

   c. $\tan 53° =$

6. In each column of the table in Item 1, the ratios that you wrote are equal. Express the ratios from the three columns as decimal numbers rounded to the nearest tenth.

   a. $\dfrac{\text{length of opposite leg}}{\text{length of hypotenuse}} =$

   b. $\dfrac{\text{length of adjacent leg}}{\text{length of hypotenuse}} =$

   c. $\dfrac{\text{length of opposite leg}}{\text{length of adjacent leg}} =$

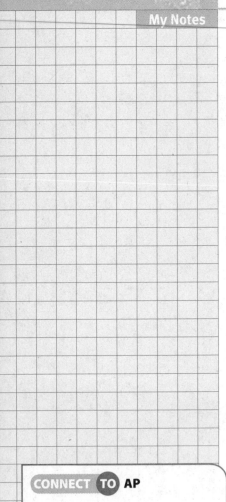

My Notes

7. Compare your answers to Items 5 and 6. Then describe each of the ratios below in terms of sin, cos, and tan. Assume that the ratios represent sides of a right triangle in relation to acute $\angle X$.

a. $\dfrac{\text{length of opposite leg}}{\text{length of hypotenuse}} =$

b. $\dfrac{\text{length of adjacent leg}}{\text{length of hypotenuse}} =$

c. $\dfrac{\text{length of opposite leg}}{\text{length of adjacent leg}} =$

8. a. For $\triangle ABC$, write the ratios in simplest form.

$\sin A =$ $\sin C =$

$\cos A =$ $\cos C =$

$\tan A =$ $\tan C =$

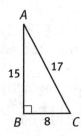

CONNECT TO AP

Trigonometric ratios are used to define functions that model periodic phenomena like the hours of daylight.

b. How are the two acute angles of $\triangle ABC$ related?

c. What is the relationship between the sine and cosine of complementary angles?

d. If you know $\sin 68° \approx 0.93$, what other trigonometric ratio do you know?

My Notes

Check Your Understanding

9. Triangle *ABC* is a 30°-60°-90° triangle. Explain how to write sin 30° as a ratio in simplest form without knowing the length of any side of the triangle.

10. Suppose you know that △*RST* is a right triangle with a right angle at ∠*R*. If cos *S* = 0.67, what other trigonometric ratio can you write?

11. Given sin *B* = $\frac{5}{13}$, draw a right triangle *ABC* with right angle *C* and label the side lengths.
    a. Determine the length of the missing side.
    b. Determine cos *B*.
    c. What is tan *B*?

LESSON 22-2 PRACTICE

12. Use a calculator to find each of the following. Round each value to the nearest hundredth.

sin 48° = _____

tan 65° = _____

cos 12° = _____

sin 90° = _____

13. Write each ratio in simplest form.

sin *X* = _____

cos *X* = _____

sin *Y* = _____

cos *Y* = _____

tan *X* = _____

tan *Y* = _____

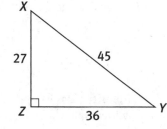

14. Attend to precision. Elena was asked to write an explanation of how to find tan *P*. She wrote, "To find the tangent of ∠*P*, I found the ratio of the length of the side opposite ∠*P* to the length of the side adjacent to ∠*P*. Since these sides have the same length, tan *P* = 1 ft." Critique Elena's statement. Is there anything she should have written differently? If so, what?

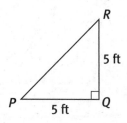

My Notes

Learning Targets:

● Use trigonometric ratios to find unknown side lengths in right triangles.
● Solve real-world problems using trigonometric ratios.

SUGGESTED LEARNING STRATEGIES: Quickwrite, Create Representations, Identify a Subtask

1. For each of the following triangles, determine the ratios requested. Then use a scientific or graphing calculator to evaluate each trigonometric function to the nearest thousandth and solve each equation for *y*. Round final answers to the nearest tenth.

   a.

   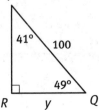

   b.

   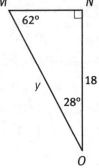

   $\sin 41° =$ $\cos 28° =$

2. Use your knowledge of trigonometric functions to find the value of *x* in △*ABC*.
   a. Choose an acute angle in △*ABC*.

   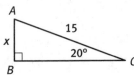

   b. Identify sides as opposite, adjacent, or hypotenuse with respect to the acute angle chosen.

   c. Use the sides to choose an appropriate trigonometric function.

   d. Write an equation using the identified sides, acute angle, and trigonometric function chosen.

   e. Solve for *x*.

3. Use your knowledge of trigonometric functions to find the value of *y* in the triangle below.

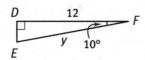

a. Choose an acute angle in △*DEF* and identify sides as adjacent, opposite, or hypotenuse with respect to the angle you chose.

b. Use the sides to choose an appropriate trigonometric ratio and write an equation using the identified sides, acute angle, and trigonometric function. Then solve for *y*.

4. Make sense of problems. Tricia did such an exceptional job creating logos that she was given the task of making a banner and representing her company at a job fair. When Tricia got to the job fair, she was relieved to see there was a ladder she could use to hang the banner. While Tricia waited for someone to help her, she leaned the 12-foot ladder against the wall behind the booth. The ladder made an angle of 75° with the floor.

a. Use the information above to draw and label a right triangle to illustrate the relationship between the ladder and the wall.

b. Set up and solve an equation to find how far up the wall the top of the ladder reaches.

c. Find the distance from the base of the wall to the base of the ladder using two different methods.

Check Your Understanding

5. Explain how to find the length of the hypotenuse of △*DEF* without using the Pythagorean Theorem.

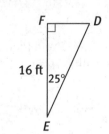

6. Jo says she can find *BC* using the equation $\sin 40° = \dfrac{BC}{62}$. Liam says he can find *BC* using the equation $\cos 50° = \dfrac{BC}{62}$. Who is correct? Explain.

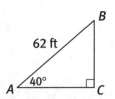

LESSON 22-3 PRACTICE

7. Find each unknown side length.

  a. $x =$ ____
     $y =$ ____

  b. $x =$ ____
     $y =$ ____

  c. $x =$ ____
     $y =$ ____

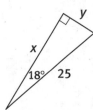
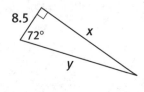
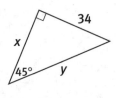

8. Reason quantitatively. Jackson has the triangular garden shown in the figure. Find the perimeter and area of the garden. Be sure to check that your answers are reasonable.

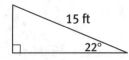

9. Construct viable arguments. The longer diagonal of a rhombus measures 20 cm. The rhombus has an angle that measures 100°. Determine the perimeter of the rhombus, to the nearest tenth. Explain how you found the answer.

Learning Targets:

- Calculate angle measures from trigonometric ratios.
- Solve right triangles.

> **SUGGESTED LEARNING STRATEGIES:** Predict and Confirm, Summarizing, Quickwrite

1. In a right triangle ABC with acute angle A, you know that $\sin A = \dfrac{\sqrt{3}}{2}$.

   a. Draw a possible right triangle ABC.

   b. Determine what must be true about $\angle A$ using what you know about special right triangles.

In Item 1, you are given the sine of acute angle A and are asked to find the angle whose sine is equal to that ratio. In other words, you are finding an inverse sine function. This is written as $\sin^{-1}\left(\dfrac{\sqrt{3}}{2}\right) = 60°$. The expression $\sin^{-1} x$ is read as "the inverse sine of x."

The ***inverse trigonometric functions*** for sine, cosine, and tangent are defined as follows:

Inverse Trig Functions
If $\sin A = x$, then $\sin^{-1} x = m\angle A$.
If $\cos A = x$, then $\cos^{-1} x = m\angle A$.
If $\tan A = x$, then $\tan^{-1} x = m\angle A$.

2. Use a scientific or graphing calculator to evaluate each of the following to the nearest tenth. Make sure your calculator is in DEGREE mode.

   a. $\sin^{-1}\dfrac{1}{2} =$ **b.** $\cos^{-1}\dfrac{1}{2} =$

   c. $\tan^{-1}\dfrac{1}{2} =$ **d.** $\sin^{-1}\dfrac{3}{4} =$

   e. $\cos^{-1}\dfrac{3}{4} =$ **f.** $\tan^{-1}\dfrac{3}{4} =$

Using known measures to find all the remaining unknown measures of a right triangle is known as *solving a right triangle*.

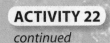

My Notes

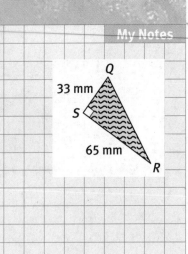

Tricia designs the logo shown for one of her clients. She needs to know all the missing dimensions and angle measures of the logo.

3. **Model with mathematics.** Use an inverse trigonometric function to find the measure of angle Q.

4. Describe two ways to find the measure of angle R, without finding the length of the hypotenuse. Find the angle measure using both methods.

5. Describe two ways to find the length of the hypotenuse. Find the length using both methods.

Check Your Understanding

6. What is the minimal amount of information needed to solve a right triangle? Explain.

7. Explain the difference between the two expressions $\sin 15°$ and $\sin^{-1}(0.2558)$. How are the expressions related?

LESSON 22-4 PRACTICE

8. Angle X is an acute angle in a right triangle. What measure of angle X makes each statement true? Round angle measures to the nearest tenth.
   a. $\cos X = 0.59$ **b.** $\tan X = 3.73$ **c.** $\sin X = 0.87$
   d. $\tan X = 0.18$ **e.** $\cos X = 0.02$ **f.** $\sin X = 0.95$

9. Solve each right triangle if possible. Round your measures to the nearest tenth.

   a. 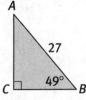   **b.** 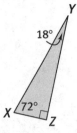   **c.** 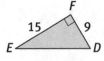   **d.**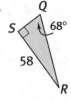

10. **Construct viable arguments.** Without using a calculator, explain how you can find the value of $\tan^{-1}(1)$.

11. Consider rhombus ABCD, where $\overline{AC} = 8$ in. and $\overline{BD} = 12$ in. What are the measures of the sides and angles of the rhombus? Round your answers to the nearest tenth.

ACTIVITY 22 PRACTICE

Write your answers on notebook paper.
Show your work.

Lesson 22-1

1. Which side of △ABC is the side opposite angle A?

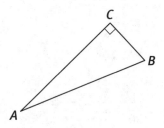

   A. $\overline{AB}$
   B. $\overline{AC}$
   C. $\overline{BC}$

2. In △PQR, identify the hypotenuse, adjacent leg, and opposite leg for ∠R.

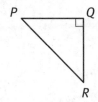

3. a. Find the missing measures in the given triangle.

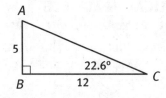

   b. Draw and label a triangle similar to the triangle given in Part a. Include each side length and angle measure.
   c. State the scale factor of the triangle given in Part a to the triangle you drew in Part b.

4. Lisa wants to make a larger bandana similar to the bandana shown. If the shorter leg of the larger bandana is 15 inches, how long is its hypotenuse?

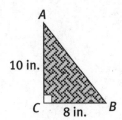

Lesson 22-2

5. Use your calculator to evaluate the following. Round to 3 decimal places.
   a. cos 54°
   b. sin 12°
   c. tan 67°

6. Find each of the following ratios. Write each ratio in simplest form.

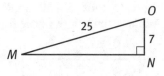

   a. sin M
   b. cos O
   c. tan M
   d. sin O
   e. cos O
   f. tan O

7. Which expression is equivalent to cos 25°?
   A. cos 65°
   B. tan 65°
   C. sin 25°
   D. sin 65°

Lesson 22-3

8. Find the perimeter and area of each triangle.
   a.

   b.

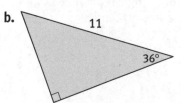

   c.

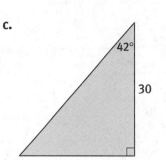

9. Find x and y. Round final answers to tenths.

10. A badminton net is tethered to the ground with a strand of rope that forms a 50° angle with the ground. What is the length of the rope, x?

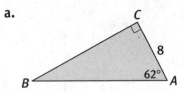

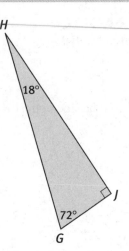

Lesson 22-4

11. Use a scientific or graphing calculator to evaluate each of the following to the nearest tenth.

   a. $\sin^{-1} \frac{1}{2} =$

   b. $\cos^{-1} \frac{1}{4} =$

   c. $\tan^{-1} 0.6 =$

12. Solve each right triangle if possible. Round your measures to the nearest tenth.

   a.

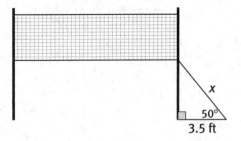

   b.

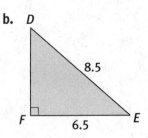

13. A skateboard ramp has a slope of $\frac{4}{9}$. What is the measure of the angle the ramp forms with the ground?

14. Which expression is equivalent to $\sin^{-1}(0.5)$?

   A. $\cos^{-1}(0.5)$

   B. $\dfrac{\cos^{-1}(0.5)}{\tan^{-1}(0.5)}$

   C. $90° - \cos^{-1}(0.5)$

   D. $90° - \tan^{-1}(0.5)$

MATHEMATICAL PRACTICES
Look For and Make Use of Structure

15. Compare the values of the sine and cosine ratios as the measure of an angle increases from 0° to 90°.

The Law of Sines and Cosines

There Ought to Be a Law

Lesson 23-1 The Law of Sines

Learning Targets:

- Prove the Law of Sines.
- Apply the Law of Sines.

> **SUGGESTED LEARNING STRATEGIES:** Create Representations, Graphic Organizer, Predict and Confirm, Visualization, Think-Pair-Share

The location of a fire spotted from two fire observation towers can be determined using the distance between the two towers and the angle measures from the towers to the fire. This process is known as *triangulation*.

You have already solved right triangles. In this lesson you will learn how to solve any triangle.

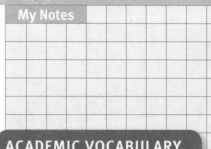

ACADEMIC VOCABULARY

Triangulation is also used in surveying, navigation, and cellular communications.

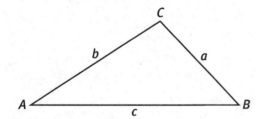

1. Begin with triangle *ABC*. Draw altitude $\overline{CD}$ from vertex *C* to $\overline{AB}$. Label the altitude *h*.

2. What two right triangles are formed?

3. **Reason abstractly.** You can use the triangles you just formed to write some trigonometric ratios.
   a. Write a ratio for sin *A*.

   b. Write a ratio for sin *B*.

MATH TIP

An altitude of a triangle is the perpendicular segment from a vertex to the opposite side.

MATH TIP

In a triangle, the side opposite ∠*A* is *a*, the side opposite ∠*B* is *b*, and so on.

4. **a.** Solve each equation from Item 3 for *h*.

   b. Set the values for *h* equal.

   c. Complete the following statement.

   $$\frac{\sin A}{\Box} = \frac{\sin B}{\Box}$$

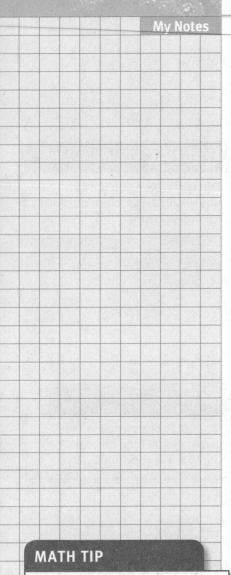

In a similar way, you can show $\dfrac{\sin A}{a} = \dfrac{\sin C}{c}$ and $\dfrac{\sin B}{b} = \dfrac{\sin C}{c}$.

You have just derived the **Law of Sines**.

Below is a formal statement of the Law of Sines.

For any triangle ABC, with side lengths a, b, and c, $\dfrac{\sin A}{a} = \dfrac{\sin B}{b} = \dfrac{\sin C}{c}$.

Example A

Fire spotters at stations located at A and B notice a fire at location C. What is the distance between station A and the fire?

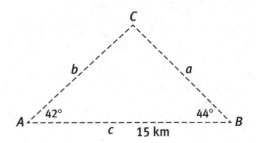

Step 1: Find $m\angle C$.

$m\angle C = 180° - 42° - 44°$

$\qquad = 94°$

Step 2: Use the Law of Sines.

$\dfrac{\sin B}{b} = \dfrac{\sin C}{c}$

$\dfrac{\sin 44°}{b} = \dfrac{\sin 94°}{15}$ Substitute.

$15 \sin 44° = b \cdot \sin 94°$ Cross Products Property

$b = \dfrac{15 \sin 44°}{\sin 94°}$ Solve for $b = AC$.

$b \approx 10.4$ Simplify.

Solution: The distance between station A and the fire is about 10.4 km.

MATH TIP

The Cross Products Property states that, for real numbers a, b, c, and d, $b \neq 0$ and $c \neq 0$, if $\dfrac{a}{b} = \dfrac{c}{d}$, then $ad = bc$.

My Notes

Try These A

Two boaters located at points *A* and *B* notice a lighthouse at location *C*. What is the distance between the boater located at point *B* and the lighthouse? Round to the nearest tenth.

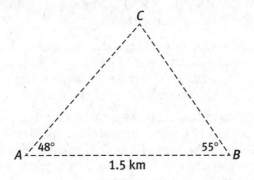

Check Your Understanding

5. **Reason quantitatively.** Show that the Law of Sines is true for a 45°-45°-90° triangle with leg lengths of 1.

6. Can you use the Law of Sines to find *ZX*? Explain.

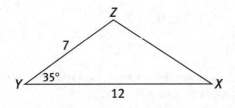

LESSON 23-1 PRACTICE

7. Find each measure. Round to the nearest tenth.
   a. *YZ* = _____

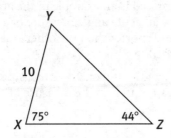

   b. *DE* = _____

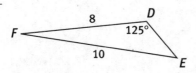

8. **Construct viable arguments.** When can you use the Law of Sines to find the measure of an angle of a triangle? Explain your thinking.

MATH TIP

You may need to use the Law of Sines to find an angle measure *before* finding the measure of a side. This may require the use of an inverse trigonometric function.

TECHNOLOGY TIP

You can also use geometry software to complete Item 1.

Learning Targets:

● Understand when the ambiguous case of the Law of Sines occurs.
● Solve problems using the Law of Sines.

SUGGESTED LEARNING STRATEGIES: Create Representations, Use Manipulatives, Predict and Confirm

Fire spotters at stations located at Q and R notice a fire at location S. The distance between stations Q and R is 15 km, and the distance between station R and the fire is 12 km. Station Q forms a 38° angle with station R and the fire. What is the distance between station Q and the fire?

1. **Use appropriate tools strategically.** Cut straws or coffee stirrers that are 15 cm and 12 cm long to model the distances between the locations. Use a protractor to form a 38° angle at vertex Q. How many different triangles can you make using a 38° angle and side lengths of 15 cm and 12 cm? Sketch the triangles.

2. Why could you form two different triangles in Item 1?

3. Is there an SSA criterion for proving two triangles are congruent? How does this help explain your answer to Item 2?

The problem you just explored is an example of the ambiguous case of the Law of Sines. If you know an acute angle measure of a triangle and the side that is opposite the angle is shorter than the other side length you know, then two triangles can be formed.

4. You know two side lengths and an angle measure. Use the Law of Sines to complete the equation to find the measure of angle S. Round to the nearest degree.

   a. $\dfrac{\sin 38°}{\boxed{}} = \dfrac{\sin S°}{\boxed{}}$

   b. $m\angle S \approx \boxed{}°$

5. There are two angles between $0°$ and $180°$ whose sine is 0.7660, one acute and one obtuse. Your calculator gives you the measure of the acute angle, $50°$. The obtuse angle uses $50°$ as a reference angle.

a. Find the measure of the obtuse angle whose sine is 0.7660.

$$m\angle S = 180° - 50° = \boxed{}°$$

b. Now find the measure of $\angle R$ for the two possible triangles.

$$m\angle R = 180° - 38° - \boxed{}° = \boxed{}°$$

$$m\angle R = 180° - 38° - \boxed{}° = \boxed{}°$$

c. Use the Law of Sines to complete the equations to find the two possible values of QS. Round to the nearest tenth.

$$\frac{\sin 38°}{12} = \frac{\sin \boxed{}°}{QS} \qquad \frac{\sin 38°}{12} = \frac{\sin \boxed{}°}{QS}$$

$$QS = \underline{} \text{ or } QS = \underline{}$$

Check Your Understanding

6. Given: $\triangle ABC$ with $m\angle B = 40°$, $AB = 12$, $AC = 8$. Find two possible values for each measure.
   a. $m\angle C$
   b. $m\angle A$
   c. BC

LESSON 23-2 PRACTICE

7. Given: $\triangle ABC$ with $m\angle A = 70°$, $BC = 85$, $AB = 88$. Find two possible values for each measure.
   a. $m\angle C$
   b. AC

8. Given: $\triangle ABC$ with $m\angle A = 40°$, $BC = 26$, $AB = 32$. Find two possible values for each measure.
   a. $m\angle C$
   b. AC

9. **Reason abstractly.** Three radio towers are positioned so that the angle formed at vertex A is $65°$. The distance between tower A and tower B is 28 miles. The distance between tower B and tower C is 26 miles. What are the two possible distances between tower A and tower C? Draw a diagram to support your answers. Round to the nearest whole number.

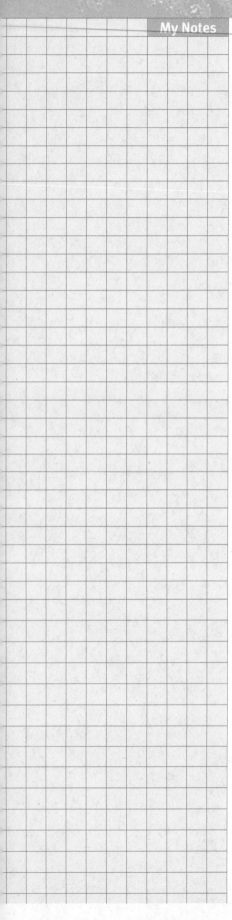

Learning Targets:

- Prove the Law of Cosines.
- Solve problems using the Law of Cosines.

> **SUGGESTED LEARNING STRATEGIES:** Create Representations, Predict and Confirm, Think-Pair-Share

Fire spotters at stations located at *A* and *B* notice a fire at location *C*. What is the distance between station *B* and the fire?

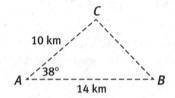

1. Can you use the Law of Sines to solve the problem? Explain.

You need a different relationship to solve this problem. You can solve the problem using the **Law of Cosines**.

For any triangle *ABC*, with side lengths *a*, *b*, and *c*,

$$a^2 = b^2 + c^2 - 2bc \cos A$$
$$b^2 = a^2 + c^2 - 2ac \cos B$$
$$c^2 = a^2 + b^2 - 2ab \cos C$$

Follow these steps to prove the Law of Cosines.

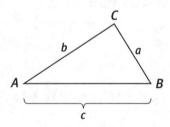

2. Begin with triangle *ABC*. Draw altitude $\overline{CD}$ from vertex *C* to $\overline{AB}$.
   a. Label the altitude *h*.
   b. Label $\overline{AB}$ as *c*.
   c. Label $\overline{AD}$ in terms of *x* and *c*.

3. Complete the following ratio.
   $$\cos A = \frac{x}{\square}$$

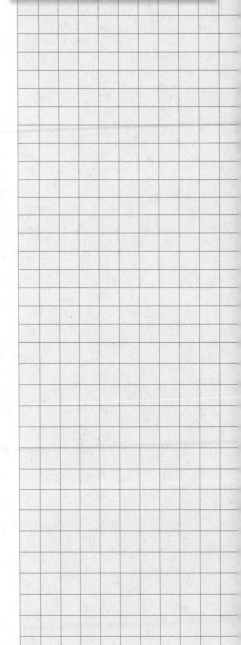

My Notes

4. Solve the equation from Item 3 for x.

5. Use the Pythagorean Theorem to complete the following statements.
   a. $x^2 + \boxed{} = b^2$
   b. $(\boxed{})^2 + h^2 = a^2$

6. **Make sense of problems.** Solve for h^2 in each equation. Expand the equation from Item 5 and set them equal to each other. Then use substitution to prove the Law of Cosines.

> **MATH TIP**
>
> The *Pythagorean Theorem* states that the square of the length of the hypotenuse of a right triangle is equal to the sum of the squares of the lengths of the legs of the right triangle. In other words, for a right triangle with hypotenuse c and legs a and b, $c^2 = a^2 + b^2$.

7. Suppose $\angle B$ was a right angle. Show how the Law of Cosines would relate to the Pythagorean Theorem.

The Law of Cosines is a generalization of the Pythagorean Theorem.

Now you can solve the problem that was posed at the beginning of the lesson.

8. Fire spotters at stations located at A and B notice a fire at location C. What is the distance between station B and the fire? Round to the nearest tenth.
   a. Use the Law of Cosines to complete the equation.

   $$CB^2 = 10^2 + \boxed{}^2 - 2(\boxed{})(\boxed{})\cos(\boxed{}°)$$

   b. Solve the equation for CB. Round to the nearest tenth.

   The distance between station B and the fire is _____.

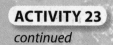

My Notes

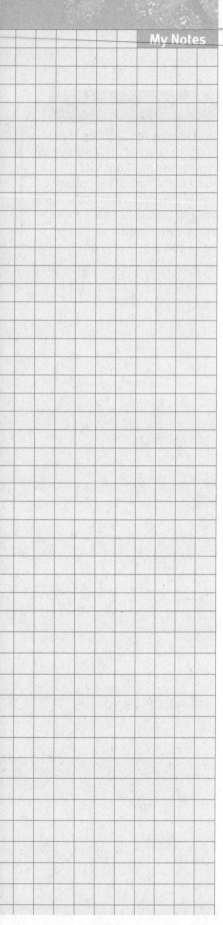

9. Fire station towers are located at points A, B, and C. The distances between the towers are known. Spotters need to know the measures of angles A, B, and C. What is the measure of angle C? Round to the nearest degree.

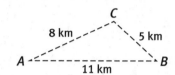

a. Which equation of the Law of Cosines do you use to find the measure of angle C?

b. Write the equation.

c. What is the measure of angle C?

Check Your Understanding

10. Given $\triangle XYZ$ and the lengths of $\overline{XY}$ and $\overline{XZ}$, do you have enough information to use the Law of Cosines to find $m\angle X$? Explain.

11. An equilateral triangle has sides of length 1. Use the Law of Cosines to show that each angle of the triangle measures $60°$.

LESSON 23-3 PRACTICE

12. Make use of structure. Once you know the measure of angle C in Item 9, describe two ways to find the measures of the remaining angles of the triangle.

13. Find each measure. Round to the nearest tenth.

a. $QR =$ _____   **b.** $m\angle D =$ _____

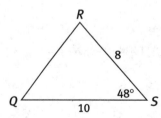

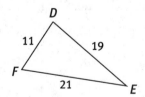

Learning Targets:

- Determine when to use the Law of Sines and when to use the Law of Cosines.
- Solve problems using the Law of Cosines and/or the Law of Sines.

SUGGESTED LEARNING STRATEGIES: Create Representations, Predict and Confirm, Think-Pair-Share, Visualization

To solve a triangle, you find all its angle measures and all its side lengths. It is important that you know when you can use the Law of Sines and when you can use the Law of Cosines to solve triangles.

1. Complete the table below and use it as a reference.

Case	Description	Use Law of Sines or Law of Cosines to solve?
AAS	Two angle measures and the length of a nonincluded side are known.	
ASA	Two angle measures and the length of the included side are known.	
SSA	The lengths of two sides and the angle opposite are known.	
SAS	Two side lengths and the included angle measure are known.	
SSS	Three side lengths are known.	

2. Fire spotters at stations located at *B* and *C* notice a fire at location *A*. Solve the triangle.
   a. What information do you know?

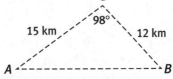

   b. Describe the first step in solving the problem.

   c. **Make sense of problems.** Draw a flowchart to plan a solution pathway for the problem.

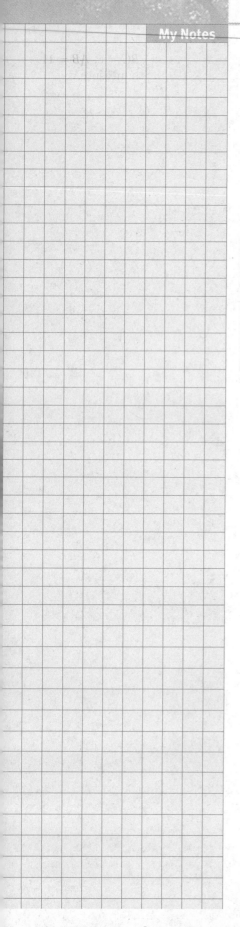

My Notes

d. Does your plan include using the Law of Sines, the Law of Cosines, or both? Explain.

e. Solve the triangle. Round all side measures to the nearest tenth and angle measures to the nearest degree.

Check Your Understanding

3. Suppose you know the lengths of the three sides of a triangle. Describe how you would find the measure of each angle of the triangle.

4. Suppose you know the measures of the three angles of a triangle. Can you use the Law of Sines and/or the Law of Cosines to solve the triangle? Explain.

LESSON 23-4 PRACTICE

5. Solve each triangle. Round all side measures to the nearest tenth and angle measures to the nearest degree.

a.

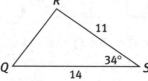

b.

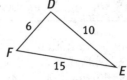

c.

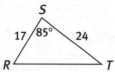

d.

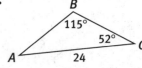

6. **Reason quantitatively.** Two lifeguards on the towers at vertex *A* and vertex *B* are watching a swimmer in the ocean at vertex *C*. Which lifeguard is closer to the swimmer? Show your work.

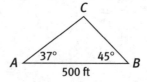

ACTIVITY 23 PRACTICE
Write your answers on notebook paper.
Show your work.

Unless otherwise indicated, round all side measures to the nearest tenth and angle measures to the nearest degree.

Lesson 23-1

1. Solve for x: $\dfrac{\sin 28°}{x} = \dfrac{\sin 52°}{15}$

2. Solve for A: $\dfrac{\sin 82°}{28} = \dfrac{\sin A°}{8}$

3. Describe how to use the Law of Sines to find the lengths of the other two sides of a triangle, if you know the measures of two angles and the included side.

4. To the nearest tenth, what is RS?

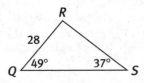

A. 21.2   **B.** 29
C. 35.1   **D.** 37

5. Find each measure.

   a. $AC =$ _____

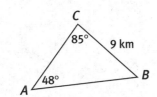

   b. $HJ =$ _____

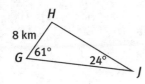

   c. $m\angle R =$ _____

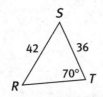

Lesson 23-2

6. Given: $\triangle ABC$ with $m\angle A = 28°$, $BC = 6$, $AB = 11$. Find two possible values for each measure.
   a. $m\angle C$
   b. AC

7. Given: $\triangle ABC$ with $m\angle A = 65°$, $BC = 19$, $AB = 21$. Find two possible values for each measure.
   a. $m\angle C$
   b. AC

8. Three fire towers are positioned so that the angle formed at vertex R is $31°$. The distance between tower R and tower S is 8 miles. The distance between tower S and tower T is 6 miles. What are the two possible distances between tower R and tower T?

Lesson 23-3

9. Solve for b:
   $b^2 = 22^2 + 28^2 - 2(22)(28)\cos 36°$

10. Solve for C:
   $5^2 = 8^2 + 11^2 - 2(8)(11)\cos C°$

11. To the nearest degree, what is $m\angle S$?

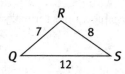

A. $34°$
B. $40°$
C. $50°$
D. $106°$

12. Find each measure.
a. $m\angle C =$ _____

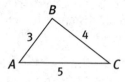

b. $m\angle S =$ _____

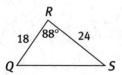

13. What is the distance across the lake, AB?

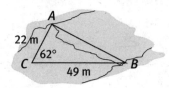

Lesson 23-4

14. Solve each triangle.
a.

b.

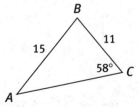

MATHEMATICAL PRACTICES
Construct Viable Arguments and Critique the Reasoning of Others

15. Chandra wants to find the measure of angle B in triangle ABC. Is her work correct? Explain. If it is not, then fix the error and find the measure of angle B.

$$\cos B = \frac{36^2 - 20^2 + 30^2}{2(20)(30)}$$

Chloe wants to ride a zip line. She looked online and found a zip line tour near her home, and she needs to decide whether to ride the Beginner's zip line or the Daredevil's zip line. The tour company's Web page gives some of the measurements for the two zip lines, but Chloe wants to find some additional measurements before she decides. The image below is shown on the tour company's Web page.

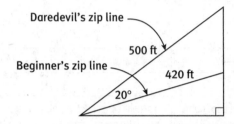

1. Chloe printed the image and added labels to help her identify sides and angles. Describe how to find BC, the difference in the heights of the starting points.

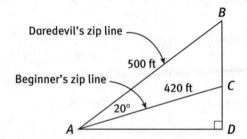

2. Find each of the following measures. Round your answer to the nearest whole number or degree.
   a. $BC = $ _____
   b. $m\angle B = $ _____
   c. $m\angle BCA = $ _____
   d. $m\angle CAD = $ _____
   e. $m\angle DCA = $ _____
   f. $AD = $ _____

3. What is the height of the starting point of the Beginner's zip line, CD?

4. What is the height of the starting point of the Daredevil's zip line, BD?

To prepare for her zip line adventure, Chloe's father helps her build a smaller zip line in her backyard. Chloe made a diagram of her zip line.

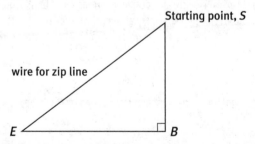

5. The height of the starting point, SB, is 20 feet and $EB = 26$ feet. Determine the angle of elevation from the ending platform, E, to the starting point, S. Show the work that leads to your response. Round your angle to the nearest degree.

6. Chloe decides she wants the length of the wire for the zip line to be 60 feet long and the angle of elevation to be 40°. Chloe and her father need to determine the distance from B to E to decide if there is enough room in her yard for this zip line. Her father uses the equation $\sin 50° = \dfrac{EB}{60}$ and Chloe uses the equation $\cos 40° = \dfrac{EB}{60}$. Who is correct? Justify your answer.

Scoring Guide	Exemplary	Proficient	Emerging	Incomplete
	The solution demonstrates these characteristics:			
Mathematics Knowledge and Thinking (Items 1, 2, 3, 5, 6)	• Accurate use of right triangle trigonometry, Law of Cosines, Law of Sines, and the Triangle Angle Sum Theorem to determine missing measures in triangles • Clear and accurate understanding of the relationship between trigonometric ratios of co-functions of complementary angles	• Mostly correct use of right triangle trigonometry, Law of Cosines, Law of Sines, and the Triangle Angle Sum Theorem to determine missing measures in triangles • A functional understanding of the relationship between trigonometric ratios of co-functions of complementary angles	• Partially correct use of right triangle trigonometry, Law of Cosines, Law of Sines, and the Triangle Angle Sum Theorem to determine missing measures in triangles • Partial understanding of the relationship between trigonometric ratios of co-functions of complementary angles	• Incorrect or incomplete use of right triangle trigonometry, Law of Cosines, Law of Sines, and the Triangle Angle Sum Theorem to determine missing measures in triangles • Little or no understanding of the relationship between trigonometric ratios of co-functions of complementary angles
Problem Solving (Items 2, 3, 4, 5)	• An appropriate and efficient strategy that results in correct answers	• A strategy that may include unnecessary steps but results in correct answers	• A strategy that results in some incorrect answers	• No clear strategy when solving problems
Mathematical Modeling / Representations (Items 2, 5)	• Clear and accurate understanding of creating equations using right triangle trigonometry, Law of Cosines, Law of Sines, and the Triangle Angle Sum Theorem to determine missing measures in triangles	• Mostly accurate understanding of creating equations using right triangle trigonometry, Law of Cosines, Law of Sines, and the Triangle Angle Sum Theorem to determine missing measures in triangles	• Partial understanding of creating equations using right triangle trigonometry, Law of Cosines, Law of Sines, and the Triangle Angle Sum Theorem to determine missing measures in triangles	• Little or no understanding of creating equations using right triangle trigonometry, Law of Cosines, Law of Sines, and the Triangle Angle Sum Theorem to determine missing measures in triangles
Reasoning and Communication (Items 1, 6)	• Precise use of appropriate mathematics and language to describe how to determine *BC* • Precise use of appropriate language to explain which equation is correct in Item 6	• Adequate use of appropriate language to explain which equation is correct in Item 6	• Misleading or confusing use of appropriate language to explain which equation is correct in Item 6	• Incomplete or inaccurate use of appropriate language to explain which equation is correct in Item 6

Circles, Coordinates, and Constructions

Unit Overview

In this unit you will study many geometric concepts and theorems related to circles, including angles, arcs, and segments of circles. You will study coordinate geometry to prove some theorems about triangles and line segments in order to enhance your understanding of the relationships between algebra and geometry. You will derive the equation for a circle and for a parabola. Then you will apply what you have learned, along with your knowledge of geometric constructions, in order to model and solve various geometric problems.

Key Terms

As you study this unit, add these and other terms to your math notebook. Include in your notes your prior knowledge of each word, as well as your experiences in using the word in different mathematical examples. If needed, ask for help in pronouncing new words and add information on pronunciation to your math notebook. It is important that you learn new terms and use them correctly in your class discussions and in your problem solutions.

Academic Vocabulary
- conjecture

Math Terms
- circle
- tangent
- radius
- diameter
- chord
- arc
- equidistant
- tangent segment
- bisecting ray
- minor arc
- major arc
- central angle
- inscribed angle
- coordinate proof
- biconditional statement
- directed line segment
- parabola
- focus
- directrix
- geometric construction
- inscribed
- circumscribed

ESSENTIAL QUESTIONS

? How are the geometric properties of circles, their coordinates, and constructions used to model and describe real-world phenomena?

? Why is it important to understand coordinate geometry and geometric constructions?

EMBEDDED ASSESSMENTS

This unit has two embedded assessments, following Activities 25 and 29. The first will give you the opportunity to apply theorems relating to circles. You will also be asked to apply the relationships among angles, radii, chords, tangents, and secants to a real-world context. The second assessment focuses on coordinate geometry and directed line segments to determine possible locations for a company, given certain criteria.

Embedded Assessment 1:

Circles	p. 371

Embedded Assessment 2:

Coordinates and Constructions	p. 429

Getting Ready

Write your answers on notebook paper.
Show your work.

1. Simplify.
   a. $\sqrt{75}$
   b. $\sqrt{32} + \sqrt{18}$

2. Solve the following for x.
   a. $x^2 - 7x + 10 = 0$
   b. $4(x + 2) = 6x$
   c. $x(x + 1) = 2(x + 1)$

3. Find the following products.
   a. $(5x^2)(3x^2)$
   b. $2y(3y + 5)$

4. Find the distance between the following:
   a. $(3, 4)$ and $(-2, 6)$
   b. $(1, 3)$ and $(5, 3)$

5. Find the measure of $\angle A$.

6. In the figure below, $AC = 14$ units, $BD = 12$ units, and $AD = 20$ units. Find BC and AB.

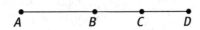

7. Compare and contrast the characteristics of a radius, a diameter, and a chord of a circle.

8. Sketch a line, b, that is the perpendicular bisector of a segment, AC. Describe the geometric characteristics of your sketch.

9. Complete the square to create a perfect square trinomial.
   a. $x^2 + 16x$
   b. $x^2 - 10x$

10. Determine the type of function graphed below. Then identify the line of symmetry.

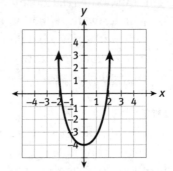

11. Describe how the graph of $y = x^2$ differs from the graph of $y = -x^2$.

12. What is true about the slopes of parallel lines? What is the relationship of the slopes of perpendicular lines?

Tangents and Chords

Off on a Tangent

Lesson 24-1 Circle Basics

Learning Targets:

- Describe relationships among tangents and radii of a circle.
- Use arcs, chords, and diameters of a circle to solve problems.

> **SUGGESTED LEARNING STRATEGIES:** Create Representations, Interactive Word Wall, Use Manipulatives, Think-Pair-Share, Quickwrite

A *circle* is the set of all points in a plane at a given distance from a given point in the plane. Lines and segments that intersect the circle have special names. The following illustrate *tangent* lines to a circle.

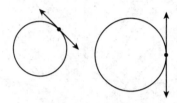

> **MATH TERMS**
>
> A **circle** consists of an infinite number of points.

1. On the circle below, draw three unique examples of lines or segments that are not tangent to the circle.

2. **Attend to precision.** Write a definition of tangent lines.

3. Using the circle below,
   a. Draw a tangent line and a *radius* to the point of tangency.

> **MATH TERMS**
>
> The **radius** of a circle is a segment, or length of a segment, from the center to any point on the circle.

   b. Describe the relationship between the tangent line and the radius of the circle drawn to the point of tangency.

MATH TERMS

The **diameter** is a segment, or the length of a segment, that contains the center of a circle and two end points on the circle.

MATH TERMS

A **chord** is a segment whose endpoints are points on a circle.

An **arc** is part of a circle consisting of two points on the circle and the unbroken part of the circle between the two points.

DISCUSSION GROUP TIPS

In your discussion groups, read the text carefully to clarify meaning. Reread definitions of terms as needed to help you comprehend the meanings of words, or ask your teacher to clarify vocabulary words.

Chuck Goodnight dug up part of a wooden wagon wheel. An authentic western wagon has two different-sized wheels. The front wheels are 42 inches in diameter while the rear wheels are 52 inches in diameter. Chuck wants to use the part of the wheel that he found to calculate the *diameter* of the entire wheel, so that he can determine if he has found part of a front or rear wheel. A scale drawing of Chuck's wagon wheel part is shown below.

4. Trace the outer edge of the portion of the wheel shown onto a piece of paper.

5. Draw two *chords* on your *arc*.

6. **Use appropriate tools strategically.** Using a ruler, draw a perpendicular bisector to each of the two chords and extend the bisectors until they intersect.

The perpendicular bisectors of two chords in a circle intersect at the center of the circle.

7. Determine the diameter of the circle that will be formed. Explain how you arrived at your answer.

8. The scale factor for the drawing is 1:12. Determine which type of wheel can contain the part Chuck found. Justify your answer.

Check Your Understanding

9. On the figure below, draw a tangent line and a diameter to the point of tangency.

10. Describe the relationship between the tangent line and the diameter of the circle drawn to the point of tangency.

11. **Critique the reasoning of others.** Josie states that in some cases a chord can also be a tangent. Wyatt states that a chord can never be a tangent. Which statement is valid? Explain your reasoning.

12. A farmer is standing at Point X. Point X is 36 feet from the base of a cylindrical storage silo and 42 feet from point Y. Find the radius of the silo, to the nearest tenth, given that $\overline{XY}$ is tangent to circle O at Y.

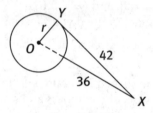

TECHNOLOGY TIP

You can use geometry software to draw a circle. Use the circle tool to draw the circle and the point on object command to draw a point on the circle.

MATH TIP

The base of a cylinder is a circle.

My Notes

LESSON 24-1 PRACTICE

13. **Use appropriate tools strategically.** Use graphing software, or a compass and a straightedge, to draw a circle with the following parts. Identify each part with a label.
    a. center point
    b. radius
    c. diameter
    d. arc
    e. chord (that is not a diameter)
    f. tangent line
    g. non-tangent line

14. Describe how to create a tangent to a circle given a point on the circle.

Use the figure to answer Items 15 to 17.

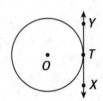

15. **Construct viable arguments.** Given that $OT = 5$, $XT = 12$, and $OX = 13$, is $\overline{XY}$ tangent to circle O at T? Explain your reasoning.

16. Given that $OT = 4$, $YT = 8$, and $OY = 10$, is $\overline{XY}$ tangent to circle O at T? Explain how you determined your answer.

17. Given that $\overline{XY}$ is tangent to circle O at T, what is YT if $OT = 18$ and $OY = 24$?

18. The radius of a circular-shaped fountain is 10 feet.
    a. Use geometry software, or a compass and a straightedge, to draw the fountain using a scale of 1 cm = 6 in.
    b. Draw two chords on your drawing. Use the perpendicular bisectors of the chords to find the center of the fountain.

WRITING MATH

When writing a description of a process, go step-by-step and use proper mathematical terminology.

Learning Targets:

● Describe relationships among diameters and chords of a circle.
● Prove and apply theorems about chords of a circle.

> **SUGGESTED LEARNING STRATEGIES:** Look for a Pattern, Use Manipulatives, Quickwrite, Sharing and Responding

The diameter of a circle and a chord of a circle have a special type of relationship.

1. In the circle below:
   • Draw a diameter.
   • Draw a chord that is perpendicular to the diameter.

   a. Use a ruler to take measurements in this figure. What do you notice?

   b. Compare your answer with your neighbor's answer. What *conjecture* can you make based on your investigations of a diameter perpendicular to a chord?

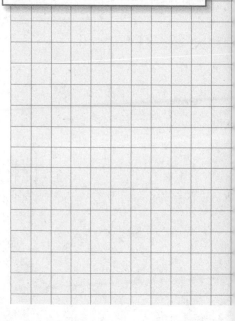

ACADEMIC VOCABULARY

A *conjecture* is an assertion that is likely to be true but has not been formally proven.

2. For the theorem below, the statements for the proof have been scrambled. Rearrange them in logical order.

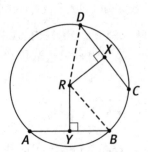

Theorem: In a circle, two congruent chords are *equidistant* from the center of the circle.

Given: $\overline{AB} \cong \overline{CD}$; $\overline{RX} \perp \overline{CD}$; $\overline{RY} \perp \overline{AB}$

Prove: $\overline{RY} \cong \overline{RX}$

MATH TERMS

If two segments are the same distance from a point, they are **equidistant** from it.

Draw radii $\overline{RB}$ and $\overline{RD}$.
$\overline{RY} \cong \overline{RX}$
$\overline{AB} \cong \overline{CD}$; $\overline{RX} \perp \overline{CD}$; $\overline{RY} \perp \overline{AB}$
$AB = CD$
$\triangle DXR$ and $\triangle BYR$ are right triangles.
$\overline{RB} \cong \overline{RD}$
$\frac{1}{2}AB = \frac{1}{2}CD$
$\overline{BY} \cong \overline{DX}$
$\angle DXR$ and $\angle BYR$ are right angles.
$BY = DX$
$BY = \frac{1}{2}AB$; $DX = \frac{1}{2}CD$
$\triangle DXR \cong \triangle BYR$

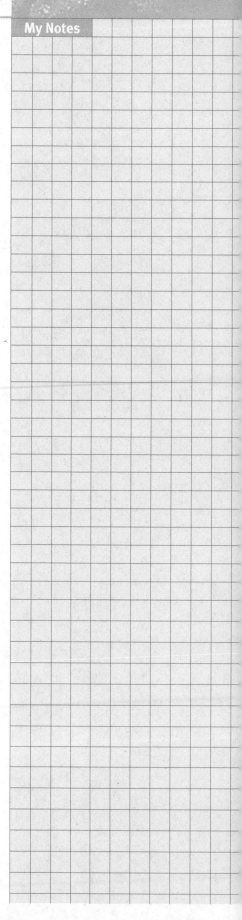

3. The reasons for the proof in Item 2 are scrambled below. Rearrange them so they match the appropriate statement in your proof.

Through any two points there is exactly one line.
Definition of right triangle
Definition of congruent segments
Definition of congruent segments
Multiplication Property
C.P.C.T.C.
HL Theorem
Given
Definition of perpendicular lines
All radii of a circle are congruent.
A diameter perpendicular to a chord bisects the chord.
Substitution Property

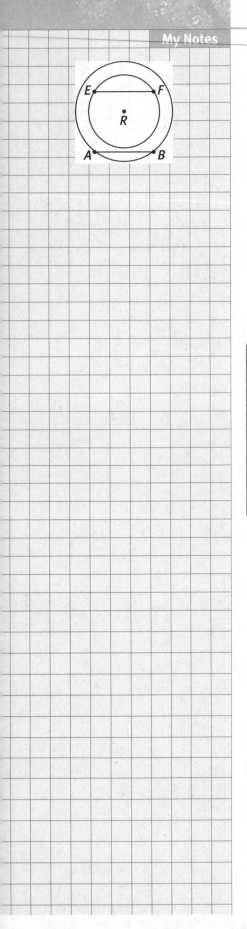

My Notes

4. Given $\overline{EF} \cong \overline{AB}$, explain how you know that $\overline{EF}$ and $\overline{AB}$ are not equidistant from the center, R.

5. **Critique the reasoning of others.** Michael said that if two chords are the same length but are in different circles that are not necessarily concentric circles, then they will not be the same distance from the center of the circle. Is he correct? If he is, give a justification. If not, give a counterexample.

Check Your Understanding

6. A chord of a circular clock is 12 in. long, and its midpoint is 8 in. from the center of the circle.
   a. What theorem(s) can you use to determine the length of the radius of the circle?
   b. Calculate the radius of the circle.

7. A chord of a circle is 15 in. long, and its midpoint is 9 in. from the center of the circle. Calculate the length of the diameter of the circle.

Intersecting chords in a circle also have a special relationship.

8. Using a protractor and a ruler, draw a circle with chord *AB* and chord *CD* so that the chords intersect. Label the intersection point *X*.
   a. Measure the following lengths.
      - *AX*
      - *XB*
      - *CX*
      - *XD*

   b. Find the product of *AX* • *XB* and the product of *CX* • *XD*. What do you notice?

   c. Compare your answer with your neighbor's answer. What conjecture can you make based on your investigations of the intersecting chords of a circle?

My Notes

9. Complete the statements for the following proof.

   Given: Chords $\overline{AB}$ and $\overline{CD}$

   Prove: $AX \cdot XB = CX \cdot XD$

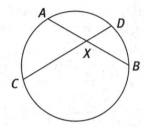

Statements	Reasons
1.	1.
2. Draw $\overline{AD}$ and $\overline{CB}$.	2. Through any two points there is exactly one line.
3. $\angle XAD \cong \angle XCB$ and $\angle XDA \cong \angle XBC$	3. Two inscribed angles intercepting the same arc are congruent.
4. $\triangle ADX$ and $\triangle CBX$	4.
5. $\dfrac{AX}{CX} = \dfrac{XD}{XB}$	5.
6.	6. The product of the means equals the product of the extremes in a proportion.

Check Your Understanding

10. In the circle shown, what is the measure of x? Show your work.

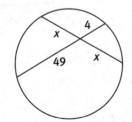

My Notes

CONNECT TO STEM

Chemical engineers consider piping specifications, such as inside and outside diameters, when designing a process flow diagram.

LESSON 24-2 PRACTICE

11. **Reason abstractly.** How can you use geometry terminology to explain why the inside diameter of a pipe is not the same measure as the outside diameter?

12. The diameter of a circle with center P bisects $\overline{AB}$ at point X. Points A and B lie on the circle. Classify the triangle formed by points A, X, and P.

13. Seth states that all diameters of a circle are chords. Sara states that all chords of a circle are diameters. Which statement, if any, is true? Justify your reasoning.

14. The distance between a 16 feet long chord and the center of a circle is 15 feet.
    a. Use technology to draw a diagram.
    b. Compute the diameter of the circle.

15. The radius of a circular-shaped metal gasket is 13 cm. A machinist wants to make a straight 10 cm cut across the gasket.
    a. Use geometry software, or a compass and a straightedge, to draw the gasket. Draw a chord to indicate the cut the machinist wants to make.
    b. Determine the distance between the center of the sheet of metal and the cut edge.

16. **Use appropriate tools strategically.** Use geometry technology, or a compass and a straightedge, to construct a circle with chords $\overline{SV}$ and $\overline{QR}$ intersecting at point C. Use your construction to prove or disprove the conjecture that $\dfrac{SC}{QC} = \dfrac{CR}{CV}$.

17. In the diagram shown, explain a method for determining the values of x and y. Then, find x and y, to the nearest tenth.

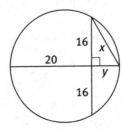

Learning Targets:

- Prove that tangent segments to a circle from a point outside the circle are congruent.
- Use tangent segments to solve problems.

> **SUGGESTED LEARNING STRATEGIES:** Think-Pair-Share, Create Representations, Self Revision/Peer Revision

Theorem: The *tangent segments* to a circle from a point outside the circle are congruent.

1. Use the theorem above to write the prove statement for the diagram below. Then, prove the theorem. Share your ideas with your group.

   Given: $\overline{BD}$ and $\overline{DC}$ are tangent to circle A.

   Prove:

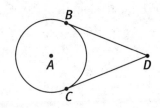

MATH TERMS

A **tangent segment** to a circle is part of a tangent line with one endpoint outside the circle and the second endpoint at a *point of tangency* to the circle.

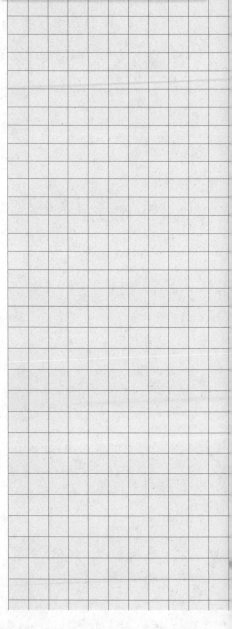

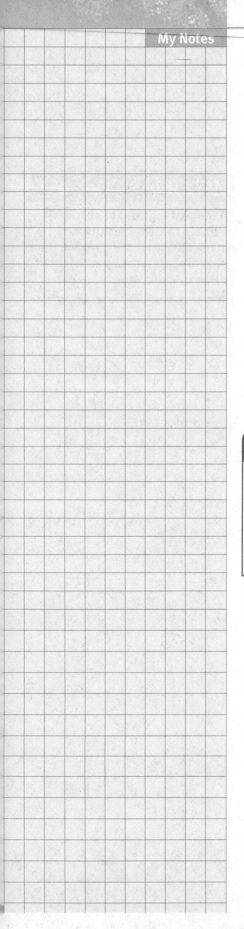

2. **Reason abstractly.** In the diagram, $RT = 12$ cm, $RH = 5$ cm, and $MT = 21$ cm.
   a. Determine the length of $\overline{RM}$. Explain how you arrived at your answer.

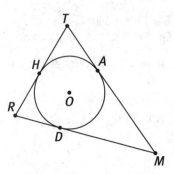

   b. If $OH = 4$ cm, determine the length of $\overline{OT}$. Explain how you arrived at your answer.

Check Your Understanding

3. Refer to the proof in Item 1.
   a. What auxiliary lines, if any, did you draw?
   b. What do you know about those lines?

4. In the diagram in Item 2, if $RM = 40$ cm and $AM = 32$ cm, name the other measures you can find. Then find the measures.

LESSON 24-3 PRACTICE

5. In the diagram, $\overline{NM}$ and $\overline{QN}$ are tangent to circle P, the radius of circle P is 5 cm, and $MN = 12$ cm.
   a. What is QN?
   b. What is PN?

6. **Make sense of problems.** In the diagram below, $\overline{AH}$, $\overline{AD}$, and $\overline{DH}$ are each tangent to circle Q. $AT = 9$, $AH = 13$, and $AD = 15$. What is HD?

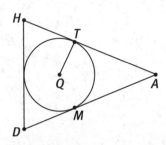

ACTIVITY 24 PRACTICE

**Write your answers on notebook paper.
Show your work.**

Lesson 24-1

For Items 1–3, use the diagram.

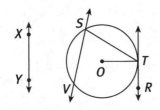

1. Identify the line tangent to the circle.

2. Identify a chord.

3. Which segment is perpendicular to the tangent line? What is the proper name for this segment?

4. Marta claims that it is possible to draw one line tangent to a circle at two points on the circle. Is Marta's claim reasonable? Explain.

The top half of a box fan is shown in the diagram. Use the diagram for Items 5–6.

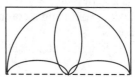

5. How many chords can you draw to represent the distance between the ends of the blades of the fan?

6. In the diagram, $\overline{CA}$ is tangent to circle P. The radius of circle P is 8 cm and $BC = 9$ cm. What is AC?

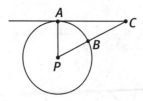

A. 7 cm   B. 12 cm

C. 15 cm   D. 17 cm

Lesson 24-2

7. Suppose a chord of a circle is 5 cm from the center and is 24 cm long.
   a. Draw the diagram using a compass and straightedge.
   b. What is the length of the diameter of the circle?
   c. What is the measure of the radius if the circle is dilated by a scale factor of 125%?

8. What part of a circle is considered to be the longest chord?

9. The distance between a chord and the center of a circle is 4 cm. What is the radius of the circle if the chord measures 16 cm?

Lesson 24-3

10. Given that the radius of the circle shown is 4, what is the value of *x*?

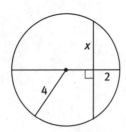

   A. $x = 2$
   B. $x = 2\sqrt{3}$
   C. $x = 8\sqrt{3}$
   D. $x = 8$

11. Two tangents are drawn from point *A*, which is 37 cm from the center of the circle. The diameter of the circle is 24 cm. What is the length of each tangent from point *A* to the point of tangency?
   A. 13 cm
   B. 32 cm
   C. 35 cm
   D. 44 cm

12. Explain what theorem you can use to determine the perimeter of triangle *ABC*. Then, compute the perimeter.

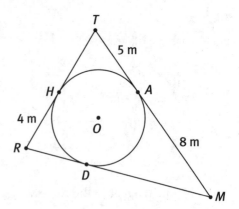

MATHEMATICAL PRACTICES
Construct Viable Arguments and Critique the Reasoning of Others

13. Explain how to prove the following conjecture: If a diameter is perpendicular to a chord, then the diameter bisects the chord.

Arcs and Angles
Coming Full Circle
Lesson 25-1 Arcs and Central Angles

Learning Targets:

- Understand how to measure an arc of a circle.
- Use relationships among arcs and central angles to solve problems.

> **SUGGESTED LEARNING STRATEGIES:** Visualization, Use Manipulatives, Create Representations, Interactive Word Wall

Chris plays soccer for his high school team. His coach wants Chris to improve his accuracy on his goal shots. At practice, the coach stands centered between the goalposts; he has Chris try to kick a goal from different positions on the field. He has noticed that Chris's shots go anywhere from right on target to 15° on either side of his target. With this information, the coach thinks that he and Chris can find locations on the soccer field from which Chris can be sure of kicking between the goalposts.

Your teacher will provide you with a diagram of part of the soccer field, the 24-foot-wide goal, and the point *X* at which the coach plans to stand. Points *A* and *B* represent the goalposts, which are 24 feet apart. Chris will aim his kicks directly at the coach from various points on the playing field to try to find the locations where, even with his margin of error, his shots will land between the goalposts.

Your teacher will also provide you with a diagram of a 30° angle that has a *bisecting ray*. The vertex *S* represents the point from which Chris makes his kick, the bisecting ray represents the path to the target at which Chris is aiming, and the sides of the 30° angle form the outer boundaries of Chris's possible kicks, given that his margin of error is up to 15° on either side of the target. You will use this angle diagram as a tool in estimating the outer boundaries of Chris's kicks when he aims at point *X* from various locations on the soccer field.

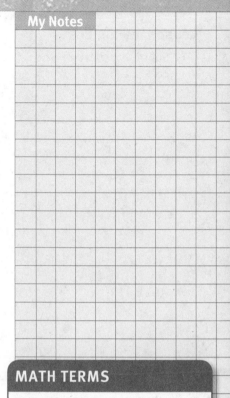

> ### MATH TERMS
>
> A **bisecting ray** is a ray whose end point is the vertex of the angle and which divides the angle into two congruent angles.

1. The three points labeled Points 1, 2, and 3 on the soccer field diagram represent the different positions on the field from which Chris will attempt his shot at the goal. Place the vertex of your angle at Point 1 and make certain that Point *X* lies on the angle bisector. Will Chris's shot be guaranteed to end up between the goalposts from this position on the field? Explain.

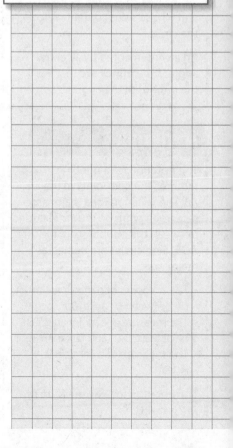

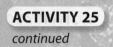

My Notes

2. One at a time, place the vertex of the angle on Point 2 and then on Point 3. Each time, make certain that Point *X* lies on the angle bisector. Determine whether Chris's shots are guaranteed to end up between the goalposts from these positions on the field. Which, if either, position is a sure shot at the goal for Chris?

3. With continued experimentation, you should find that there is a region of the playing field from which Chris is certain to have a shot into the goal zone, despite his margin of error. Use the soccer field diagram and the angle diagram to test points on the field until you can make an informed conjecture as to the shape of this region. Write a description of the region. On the soccer field diagram, clearly identify at least eight points on the outer boundary of this region.

MATH TERMS

A **central angle** is an angle whose vertex is at the center of a circle and whose sides contain radii of the circle.

An arc intercepted by a central angle is the **minor arc** that lies in the interior of the angle.

4. In the diagram of circle *O*, what is the proper math term that describes $\overline{OA}$ and $\overline{OB}$?

Points *A* and *B* divide the circle *O* into two arcs. The smaller arc is known as the ***minor arc*** $\overset{\frown}{AB}$, and the larger arc is known as ***major arc*** $\overset{\frown}{AQB}$. The angle formed by the two radii, $\angle AOB$, is called a ***central angle*** of this circle.

Notice that the major arc associated with points *A* and *B* lies outside $\angle AOB$, while the minor arc lies in the interior of $\angle AOB$. $\overset{\frown}{AB}$ is said to be intercepted by $\angle AOB$. By definition, the measure of a minor arc is equal to the measure of the central angle that intercepts the minor arc.

MATH TIP

The notation for a minor arc requires the endpoints of the arc, $\overset{\frown}{AB}$. The notation for a major arc requires a point on the arc included between the endpoints of the arc, $\overset{\frown}{AQB}$. Semicircles are named as major arcs.

- The measure of a minor arc must be between 0° and 180°.
- The measure of a major arc must be at least 180° and less than 360°.
- The measure of a semicircle is 180°.

The notation for "the measure of $\overset{\frown}{AB}$" is $m\overset{\frown}{AB}$.

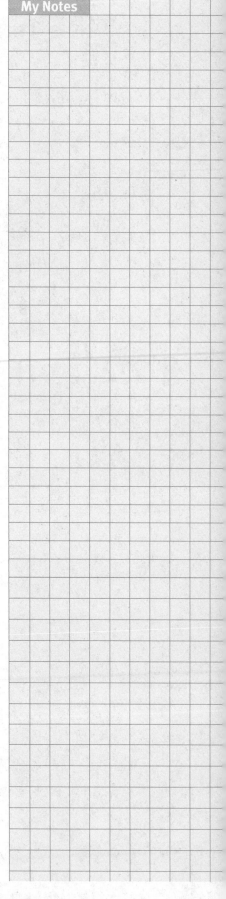

5. Given circle *C*, with diameters $\overline{JR}$ and $\overline{KQ}$ and $m\angle RCQ = 50°$, use the definitions for central angle and intercepted arc along with triangle properties to find each of the following.

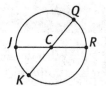

a. $m\widehat{RQ} = $ _____ °

b. $m\widehat{JQ} = $ _____ °

c. $m\angle CRQ = $ _____ °

d. $m\widehat{JQR} = $ _____ °

e. $m\widehat{JKQ} = $ _____ °

f. $\widehat{JK} \cong$ _____

6. Attend to precision. Write a definition for congruent arcs.

7. Given circle *C* with diameters $\overline{JR}$, $\overline{KQ}$, and $\overline{PL}$, and $\overline{PL} \perp \overline{JR}$ and $\overline{KQ}$ bisects $\angle PCR$, answer the following questions.

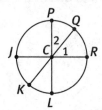

a. Explain why $\widehat{PQ} \cong \widehat{QR}$.

b. $m\angle 1 + m\angle 2 = $ _____ °

c. $m\widehat{JP} + m\widehat{PQ} = m$ _____ °. Provide justification of your reasoning.

d. $m\widehat{JQ} = $ _____ °

e. $m\angle JRQ = $ _____ °

f. $m\widehat{JL} = $ _____ °

g. $m\angle JRL = $ _____ °. Provide justification for your answer.

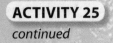
My Notes

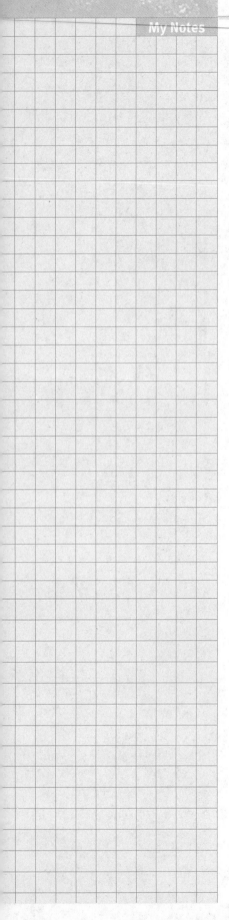

Check Your Understanding

8. What do a vertex of a central angle and the center of a circle have in common?

9. What is another name for the sides of a central angle?

10. Why is the major arc of a circle designated by three points on the circle?

11. Write the range of possible measures of a major arc as an inequality. Explain why a major arc cannot be equal to 360°.

LESSON 25-1 PRACTICE

12. Using a compass or geometry software, construct a circle with a central angle of 50°. Label the major arc and minor arc. What is the measure of the minor arc? Major arc?

13. If you know the measure of the central angle, how can you find the measure of the major arc?

14. Use the circle shown below to determine the following.

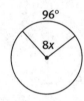

96°

8x

a. What is the measure of the central angle?
b. Write and solve an equation for x.
c. What is the measure of the angle that bisects the minor arc?
d. Write an expression that can be used to determine the measure of the major arc.

15. **Critique the reasoning of others.** To find the measure of x in circle C shown below, Emma set up the following equation: $(12x + 6) + (3x - 6) = 360$. Is Emma on her way to a correct answer? If so, solve for x. If not, explain your reasoning.

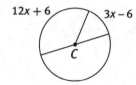

12x + 6   3x − 6

C

Learning Targets:

● Describe the relationship among inscribed angles, central angles, and arcs.

● Use inscribed angles to solve problems.

> **SUGGESTED LEARNING STRATEGIES:** Think-Pair-Share, Look for a Pattern, Quickwrite, Vocabulary Organizer, Create Representations

The soccer coach needs to create a logo for the new team jerseys. He starts with a circle, since it best mimics a soccer ball. Chris suggests that the coach experiment with central and inscribed angles in order to color block the design.

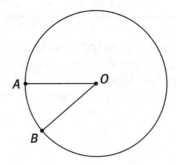

1. Use a protractor to find the measure of central angle ∠AOB.

   $m\angle AOB =$ _____ and $m\overset{\frown}{AB} =$ _____

2. Choose any point on the major arc and label the point *P*. Draw $\overline{PA}$ and $\overline{PB}$. $\overline{PA}$ and $\overline{PB}$ form an ***inscribed angle***.

   a. Name the arc intercepted by ∠APB.

   b. Attend to precision. List the characteristics of an inscribed angle.

3. Use a protractor to find the measure of inscribed angle ∠APB.

   $m\angle APB =$ _____

4. Draw a different point *R* on the circle. Then draw a new inscribed angle that has a vertex *R* and that intercepts $\overset{\frown}{AB}$. Find the measure of the new inscribed angle. $m\angle ARB =$ _____

5. Make a conjecture about the measure of any inscribed angle of this circle that intercepts $\overset{\frown}{AB}$. Test your conjecture by creating and measuring three more inscribed angles that intercept $\overset{\frown}{AB}$.

> **MATH TERMS**
>
> An **inscribed angle** is an angle formed by two chords with a common endpoint.

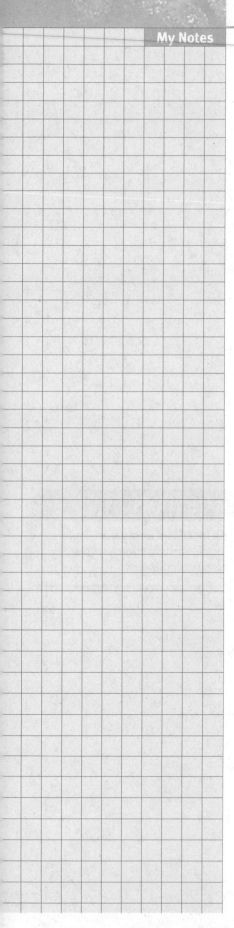

6. Refer to your answers in Items 5 and 7 of Lesson 25-1 and Items 1 and 3 of this lesson to complete the following table.

	Measure of the Intercepted Arc	Measure of the Central Angle	Measure of the Inscribed Angle
Item 5	$m\widehat{JQ} =$	$m\angle JCQ =$	$m\angle JRQ =$
Item 7	$m\widehat{JQ} =$	$m\angle JCQ =$	$m\angle JRQ =$
Item 7	$m\widehat{JL} =$	$m\angle JCL =$	$m\angle JRL =$
Items 1 & 3	$m\widehat{AB} =$	$m\angle AOB =$	$m\angle APB =$

7. Express regularity in repeated reasoning. Based upon any patterns that you see in the table above, write a conjecture about the relationship between the measure of an inscribed angle and the measure of the central angle that intercepts the same arc.

8. Given circle C with diameter $\overline{AR}$ and $m\angle HCA = 50°$, find each of the following.

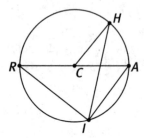

a. $m\angle HIA =$ _____°

b. $m\angle HCR =$ _____°

c. $m\angle HIR =$ _____°

d. $m\angle AIR =$ _____°

e. Write a conjecture about inscribed angles on the diameter of a circle.

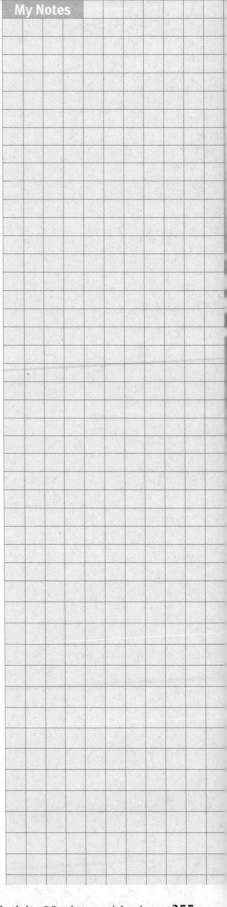

Now, Chris suggests to the coach to inscribe a quadrilateral inside of the circle to create a more appealing logo. Chris and the coach soon realize that a quadrilateral inscribed inside of a circle also has some interesting relationships.

9. Draw circle O. Draw quadrilateral $ABCD$ inscribed in circle O.

   a. Use your drawing to complete the proof that $m\angle ABC + m\angle ADC = 180°$.

Statements	Reasons
Quadrilateral $ABCD$ is inscribed in circle O.	Given
$m\widehat{ABC} = 360 - m\widehat{ADC}$	
$m\angle ABC = \dfrac{1}{2}m\widehat{ADC}$	
$m\angle ADC = \dfrac{1}{2}m\widehat{ABC}$	
	Substitution
$m\angle ADC = 180 - \dfrac{1}{2}m\widehat{ADC}$	
$m\angle ABC + m\angle ADC =$	Substitution

   b. Predict the sum of $m\angle BAD + m\angle BCD$.

   c. Write the theorem suggested by this proof.

All of this exploration into inscribed quadrilaterals and angles has led the soccer coach to revisit his findings about the points from where Chris is certain to make a goal.

My Notes

In the circle below, the inscribed angle is ∠APB and m∠APB = 30°. $\overline{PX}$ bisects ∠APB.

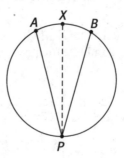

10. Place the 30°-angle diagram that you used at the beginning of the activity so that the vertex, S, is at point P and the angle bisectors coincide. Slide S so that it is closer to X than P, keeping the angle bisectors on top of each other. Then slide S away from X, so that S is outside the circle and so that the angle bisectors are still aligned. Think about locations of S from which Chris will be certain to make a shot into the goal zone. Using the circle as a point of reference, from which points along $\overrightarrow{PX}$ will Chris be certain of making a shot into the goal zone?

11. On the circle below, select a new point W on the major arc determined by points A and B, and carefully draw ∠AWB.

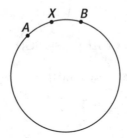

12. m∠AWB = _____°. Explain.

13. **Use appropriate tools strategically.** By careful use of a protractor or by construction, draw the angle bisector of ∠AWB. Does your new angle bisector also go through point X? Use the properties that you have learned in this activity to support your conclusion.

14. Place vertex S of your 30° angle on the circle above so the angle bisectors coincide. Slide S from a starting position at W closer and farther from point X. Using the circle as a point of reference, from which points along this angle bisector will Chris be certain of making a shot into the goal zone?

15. Restate or revise your conjecture, in Item 3 of the previous lesson, about the region in which Chris wants to be when kicking a goal.

Check Your Understanding

16. If an inscribed angle in a circle intercepts a semicircle, what is true about the measure of the angle?

17. Refer to circle O where $ABCD$ is inscribed in circle O, $\overline{AC}$ is the diameter, and $m\angle DAB = 122°$.

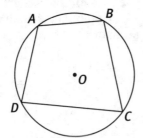

  a. Find $m\angle BCD$.
  b. What are the measures of $\angle ADC$ and $\angle ABC$? Explain your reasoning.
  c. Janet states that $\overline{AC}$ is a line of symmetry. Name a property about kites that can help Janet support her statement.

18. How can you use what you learned in this lesson to prove that the sum of the measures of a quadrilateral inscribed in a circle is 360°?

LESSON 25-2 PRACTICE

19. Draw an angle inscribed in a circle such that its intercepted arc is a semicircle. Label the measure of the inscribed angle.

Use the diagram to answer Items 20–22.

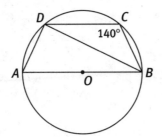

20. Which angle(s), if any, are right angles?

21. What is the sum of $m\angle DAB$ and $m\angle DCB$? Explain.

22. Identify the angle with a measure of 40°.

23. **Make use of structure.** Name the quadrilateral that when inscribed in a circle has angle pairs in which one angle measures twice the measure of the other.

Learning Targets:

- Describe a relationship among the angles formed by intersecting chords in a circle.
- Use angles formed by chords to solve problems.

SUGGESTED LEARNING STRATEGIES: Visualization, Group Presentation, Think-Pair-Share, Quickwrite, Self Revision/Peer Revision

Chris has been asked to consult on the design of a new soccer hall of fame in which names of former players from his high school are written on tiles around the edge of a circular reflecting pool. The pool has tiles along the inside edges that were designed by art students. For the tiles to have the desired visual effect, they need to be illuminated by spotlights. Students have been submitting their suggestions for the placement of the light fixtures.

The light fixtures that are to be used for this project illuminate objects that are within 30° of the center of the bulb. The diagram below represents an overhead view of a single light fixture.

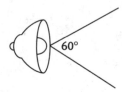

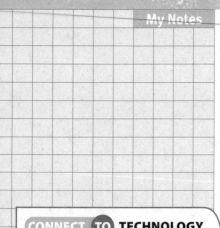

CONNECT TO TECHNOLOGY

To help visualize this part of the activity, use geometry software to draw a diagram with two concentric circles: one that represents the outer edge of the pool, and one that represents the points that are halfway between the center and the edge of the pool.

1. **Model with mathematics.** If the light fixtures are placed at the center of the circular pool and aimed outward toward the edge of the pool, how many would be needed to illuminate the entire pool? Explain.

2. If the same light fixtures in Item 1 are placed halfway between the center and the pool edge and aiming outward, about how much of the pool wall do you think would be illuminated? Estimate the number of additional light fixtures that would be needed to illuminate the entire pool.

3. If the light fixtures were placed on the pool edge and aimed toward the center, how many light fixtures would be needed to illuminate the entire pool? Explain.

Chris is considering a design that involves attaching two light fixtures back-to-back and placing the pairs in various locations in the pool.

4. The figure below represents an overhead view of the pool and one of the light fixture pairs located at the center of the pool, *C*. Find the degree measure of each of the illuminated portions of the pool, $\overset{\frown}{AB}$ and $\overset{\frown}{PQ}$.

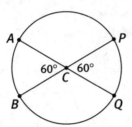

5. As Chris moves the pair of spotlights (point *L* in the figure below) left or right of the center, he notices that the sizes of the illuminated portions of the pool change. As one of the arcs increases in measure, the other arc decreases in measure. Chris needs to know if there is a relationship between the measure of the vertical angles, *x*, and the measure of the two intercepted arcs, *a* and *b*.

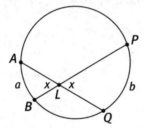

a. Draw $\overline{AP}$.

b. Each of the angles, *x*, is an exterior angle to $\triangle ALP$. Therefore,
$x = m\angle \underline{\hspace{2cm}} + m\angle \underline{\hspace{2cm}}$.

c. Use the Inscribed Angle Measure Theorem to find the measure of $\angle APB$ and $\angle PAQ$ in terms of *a* and *b*.

d. Use your responses in parts b and c to find an expression for *x* in terms of *a* and *b*.

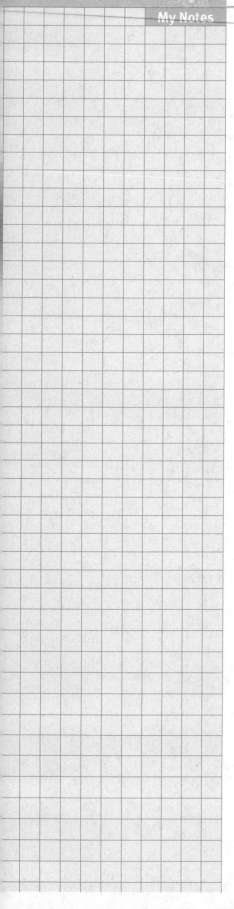

My Notes

6. Complete the following theorem:

When two chords intersect in the _____ of a circle, then the measure of each angle formed is _____ the sum of the measures of the arcs intercepted by the angle and its _____.

The theorem in Item 6 is also true for an intersecting chord and a secant, and for two intersecting secants.

7. Refer to Item 5. Use the formula you discovered in Item 5d to write a formula for *a*.

8. Chris decided that he liked the effect when the back-to-back light fixture pairs were placed off-center because some of the tiles would be lit up more brightly than others. In the figure below, point *A* represents the location of a pair of the spotlights, and the arcs $\overset{\frown}{WX}$ and $\overset{\frown}{YZ}$ represent the parts of the pool edge illuminated by the spotlights.

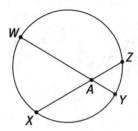

a. Recall that $m\angle WAX = 60°$. If $m\overset{\frown}{WX} = 100°$, then $m\overset{\frown}{YZ} =$ _____.

b. $m\overset{\frown}{WX} + m\overset{\frown}{YZ} =$ _____.

c. If $m\overset{\frown}{WX} = 100°$, then which arc in the figure represents the part of the pool edge where the tiles are most brightly lit? Explain.

9. In his design for the reflecting pool, Chris placed three of the back-to-back light fixture pairs as depicted in the figure below. Points *A*, *B*, and *C* represent the location of each pair. Each pair of lights is equidistant from the center of the circle. $\overset{\frown}{ES} \cong \overset{\frown}{IG} \cong \overset{\frown}{DN}$

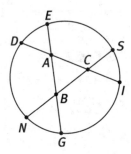

a. Will the entire pool edge be illuminated in this design? Explain.

b. Shade in the region of the pool that will be illuminated by more than one spotlight.

c. If $\overset{\frown}{ES}$ is one-fourth of the circumference of the pool, then what is $m\overset{\frown}{DE}$? Show the work that supports your response.

d. What fraction of the pool edge will be in brighter light than the rest of the pool edge?

Check Your Understanding

10. Use the figure below and the relationship that you discovered in Item 5d to find each of the following.

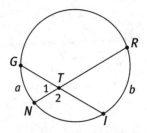

a. If $a = 40°$ and $b = 80°$, then
$m\angle 1 =$ _____° and $m\angle 2 =$ _____°.

b. If $a = 40°$ and $m\angle 1 = 65°$, then $b =$ _____° and $m\overset{\frown}{GR} + m\overset{\frown}{NI} =$
_____°.

My Notes

c. If $m\widehat{GR} = 100°$, $m\widehat{NI} = 160°$, and $m\widehat{RI} = 80°$, then $m\angle 1 = $ _____°.

d. If $a = 4x - 4$, $b = 100°$, and $m\angle 1 = 5x + 3$, write an equation and solve for x.

LESSON 25-3 PRACTICE

Use the diagram for Items 11 and 12.

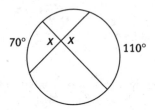

11. What is the value of x?

12. **Make use of structure.** How can you describe the two chords inscribed in this circle?

13. Write an expression to determine the value of x.

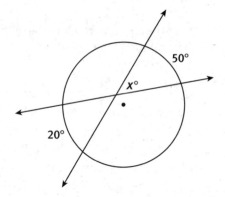

14. Find $m\widehat{AC}$.

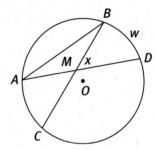

15. Solve for t.

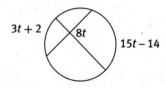

Learning Targets:

- Describe relationships among the angles formed by tangents to a circle or secants to a circle.
- Use angles formed by tangents or secants to solve problems.

SUGGESTED LEARNING STRATEGIES: Shared Reading, Questioning the Text, Summarizing, Paraphrasing, Quickwrite, Think-Pair-Share

Chris realized that he could illuminate the pool with fewer spotlights by placing the spotlights outside the pool and pointing them toward the center.

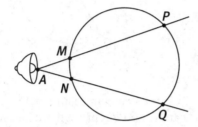

1. If point A represents the light source, which part of the pool edge will be illuminated and which part will not be illuminated?

2. Chris places the spotlight as close to the pool as possible, while at the same time illuminating the largest possible part of the pool's edge. In the figure below, point A represents the light source and point C represents the center of the pool.

   a. $\overline{CP}$ and $\overline{CQ}$ are called _____.

   b. $\overrightarrow{AP}$ and $\overrightarrow{AQ}$ are called _____.

   c. $m\angle APC = m\angle AQC = $ _____°.

   d. Recall that $m\angle A = 60°$. Find $m\angle C$. (*Hint*: consider the angles in quadrilateral $APCQ$.)

   e. What fraction of the pool edge will be illuminated by the spotlight and what fraction will not be illuminated?

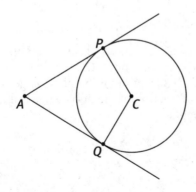

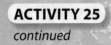

3. **Reason abstractly.** In the diagram below, point *C* represents the center of the circle. $\overrightarrow{AP}$ and $\overrightarrow{AQ}$ are tangent to the circle. If $m\angle A = x°$, then find an expression for $m\widehat{PQ}$ in terms of *x*.

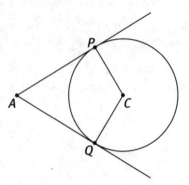

4. In the figure below, *x* is the degree measure of an angle whose sides are tangent to the circle and *a* and *b* represent arc measures (in degrees). Use the relationship that you discovered in Item 2 to find each of the following.

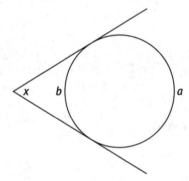

   a. Find *a* and *b* if $x = 45$.

   b. Find *x* if $b = 100$.

   c. Find *x* if $a = 270$.

   d. Solve for *y* if $x = 4y$ and $b = 20y - 12$.

5. In his design, Chris decided to use three spotlights (as in Item 2) evenly spaced around the reflection pool. Draw a sketch of the overhead view of Chris's design. What fraction of the pool's edge is not illuminated by the spotlight? What fraction of the pool's edge is illuminated by two or more of the spotlights?

Even though he did not use them in his design, Chris investigated two additional situations in which the spotlight is located outside the circle.

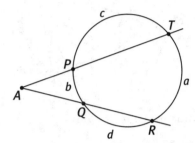

6. a. In the figure above, $\overrightarrow{AT}$ and $\overrightarrow{AR}$ intersect the circle in two points. What name can be given to these two segments?

b. The points P, T, R, and Q divide the circle into four arcs. Which of the arcs lie in the interior of $\angle A$ and which lie in the exterior?

c. Which of the arcs are intercepted by $\angle A$?

d. If the variables a, b, c, and d represent the measures of each of the four arcs, then $a + b + c + d =$ _____ °.

7. Inscribed angles are formed when $\overline{RT}$ is drawn.

In terms of a, b, c, and d,

$m\angle 3 =$ _____ and $m\angle 4 =$ _____.

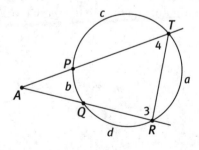

> **CONNECT TO AP**
>
> In calculus, you will study how the tangent and secant lines relate to the concept of a derivative.

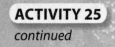

My Notes

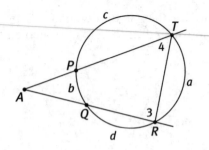

8. a. Let x represent the measure of $\angle A$.

$$x + m\angle 3 + m\angle 4 = \underline{\qquad}^\circ$$

b. Substitute the expressions that you found for $m\angle 3$ and $m\angle 4$ (in Item 7) into the equation that you wrote in Item 8a. Simplify your new equation.

c. Refer to the equation in Item 6d. Solve this equation for $c + d$.

d. Use your responses in Items 8b and 8c to find an expression for x in terms of a and b.

e. Complete the following theorem:

Theorem The measure of an angle formed by two secants drawn to a circle from a point outside the circle is equal to \underline{\qquad\qquad}.

Example A

In circle C below where $m\angle PAQ = 40°$, $m\widehat{PQ} = 50°$, and $\overrightarrow{AP}$ and $\overrightarrow{AQ}$ are tangents, what is $m\angle PRQ$?

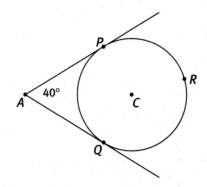

$$m\angle PAQ = \frac{1}{2}(m\angle PRQ - m\widehat{PQ})$$

$$40° = \frac{1}{2}(m\angle PRQ - 50°)$$

$$80° = m\angle PRQ - 50°$$

$$130° = m\angle PRQ$$

Try These A

Find each of the following.

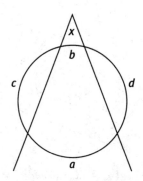

a. Find x if $a = 125°$ and $b = 35°$.

b. Find a if $x = 35°$ and $b = 40°$.

c. Find x if $a = 160°$, $c = 80°$, and $d = 70°$.

d. Write an equation and solve for t if $a = 10t$, $b = 3t - 10$, and $x = 4t - 1$.

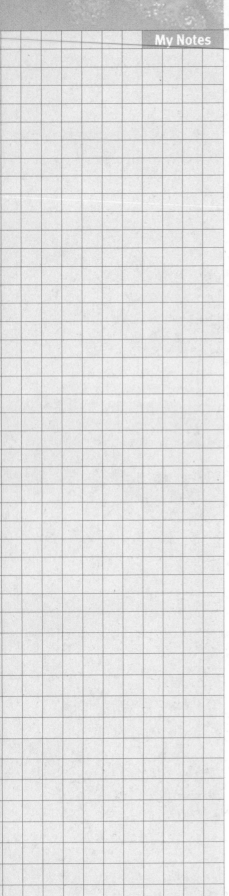

My Notes

Check Your Understanding

9. **Construct viable arguments.** Given the diagram, write a clear and convincing argument that $m\angle A = \frac{1}{2}(a-b) = 180 - b$.

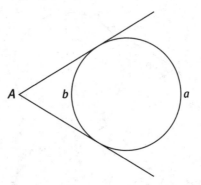

10. Using geometry software, draw circle P with points X and Y on circle P. Draw tangent segments $\overline{XW}$ and $\overline{YW}$. Adjust $m\angle XPY$ from $10°$ to almost $180°$ and write a description about the effect this has on $m\angle XWY$.

LESSON 25-4 PRACTICE

11. Determine $m\angle 2$ if $m\angle 1 = 34°$.

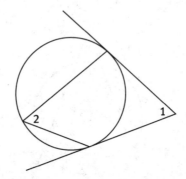

12. **Reason quantitatively.** A farmer woke up one morning to find crop circles in his wheat field as shown below. If $m\angle P = 16°$ and $m\overset{\frown}{CO} = 96°$, determine each of the following.

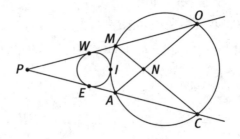

a. $m\overset{\frown}{WE}$ b. $m\overset{\frown}{WIE}$ c. $m\angle OAC$

d. $m\angle MOA$ e. $m\overset{\frown}{AM}$ f. $m\angle CNO$

g. If $\overset{\frown}{AC} \cong \overset{\frown}{OM}$, then determine $m\angle AOC$.

ACTIVITY 25 PRACTICE

Write your answers on notebook paper.
Show your work.

Lesson 25-1

1. Given a circle with center C and $m\angle SCR = 42°$, determine each of the following.

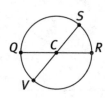

   a. $m\widehat{SR}$ b. $m\angle SCQ$
   c. $m\widehat{SQR}$ d. $m\widehat{QV}$
   e. $m\angle QSV$ f. $m\angle QVR$

2. Use the fact that $m\angle LCR = 90°$ in circle C below to answer the following items.

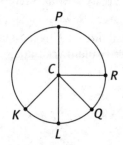

   a. If $\overline{CQ}$ is an angle bisector of $\angle LCR$, what is $m\angle LCQ$?
   b. Identify two major arcs.
   c. Name two congruent minor arcs.
   d. Name three adjacent arcs that form a semicircle.

Lesson 25-2

3. In circle O shown, let $\overline{BE} \perp \overline{IS}$ and $m\angle TOE = 36°$. Find each of the following.

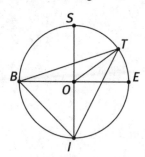

   a. $m\widehat{TE}$ b. $m\widehat{ST}$
   c. $m\angle SIT$ d. $m\widehat{SB}$
   e. $m\angle BIS$ f. $m\angle IOT$
   g. $m\widehat{IT}$ h. $m\angle TBI$

4. What is the value of x?

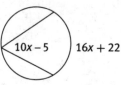

   A. 4.5   **B.** 8
   C. 25.5   **D.** 75

5. Use the circle below to complete the following.

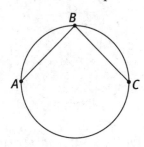

   a. If $\overline{AB} \cong \overline{BC}$, then $\widehat{AB} \cong$ _____.
   b. Write a convincing argument that supports your response to part a. *Hint*: Draw $\overline{AC}$ or the three radii that contain points A, B, and C.

6. If a polygon is inscribed in a circle, then each of its vertices lies on the circle. Which of the following correctly depict an inscribed polygon?

   A.

   B.

   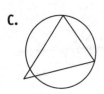

   C.

   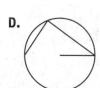

   D.

7. Find the length of one side of a square inscribed in a circle that has a radius of 4 cm.
 A. 4 cm
 B. $4\sqrt{2}$ cm
 C. 8 cm
 D. $8\sqrt{2}$ cm

Lesson 25-3

8. Use the diagram to answer each of the following.

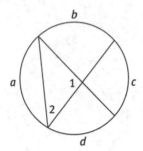

 a. If $a = 120°$, $c = 84°$, and $d = 108°$, then how much greater is $m\angle 1$ than $m\angle 2$? Explain.
 b. If $a = 110°$ and $m\angle 1 = 88°$, then
  $c =$ _____ and $b + d =$ _____.

9. Use *always*, *sometimes*, or *never* to make each of the following statements true.
 a. A parallelogram inscribed in a circle is a rectangle.
 b. An inscribed angle that intercepts an arc whose measure is greater than $180°$ is acute.
 c. If two angles intercept the same arc, they are congruent.

Lesson 25-4

Use the diagram for Items 10–13.

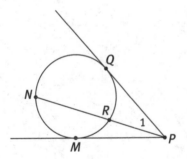

10. If $m\angle MPQ = 48°$, find $m\widehat{QM}$.

11. If $m\widehat{NQM} = 200°$, then what is $m\angle MPQ$?

12. If $m\widehat{QN} = 125°$ and $m\widehat{QR} = 83°$, find $m\angle 1$.

13. If $m\widehat{NQR} = 260°$ and $m\angle 1 = 45°$, then what is $m\widehat{QN}$?

MATHEMATICAL PRACTICES
Reason Abstractly and Quantitatively

14. $\overline{AB}$ and $\overline{AD}$ are tangent to the circle with center C as shown below. Imagine point A moving out to the left to increase AC. As it moves, $\angle A$ and points of tangency B and D will change.

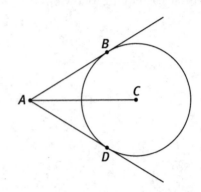

 a. As AC increases, what is happening to $m\angle A$?
 b. As AC increases, what is happening to BD?
 c. How small does $\angle A$ have to be for $\overline{BD}$ to be a diameter? Explain your answer.

The renowned architect and graduate of the MIU School of Design, Drew Atower, designed a hotel, all of whose floors spin on a circular track. As it spins, each floor pauses every 45°. (Otherwise, getting on and off the elevator would be tricky.) The figure below shows an overhead view of one of the square floors and its circular track. Points *A*, *B*, *C*, and *D* are located at each of the four corners of the building. $\overline{AO}$ bisects $\widehat{ZW}$. *Z*, *O*, and *X* are collinear. *A*, *O*, and *C* are collinear.

1. The circular track is tangent to each side of Quadrilateral *ABCD*, and all of the angles in Quadrilateral *ABCD* are right angles. Points *W*, *X*, *Y*, and *Z* are the points of tangency. Find each of the following.

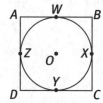

   a. $m\widehat{ZW}$
   b. $m\widehat{WXZ}$

2. Draw $\overline{AX}$ and label the point of intersection with the circle as point *M*. If $m\widehat{ZM} = 53°$, find $m\angle AXB$.

3. Draw $\overline{AC}$ and radius $\overline{OX}$. Find each of the following.
   a. $m\angle AOX$
   b. $m\angle OXA$
   c. $\angle CAX$ intercepts two arcs. Find their measures.

When the building rotates 45°, the corner that was located at point *A* is now located at point *E*. Points *P*, *Q*, *R*, and *S* are the points of tangency.

4. Draw $\overline{PS}$ and $\overline{RZ}$. Find the measure of the angles formed by $\overline{PS}$ and $\overline{RZ}$.

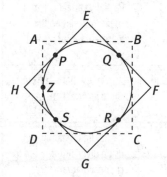

5. A circular stained glass and wrought iron window is to be installed above the front entrance. One of the stained glass window designs being considered has a radius of 90 cm and several wrought iron chords each 60 cm long. How far are the chords from the center of the circle? Draw a diagram and show your work.

In the main lobby of the hotel, there is a circular hospitality area that also rotates. The radius of the hospitality area is 3 m. The distance from the front door, at point *A*, to the far side of the hospitality area, at point *C*, is 20 m. At a certain moment the dessert bar is located at point *B* and the tourist information desk is located at point *E*.

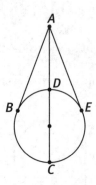

6. Assuming $\overline{AB}$ and $\overline{AE}$ are tangent to the circle, find *CD* and *AD*. Explain how you arrived at your answers.

Scoring Guide	Exemplary	Proficient	Emerging	Incomplete
	The solution demonstrates these characteristics:			
Mathematics Knowledge and Thinking (Items 1, 2, 3, 4, 5, 6)	• Clear and accurate understanding of the relationship between the measures of angles and arcs of a circle • Accurate use of theorems relating the length of segments in a circle	• A functional understanding of the relationship between the measures of angles and arcs of a circle • Mostly correct use of theorems relating the length of segments in a circle	• Partial understanding of the relationship between the measures of angles and arcs of a circle • Partially correct use of theorems relating the length of segments in a circle	• Little or no understanding of the relationship between the measures of angles and arcs of a circle • Incorrect or incomplete use of theorems relating the length of segments in a circle
Problem Solving (Items 1, 2, 3, 4, 5, 6)	• An appropriate and efficient strategy that results in correct answers	• A strategy that may include unnecessary steps but results in correct answers	• A strategy that results in some incorrect answers	• No clear strategy when solving problems
Mathematical Modeling / Representations (Items 2, 4, 5)	• Clear and accurate understanding of using given information to create a diagram to determine missing measures in circles	• Mostly accurate understanding of using given information to create a diagram to determine missing measures in circles	• Partial understanding of using given information to create a diagram to determine missing measures in circles	• Little or no understanding of using given information to create a diagram to determine missing measures in circles
Reasoning and Communication (Items 5, 6)	• Precise use of appropriate mathematics and language to justify the lengths of segments in a circle	• Mostly correct use of appropriate mathematics and language to justify the lengths of segments in a circle	• Misleading or confusing use of appropriate mathematics and language to justify the lengths of segments in a circle	• Incomplete or inaccurate use of appropriate mathematics and language to justify the lengths of segments in a circle

Coordinate Proofs

Prove It!

Lesson 26-1 Proving the Midpoint Formula

Learning Targets:

- Write coordinate proofs.
- Prove the midpoint formula.

> **SUGGESTED LEARNING STRATEGIES:** Create Representations, Look for a Pattern, Create a Plan

A **coordinate proof** is a proof of a geometric theorem, corollary, conjecture, or formula that uses variables as the coordinates of one or more points on the coordinate plane. Coordinate proofs can be used to justify many of the theorems and formulas you have learned so far. To form an argument using coordinate geometry, you will need to rely heavily on your knowledge of geometric and algebraic principles.

1. Draw $\overline{AB}$ on the coordinate plane, with endpoints $A(-4, 3)$ and $B(2, 1)$.

2. Find and plot the midpoint M of $\overline{AB}$. State the formula you used to determine the midpoint.

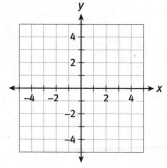

The steps in Item 3 will show you how to use a coordinate proof to justify that the midpoint formula is valid. You will be able to show the following:

Given: $P(x_1, y_1)$ and $Q(x_2, y_2)$ and

$$M\left(\frac{x_1 + x_2}{2}, \frac{y_1 + y_2}{2}\right).$$

Prove: M is the midpoint of $\overline{PQ}$.

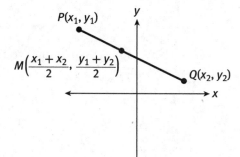

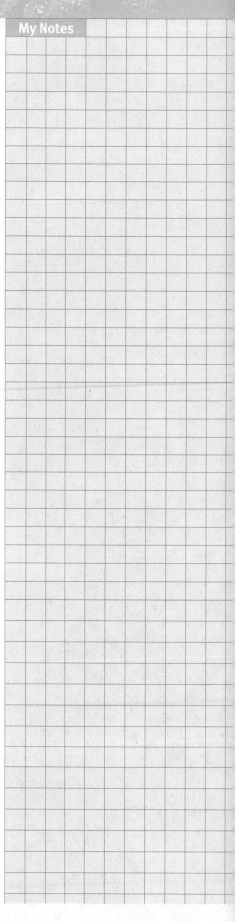

3. **Construct viable arguments.** To prove that M is the midpoint of $\overline{PQ}$, you need to show the following:

$PM = MQ$

$PM = \dfrac{1}{2}PQ$ and $MQ = \dfrac{1}{2}PQ$

a. Use the distance formula to find PQ. Substitute the coordinates of P and Q into the distance formula and write the resulting expression.

b. Use the distance formula to find PM.

• Substitute the coordinates of P and M into the distance formula and write the resulting expression.

• Simplify the expression. First, use a common denominator to combine terms within each set of parentheses.

• Then simplify so that there are no functions under the square root sign.

c. Use the distance formula to find MQ, and simplify the same way you did in part b.

d. Compare PM and MQ.

Compare PM and PQ, and compare MQ and PQ.

e. Complete the statement.
Since $PM =$ _____, $PM =$ _____ and $MQ =$ _____. Therefore, M is the midpoint of $\overline{PQ}$.

My Notes

Check Your Understanding

4. Sasha said it is enough to show that $PM = MQ$ to prove that point M is the midpoint of $\overline{PQ}$. Do you agree with Sasha? Why or why not? If not, what does this allow you to conclude about point M?

5. The coordinates of three collinear points are $M(a, b)$, $N(c, d)$, and $X\left(\dfrac{a+c}{2}, \dfrac{b+d}{2}\right)$.

   a. To show that X is the midpoint of $\overline{MN}$, what do you need to prove? Explain your answer.
   b. Use Item 3 as a guide to prove that X is the midpoint of $\overline{MN}$.
   c. Suppose you did not know that the points were collinear. Show the additional work that you would use to prove that X is the midpoint of $\overline{MN}$.

LESSON 26-1 PRACTICE

6. **Make use of structure.** Suppose you swapped points (x_1, y_1) and (x_2, y_2) in the proof in Item 3. Would the midpoint still be in the same location? Would it still have the same coordinates?

7. The endpoints of a line segment are $P(x, y)$ and $Q(r, s)$.
   a. Write the statements that you can use to prove that $X\left(\dfrac{x+r}{2}, \dfrac{y+s}{2}\right)$ is the midpoint of $\overline{PQ}$.
   b. Prove that $X\left(\dfrac{x+r}{2}, \dfrac{y+s}{2}\right)$ is the midpoint of $\overline{PQ}$.

8. Given that points P and Q lie on a vertical line, write a coordinate proof to validate the midpoint formula.

Learning Targets:

- Write coordinate proofs.
- Prove the slope criteria for parallel and perpendicular lines.

SUGGESTED LEARNING STRATEGIES: Create Representations, Predict and Confirm, Critique Reasoning

You can also use coordinate geometry to prove properties and theorems about parallel and perpendicular lines.

Maria and Eric have been asked to prove the following theorem. *Two nonvertical lines are parallel if and only if they have the same slope.*

Maria says she will prove one part of the theorem if Eric proves the other part of the theorem.

1. Maria's Coordinate Proof

Given: Line *l* and line *n* are parallel.

Prove: Line *l* and line *n* have the same slope.

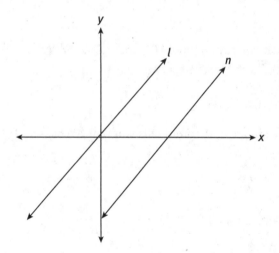

a. In the figure, line *l* ‖ line *n*, as shown. Draw a vertical line *p* that intersects line *l* at point *A* and another vertical line *q* that intersects line *n* at point *D*.

b. Draw a horizontal line *r* that intersects line *l* at point *C* and line *n* at point *F*.

c. Label the intersection of line *p* and line *r* as point *B*. Label the intersection of line *q* and line *r* as point *E*.

MATH TERMS

An *if and only if* statement is known as a **biconditional statement.** To prove a biconditional statement, you have to prove that both directions of the statement are true.

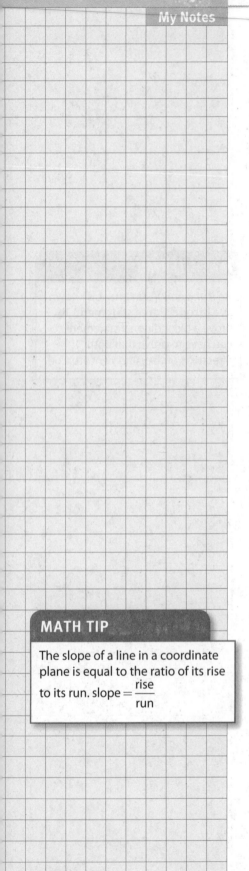

My Notes

d. Identify the segments that are parallel to the *x*-axis.

e. Identify the segments that are parallel to the *y*-axis.

f. What type of angle is formed by ∠*ABC* and by ∠*DEF*?

g. What do you know about ∠*ABC* and ∠*DEF*?

h. What can you say about ∠*ABC* and ∠*DEF*? Why?

i. What postulate or theorem tells you that △*ABC* ~ △*DEF*?

j. What reasoning supports the fact that $\dfrac{AB}{BC} = \dfrac{DE}{EF}$?

k. Use the figure to complete the following:
By the definition of slope, the slope of line *l* is
and the slope of line *n* is   .

MATH TIP

The slope of a line in a coordinate plane is equal to the ratio of its rise to its run. slope $= \dfrac{\text{rise}}{\text{run}}$

l. What does this prove about the slopes of parallel lines?

2. Eric's Coordinate Proof

Given: Line *l* and line *n* have the same slope.

Prove: Line *l* and line *n* are parallel lines.

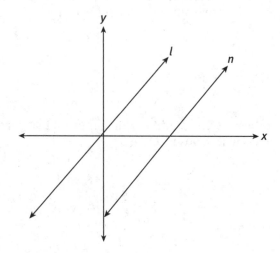

a. In the figure, line *l* and line *n* have the same slope. Draw a vertical line *p* that intersects line *l* at point *A* and another vertical line *q* that intersects line *n* at point *D*.

b. Draw a horizontal line *r* that intersects line *l* at point *C* and line *n* at point *F*.

c. Label the intersection of line *p* and line *r* as point *B*. Label the intersection of line *q* and line *r* as point *E*.

d. Based on the figure, can you conclude that $\dfrac{AB}{BC} = \dfrac{DE}{EF}$? Why?

e. As the next step in Eric's proof, he states that $\triangle ABC \sim \triangle DEF$ by SAS Similarity Criterion. How can he justify making this claim?

f. What is true about the angles of two similar triangles?

g. Eric states that $\angle BCA \cong \angle EFD$. Do you agree?

h. Can Eric now claim that line *l* is parallel to line *n*? Explain.

Check Your Understanding

3. Explain why $\dfrac{AB}{BC}$ represents the slope of line *l*.

4. What is true about the slope of all vertical lines used in coordinate proofs?

5. If Maria and Eric had drawn lines *l* and *n* as vertical lines, would their proofs still work? Is the theorem still valid in this case?

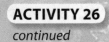

Maria challenged Eric to another proof about slope. She asked him to help her prove that two nonvertical lines are perpendicular if and only if the product of their slopes is −1.

6. **Make sense of problems.** Is the theorem that Maria wants to prove a biconditional? If so, what two statements need to be proven to prove the theorem?

7. Maria draws these two diagrams to help her prove that perpendicular lines have slopes whose product is −1.

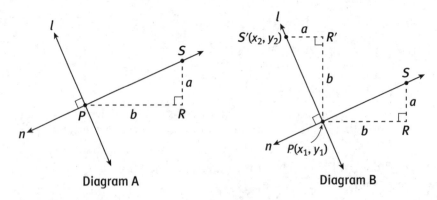

Diagram A   Diagram B

a. What information is given in Diagram A?

b. Assuming that *a* and *b* are both positive, is the slope of *n* positive or negative? Write an expression for the slope of line *n*.

c. Describe how you can use the coordinates of the vertices of $\triangle PR'S'$ in Diagram B to find the slope of line *l*. Is the slope of line *l* positive or negative?

d. Compute the product of the slope of line *l* and the slope of line *n*.

Lesson 26-2
Proofs About Slope

Check Your Understanding

8. Describe how Maria transformed △PRS to obtain △$PR'S'$.

9. Why didn't Maria draw either line l or line n as a horizontal line?

10. How did you know that the slope of line l was negative?

LESSON 26-2 PRACTICE

11. **Construct viable arguments.** Use the diagram below to write a coordinate proof of the second part of the theorem: Lines with slopes whose product is -1 are perpendicular. (*Hint:* First show $\angle 1 \cong \angle 3$. Then show that $\angle 1$ and $\angle 2$ must form a right angle.)

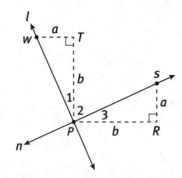

12. If two nonvertical lines are perpendicular, what can you assume about the signs of the slopes of the lines?

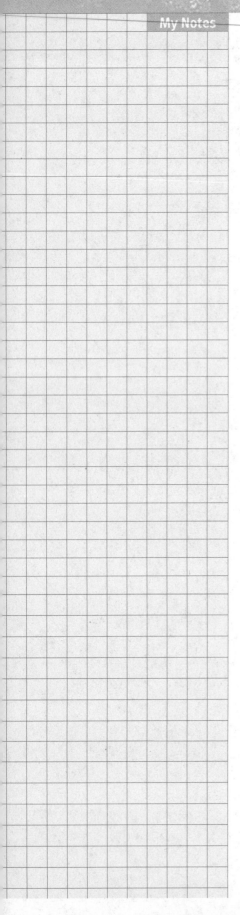

Learning Targets:
● Write coordinate proofs.
● Prove that the medians of a triangle are concurrent.

> **SUGGESTED LEARNING STRATEGIES:** Create Representations, Construct an Argument, Identify a Subtask, Simplify the Problem

When writing a coordinate proof, it is helpful to think about what you know about the concept at hand before delving into the proof. Getting an idea of the big picture will help you organize a step-by-step method for proving the conjecture or theorem.

A group of students has been asked to write a coordinate proof of the following theorem:

The medians of a triangle are concurrent.

1. State what you already know about the medians of a triangle.

2. Write a definition of *concurrent*.

3. What does the proof need to show?

4. **Make sense of problems.** There are four items or steps that need to be included in the proof of this theorem. Brainstorm to think of what these items might be. Create a list of these four items in the most logical, step-by-step order. Include any pertinent details in your outline.

   Step 1:

   Step 2:

   Step 3:

   Step 4:

Write a coordinate proof of the theorem following the steps you outlined in Item 4.

5. Step 1: Draw $\triangle XYZ$ with vertices $X(0, 0)$, $Y(2b, 2c)$, and $Z(2a, 0)$.

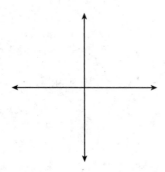

6. Step 2: Write the coordinates of the midpoint of each side of the triangle.
   a. Midpoint of $\overline{XY}$

   b. Midpoint of $\overline{YZ}$

   c. Midpoint of $\overline{XZ}$

   d. Label the midpoints in your drawing.

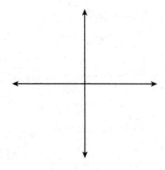

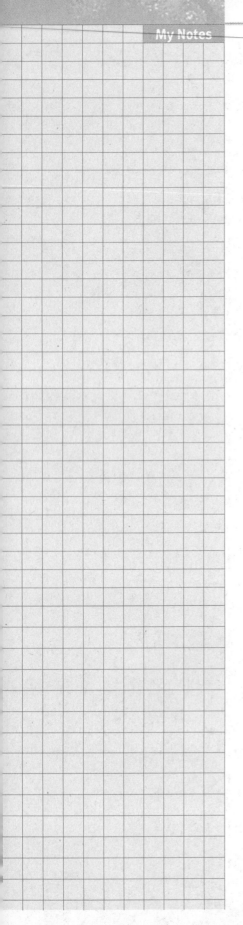

My Notes

7. **Step 3:** Write the equation of each median.

   a. Equation of median #1 using points (b, c) and $(2a, 0)$:
   Write an expression for the slope.

   Use the slope and point $(2a, 0)$ to write the equation of median #1.

   b. Equation of median #2 using points $(a, 0)$ and $(2b, 2c)$:
   Find the slope.

   Use the slope and a point $(2a, 0)$ to write the equation of median #2.

   c. Equation of median #3 using points $(a + b, 0)$ and $(0, 0)$:
   Find the slope.

   Use the slope and a point $(2a, 0)$ to write the equation of median #3.

Lesson 26-3
Proving Concurrency of Medians

My Notes

8. **Step 4:** Find the point where two of the medians intersect.

    a. Choose two of the equations and find their intersection point.

    b. Set the two equations equal and solve for x.

    c. Solve for y.

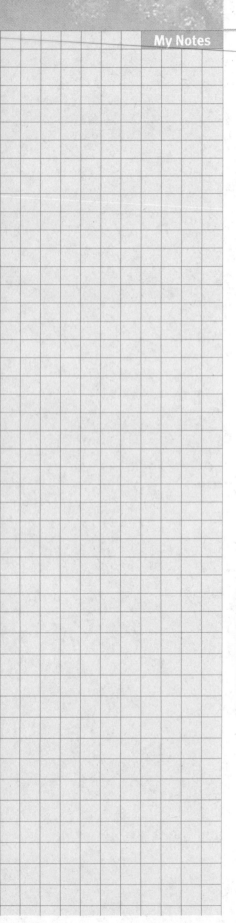

My Notes

d. Identify the point where $y = \dfrac{-c}{2a-b}x + \dfrac{2ac}{2a-b}$ and $y = \dfrac{c}{a+b}x$ intersect.

e. Verify that $\left(\dfrac{2(a+b)}{3}, \dfrac{2c}{3}\right)$ is a solution to the third equation, $y = \dfrac{2c}{2b-a}x - \dfrac{2ac}{2b-a}$.

f. Is $\left(\dfrac{2(a+b)}{3}, \dfrac{2c}{3}\right)$ a solution to all three equations?

9. What conclusion can you make about your findings?

Check Your Understanding

10. Describe a benefit in a coordinate proof of placing one of the edges of the triangle along the x-axis.

11. Point T is the centroid of $\triangle QRS$. Write a summary about the properties of point T.

LESSON 26-3 PRACTICE

12. Use appropriate tools strategically. Cut out a large triangle and use paper folding to construct the medians of the triangle. Verbally describe how this construction demonstrates the theorem that the medians of a triangle are concurrent.

13. Explain how to adapt the proof shown above to prove that a triangle with two congruent medians is an isosceles triangle.

Learning Targets:

- Find the coordinates of the point that is a given fractional distance along a line segment.
- Find the coordinates of the point that partitions a line segment in a given ratio.

> **SUGGESTED LEARNING STRATEGIES:** Create Representations, Activating Prior Knowledge

Maria tells Eric that she is going to walk from her math classroom to the cafeteria. Before leaving, she depicts her movement on a coordinate plane. Her movement is an example of a ***directed line segment***.

Maria indicates the math classroom on the coordinate plane as point M and the cafeteria as point C. Each endpoint of the segment is designated by an ordered pair.

Suppose Eric asks Maria to stop at the school's office before heading to the cafeteria. He indicates the location of the office as point O.

Suppose the math classroom is located at $M(-2, -1)$ and the cafeteria is at $C(2, 7)$. The office, point O, is located $\frac{1}{4}$ of the distance from point M to point C.

1. **Model with mathematics.** Plot points M and C on a coordinate grid.

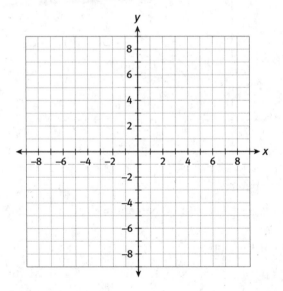

2. Estimate the location of point O. Should point O be closer to point M or to point C?

3. Compute the slope of $\overline{MC}$.

4. Devise a method to determine the coordinates of point O. Then find the coordinates of point O.

> **MATH TERMS**
>
> A **directed line segment** is a line segment that is designated with direction.

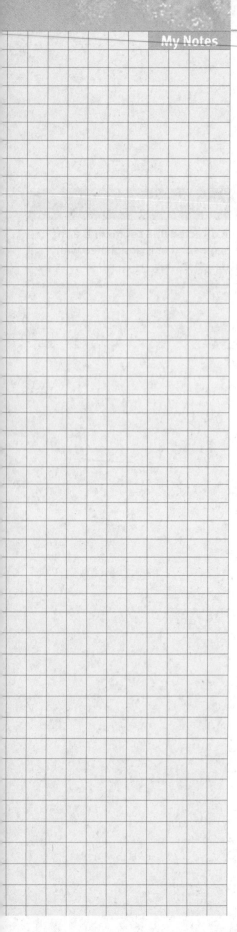

5. In which quadrant would you expect point *O* to be located?

6. Compare your method with a partner and check the reasonableness of your answer. Justify why the coordinate pair for point *O* is correct or incorrect.

7. If the office were located $\frac{3}{4}$ of the way from the math classroom to the cafeteria, would you expect either the *x*- or *y*-coordinate of point *O* to be negative? Explain.

Example A

Refer to the directed line segment Maria and Eric plotted on the coordinate grid. Find the coordinates of point *O* that lies along the directed line segment from *M*(1, 1) to *C*(7, 6) and partitions the segment into the ratio 3 to 2.

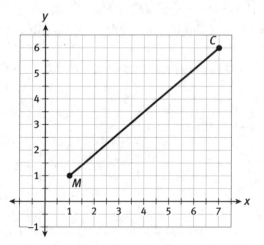

Step 1: Find the percent.

Point *O* is $\frac{3}{3+2} = \frac{3}{5}$, or 60 percent of the distance from point *M* to point *C*.

Step 2: Compute the slope.

The slope of $\overline{MC} = \frac{6-1}{7-1} = \frac{5}{6}$. The rise is 5 and the run is 6.

Step 3: Determine the coordinates of point *O*.

Since points *M*, *O*, and *C* are collinear, the slope of $\overline{MO}$ must be the same as $\overline{MC}$.

Find the *x*-coordinate of point *O* by multiplying the run of the slope by 60 percent and adding this value to the *x*-coordinate of point *M*.

x-coordinate of point *O*: $6(0.6) + 1 = 4.6$

Find the *y*-coordinate of point *O* by multiplying the rise of the slope by 60 percent and adding this value to the *y*-coordinate of point *M*: $5(0.6) + 1 = 4$

The ordered pair for point *O* is (4.6, 4).

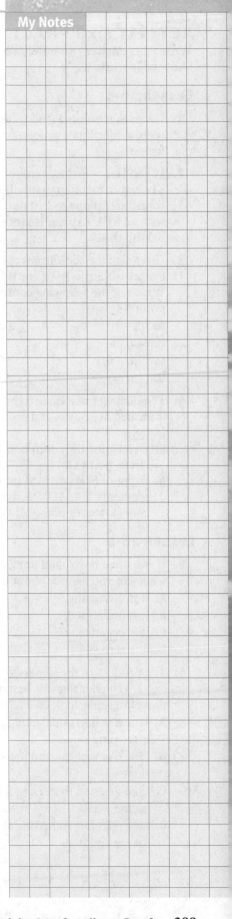

My Notes

Try These A

a. Find the coordinates of point T that lies $\frac{1}{2}$ of the way along the directed line segment from $B(2, 0)$ to $C(6, 4)$.

b. Point S lies along the directed line segment from $A(2, 0)$ to $R(6, 4)$. Point S partitions the segment into the ratio 1:3. Find the coordinates of point S.

c. Find the coordinates of point V that divides the directed line segment from $M(2, 4)$ to $C(5, 10)$ and partitions the segment into the ratio 3 to 2.

Check Your Understanding

8. Critique the reasoning of others. A line segment is partitioned into the ratio 5:6. Danny states that he needs to multiply the rise and the run of the slope by 83.3 percent. Do you agree or disagree with his process?

9. Plot the points in Try These A to determine if your ordered pair for point V is reasonable.

LESSON 26-4 PRACTICE

10. Make use of structure. Point R lies along the directed line segment from $Y(-1, -4)$ to $X(7, 6)$ and partitions the segment into the ratio 1 to 4. What is the slope of $\overline{YX}$, and how does this slope compare to the slope of $\overline{YR}$?

11. Find the coordinates of point B that lies along the directed line segment from $F(1, 1)$ to $G(7, 6)$ and partitions the segment into the ratio 2 to 4.

12. Find the coordinates of point W that lies along the directed line segment from $U(0, 5)$ to $S(8, 10)$ and partitions the segment into the ratio 1 to 5.

ACTIVITY 26 PRACTICE

Write your answers on notebook paper.
Show your work.

Lesson 26-1

1. Given that points *P* and *Q* lie on a horizontal line, write a coordinate proof to validate the midpoint formula.

2. When Henry writes a coordinate proof about a polygon, he often draws the polygon on the coordinate plane so that one of its sides aligns with an axis. Explain Henry's reasoning behind this.

3. Given that the coordinates of two vertices of isosceles triangle *WXY* are *W*(0, 0) and *Y*(2*d*, 4*f*). Which of the following coordinate pairs describes point *X*?
   A. $(0, -f)$
   B. $(4d, 0)$
   C. $(2d, -6f)$
   D. $(1d, 4f)$

4. The diameter of a circle is indicated by $\overline{FG}$. Point *F* is located at (x_1, y_1), and point *G* is located at (x_2, y_2).
   a. Determine the coordinates of the center of the circle, point *O*.
   b. Suppose $\overline{FG}$ is divided into four congruent segments: $\overline{FA}, \overline{AO}, \overline{OB}$, and $\overline{BG}$. Determine the coordinates of points *A*, *O*, and *B*.

Lesson 26-2

5. If you use a horizontal line in a coordinate proof, what can you assume about the slope of the line?
   A. It is increasing.
   B. It is undefined.
   C. It is negative.
   D. It is zero.

6. The product of the slopes of line *a* and line *b* is −1. Which statement best describes how these lines may look on a coordinate plane?
   A. Line *a* is horizontal, and line *b* has an increasing slope.
   B. Line *a* is vertical, and line *b* has a decreasing slope.
   C. Line *a* has an increasing slope, and line *b* lies on the *y*-axis.
   D. Line *a* has an increasing slope, and line *b* has a decreasing slope.

Lesson 26-3

7. In triangle *XYZ*, the medians of the triangle are also angle bisectors. In which type of triangle is this possible?
   A. Equilateral triangles   **B.** Isosceles triangles
   C. Right triangles   **D.** Scalene triangles

8. In triangle *QRS*, one of the medians is also an angle bisector. You have been asked to write a coordinate proof showing that this is true. Which type of triangle should you sketch?
   A. Equilateral triangle   **B.** Isosceles triangle
   C. Right triangle   **D.** Scalene triangle

Lesson 26-4

9. Point *S* partitions the segment into the ratio 2:3.

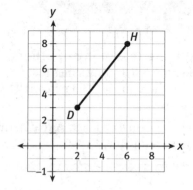

   a. Convert the ratio to a percent.
   b. Find the slope of $\overline{DH}$.
   c. Find the coordinates of point *S*.

10. Point *Q* lies along the directed line segment from *R*(2, 1) to *T*(6, 4). Point *Q* partitions the segment into the ratio 5:3. Find the coordinates of point *Q*.

11. Find the coordinates of point *H* that divides the directed line segment from *M*(2, 4) to *X*(5, 6) and partitions the segment into the ratio 5 to 1.

MATHEMATICAL PRACTICES
Construct Viable Arguments and Critique the Reasoning of Others

12. Work in small groups to determine how to set up a coordinate proof of the following theorem using the proofs learned in this lesson:

    The medians of a triangle are concurrent. The length of the segment of a median from the vertex to the point of concurrency is $\frac{2}{3}$ the length of the entire median.

Equation of a Circle

Round and Round
Lesson 27-1 Circles on the Coordinate Plane

Learning Targets:

- Derive the general equation of a circle given the center and radius.
- Write the equation of a circle given three points on the circle.

> **SUGGESTED LEARNING STRATEGIES:** Quickwrite, Think-Pair-Share, Create Representations, Vocabulary Organizer

How can the path of a windmill be described mathematically? Suppose the coordinate plane is positioned so that the center of the windmill's face is at the origin.

1. Show that the points given in the diagram are on the circle by showing that the coordinates of the points satisfy the equation given for the circle.

a. $x^2 + y^2 = 4$

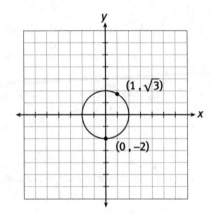

b. $x^2 + y^2 = 36$

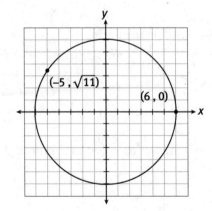

CONNECT TO STEM

A wind farm is an array of windmills used for generating electrical power. The world's largest wind farm at Altamont Pass, California, consists of 6,000 windmills. Wind farms supply about 1.5% of California's electricity needs.

My Notes

My Notes

Consider the circle below, which has its center at (0, 0) and has a radius of 5 units.

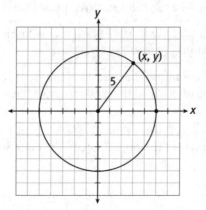

2. Suppose (x, y) is a point on the circle.
   a. Use the distance formula to write an equation to show that the distance from (x, y) to $(0, 0)$ is 5.

   b. Square both sides of your equation to eliminate the square root.

Consider a circle that has its center at the point (h, k) and has radius r.

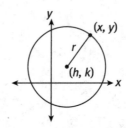

3. Suppose (x, y) is a point on the circle.
   a. Use the distance formula to write an equation to show that the distance from (x, y) to (h, k) is r.

   b. Square both sides of your equation to eliminate the square root.

My Notes

Check Your Understanding

4. Write the equation of the circle described.
   a. center $(0, 0)$ and radius 7
   b. center $(0, 2)$, radius $= 10$
   c. center $(9, -4)$, radius $= \sqrt{15}$

5. Identify the center and radius of the circle.
   a. $(x - 2)^2 + (y + 1)^2 = 9$
   b. $(x + 3)^2 + y^2 = 10$

Suppose the center of the windmill is not positioned at the origin of a coordinate plane but at $(2, -3)$.

6. Draw a circle with center $(2, -3)$ that contains the point $(5, 1)$.
   a. Write the equation of any circle with radius r and center $(2, -3)$.

   b. Substitute $(5, 1)$ for (x, y) in the equation from Item 6a. Explain what information this gives about the circle.

   c. Write the equation of the circle with center $(2, -3)$ that contains the point $(5, 1)$.

7. **Critique the reasoning of others.** Wyatt made the statement that the point $(2, \sqrt{6})$ lies on the circle centered at the origin and contains the point $(0, 4)$. He gave the following proof to support his statement:

   radius $= 4$;
   Equation of circle: $(x - 0)^2 + (y - 0)^2 = 4^2$
   $$x^2 + y^2 = 16$$

   Substitute $(2, \sqrt{6})$ for (x, y) in the equation.
   $$2^2 + \sqrt{6}^2 = 16$$
   $$4 + 12 = 16$$
   $$16 = 16$$

   Do you agree with Wyatt? If not, provide justification to support your answer.

8. Consider the circle that has a diameter with endpoints $(-1, 4)$ and $(9, -2)$.

   a. Determine the midpoint of the diameter. What information does this give about the circle?

   b. Using one of the endpoints of the diameter and the center of the circle, write the equation of the circle.

   c. Using the other endpoint of the diameter and the center of the circle, write the equation of the circle.

   d. What do you notice about your responses to parts b and c above? What does that tell you about writing the equation of a circle given the endpoints of the diameter?

9. Follow the steps below to write the equation of the circle that contains the following three points:

   $A(-4, -1)$, $B(6, -1)$, and $C(6, 5)$.

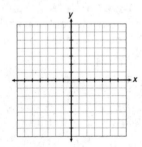

   a. Graph the three points.
   b. Draw the chords $\overline{AB}$ and $\overline{BC}$.
   c. Graph the perpendicular bisectors of the chords.
   d. What are the coordinates of the center of this circle?

   e. Write the equation of the circle using the center and any one of the given points A, B, or C.

MATH TIP

Recall that the perpendicular bisectors of chords of a circle intersect at the center of the circle.

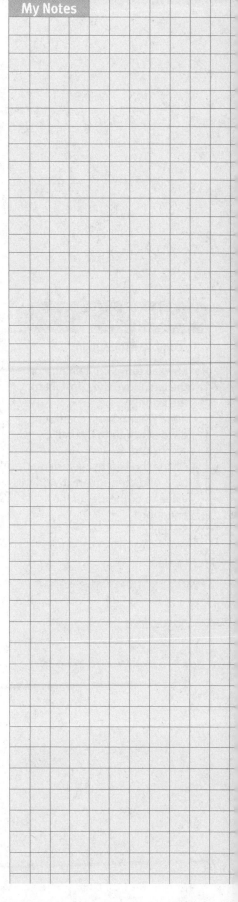

Check Your Understanding

10. Explain how to use absolute value to determine the radius of a circle centered at the origin, given a point on the *x*-axis.

11. Write the equation of the circle described.
    a. center (3, 6) passes through the point (0, −2)
    b. diameter with endpoints (2, 5) and (−10, 7)
    c. contains the points (−2, 5), (−2, −3), and (2, −3)

LESSON 27-1 PRACTICE

12. Write the equation of a circle centered at the origin with the given radius.
    a. radius = 6
    b. radius = $\sqrt{12}$

13. Write the equation of a circle given the center and radius.
    a. center: (7, 2); radius = 5
    b. center: (−4, −2); radius = 9

14. Identify the center and radius of the circle.
    a. $(x - 5)^2 + y^2 = 225$
    b. $(x + 4)^2 + (y - 2)^2 = 13$

15. **Model with mathematics.** An engineer draws a cross-sectional area of a pipe on a coordinate plane with the endpoints of the diameter at (2, −1) and (−8, 7). Determine the equation of the circle determined by these endpoints.

16. Points $A(2, -4)$, $B(6, -2)$, and $C(5, 5)$ lie on circle P.
    a. Determine the center of circle P.
    b. Determine the radius of circle P.

17. Points $X(2, 2)$, $Y(2, 14)$, and $Z(8, 8)$ lie on circle O. Determine the equation of circle O.

My Notes

Learning Targets:

● Find the center and radius of a circle given its equation.
● Complete the square to write the equation of a circle in the form $(x - h)^2 + (y - k)^2 = r^2$.

SUGGESTED LEARNING STRATEGIES: Vocabulary Organizer, Create Representations, Think-Pair-Share

When an equation is given in the form $(x - h)^2 + (y - k)^2 = r^2$, it is easy to identify the center and radius of a circle, but equations are not always given in this form. For instance, the path of a windmill is more realistically represented by a more complicated equation.

1. Suppose the path of a windmill is given by the equation $x^2 + 6x + (y - 2)^2 = 16$. Describe how this equation is different from the standard form of the circle equation.

In algebra, you learned how to complete the square to rewrite quadratic polynomials, such as $x^2 + bx$, as a factor squared. The process for completing the square is depicted below.

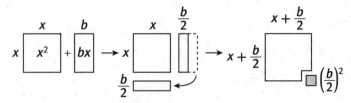

MATH TIP

To complete the square:

• Keep all terms containing *x* on the left. Move the constant to the right.
• If the x^2 term has a coefficient, divide each term by that coefficient.
• Divide the *x*-term coefficient by 2, and then square it. Add this value to both sides of the equation.
• Simplify.
• Write the perfect square on the left.

2. What term do you need to add to each side of the equation $x^2 + 6x + (y - 2)^2 = 16$ to complete the square for $x^2 + 6x$?

3. Complete the square and write the equation in the form $(x - h)^2 + (y - k)^2 = r^2$.

4. **Make use of structure.** Identify the center and the radius of the circle represented by your equation in Item 3.

Check Your Understanding

5. Complete each square, and write the equation in the form $(x - h)^2 + (y - k)^2 = r^2$.

   a. $x^2 - 2x + y^2 = 3$

   b. $x^2 + 3x + (y + 2)^2 = 1$

Sometimes equations for circles become so complicated that you may need to complete the square on both variables in order to write the equation in standard circle form.

Example A

A mural has been planned using a large coordinate grid. An artist has been asked to paint a red circular outline around a feature according to the equation $x^2 - 4x + y^2 + 10y = 6$. Determine the center and the radius of the circle that the artist has been asked to paint.

Follow these steps to write the equation in standard circle form.

Step 1: Write the equation.
$$x^2 - 4x + y^2 + 10y = 7$$

Step 2: Complete the square on both the x- and y-terms.

To complete the square on $x^2 - 4x$, take half of 4 and square it. Add this term to both sides of the equation. Then simplify, and write $x^2 - 4x + 4$ as a perfect square.

$$x^2 - 4x + 4 + y^2 + 10y = 7 + 4$$
$$(x - 2)^2 + y^2 + 10y = 11$$

To complete the square on $y^2 + 10$, take half of 10 and square it. Add this term to both sides of the equation. Then simplify, and write $y^2 + 10y + 25$ as a perfect square.

$$(x - 2)^2 + y^2 + 10y + 25 = 11 + 25$$
$$(x - 2)^2 + (y + 5)^2 = 36$$

Step 3: Determine the center and radius of the circle.

Using the equation, the center of the circle is at $(2, -5)$ and the radius is 6.

> **CONNECT TO AP**
>
> You can use what you know about circles to determine the equation for a sphere. In calculus, you will learn to compute how fast the radius and other measurements of a sphere are changing at a particular instant in time.

Try These A

Find the center and radius of each circle.

a. $(x - 5)^2 + y^2 - 2y = 8$

b. $x^2 + 4x + (y - 4)^2 = 12$

c. $x^2 - 8x + y^2 - 14y = 16$

d. $x^2 + 6x + y^2 + 12y = 4$

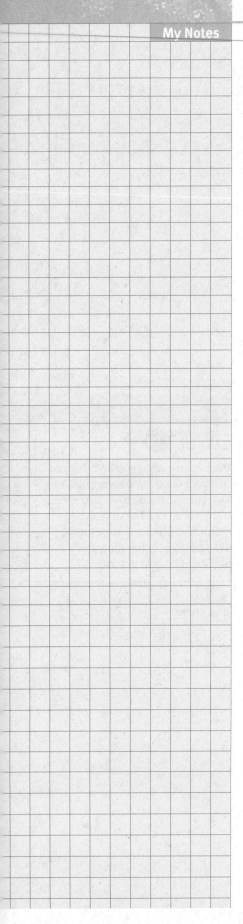

Check Your Understanding

6. Refer to Example A. Explain how you know the x-coordinate of the center of the circle is a positive value and the y-coordinate is negative.

7. Circle Q is represented by the equation $(x + 3)^2 + y^2 + 18y = 4$. Bradley states that he needs to add 18 to each side of the equation to complete the square on the y-term. Marisol disagrees and states that it should be 9. Do you agree with either student? Justify your reasoning.

8. Circle P is represented by the equation $(x - 8)^2 + 9 + y^2 + 6y = 25$.
   a. What is the next step in writing the equation in standard form for a circle?
   b. What is the radius of the circle?

LESSON 27-2 PRACTICE

9. Determine if the equation given is representative of a circle. If so, determine the coordinates of the center of the circle.
   a. $x^2 + y^2 - 6y = 16$
   b. $x - 49 + y^2 - 6y = 4$
   c. $x^2 - 2x + y^2 + 10y = 0$

10. Determine the center and radius of each circle.
    a. $(x - 6)^2 + y^2 - 8y = 0$
    b. $x^2 - 20x + y^2 - 12y = 8$
    c. $x^2 + 14x + y^2 + 2y = 14$

11. **Reason quantitatively.** On a two-dimensional diagram of the solar system, the orbit of Jupiter is represented by circle J. Circle J is drawn on the diagram according to the equation $x^2 - 4x - 9 + y^2 + 5 = 0$.
    a. The center of the circle falls on which axis?
    b. What are the coordinates of the center of the circle?
    c. What is the radius?

ACTIVITY 27 PRACTICE
Write your answers on notebook paper.
Show your work.

Lesson 27-1

1. A circle is drawn on the coordinate plane to represent an in-ground swimming pool. The circle is represented by the equation $(x - 3)^2 + y^2 = 4$. Which of the following points lies on the circle?
   A. $(1, 0)$
   B. $(2, 1)$
   C. $(1, -2)$
   D. $(3, 0)$

2. Two points on the circle given by the equation $(x - 1)^2 + (y + 3)^2 = 100$ have the x-coordinate -7. What are the y-coordinates of those two points?

3. Write an equation for the circle described.
   a. center $(-3, 0)$ and radius $= 7$
   b. center $(4, 3)$, tangent to the y-axis
   c. center $(2, -1)$ and contains the point $(4, 5)$
   d. diameter, with endpoints $(2, -5)$ and $(4, 1)$
   e. contains the points $(-2, 3)$, $(-2, 7)$, and $(6, 3)$

4. Explain how you can tell by looking at the equation of the circle that the center of the circle lies on the y-axis.

5. Write the equation of a circle centered at the origin with the given radius.
   a. radius $= 3$
   b. radius $= \sqrt{11}$

6. Which equation represents a circle with a diameter at endpoints $(-1, 5)$ and $(3, 7)$?
   A. $(x - 1)^2 + (y - 6)^2 = 5$
   B. $(x - 2)^2 + (y - 10)^2 = 4$
   C. $(x + 6)^2 + (y + 1)^2 = 25$
   D. $(x + 10)^2 + (y - 2)^2 = 10$

7. Which circle has a center of $(0, -4)$?
   A. $(x - 4)^2 + y^2 = 4$
   B. $(x + 1)^2 + (y - 4)^2 = 4$
   C. $x^2 + (y + 4)^2 = 16$
   D. $(x + 4)^2 + (y - 4)^2 = 16$

8. Suppose a cross-sectional area of a pipe is drawn on a coordinate plane. The circle contains points $(1, 4)$, $(9, 4)$, and $(9, -2)$. Determine the equation of the circle.

9. Identify the center and radius of the circle given by each equation.
   a. $(x - 3)^2 + y^2 = 1$
   b. $(x + 2)^2 + (y + 1)^2 = 16$

Lesson 27-2

10. Identify the center and radius of the circle represented by the equation $(x + 4)^2 + y^2 - 10y = 11$.

11. Circle Q is represented by the equation $(x + 1)^2 + y^2 + 6y = 5$. Howard states that the center of the circle lies in Quadrant III. Do you agree? Justify your reasoning.

12. Circle P is represented by the equation $(x - 11)^2 + y^2 + 10y = 25$. What is the radius of the circle?
    A. $\sqrt{5}$
    B. 10
    C. 25
    D. $\sqrt{50}$

13. Determine if the equation given is representative of a circle. If it is, determine the coordinates of the center of the circle.
    a. $x + 5 - y^2 - y = 5$
    b. $x^2 - 2 + y^2 - 8y = 7$
    c. $x^2 + 2x + y^2 - 16y = 0$

14. For any equations in Item 13 that are not equations of a circle, explain how you determined your answer.

MATHEMATICAL PRACTICES
Look For and Make Use of Structure

15. Given an equation of a circle, how can you determine when you need to complete the square to determine the coordinates of the center of the circle? Write an example of an equation of a circle where you would have to complete the square to determine that the circle has a radius of 10 and a center of $(4, 6)$.

Equations of Parabolas
Throwing a Curve
Lesson 28-1 Parabolas on the Coordinate Plane

Learning Targets:
- Derive the general equation of a parabola given the focus and directrix.
- Write the equation of a parabola given a specific focus and directrix.

> **SUGGESTED LEARNING STRATEGIES:** Create Representations, Interactive Word Wall, Critique Reasoning

Recall from your study of quadratic functions that the graph of a function in the form $ax^2 + bx + c = y$ is a curve called a parabola. A **parabola** is defined geometrically as the set of points in a plane that are equidistant from a given point, called the **focus**, and a given line, called the **directrix**.

Consider the graph below, on which the focus is located at (0, 1) and the directrix is given by the linear equation $y = -1$. For the curve to be a parabola, the distance from any point A on the curve to the focus and the distance from point A to the directrix must be equal.

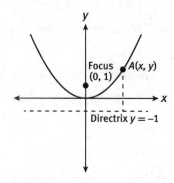

MATH TIP

To determine the distance from a point to a line, find the length of the perpendicular line segment from the line to the point.

Use the graph of the parabola shown above to derive an equation for the parabola.

1. The ordered pairs and equation for the focus, directrix, and point A on the parabola are as follows:

    Focus   (0, 1)
    Directrix $y = -1$
    Point A (x, y)

    Write an expression in terms of y for the distance between point A and the directrix.

2. Write an expression for the distance between the focus and point A.

My Notes

3. Set the expressions in Items 1 and 2 equal and solve for y. Show your work.

4. Suppose the ordered pair for the focus is given as $(0, p)$ and the line for the directrix is given as $y = -p$. How would you modify your equation in Item 3 to generalize for *any* parabola? Show your work by completing the following.

   a. Write an expression for the distance between point A and the directrix.

   b. Write an expression for the distance between the focus and point A.

   c. Set the expressions equal and solve for y.

CONNECT TO **AP**

In calculus, you will use vectors as well as parametric equations to find the distance from a point to a line.

5. Write the general equation of a parabola given the focus $(0, p)$ and directrix $y = -p$.

6. Based on what you know about quadratic equations, what can be determined about the vertex of the parabola in Item 5?

Check Your Understanding

7. Write the equation of the parabola with vertex at the origin, focus $(0, 8)$, and directrix $y = -8$.

8. Suppose a point on a parabola is $(4, 5)$ and the directrix is $y = -1$. Describe two methods you could use to determine the distance between the point and the directrix.

In your study of quadratic functions, you learned that some parabolas open up or down. Some parabolas also open to the left or to the right.

9. If a parabola opens to the left or to the right, what must be true about the directrix?

10. Given that the focus is $(p, 0)$, determine a general equation that can be used for a parabola that opens to the left or right.

11. **Make use of structure.** How can you determine if a parabola with focus $(p, 0)$ opens to the left or to the right?

Example A

Write the equation of a parabola with focus $(-3, 0)$ and directrix $x = 3$.

Step 1: Graph the focus and directrix on the coordinate plane.

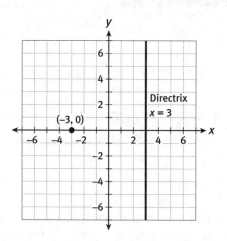

Step 2: Find p.

Since the focus and the directrix must be equidistant from any point on the parabola, find p by finding half the distance between the focus and the directrix.

Distance = 6, so $p = 3$.

Step 3: Write the equation of the parabola.

Substitute the value of p into the general equation for a parabola that opens left or right. Since the parabola opens to the left, substitute $p = -3$ into the equation.

$$x = \frac{1}{4p} y^2$$

$$x = \frac{1}{4(-3)} y^2$$

$$x = -\frac{1}{12} y^2$$

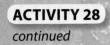

Try These A

Write the equation of a parabola with its vertex at the origin for each focus and directrix.

a. focus: $(0, -5)$; directrix: $y = 5$

b. focus: $(-4, 0)$; directrix: $x = 4$

12. Explain how you know if the parabola in Try These Item a opens up, down, left, or right.

Check Your Understanding

13. Write the equation of the parabola with vertex $(0, 0)$ and directrix $y = 9$.

LESSON 28-1 PRACTICE

14. Write the equation of the parabola with focus $(0, 4)$ and directrix $y = -4$.

15. Write the equation of the parabola with vertex $(0, 0)$, focus $(0.25, 0)$, and directrix $x = -0.25$.

16. **Critique the reasoning of others.** Hans describes a parabola by saying that the vertex of the parabola is at the origin, the focus is at $(0, -6)$, and the directrix is $y = -10$. Mei says that the curve Hans is describing is not a parabola. With whom do you agree? Explain.

Learning Targets:

- Derive the general equation of a parabola given the vertex and directrix.
- Write the equation of a parabola given a specific vertex and directrix.

> **SUGGESTED LEARNING STRATEGIES:** Create Representations, Look for a Pattern, Summarizing, Predict and Confirm

The graph of a quadratic function in the form $y = ax^2$ is a parabola with its vertex at the origin. The graph of a quadratic function in the form $y = ax^2 + bx + c$ is also a parabola, but its vertex is not necessarily at the origin.

A parabolic satellite dish is modeled by the parabola $y + 1 = \frac{1}{4}(x - 2)^2$.

1. To graph the equation, first rewrite the equation by isolating the y–term.

2. Consider what you have learned about transformations to predict how the graph of the parabola compares to the graph of $y = \frac{1}{4}x^2$.

3. **Model with mathematics.** Graph $y = \frac{1}{4}x^2$ on the coordinate plane. Then graph the translations from Item 2 to draw the graph of $y + 1 = \frac{1}{4}(x - 2)^2$.

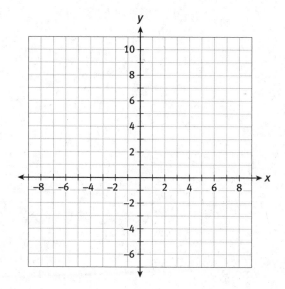

My Notes

> **TECHNOLOGY TIP**
>
> Check your graphs using a graphing calculator. Use the trace feature to identify the vertex of a parabola.

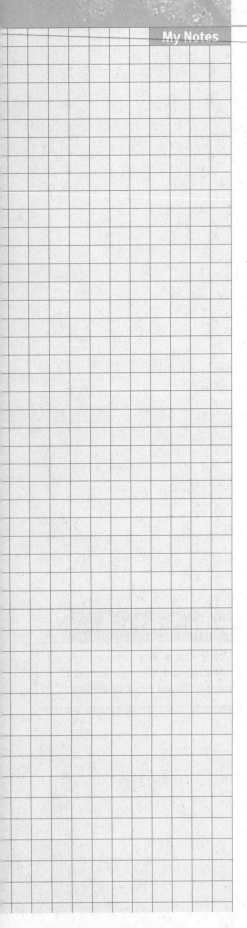

My Notes

4. Determine the vertex of the translated parabola in Item 3.

5. **Make sense of problems.** Examine the equation $y + 1 = \frac{1}{4}(x - 2)^2$, the vertex, and the graph of the parabola. Write a summary statement explaining what you just discovered.

6. Draw a conclusion about how to use the equation of a parabola in the form $y - k = \frac{1}{4p}(x - h)^2$ to determine the vertex of the parabola.

Lesson 28-2
Parabolas with Vertex (h, k)

Example A

Write the equation of a parabola with vertex (2, 3) and directrix $y = 2$.

Step 1: Graph the vertex and directrix on the coordinate plane.

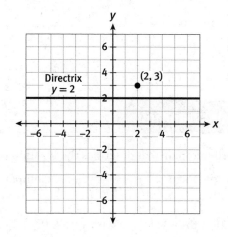

Step 2: Find p.

The focus and the directrix must be equidistant from any point on the parabola, and p is the distance between the vertex and the directrix.

$p = 1$

Step 3: Write the equation of the parabola.

Substitute the value of the vertex (h, k) and the value of p into the general equation for a parabola that opens up or down.

Substitute $h = 2$, $k = 3$, and $p = 1$.

$$y - k = \frac{1}{4p}(x - h)^2$$

$$y - 3 = \frac{1}{4(1)}(x - 2)^2$$

$$y - 3 = \frac{1}{4}(x - 2)^2$$

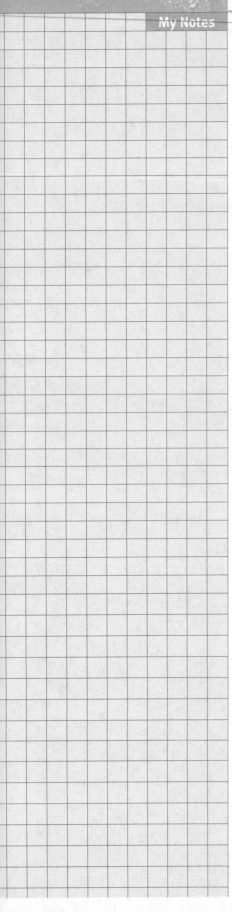

My Notes

Try These A

Write the equation of a parabola with the given vertex and directrix.

   a. vertex: (4, 1); directrix: $y = -3$

   b. vertex: (1, 1); directrix: $y = -11$

Check Your Understanding

7. Identify the ordered pair that describes the location of the vertex for an equation in the form $x - h = \dfrac{1}{4p}(y - k)^2$. Compare this to your response to Item 6.

8. Write an equation for a parabola with vertex (5, −2) and directrix $y = -4$.

LESSON 28-2 PRACTICE

9. Write an equation for a parabola with vertex (−1, 5) and directrix $y = 2$.

10. Write the equation of the parabola with focus (1, 1) and directrix $y = -3$.

11. **Model with mathematics.** Alberto models the parabolic path of a seagull using the equation $y - 4 = (x - 3)^2$. The vertex of the parabola represents the point at which the seagull snatches a crab off the beach. What is the vertex of the parabola?

12. Write the equation of the parabola with vertex (−3, −1) and focus (−3, −3).

13. Write the equation of the parabola with focus (1, 4) and directrix $x = 3$.

14. Casey throws a football for 40 yards. The maximum height the ball reaches is 12 yards. Model the path of the football with the equation of a parabola.

ACTIVITY 28 PRACTICE

Write your answers on notebook paper.
Show your work.

Lesson 28-1

For Items 1–3, write the equation of the parabola shown.

1.

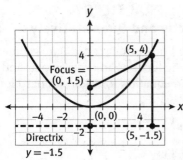

2.

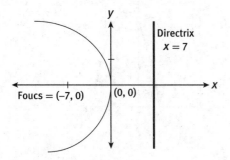

3.

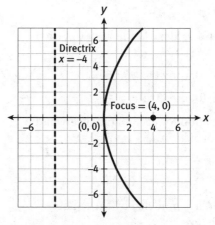

4. The equation of a parabola is $y = \frac{1}{12}x^2$. The vertex of the parabola is at the origin. What are the coordinates of the focus?
  A. $(0, 3)$
  B. $(3, 0)$
  C. $(4, 3)$
  D. $(0, -4)$

5. Write the equation of the parabola with focus $(2, 0)$ and directrix $x = -2$.

6. Write the equation of the parabola with focus $(0, -6)$ and directrix $y = 6$.

7. Write the equation of the parabola with focus $(0, 10)$ and directrix $y = -10$.

Lesson 28-2

For Items 8 and 9, identify the vertex of each parabola.

8. focus $(4, 4)$; directrix $y = 6$

9. focus $(2, 0)$; directrix $x = -4$

Write the equation for each parabola given the following information.

10. vertex $(0, -2)$; directrix $y = 2$

11. focus $(3, 1)$; directrix $x = -2$

12. A parabola is modeled by the equation
$(y + 2) = \dfrac{(x - 5)^2}{12}$. Identify the vertex and directrix.

13. Which equation represents a parabola with focus $(2, 6)$ and directrix $y = 2$?

   A. $y + 4 = \dfrac{1}{10}(x - 2)^2$

   B. $y - 4 = \dfrac{1}{8}(x - 2)^2$

   C. $y + 6 = -\dfrac{1}{8}(x - 2)^2$

   D. $y - 6 = -\dfrac{1}{10}(x + 2)^2$

14. Determine the equation of the parabola graphed on the coordinate plane below.

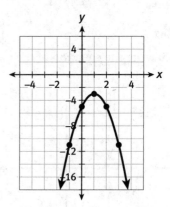

MATHEMATICAL PRACTICES
Reason Abstractly and Quantitatively

15. Use what you know about coordinate geometry to represent the focus as an ordered pair and the directrix as an equation for each standard form of a parabola.

   a. $y - k = \dfrac{1}{4p}(x - h)^2$

   b. $x - h = \dfrac{1}{4p}(y - k)^2$

Constructions

Constructive Thinking
Lesson 29-1 Constructions with Segments and Angles

Learning Targets:
- Use constructions to copy a segment or an angle.
- Use constructions to bisect a segment or an angle.

> **SUGGESTED LEARNING STRATEGIES:** Construct an Argument, Look for a Pattern, Create a Plan

An architect is working on plans for a new museum. The architect often relies on CAD programs to create her architectural drawings, but sometimes she uses geometric constructions to make additional drawings directly on printouts.

Geometric constructions were used to make architectural drawings prior to CAD programs and other advances in computer technology. The only tools involved in *geometric constructions* are a compass and straightedge. A *compass* is used to draw circles and arcs, and a *straightedge* is used to draw segments, rays, and lines.

The architectural plan shows a circular opening for a window above the front museum entrance. The architect wants to construct a square pane of glass in the circular opening.

1. **Use appropriate tools strategically.** Draw a point *P*. Use your compass to draw various circles with center at point *P*.

2. Describe the effect of the compass setting on the size of a circle.

To construct the square pane of glass, the architect first needs to know how to construct congruent segments.

3. Construct a segment congruent to a given segment.
   a. Use a straightedge to draw a line segment. Label the endpoints *E* and *Z*.

   b. Now use the straightedge to draw another segment, slightly longer than $\overline{EZ}$. Mark a point on the segment and label it *C*.

   c. Set the compass to the length of $\overline{EZ}$.

   d. Describe how to use the compass to draw a segment congruent to segment *EZ* that has point *C* as one of the endpoints.

   e. How can you use the properties of a circle to verify that the two segments have the same length?

MATH TIP

In geometry, the terms *construct*, *sketch*, and *draw* have very different, specific meanings. In an instruction to *construct* a geometric figure, it is implied that only a compass and a straightedge are permitted to complete the task. In an instruction to *sketch* a figure, a quick jotted picture is intended to illustrate relative geometric relationships. Accurate measurements are not required in a sketch. A *drawing* usually implies a more careful image made with a ruler and/or a protractor.

CONNECT TO HISTORY

This table of geometry, from the 1728 publication titled *Cyclopaedia*, illustrates classic constructions.

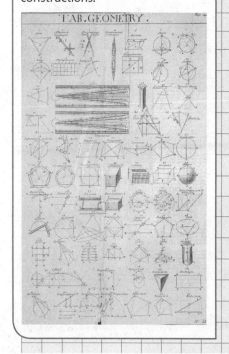

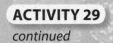

My Notes

To create visual interest for the museum ceiling, the architect plans to design a triangular pattern with some of the support beams. The architect needs to determine which sets of beams can be used to form a triangle.

4. The architect is examining the following segments to use in her drawing.

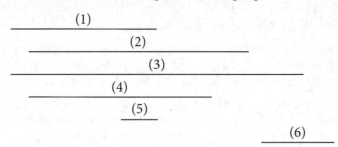

    (1)

      (2)

        (3)

    (4)

    (5)

          (6)

a. Try to construct a triangle using segments 1, 3, and 4. Do these segments form a triangle?

b. Try to construct a triangle using segments 2, 5, and 6. Do these segments form a triangle?

c. Experiment with other combinations of three segments. Name a set of segments that forms a triangle and a set of segments that does not form a triangle.

d. Construct viable arguments. Make a conjecture as to why some of the segments form a triangle and some do not.

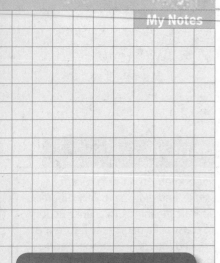

MATH TIP

The Triangle Inequality Theorem states that the sum of the lengths of any two sides of a triangle must be greater than the length of the third side.

The architect decides to use segments 1, 2, and 4 to create triangular windows in the museum library. In order to duplicate the triangle, the architect needs to make sure that the angles of the windows are congruent.

5. Construct an angle congruent to a given angle.

   a. Use a straightedge to draw an acute angle. Label the angle *CAT*. Use the compass to draw an arc through the angle as shown.

   b. Now use the straightedge to draw a new ray, and label the endpoint *O*.

   c. Place one end of your compass on point *O* and draw a large arc. Using the same radius as in Step 5a, place the center of your compass at point *O* and draw an arc. Label the point of intersection with the ray as *G*.

   d. Describe how to use the compass to measure the opening of ∠*CAT*.

   e. Explain a method for constructing ray *OD* to form ∠*DOG* so that ∠*CAT* is congruent to ∠*DOG*.

   f. **Critique the reasoning of others.** Maria says that it will not matter whether the radius of the compass changes from Step d to Step e. Is she correct or incorrect? Explain your answer.

6. How can you use the properties of a circle to verify that the two angles you constructed in Item 5 have the same measure?

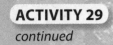
My Notes

Check Your Understanding

7. Use the given figures to create the following constructions on a separate sheet of unlined paper.

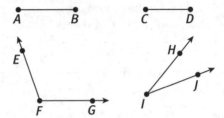

a. Construct and name a segment congruent to $\overline{AB}$.
b. Construct and name a segment with length equal to $3CD - AB$.
c. Construct and name an angle congruent to $\angle EFG$.
d. Construct an angle with measure equal to $m\angle EFG + m\angle HIJ$.

The architect's plans include a column in the museum foyer that intersects the second floor as a perpendicular bisector.

8. Suppose $\overline{WO}$ represents the second floor of the museum.

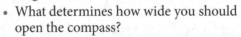

a. **Make sense of problems.** What must be true about the column for it to be considered a perpendicular bisector?

b. To draw the perpendicular bisector of $\overline{WO}$, you will first draw a large arc with the compass point at point W, as shown in the figure.
   • What determines how wide you should open the compass?

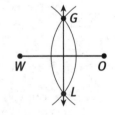

   • What arc do you need to draw next? Will you adjust your compass setting?

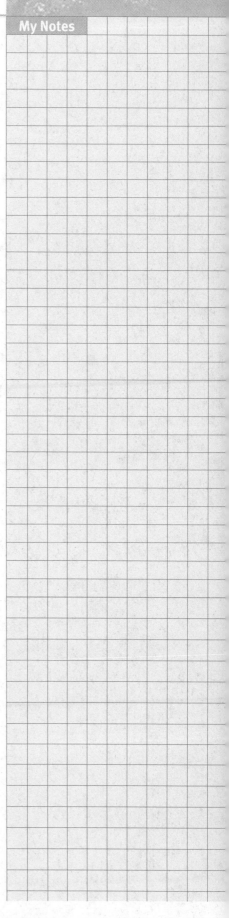

c. Draw the final arc. Make sure the arc is large enough to intersect the other arc above and below the line segment. Then align a straightedge with the intersection points of the arcs (above and below the line segment) to draw the perpendicular bisector.

Explain why the construction guarantees that the constructed line is the perpendicular bisector of $\overline{WO}$.

9. A step-by-step process for constructing an angle bisector follows. Use what you have learned about constructions and your knowledge of bisectors to describe the step-by-step process. Be sure to identify the tools used in each step.

a. Given $\angle A$.

b.

My Notes

c.

d.

e.

10. **Construct viable arguments.** Explain why the construction in Item 9 guarantees that the constructed ray is the bisector of the given angle.

Lesson 29-1
Constructions with Segments and Angles

ACTIVITY 29
continued

Check Your Understanding

11. Make sense of problems. Explain how you could construct a segment whose length is half the length of $\overline{WO}$.

12. Perform the construction you described in Item 11.

LESSON 29-1 PRACTICE

13. Describe a way to divide $\overline{WO}$ into four congruent segments.

14. Explain why the construction in Item 5 guarantees that the constructed angle is congruent to the original angle.

15. Attend to precision. Construct the angle bisector of $\angle Z$.

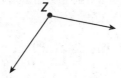

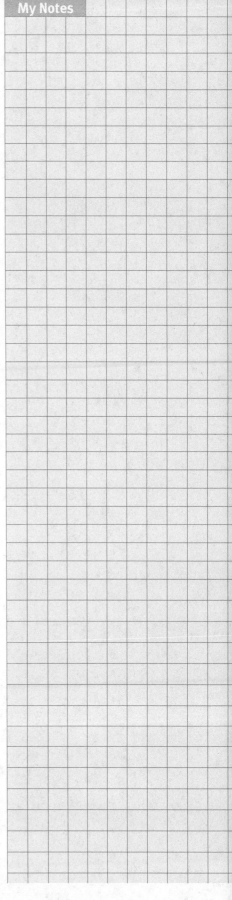

Activity 29 • Constructions   **417**

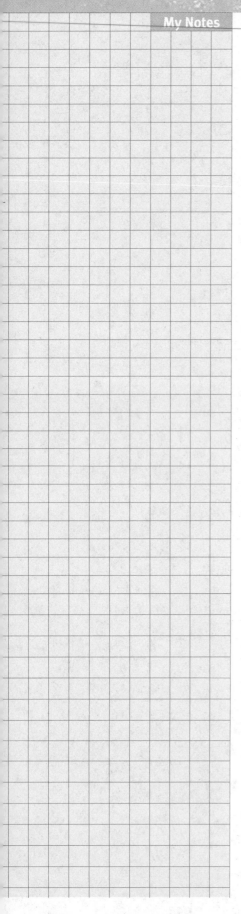

My Notes

Learning Targets:

● Construct parallel and perpendicular lines.

● Use constructions to make conjectures about geometric relationships.

SUGGESTED LEARNING STRATEGIES: Predict and Confirm, Simplify the Problem, Think-Pair-Share, Critique Reasoning, Sharing and Responding

A designer working with the architect wants to design the children's part of the museum with exposed ducts and pipes.

The designer requests that the pipes run parallel to each other across the top of the room.

1. The architect constructs line ℓ to represent one pipe. She then marks point H on the drawing to indicate where the next pipe should be located.

   a. What must be true about the line drawn through point H?

   b. **Use appropriate tools strategically.** Draw a point on line ℓ and label it A. Use your compass to draw an arc through point H and line ℓ. Label the intersection of the arc with line ℓ as point T.

   c. Since two points determine a line, you need to use your compass setting to draw one more point. How many intersecting arcs do you need to draw to create a point?

   d. Examine the figure. At which points should you place your compass next to draw the arcs for point P? Should you change your compass setting?

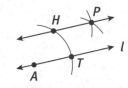

   e. Draw the arcs to locate a point on your diagram. Label it P. Then use your straightedge to draw the line that passes through points H and P.

2. In Item 1, if you were to draw segments $\overline{HA}$ and $\overline{PT}$, what type of quadrilateral would be formed?

My Notes

3. Explain why the construction in Item 1 guarantees that the constructed line is parallel to the given line. Review your answer. Be sure to check that you have described the situation with specific details, included the correct mathematical terms to support your reasoning, and that your sentences are complete and grammatically correct.

Now the architect needs to draw a post to support the handrail for a sloped access ramp, indicated by line ℓ below. The post needs to be perpendicular to line ℓ at point O.

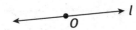

4. Sonia suggests that the architect use point O as the center of a circle and draw arcs on both sides of point O in order to determine the endpoints of the diameter of a circle.
   a. How do the two points that indicate the endpoints of the diameter of circle O help the architect find the perpendicular to line ℓ at point O?

   b. Use the above idea and what you learned from Item 8 of the previous lesson to construct a line perpendicular to line ℓ through point O. Show your construction in the space below.

5. **Attend to precision.** Kendrick said the line constructed in Item 4 is actually the perpendicular bisector of line ℓ. Do you agree? Why or why not?

6. Could you use the construction you discovered in Item 4 to construct a rectangle? Explain.

My Notes

Check Your Understanding

7. Construct a line through point *C* that is parallel to line *m*.

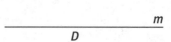

8. Construct a line through point *H* that is perpendicular to line *l*.

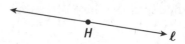

Basic constructions involving line segments and congruent angles can be used to discover other geometric relationships.

9. Model with mathematics. You will now use constructions to investigate the location of a point of concurrency of the perpendicular bisectors of the sides of a right triangle.

a. First, construct a large right triangle given line *l* and point *H*.

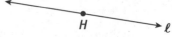

b. Now construct the perpendicular bisector of each side of the triangle.

c. Compare your findings with those of your classmates. Make a conjecture about the point of concurrency of the perpendicular bisectors in any right triangle.

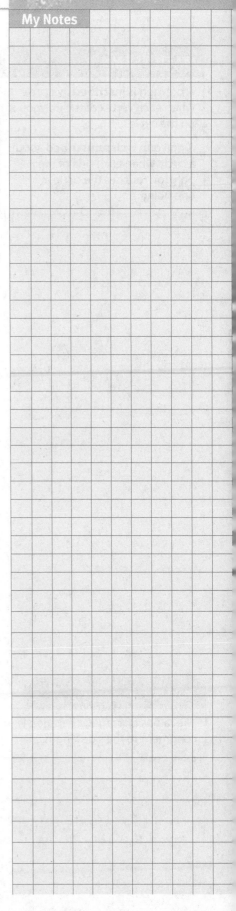

Check Your Understanding

10. For an acute triangle, does the point of concurrency of the perpendicular bisectors ever lie on a side of the triangle? Perform a few constructions to experiment, and then use your results to justify your answer.

11. To construct a kite, Omar starts by constructing two segments that are perpendicular to each other. Perform the construction, and then explain his reasoning for beginning the construction this way.

LESSON 29-2 PRACTICE

For each construction, show your construction lines.

12. Construct and label a right triangle with legs of lengths *HI* and *JK*. (*Hint*: Extend $\overline{JK}$ and construct a perpendicular line at point *J*. Then construct a segment congruent to $\overline{HI}$ on the perpendicular line.)

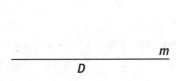

13. Construct a line through point *C* that is perpendicular to line *m*. (*Hint*: First place the point of your compass at *C* and draw an arc that intersects line *m* in two points. Then consider what you know about constructing a perpendicular bisector of a segment.)

14. **Construct viable arguments.** Describe how to verify, using constructions, that corresponding angles of two parallel lines cut by a transversal are congruent. Use the figure below to help you.

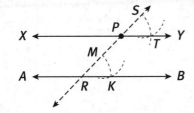

MATH TERMS

A polygon is **inscribed** in a circle when each vertex of the polygon is on the circle.

A polygon is **circumscribed** about a circle when each side of the polygon touches the circle at one point.

Learning Targets:

- Construct inscribed and circumscribed circles.
- Construct tangents to a circle.

> **SUGGESTED LEARNING STRATEGIES:** Construct an Argument, Identify a Subtask, Summarizing, Look for a Pattern

The architect is designing some of the light fixtures in the museum as regular polygons *inscribed* in a circle. Recall that a regular polygon has sides that are congruent and angles that are congruent.

1. Use your compass and straightedge to construct a regular hexagon in a circle.

   a. First use your compass to draw a large circle O in the space below.

   b. Keep your compass width set to the radius of the circle.

   c. How many vertices and how many edges compose a hexagon?

   d. What do you know about the side lengths of a regular hexagon? What does this indicate about your compass width throughout the construction?

   e. With the compass center positioned on the circle, draw your first arc so that it intersects the circle. This is the first vertex of the hexagon. Describe how to mark the rest of the vertices.

   f. Use your straightedge to draw a segment between each adjacent vertex.

MATH TIP

The radius of a regular hexagon is congruent to the side lengths.

2. Suppose each light fixture in Item 1 is partitioned into equilateral triangles.
   a. Explain how you can use your construction in Item 1 to draw equilateral triangles in the circle. Then draw the triangles.

   b. How many equilateral triangles did you construct?

   c. **Make use of structure.** Explain how you are certain that the triangles are equilateral.

3. Draw a circle in the space below and follow these steps to inscribe a square in the circle.

   a. What tool can you use to draw the diameter of the circle?

   b. Identify a property about the diagonals of a square that can help you decide which construction you need to perform next.

   c. Perform the construction to locate the other two vertices of the square.
   d. Use your straightedge to connect the vertices to form a square.

4. Explain why the largest hexagon that will fit in any circle is one that is inscribed in the circle.

> **MATH TIP**
>
> The endpoints of the diameter are two of the vertices of the square.

Check Your Understanding

5. Modify the last step of the construction described in Item 1 to construct an equilateral triangle that is inscribed in a circle.

My Notes

Recall that the point of concurrency of the three angle bisectors of any triangle is called the incenter. Use what you have learned about constructing angle bisectors to construct a circle inscribed in a triangle.

6. Follow the steps below to construct the inscribed circle of a triangle.

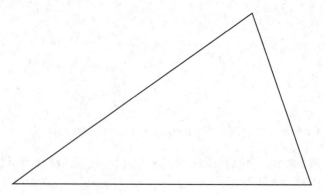

a. Construct two angle bisectors.
b. Mark the incenter at the point of concurrency.
c. Construct a perpendicular line from the incenter to one side of the triangle. Label this point X.
d. Name the part of the circle defined by the incenter and point X. Then draw the circle.

7. Use your compass to draw a triangle in the space below. Then construct the circumscribed circle of the triangle. Create a statement summarizing the construction you performed. (*Hint:* You will need to find the circumcenter. The circumcenter is the point where the perpendicular bisectors of the sides intersect.)

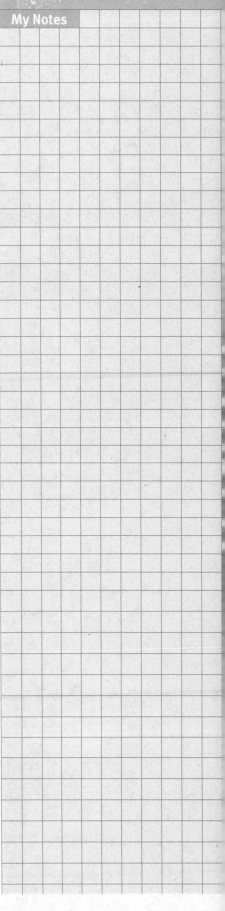

Sometimes architects have to perform more complex constructions in order to specify exactly what they are designing.

8. A truss inside the museum is to run tangent to a large, circular clock.
   a. Represent the clock by drawing any circle *A* with your compass. Plot a point *P* outside the circle. Draw a segment from the center of circle *A* to external point *P*.

   b. The next step is to find the midpoint *M* of $\overline{AP}$. What construction should you perform?

   c. If $\overline{MP}$ is the radius of circle *M*, describe how you would construct circle *M*.

   d. Is there a point that circle *A* and circle *M* have in common? If so, label this point *B*.

   e. Through which two points can you draw a segment so that it is tangent to circle *A*? Complete the construction.

9. Explain why the construction in Item 8 guarantees that the constructed line is tangent to circle *A*.

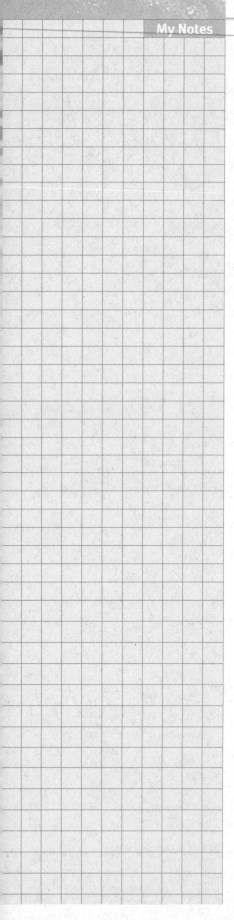

My Notes

Check Your Understanding

10. Construct an equilateral triangle with sides congruent to $\overline{AB}$. Then construct the inscribed circle of the triangle.

11. Draw a right triangle. Construct the circumscribed circle of the triangle.

Did you have to change the procedure in Item 7 to draw the circumscribed circle? Explain why or why not.

LESSON 29-3 PRACTICE

12. Construct an equilateral triangle with sides congruent to $\overline{AB}$. Then construct the circumscribed circle of the triangle.

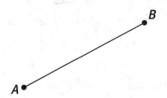

13. Use appropriate tools strategically. Explain the steps you would use to construct a tangent to circle C at point P.

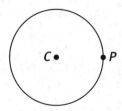

14. Vladimir is working on a construction. The first few steps of the construction are shown below, but the construction is not yet complete. What is Vladimir constructing? What is his next step?

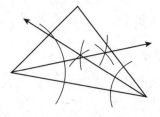

ACTIVITY 29 PRACTICE
Write your answers on notebook paper.
Show your work.

For Items 1–11, use the given figures to complete your answers. Do not erase your construction marks.

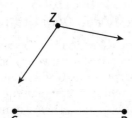

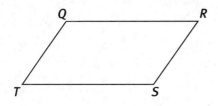

Lesson 29-1

1. Construct and name an isosceles triangle with legs of length *EF* and base of length *AB*. Describe the steps used to complete the construction.

2. Construct and name a square with sides of length *CD*. Describe the steps used to complete the construction.

3. Construct and name a triangle with sides of lengths *AB*, *CD*, and *EF*.

4. Which theorem supports the fact that $\overline{AB}$, $\overline{CD}$, and $\overline{EF}$ can form a triangle?
   A. Pythagorean Theorem
   B. Exterior Angle Theorem
   C. Isosceles Triangle Theorem
   D. Triangle Inequality Theorem

5. Construct and name an equilateral triangle with sides of length *EF*.

Lesson 29-2

6. Construct and name a rectangle with consecutive sides of lengths *CD* and *EF*.

7. Construct and name a parallelogram congruent to parallelogram *QRST*. Describe the steps used to complete the construction.

8. Construct and name a rhombus with diagonals of lengths *AB* and *EF*.

9. Construct and name a rectangle with a side of length *CD* and diagonals of length *EF*.

10. Which of the following would it **not** be possible to construct with a compass and straightedge?
    A. a line perpendicular to a given line through a point not on the line
    B. a line perpendicular to a given line through a point on the line
    C. a line parallel to a given line through a point not on the line
    D. a line parallel to a given line through a point on the line

Lesson 29-3

11. Construct and name a regular hexagon with sides of length *AB* using the following steps:
    • Construct a circle of radius *AB*.
    • Construct consecutive chords of length *AB* around the circle.

12. Summarize why the construction in Item 11 guarantees a regular hexagon.

13. Construct an equilateral triangle inscribed in a circle.

14. Construct a square inscribed in a circle.

15. Square *LMNP* is inscribed in a circle. The length of which of the following segments is also the diameter of the circle?
    A. *LM*
    B. *MN*
    C. *LN*
    D. *NP*

MATHEMATICAL PRACTICES
Reason Abstractly and Quantitatively

16. You have been asked to bisect a very long line segment, so you first open your compass to the widest setting possible. Unfortunately, the compass is not able to open far enough to construct the bisection. Devise a method to perform the geometric construction on the segment.

The owners of a grocery store chain have decided to open another store. The owners have hired a site selection consultant to help them determine possible locations for the new store. Choosing a location involves creating a list of criteria of what the owners need and/or want from a business perspective and then evaluating the criteria.

To help visualize the area of possible locations, the site selection consultant plots Town A at $(-4, -3)$ and Town B at $(6, 4)$ on a coordinate plane. Highway 1 is a straight road that connects the two towns, so he draws a line segment connecting the two points on the coordinate plane.

1. The consultant speculates—using population density—that the best place for the new grocery store is $\frac{3}{5}$ of the way from Town A to Town B. Find the coordinates for the possible location of the new grocery store.

2. The consultant states that from a product delivery standpoint, the new grocery store should be located 25 miles from a grocery distribution center. Write an equation that gives all possible locations of a grocery distribution center, based on the location of the new store in Item 1.

3. The grocery distribution center that services the current grocery store is located at $(-7, 4)$. Suppose one unit on the coordinate plane equals 5 miles. Is it feasible for the new grocery store to also be serviced by this distribution center? Explain.

The owners tell the consultant that one criterion that is important to them is for the new store to be located so that it is equidistant from the store's three main competitors.

4. The locations of the competitors' stores can be represented by the following ordered pairs: $(0, 0)$, $(8, 1)$, and $(2, 8)$.
   a. Plot the points on a coordinate plane.
   b. Use a compass and straightedge to construct the perpendicular bisectors of the three segments formed by the points.
   c. Use the circumcenter to describe the approximate location for the new grocery store.

Scoring Guide	Exemplary	Proficient	Emerging	Incomplete
	The solution demonstrates these characteristics:			
Mathematics Knowledge and Thinking (Items 1, 2, 3, 4)	• Clear and accurate understanding of how to find the point on a directed line segment between two given points that partitions the segment in a given ratio • Clear and accurate understanding of how to write the equation of a circle and determine whether a point lies in the interior or exterior of the circle • Clear and accurate understanding of perpendicular bisectors	• A functional understanding of how to find the point on a directed line segment between two given points that partitions the segment in a given ratio • A functional understanding of how to write the equation of a circle and determine whether a point lies in the interior or exterior of the circle • A functional understanding of perpendicular bisectors	• Partial understanding of how to find the point on a directed line segment between two given points that partitions the segment in a given ratio • Partial understanding of how to write the equation of a circle and determine whether a point lies in the interior or exterior of the circle • Partial understanding of perpendicular bisectors	• Little or no understanding of how to find the point on a directed line segment between two given points that partitions the segment in a given ratio • Little or no understanding of how to write the equation of a circle and determine whether a point lies in the interior or exterior of the circle • Little or no understanding of perpendicular bisectors
Problem Solving (Items 1, 4c)	• An appropriate and efficient strategy that results in correct answers	• A strategy that may include unnecessary steps but results in correct answers	• A strategy that results in some incorrect answers	• No clear strategy when solving problems
Mathematical Modeling / Representations (Items 2, 4b)	• Clear and accurate understanding of creating the equation of a circle given the center and radius • Clear and accurate understanding of constructing perpendicular bisectors of line segments	• Mostly accurate understanding of creating the equation of a circle given the center and radius • Mostly accurate understanding of constructing perpendicular bisectors of line segments	• Partial understanding of creating the equation of a circle given the center and radius • Partial understanding of constructing perpendicular bisectors of line segments	• Little or no understanding of creating the equation of a circle given the center and radius • Little or no understanding of constructing perpendicular bisectors of line segments.
Reasoning and Communication (Item 3)	• Correct answer and precise use of appropriate mathematics and language to justify whether $(-7, 4)$ is located within the circle	• Correct answer and mostly correct use of appropriate mathematics and language to justify whether $(-7, 4)$ is located within the circle	• Correct or incorrect answer and partially correct explanation to justify whether $(-7, 4)$ is located within the circle	• Incomplete or inaccurate use of appropriate mathematics and language to justify whether $(-7, 4)$ is located within the circle

Extending Two Dimensions to Three Dimensions

Unit Overview

In this unit you will study many geometric concepts related to two-dimensional and three-dimensional figures. You will derive area and perimeter formulas of polygons and circumference and area formulas of circles. You will investigate angles of a polygon and arcs and sectors of a circle. You will describe properties of prisms, pyramids, cones, cylinders, and spheres and develop and apply formulas for surface area and volume.

Key Terms

As you study this unit, add these and other terms to your math notebook. Include in your notes your prior knowledge of each word, as well as your experiences in using the word in different mathematical examples. If needed, ask for help in pronouncing new words and add information on pronunciation to your math notebook. It is important that you learn new terms and use them correctly in your class discussions and in your problem solutions.

Academic Vocabulary

- replicate
- cross section

Math Terms

- composite figure
- density
- polygon
- interior angle
- discrete domain
- regular polygon
- equilateral
- equiangular
- exterior angle
- convex polygon
- apothem
- circumference
- sector
- concentric circles
- radian measure
- net
- face
- edge
- vertex
- oblique prism
- right prism
- oblique pyramid
- polyhedron
- vertices of the polyhedron
- cylinder
- cone
- height of cone
- sphere
- great circle
- solid of rotation
- lateral area
- total surface area
- lateral surface
- Cavalieri's Principle
- slant height
- hemisphere
- antipodal points
- lune

ESSENTIAL QUESTIONS

? How do two-dimensional figures help you visualize three-dimensional figures?

? Why are geometric formulas useful in solving real-world problems?

EMBEDDED ASSESSMENTS

This unit has three embedded assessments, following Activities 32, 35, and 37. The assessments will give you the opportunity to apply what you have learned.

Getting Ready

Write your answers on notebook paper.
Show your work.

1. Solve the following equation for s.

$$P = \frac{1}{3}r(q+s)$$

2. Identify the following two- and three-dimensional figures.

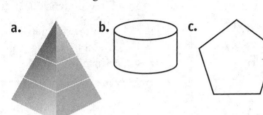

a.   b.   c.

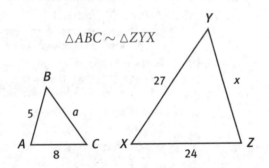

d.   e.   f.

Items 3 and 4 refer to the figures below.

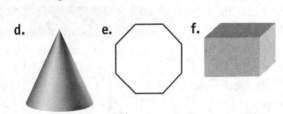

$$\triangle ABC \sim \triangle ZYX$$

3. Find the measure of sides a and x.
4. Name the pairs of angles that are congruent.
5. Give the area of a circle that has a circumference of 15π units.

6. In the figure below, a circle is inscribed in a square that has side length 8 units. Express the shaded area of the figure in terms of π.

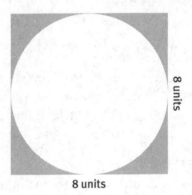

8 units

The figure below is composed of three geometric shapes. Use the figure for Items 7 and 8.

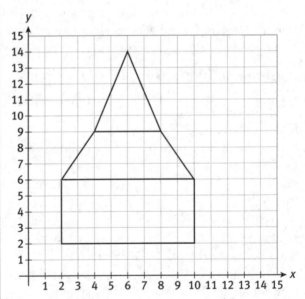

7. Name each of the figures and tell the formula you would use to find its area.
8. Find the area of the composite figure.

Deriving Area Formulas

Shape Up
Lesson 30-1 Areas of Rectangles and Parallelograms

Learning Targets:

- Solve problems using the areas of rectangles, parallelograms, and composite figures.
- Use coordinates to compute perimeters and areas of figures.

> **SUGGESTED LEARNING STRATEGIES:** Use Manipulatives, Quickwrite, RAFT

Lisa works in the billing department of A Cut Above, a company that builds custom countertops and tabletops. A new customer has contracted A Cut Above to build the tabletops for a theme restaurant, Shape Up.

Each tabletop costs $8.50 per square foot. Lisa's job is to calculate the area, compute the charge, and bill each customer properly. The tabletops, made with laminated wood, are delivered to A Cut Above in different rectangular sizes. Before there are any cuts, a cardboard template is made to use as a guide. Lisa uses the templates to investigate the areas. Shown is one of the templates for which Lisa must find the area.

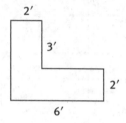

1. **a.** Find the area of this shape. Include units of measure in your answer. Describe the method used.

   b. How much should Lisa charge the customer for this tabletop?

In keeping with the theme of the restaurant, the customer wants to include tables in the shapes of triangles, parallelograms, and trapezoids. Lisa decides to investigate area formulas by first finding the formula for the area of a parallelogram.

2. **Use appropriate tools strategically.** Use the rectangle provided by your teacher.

   - Pick a point, not a vertex, on one side of the rectangle. Draw a segment from the point to a vertex on the opposite side of the rectangle.
   - Cut along the segment.
   - Put the two figures together to form a parallelogram.

   a. Explain why the area of a parallelogram is the same as the area of rectangle.

   b. **Critique the reasoning of others.** Nelson and Rashid, two tabletop designers, are discussing how to calculate the area of any parallelogram. Nelson suggests that they multiply the lengths of two consecutive sides to find the area, as they do for rectangles. Rashid claims this will not work. Explain which designer is correct and why.

My Notes

DISCUSSION GROUP TIPS

As you work in groups, read the problem scenario carefully and explore together the information provided. Discuss your understanding of the problem and ask peers or your teacher to clarify any areas that are not clear.

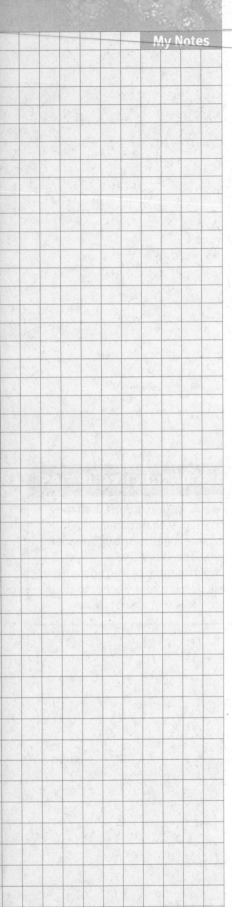

3. A scale drawing of the parallelogram tabletop template is shown below. Determine the charge for making this tabletop. Show the calculations that led to your answer.

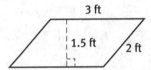

3 ft

1.5 ft   2 ft

Lisa finds the template method somewhat time-consuming and asks Rashid if there is a different way to determine the measures of the tabletops. Rashid tells Lisa that she can use a coordinate plane to determine the perimeter and area of a tabletop.

4. A diagram showing a rectangular tabletop is plotted on the coordinate plane.

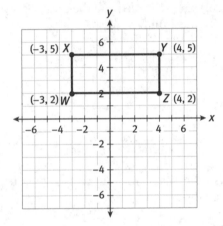

Explain how to use the coordinates to find the length and width of the rectangular tabletop. Then use the dimensions to compute the perimeter and area of the tabletop. Show the formulas that you used.

5. Points $F(-3, 4)$, $G(2, 2)$, $H(2, -4)$, and $J(-3, -2)$ are the vertices of parallelogram $FGHJ$.

   a. Draw the parallelogram on the grid.

   b. Determine the perimeter of the parallelogram to the nearest tenth.

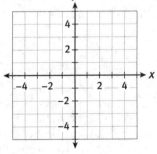

   c. What is the area of the parallelogram?

Lisa realizes that she can apply what she has learned to determine the measures of tabletops that are formed using a combination of shapes.

6. A diagram of a custom tabletop is shown. The tabletop is a *composite figure* that consists of a rectangle and parallelogram. Lisa needs to calculate the cost of the tabletop.

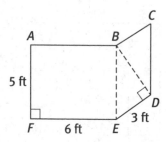

My Notes

MATH TERMS

A **composite figure** is made up of two or more simpler shapes, such as triangles, rectangles, or parallelograms. The word *composite* means made up of distinct parts. For example, in geology, a composite volcano is made up of alternating layers of lava and rocks.

a. What additional dimension(s) does Lisa need to know in order to find the area of the tabletop? How can she find this? Be sure to use properties or theorems to justify your answer.

b. What is the cost of the tabletop? Show your work.

Check Your Understanding

7. Find the area of the composite figure shown.

8. Determine the area and perimeter of a rectangle with length 12 cm and diagonal length 13 cm.

9. Determine the area and perimeter of the parallelograms shown. Round the answers to the nearest tenth.

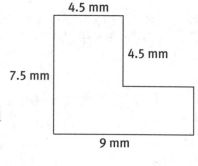

a.

b.

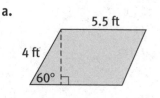

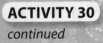

My Notes

LESSON 30-1 PRACTICE

Lisa was given the list of all of the shapes and necessary dimensions of some tabletops. In Items 10–12, determine the perimeter and area of each tabletop.

10. Table 1

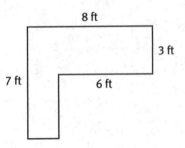

11. Table 2

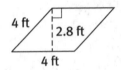

12. Table 3: Figure *QRST* with vertices $Q(-1, 4)$, $R(-1, 7)$, $S(4, 7)$, and $T(4, 4)$. Each unit of the coordinate plane represents one foot.

13. Reason quantitatively. Given that the charge for each tabletop is $8.50 per square foot, create an itemized invoice to show the cost of each tabletop from Items 10–12 and the total cost.

14. The area of the parallelogram shown is 45 square units. Find the height and base of the parallelogram.

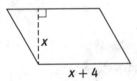

15. Explain how to use a composite figure to estimate the area of the irregular figure shown on the coordinate plane.

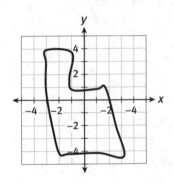

Learning Targets:

- Solve problems using the areas of triangles and composite figures.
- Use coordinates to compute perimeters and areas of figures.

> **SUGGESTED LEARNING STRATEGIES:** Marking the Text, Group Presentation, Identify a Subtask, Use Manipulatives, Quickwrite

Lisa asks Rashid to help her understand how to determine the area of triangular-shaped tabletops. Lisa and Rashid start the investigation with right and isosceles triangles.

1. Use the given triangles below to create quadrilaterals. Using what you know about these quadrilaterals, explain why the formula for the area of a triangle is Area $= \frac{1}{2} \cdot$ base $\cdot$ height.

   a.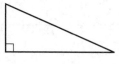

   b.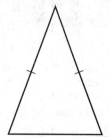

2. **Reason abstractly.** Compare and contrast the steps required to find the area of a right triangle and an isosceles triangle whose side lengths are given.

> **MATH TIP**
>
> An isosceles triangle has two congruent sides and two congruent angles.

3. Find the area and subsequent charge for each tabletop below.

   a.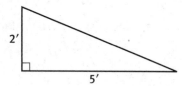

   b.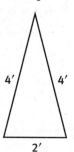

   c.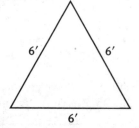

My Notes

4. **Reason abstractly.** Rashid draws several tabletops in the shape of an equilateral triangle, each having different side lengths. Derive an area formula that will work for all equilateral triangles with side length *s*.

5. Use the formula created in Item 4 to find the area of an equilateral triangle with side length 6 feet. Compare your answer to the area you found in Item 3c.

Check Your Understanding

6. Find the area of the tabletop shown on the coordinate plane.
   a. Name the shapes that make up the tabletop.
   b. **Critique the reasoning of others.** Jalen and Bree each used a different method to determine the area of the tabletop. Jalen found the sum of the areas of each of the four figures. Bree drew auxiliary lines to create a large rectangle, and then subtracted the area of the two triangular regions not in the tabletop from the large rectangle. Whose method is correct? Explain your reasoning.
   c. Compute the area of the tabletop.
   d. What are some benefits of working with composite figures on a coordinate plane?

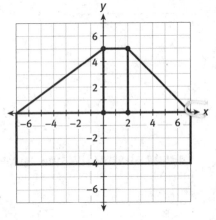

7. Determine the area of triangle *ABC*. Leave the answer in radical form.

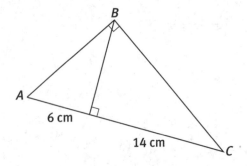

8. Explain how to determine the height of a right triangle versus the height of an equilateral triangle, given the side lengths of the triangles.

Next, Rashid shows Lisa how to determine the area of a triangular-shaped tabletop given two side lengths and the measure of the included angle.

9. **Make use of structure.** Complete the proof to discover an area formula that can be used when given a triangle with two side lengths and the measure of the included angle.

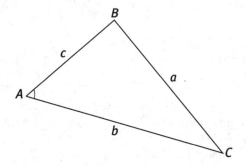

a. Write the formula for the area of a triangle.

b. Draw and label a perpendicular line, h, from point B to $\overline{AC}$. This represents the height of the triangle.

c. Complete to find sin A: $\sin A = \dfrac{opposite}{hypotenuse} =$

d. Solve for h: $= h$

e. Substitute the equivalent expression you got for h (from part d) into the formula for area of a triangle (from part a).
Area $= \frac{1}{2}bh$
$= \frac{1}{2}b$

10. The diagram shown represents tabletop ABC. The tabletop has side lengths 5 ft and 7 ft. The angle between the two sides, $\angle A$, has a measure of $49°$. Compute the area of the triangular tabletop, to the nearest tenth.

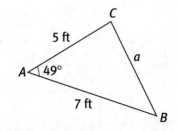

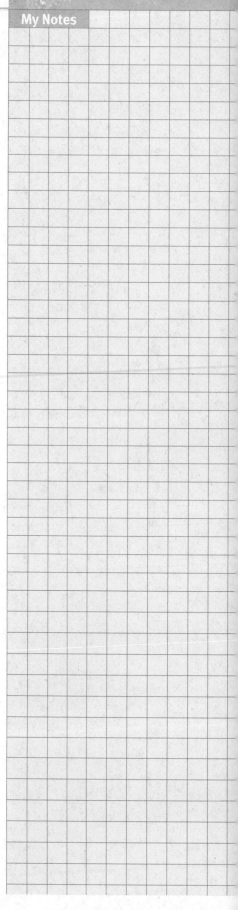

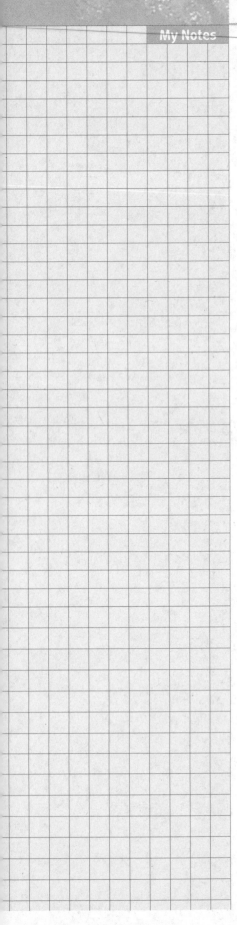

My Notes

Check Your Understanding

11. Find the area of the triangle to the nearest tenth, if $c = 10$ m, $b = 24$ m, and $m\angle A = 38°$.

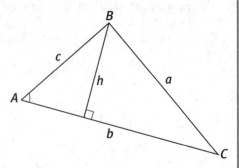

12. A parallelogram is given on a coordinate plane. Use the area formula of a triangle to derive the area formula of a parallelogram. Then compute the area of the figure.

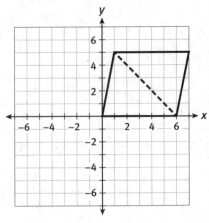

LESSON 30-2 PRACTICE

For Items 13–16, compute the area of each triangular-shaped tabletop, to the nearest tenth.

13. Equilateral triangle with 8.5 ft sides

14. Triangle *ABC* with vertices at (2, 1), (8, 1), and (6, 4)

15. Base measure of 15 ft, another side length of 12 ft, and an included angle of 30°

16. Isosceles triangle with sides of 4 ft, 7 ft, and 7 ft

17. Make sense of problems. Determine the perimeter and area of the tabletop shown on the coordinate plane below.

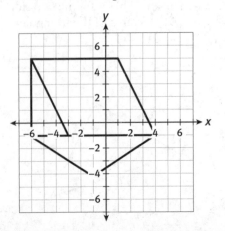

Learning Targets:

- Solve problems using the areas of rhombuses, trapezoids, and composite figures.
- Solve problems involving density.

SUGGESTED LEARNING STRATEGIES: Vocabulary Organizer, Think-Pair-Share, Create Representations, Quickwrite

Lisa begins to explore other tabletop templates. She uses what she has learned about rectangles, triangles, and parallelograms to investigate the areas of other polygons.

1. Included in the tabletop templates is the rhombus shown.

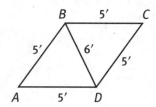

a. List the properties of a rhombus that relate to the diagonals.

b. Find the length of diagonal $\overline{AC}$.

c. Apply the formula for the area of the triangles formed by the diagonals to find the area of the rhombus.

d. Derive a formula for the area of a rhombus with diagonal lengths d_1 and d_2.

My Notes

The area of a trapezoid with base lengths b_1 and b_2 and height h can be derived by applying what you have already learned about the area of a triangle.

2. Use the figure shown to derive a formula for the area of a trapezoid. Explain how you arrived at your answer.

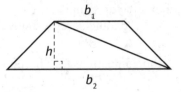

3. **Critique the reasoning of others.** Lisa states, "The area of a trapezoid is equal to the length of its median times its height." Is she correct? Why?

4. Find the area of each of the trapezoids shown below.

a.

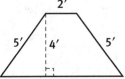

b.

To determine the total cost of a tabletop, Lisa needs to also consider the cost of shipping. The greater the mass of an object, the greater the shipping cost. The mass of the tabletop is dependent on the *density* of the material used in its construction.

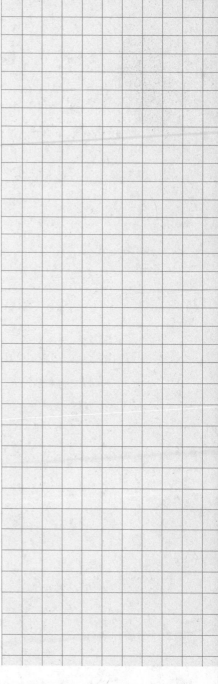

My Notes

MATH TERMS

Density is the mass per unit volume of a substance. You can determine the density of a substance using the following formula:

$$\text{density} = \frac{\text{mass}}{\text{volume}}.$$

5. A Cut Above is making the tabletop shown in Item 4a out of two different types of wood: western red cedar and maple. The volume of each tabletop is 4 ft^3. The density of western red cedar is 23 lb/ft^3, and the density of maple is 45 lb/ft^3. If the cost of shipping the tabletops is $0.50 per pound, which tabletop costs more to ship? How much more?

Check Your Understanding

6. Find the area of each trapezoid.

a.

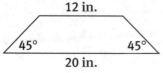

12 in.

45°   45°

20 in.

b.

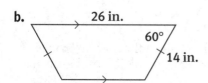

26 in.

60°

14 in.

7. The density of bamboo is about 20 lb/ft^3. What is the mass of a bamboo tabletop that has a volume of 30 ft^3?

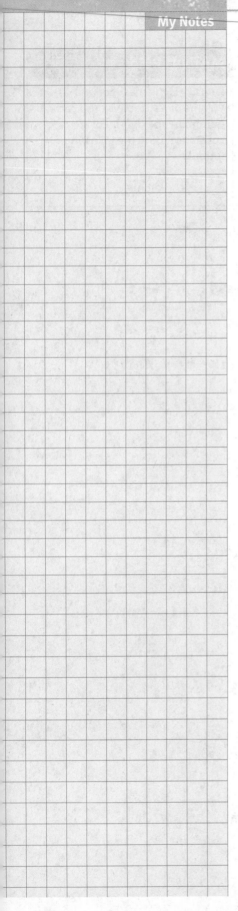

My Notes

LESSON 30-3 PRACTICE

For Items 8–11, find the area, given the measures of each figure.

8. Isosceles trapezoid with base lengths 2 ft and 5 ft and leg lengths 2.5 ft

9. Rhombus with diagonal lengths 6 in. and 10 in.

10.

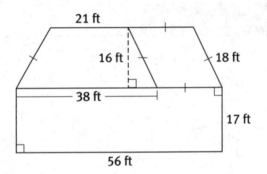

16 in.

60°   60°

30 in.

11. The area of an isosceles trapezoid is 54 square cm. The perimeter is 32 cm. If a leg is 7 cm long, find the height of the trapezoid.

12. **Attend to precision.** The front face of a manufactured home is shown in the diagram below.

21 ft

16 ft   18 ft

38 ft

17 ft

56 ft

a. Compute the area.
b. If the density of the material from which the home is made is 38 lb/ft^3, and the volume of the home is 856 ft^3, what is the mass?

ACTIVITY 30 PRACTICE

Write your answers on notebook paper.
Show your work.

Lesson 30-1

For Items 1–5, find the area of each shape described or shown.

1. Rectangle with base length 10 cm and diagonal length 15 cm

2. Equilateral triangle with perimeter 30 in.

3. Square inscribed in a circle with radius 16 mm

4. Figure *TUVW* with vertices $T(-3, 6)$, $U(-3, 7)$, $V(0, 7)$, and $W(0, 6)$

5.

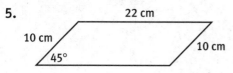

6. What is the perimeter of Figure *ABCD* with vertices at $A(2, 3)$, $B(5, 3)$, $C(5, -3)$, and $D(2, -3)$? What is the area?

Lesson 30-2

For Items 7–8, find the area of each shape described or shown.

7. Equilateral triangle with height 6 cm

8. 30°-60°-90° triangle with hypotenuse length 14 in.

9. Compute the perimeter and area of the figure shown, to the nearest tenth.

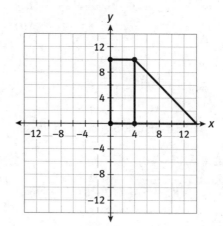

Use Figure *ABCDE* on the coordinate plane for Items 10–11.

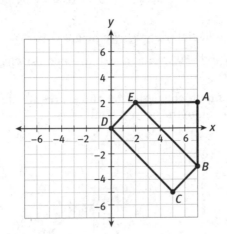

10. Which equation can be used to determine *CD*?

A. $CD = \sqrt{(5-0)^2 + (5-0)^2}$

B. $CD = \sqrt{(5-5)^2 + (0-0)^2}$

C. $CD = \sqrt{(5-0)^2 - (5-0)^2}$

D. $CD = \sqrt{(5-5)^2 + (5+5)^2}$

11. What is the area of Figure *ABCDE*?
  A. 25 ft^2
  B. 22.5 ft^2
  C. 32.5 ft^2
  D. 56 ft^2

12. The base and height of a triangular-shaped countertop have a 5 : 2 ratio. Given that the area of the countertop is 320 in.^2, what are the measures of the base and height?

Lesson 30-3

For Items 13–14, find the area of each shape described or shown.

13. The lengths of the diagonals of a rhombus are 25 cm and 40 cm.

14. Trapezoid with height of 8 in. and bases of 10 in. and 15 in.

15. The length of one diagonal of a rhombus is 10 in, and its area is 70 in.^2 Find the length of the other diagonal.

16. The pillar shown has a thickness of 0.5 ft. To find its volume, the thickness is multiplied by its area. If the pillar has a mass of 5950 lb, from which material is the pillar most likely made?

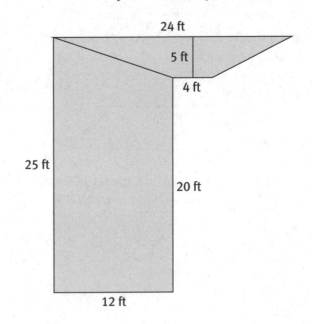

A. walnut: density $= 35 \text{ lb/ft}^3$
B. pine: density $= 30 \text{ lb/ft}^3$
C. poplar: density $= 22 \text{ lb/ft}^3$
D. balsa: density $= 9 \text{ lb/ft}^3$

MATHEMATICAL PRACTICES
Construct Viable Arguments and Critique the Reasoning of Others

17. How could you use the formula for area of a trapezoid to find the area of a parallelogram?

Regular Polygons

Plenty of Polygons

Lesson 31-1 Sum of the Measures of the Interior Angles of a Polygon

Learning Targets:

- Develop a formula for the sum of the measures of the interior angles of a polygon.
- Determine the sum of the measures of the interior angles of a polygon.

SUGGESTED LEARNING STRATEGIES: Think-Pair-Share, Create Representations, Look for a Pattern, Self Revision/Peer Revision

A **polygon** is a closed geometric figure with sides formed by three or more coplanar segments that intersect exactly two other segments, one at each endpoint. The angles formed inside the polygon are **interior angles**. Although it is difficult to measure lengths and angles exactly, tools such as rulers and protractors allow you to measure with reasonable accuracy.

Work with your group and use the polygons on the next two pages.

1. **Use appropriate tools strategically.** Measure, as precisely as possible, each interior angle, and record your results below. Complete the table by calculating the indicated sums.

	1st Angle	2nd Angle	3rd Angle	4th Angle	5th Angle	6th Angle	Total
Triangle							
Quadrilateral							
Pentagon							

2. Compare your results in the table with those of other groups in your class. What similarities do you notice?

3. Write a conjecture about the sum of the measures of the interior angles of each of the polygons.

Triangle:

Quadrilateral:

Pentagon:

TECHNOLOGY TIP

You can draw the polygons using geometry software. Then use the software to determine the angle measures and complete the table.

My Notes

My Notes

ACADEMIC VOCABULARY

To **replicate** means to duplicate or imitate. Notice the word *replica* contained within the word. In science, experiments are designed so that they can be replicated by other scientists.

Knowing that the sum of the measures of the interior angles of a triangle is a constant and that the sum of the measures of nonoverlapping angles around a single point is always 360°, you can determine the sum of the measures of any polygon without measuring.

4. Use auxiliary segments to determine a way to predict and verify the exact sum of the angles of any quadrilateral and any pentagon. Describe your methods so that another group would be able to *replicate* your results for the pentagon.

5. Use the method you described in Item 4 to answer the following.
   a. Explain how to determine the sum of the measures of the interior angles of a hexagon.

   b. Explain how to determine the sum of the measures of the interior angles for any polygon.

6. **Express regularity in repeated reasoning.** Use the method described in your answer to Item 5 to complete the table below.

Polygon	Number of Sides	Calculations	Sum of the Measures of the Interior Angles
Triangle	3		
Quadrilateral	4		
Pentagon	5		
Hexagon			
Heptagon			
Octagon			
Nonagon			
Decagon			
Dodecagon			
n-gon	*n*		

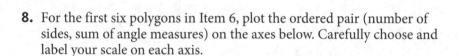

7. Observe in Item 6 that as the number of sides increases by one, the sum of the angle measures also increases by a constant amount. What type of function models this behavior?

8. For the first six polygons in Item 6, plot the ordered pair (number of sides, sum of angle measures) on the axes below. Carefully choose and label your scale on each axis.

CONNECT TO TECHNOLOGY

Use your graphing calculator to graph the ordered pairs. Create a table and then plot the points. Determine an appropriate scale for the axes.

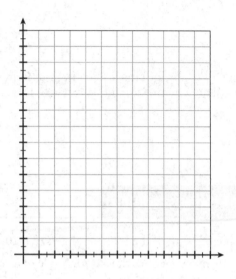

9. The data points you graphed above should appear collinear. Write an equation for the line determined by these points.

10. **Make sense of problems.** State the numerical value of the slope of the line in Item 9 and describe what the slope value tells about the relationship between the number of sides and the sum of the measures of the interior angles of a polygon. Use units in your description.

11. If the function S represents the sum of the measures of the interior angles as a function of the number of sides, n, write an algebraic rule for $S(n)$.

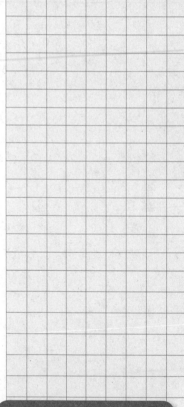

MATH TIP

Write the equation in slope-intercept form, $y = mx + b$.

12. Compare how the algebraic rule in Item 11 is similar to the slope-intercept form of a linear equation.

My Notes

13. Use $S(n)$ to determine the value of $S(7.5)$. For this value, explain the significance, if any, given that $S(n)$ represents the sum of the angle measures of an n-sided polygon.

14. What is the domain of $S(n)$?

MATH TERMS

Linear functions have *continuous* domains consisting of all real numbers. However, some contexts restrict the domain of linear functions. If the graph of a linear model consists of *discrete* points, the linear function is said to have a **discrete domain**.

15. How can you tell by looking at the graph in Item 8 that the function is linear? Explain why the domain is restricted.

Check Your Understanding

16. Determine the sum of the interior angles of a 20-sided polygon.

17. What is the measure of each interior angle of a regular polygon with 60 sides?

18. The sum of the interior angles of a polygon is 2340°. How many sides does the polygon have?

LESSON 31-1 PRACTICE

19. Does the rule in Item 11 hold true for various types of triangles? Create a way to prove the rule for a scalene triangle, a right triangle, and an isosceles triangle. Start by drawing one of the triangles, tearing it into three pieces, and rearranging the vertices.

20. **Critique the reasoning of others.** Denisha states that if you are given the sum of the interior angles of a polygon, there is no way to determine the number of sides of the polygon. Do you agree with Denisha? Justify your reasoning.

21. Use technology to create a hexagon. Label all angle measures but one. Exchange figures with a partner and find the missing angle measures in each hexagon using the rule you created in Item 11. Check answers using technology.

22. The angle measures of a stop sign are all the same. Determine the measure of each angle in a stop sign.

Learning Targets:

- Develop a formula for the measure of each interior angle of a regular polygon.
- Determine the measure of the exterior angles of a polygon.

> **SUGGESTED LEARNING STRATEGIES:** Think-Pair-Share, Create Representations, Look for a Pattern, Quickwrite

A *regular polygon* is both *equilateral* and *equiangular*. This means that each interior angle of a regular polygon has the same angle measure.

1. Complete the table to determine the angle measure of each interior angle for each regular polygon listed.

Polygon	Number of Sides	Sum of the Measures of the Interior Angles (degrees)	Measures of Each Interior Angle (degrees)
Triangle			
Quadrilateral			
Pentagon			
Hexagon			
Heptagon			
Octagon			
Nonagon			
Decagon			
Dodecagon			
n-gon			

> **MATH TERMS**
>
> **Equiangular** means that all angles of a polygon are congruent.
> **Equilateral** means all sides of a polygon are congruent.

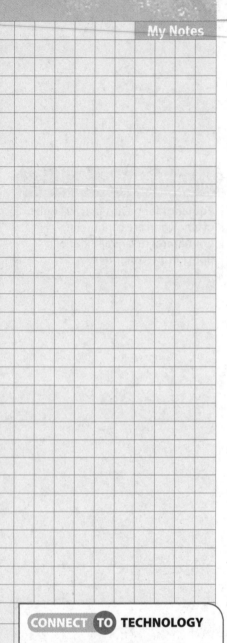

My Notes

2. For each regular polygon listed in the table in Item 1, plot the ordered pair (number of sides, measure of each interior angle) on the axes below. Carefully choose and label your scale on each axis.

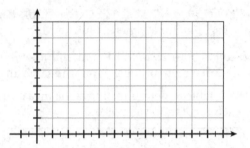

3. **Make use of structure.** The points plotted in Item 2 should not appear collinear. Explain how that conclusion could have been drawn from the data alone.

4. If the function E represents the measure of each interior angle as a function of the number of sides, n, write an algebraic rule for $E(n)$.

5. As n becomes greater, what appears to be happening to the measure of each angle? What causes this behavior?

CONNECT TO TECHNOLOGY

Use the TABLE or GRAPHING component of a graphing calculator. Enter the algebraic function for $E(n)$ in y_1 to explore the measure of individual angle measures of a regular polygon as the number of sides increases.

Exterior angles of a polygon also have a relationship. An ***exterior angle*** of a polygon is the angle formed between one side of a polygon and an extension of an adjacent side.

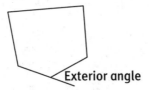

Exterior angle

6. Use geometry software to draw a ***convex*** pentagon. Extend each side.

7. **Use appropriate tools strategically.** Use the software to measure the exterior angles at each vertex. To do this you will need to mark a point on each ray.

MATH TERMS

A polygon is **convex** if no line containing a side of the polygon contains a point in the interior of the polygon. A **convex polygon** has no interior angles greater than 180°.

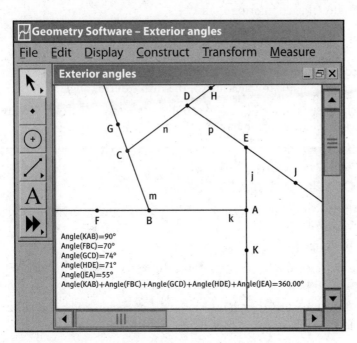

8. Find the sum of the exterior angles from Item 7.

9. Manipulate the polygon to form a convex hexagon. Measure each exterior angle and find the sum of the measures.

10. Manipulate the polygon to form a convex heptagon. Measure each exterior angle and find the sum of the measures.

11. Make a conjecture about the sum of the exterior angles of a polygon with *n* sides.

12. Predict the sum of the measure of the interior angle of a pentagon and one of its exterior angles. On what basis do you make your prediction? Use the software to measure and confirm your prediction.

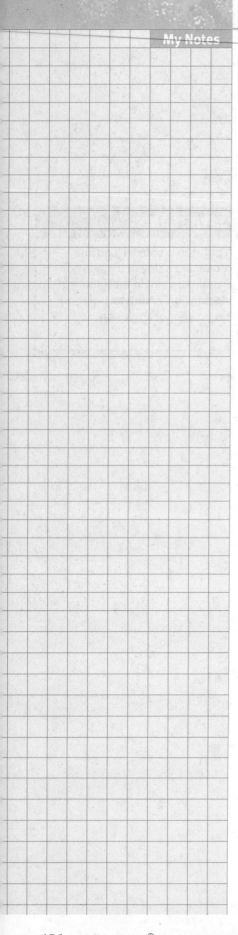

13. Use your answer from Item 12 and what you know about the angle sum of interior angles to further prove your conjecture from Item 11.

Check Your Understanding

14. What is the sum of the interior angles of a regular 24-gon? What is the measure of each interior angle?

15. How does the sum of the measure of the exterior angles of a convex polygon differ if the polygon is a regular polygon? Explain.

16. A convex pentagon has exterior angles that measure $70°$, $105°$, $28°$, and $32°$. What is the measure of the fifth exterior angle?

17. Each exterior angle of a regular polygon measures $24°$. How many sides does the polygon have?

LESSON 31-2 PRACTICE

18. Find the sum of the measures of the interior angles of each regular polygon.
   a. 15-gon   **b.** 18-gon

19. The expression $(a − 4)°$ represents the measure of an interior angle of a regular 20-gon. What is the value of a in the expression?

20. Find the measure of each interior angle of each regular polygon.
   a. 15-gon   **b.** 18-gon

21. Find the sum of the measures of the exterior angles of each polygon.
   a. 15-gon   **b.** 18-gon

22. The expression $(n + 3)°$ represents the measure of an exterior angle of a regular 18-gon. What is the value of n in the expression?

23. Construct viable arguments. Emilio said that he drew a regular polygon using a protractor and measured one of its interior angles as $100°$. Explain, using what you know about exterior angles, why this cannot be true.

24. Use graphing software to draw three quadrilaterals: a square, a rectangle, and a nonequiangular quadrilateral.
   a. Find the measure of each interior angle of each polygon.
   b. Prove that the sum of the measures of the interior angles of each quadrilateral is the same.
   c. Prove that the sum of the measures of the exterior angles of each quadrilateral is $360°$.

Learning Targets:
- Develop a formula for the area of a regular polygon.
- Solve problems using the perimeter and area of regular polygons.

> **SUGGESTED LEARNING STRATEGIES:** Think-Pair-Share, Quickwrite, Create Representations

Recall that a regular polygon is equilateral and equiangular. An **apothem** of a regular polygon is a perpendicular segment from a midpoint of a side of a regular polygon to the center of the circle circumscribed about the polygon. The apothem of a regular hexagon of side s is indicated by a in the diagram.

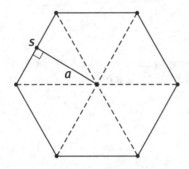

1. Consider the tabletop template of the regular hexagon shown below.

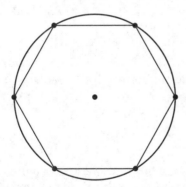

   a. Draw all radii from the center of the circumscribed circle to each vertex of the hexagon.

   b. What is the measure of each of the central angles formed by the radii? Explain how you arrived at your answer.

   c. Classify the triangles formed by the radii by their side length. Measure to verify your answer.

   d. How is the apothem of the hexagon related to the triangles formed by the radii?

   e. Find the area of a regular hexagon with side length 4 ft. Show the calculations that lead to your answer.

My Notes

Now you can use what you discovered in Item 1 to generalize the formula to determine the area of any regular polygon.

2. **Express regularity in repeated reasoning.** Refer to the diagrams of the regular polygons shown.

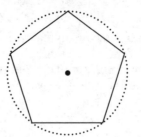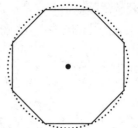

a. How many triangles are formed when the radii are drawn from the center of the polygon to each of the vertices of the polygon with *n* sides?

b. What is the measure of each of the central angles formed by the radii of the *n*-gon? Explain how you arrived at your answer.

c. Classify the triangles formed by the radii by their side length. Verify your answer.

d. Write an expression that finds the area of one triangle in an *n*-gon, using *a* to represent the apothem and *s* to represent a side of the *n*-gon. Then use the expression to write a formula that finds the area of the entire *n*-gon, where *n* represents the number of sides of the *n*-gon.

e. Explain how to determine the perimeter of a polygon, *P*.

f. Write a formula that can be used to calculate the area of a regular *n*-gon with apothem length *a* and perimeter *P*, by substituting *P* in the formula you wrote in part d.

My Notes

Example A

Calculate the area of a regular octagon with side length 8 inches.

Step 1: Find the apothem.

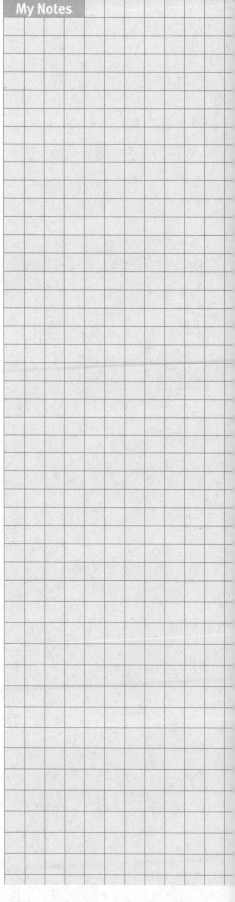

Draw the apothem, $\overline{QS}$.
The length of $\overline{QS}$ is a.

Since the polygon is a regular octagon,

$m\angle PQR = \dfrac{360°}{8} = 45°.$

So, $m\angle SQR = 22.5°.$

8 in.

Use trigonometry to find a:

$\dfrac{4}{a} = \tan 22.5°$, so $a \approx 9.7$ in.

Step 2: Find the area.

$A = \dfrac{1}{2}aP$

$= \dfrac{1}{2}(9.7 \text{ in.})(8)(8 \text{ in.})$

$= 310.4 \text{ in.}^2$

Solution: The area is approximately 310.4 square inches.

Try These A

a. Calculate the area of a regular pentagon with side length 12 m.

b. Find the area of a regular hexagon with 18 cm sides.

c. **Reason quantitatively.** Find the perimeter and area of regular polygon $ABCD$ with vertices $A(7, 8)$, $B(9, -1)$, $C(0, -3)$, and $D(-2, 6)$.

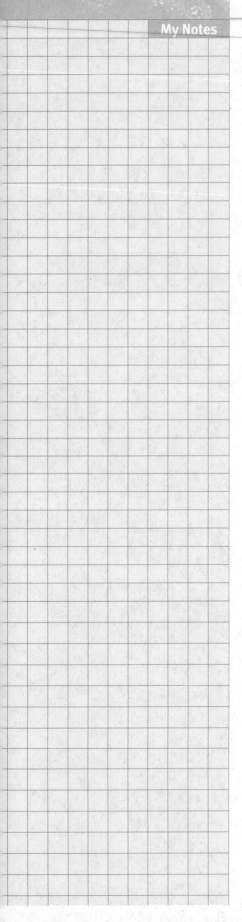

My Notes

Check Your Understanding

3. The properties of what type of triangle can be used to determine the apothem in a regular hexagon?

4. Write a formula that can be used to determine the perimeter of a regular *n*-gon.

5. Find the area of a regular octagon with 7-inch sides.

6. Seth states that the radius of a regular polygon is never less than its apothem. Do you agree? If so, provide justification. If not, provide a counterexample.

LESSON 31-3 PRACTICE

7. Determine the perimeter and area of the regular dodecagon.

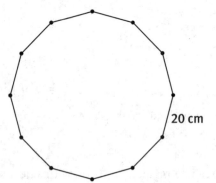

20 cm

8. **Make sense of problems.** A manufacturing company is making a design for an octagonal hazard sign. Each side of the sign measures 40 in. What is the area of the sign?

9. Find the area of regular polygon *QRST* with vertices at $Q(1, 3)$, $R(5, 0)$, $S(2, -4)$, and $T(-2, -1)$.

10. Find the area of a regular pentagon with a radius of 8 cm.

ACTIVITY 31 PRACTICE

Write your answers on notebook paper.
Show your work.

Lesson 31-1

Determine the missing angle measure for each polygon.

1.
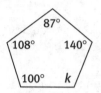

2.
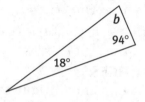

3. What is the value of x?

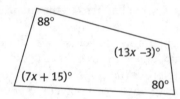

4. If the sum of the measures of the interior angles of a polygon is 2700°, how many sides does it have?
   A. 11
   B. 15
   C. 17
   D. 29

5. If the measure of each interior angle of a polygon is 150°, how many sides does it have?
   A. 10
   B. 12
   C. 14
   D. 16

6. Given $\triangle APT$ with angle measures as labeled, solve for x and calculate the measures of angles P, A, and T.

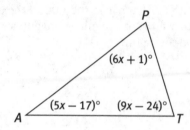

Lesson 31-2

7. What is the measure of each angle in the polygon shown?

For Items 8–10, draw polygons to satisfy the given conditions.

8. An equiangular quadrilateral that is not equilateral

9. An equilateral hexagon that is not equiangular

10. A regular polygon with an angle measuring 135°

11. What is the difference in the sum of the exterior angles measures of a regular nonagon and a regular dodecagon?
 A. 0°
 B. 90°
 C. 180°
 D. 360°

Lesson 31-3

12. A regular pentagon has sides of 4 ft. What are the perimeter and area of the pentagon?

13. Find the area of an equilateral triangle with apothem of 6 cm.

14. Find the area of a regular hexagon inscribed in a circle with a radius of 6 ft.

15. A regular triangle and a regular quadrilateral share a common side. Write a ratio of the area of the rectangle to the area of the triangle.

16. A regular octagon is plotted on the coordinate plane. The distance between each vertex is 2 units. Determine the area of the octagon.

17. What is the radius of a 1092 ft² regular heptagon?

MATHEMATICAL PRACTICES
Construct Viable Arguments and Critique the Reasoning of Others

18. a. As the number of sides of a regular polygon increases, what happens to the shape of the polygon?
 b. As a regular polygon gets smaller and smaller, what happens to the exterior angles? How does this help prove the conjecture that the sum of the exterior angles of a polygon is 360°?

Length and Area of Circles
Pi in the Sky
Lesson 32-1 Circumference and Area of a Circle

Learning Targets:
- Develop and apply a formula for the circumference of a circle.
- Develop and apply a formula for the area of a circle.

> **SUGGESTED LEARNING STRATEGIES:** Create Representations, Look for a Pattern, Identify a Subtask

Lance owns The Flyright Company. His company specializes in making parachutes and skydiving equipment. After returning from a tour of Timberlake Gardens, he was inspired to create a garden in the circular drive in front of his office building. Lance plans to hire a landscape architect to design his garden. The architect needs Lance to provide the area and circumference of the proposed garden so the architect can estimate a budget.

Lance relies on the measures of some familiar objects to help him understand the measures of a circle.

Object	Distance Around the Object, C	Diameter, d	$\frac{C}{d}$
Coin	7.85 cm	2.5 cm	
Clock	40.84 mm	13 mm	
Frisbee	62.83 in.	20 in.	

1. Complete the table to find the ratio of $C : d$.

2. Make a conjecture about the relationship between the circumference and the diameter of circular objects.

The **circumference** of a circle is the distance around the circle. Circumference is measured in linear units. The ratio of the circumference to the diameter of any circle is designated by the Greek letter π (pi).

3. Write a formula, in terms of diameter, d, that can be used to determine the circumference of a circle, C.

4. Write a formula, in terms of the radius, r, that can be used to determine the circumference of a circle, C.

5. What information does the circumference provide about the garden Lance wants to create?

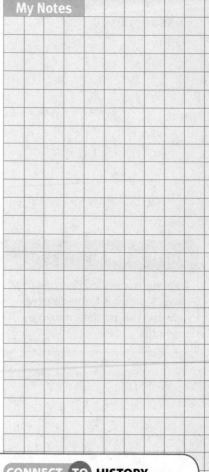

CONNECT **TO** **HISTORY**

The first known calculation of π (pi) was done by Archimedes of Syracuse (287–212 BCE), one of the greatest mathematicians of the ancient world. Archimedes approximated the area of a circle using the Pythagorean Theorem to find the areas of two regular polygons: the polygon *inscribed within the circle* and the polygon *within which the circle was circumscribed*. Since the actual area of the circle lies between the areas of the inscribed and circumscribed polygons, the areas of the polygons gave upper and lower bounds for the area of the circle. Archimedes knew that he had not found the value of pi but only an approximation within those limits. In this way, Archimedes showed that pi is between $3\frac{10}{71}$ and $3\frac{1}{7}$.

My Notes

Lance uses a compass and paper folding to develop the formula for the area of a circle.

6. **Use appropriate tools strategically.** Use a compass to draw a large circle. Use scissors to cut the circle out.

7. Divide the circle into 16 equal *sectors*.

8. Cut the sectors out and arrange the 16 pieces to form a parallelogram.

9. Write the formula for the area of a parallelogram, in terms of base b and height h.

MATH TERMS

A **sector** is a pie-shaped part of a circle. A sector is formed by two radii and the arc determined by the radii.

---

10. Explain how the height of the parallelogram is related to the radius of the circle.

11. Explain how the base of the parallelogram is related to the circumference of the circle.

12. How does the area of the parallelogram compare to the area of the original circle?

13. **Construct viable arguments.** Use your knowledge of area of parallelograms to prove the area formula of a circle.

14. What information does the area provide about the garden Lance wants to create?

The layout of The Flyright Company's building and parking lot is shown below.

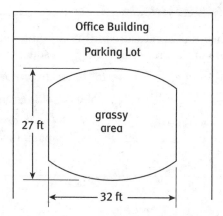

The dimensions of the grassy area of the parking lot are 32 ft by 27 ft.

15. What are the radius, circumference, and area of the largest circle that will fit in the grassy area? Justify your answer.

Even though larger circular gardens will fit in the grassy area, Lance decides that he would like the garden to have a diameter of 20 feet.

16. The landscape architect recommends surrounding the circular garden with decorative edging. The edging is sold in 12-foot sections that can bend into curves. How many sections of the edging will need to be purchased to surround the garden? Justify your answer.

17. To begin building the garden, the landscape architect needs to purchase soil. To maintain a depth of one foot throughout the garden, each bag can cover 3.5 square feet of the circle. How many bags of soil need to be purchased? Show the calculations that lead to your answer.

18. Lance and the architect are discussing the possibility of installing a sidewalk around the outside of the garden, as shown in the diagram. Determine the area of the sidewalk.

19. Critique the reasoning of others. Darnell claims that the circumference of a circular garden with radius 12 meters is greater than the perimeter of a square garden with side 18 meters. Do you agree? Explain your reasoning.

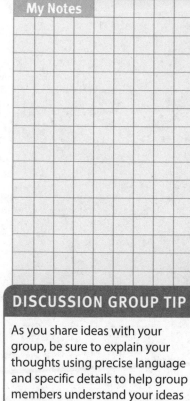

My Notes

DISCUSSION GROUP TIP

As you share ideas with your group, be sure to explain your thoughts using precise language and specific details to help group members understand your ideas and reasoning.

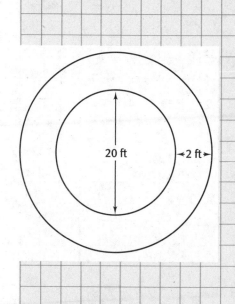

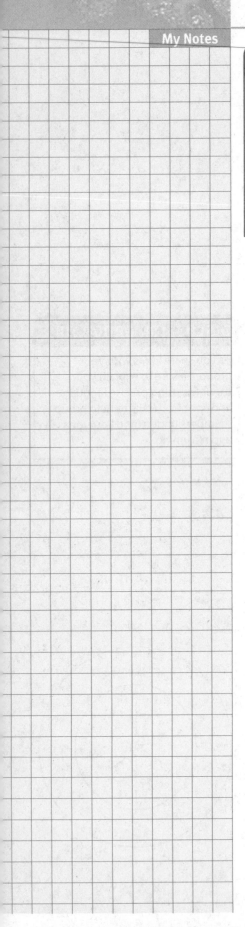

My Notes

Check Your Understanding

20. Explain why the units of measure for the circumference of a circle are linear, and those of the area of a circle are in square units.

21. Express the radius of a circle in terms of its circumference.

22. Express the area of a circle in terms of its circumference.

23. If Lance decides to increase the width of the walkway to 3 feet and keep the outer radius at 12 feet, what will happen to the area of the garden?

LESSON 32-1 PRACTICE

24. A circular rotating sprinkler sprays water over a distance of 9 feet. What is the area of the circular region covered by the sprinkler?

25. **Reason quantitatively.** What is the greatest circumference of the circle that can be inscribed in the square below?

10 cm

26. Suppose a landscaper pushes a wheelbarrow so that the wheel averages 25 revolutions per minute. If the wheel has a diameter of 18 inches, how many feet does the wheelbarrow travel each minute?

27. **Construct viable arguments.** Can the area of a circle ever equal the circumference of a circle? Support your answer with proof.

Learning Targets:

● Develop and apply a formula for the area of a sector.
● Develop and apply a formula for arc length.

SUGGESTED LEARNING STRATEGIES: Interactive Word Wall, Vocabulary Organizer, Create Representations, Quickwrite

Lance told the landscape architect that he would like the garden to resemble a colorful parachute with different flowers in alternating areas of the garden. The landscaper developed the sketch shown below.

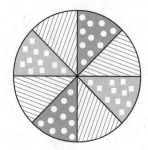

1. **Model with mathematics.** The circular garden is divided into 8 equal parts.
   a. What portion of the total area of the circle is each part?

   b. Recall that Lance would like the diameter of the circular garden to be 20 feet. Determine the area of each sector of the garden. Show the calculations that led to your answer.

   c. What is the measure of the central angle for the sector from part a?

   d. Write the fraction that is equivalent to your answer in part a and that has a denominator of 360. Explain the meaning of both the numerator and denominator using circle terminology.

2. Write an equation that will allow Lance to calculate the area of a sector with a central angle of $n°$ and radius r.

CONNECT TO AP

You will work with sectors of circles when you study polar equations in calculus.

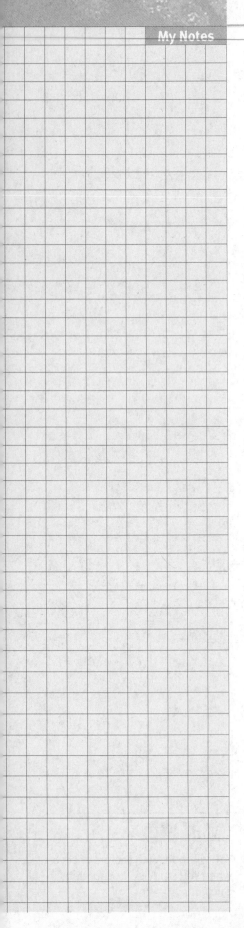

3. Determine the arc length of each sector of the garden.

4. Write an equation that will allow Lance to calculate the arc length of a sector with a central angle of $n°$ and radius r.

5. Compare and contrast the arc length of a sector and the area of a sector.

6. The architect submits his estimate to Lance. Lance notices that the architect has used the following formulas to calculate the area of each sector and length of each arc in the garden.

$$\frac{\text{degree measure of the central angle}}{360°} = \frac{\text{area of sector}}{\text{area of the circle}}$$

$$\frac{\text{degree measure of the central angle}}{360°} = \frac{\text{arc length of a sector}}{\text{circumference of the circle}}$$

Are the equations you developed in Item 2 and Item 4 equivalent to the architect's equations? Explain your answer.

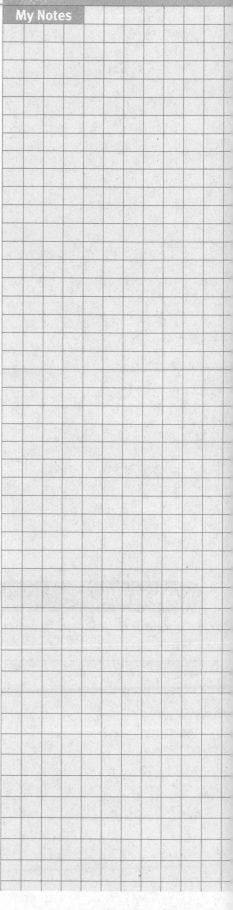

Check Your Understanding

7. If a circle has six equal sectors, explain how to determine the measure of the central angle of each sector.

8. Name the term for the sum of all the arc lengths in a circle.

9. **Critique the reasoning of others.** Juliet claims that the length of an arc is the same thing as the measure of an arc. Do you agree? Explain why.

10. The length of an arc in a circle with diameter 10 inches is 1.25π inches. Determine the measure of the arc.

11. The measure of the central angle of a sector is $36°$ and the radius of the circle is 5 inches. What is the area of the sector?

LESSON 32-2 PRACTICE

12. The length of an arc in a circle with radius 8 inches is 3.2π inches. Determine the measure of the arc.

13. The measure of the central angle of a sector is $60°$ and the area of the sector is 6π inches². Calculate the radius of the circle.

14. **Attend to precision.** Use circle B below to find the following measures.

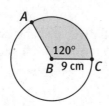

a. area of circle B
b. area of shaded sector of circle B
c. circumference of circle B
d. length of minor $\overarc{AC}$

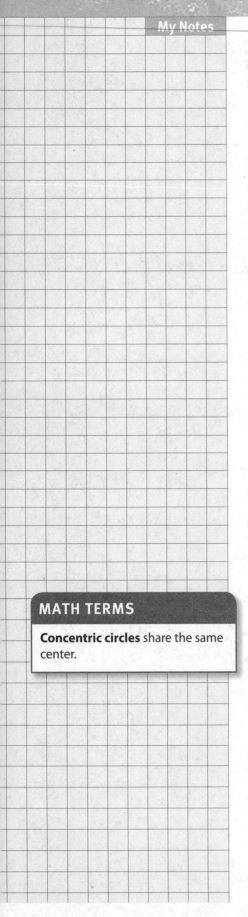

Learning Targets:
● Prove that all circles are similar.
● Describe and apply radian measure.

> **SUGGESTED LEARNING STRATEGIES:** Interactive Word Wall, Vocabulary Organizer, Create Representations, Look for a Pattern

Lance likes the design ideas generated by the landscape architect. The architect asks Lance if he will consider making the garden larger in order to include a circular fountain in the center of the garden. Lance is concerned that it will take a long time to update the current sketches and budgets to accommodate the larger garden. The architect assures him that similarity properties apply to all circles and that the changes will be quick and easy.

Lance asks, "Are you sure that all circles are similar?"

The architect draws circle O with radius r to represent the original design of the garden, and circle P with radius s to represent the sketch of the new garden.

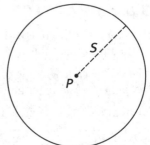

1. **Reason abstractly.** If it is true that any two circles are similar, can one circle be mapped onto the other? Explain your answer.

2. The architect maps the center of circle O onto the center of circle P, as shown in the diagram.

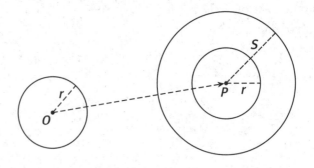

   a. What transformations are performed?

   b. If O' is the image of circle O, then identify the location of O'.

> **MATH TERMS**
>
> **Concentric circles** share the same center.

My Notes

3. **Make use of structure.** What is the scale factor between the circles?

4. Two circles share the same center. The radius of one circle is 12, and the radius of the other circle is 8.
   a. Describe how the smaller circle was dilated to generate the larger circle.

   b. Compare the ratios of the circumferences of the two circles.

   c. Compare the ratios of the two areas of the two circles.

   d. Compare the ratios you found in parts b and c to the scale factor. Describe any patterns you notice.

Check Your Understanding

5. Circle *S* is located at (0, 0). It has a radius of 4 units. Circle *T* is located at (2, 5). It has a radius of 10 units. Describe the sequence of transformations that proves that circle *S* is similar to circle *T*.

6. Circle *Q*, with radius of 18 feet, is reduced by 60 percent. What is the radius of the new circle?

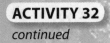

My Notes

To finalize the design of the garden, the landscape architect is using a landscaping software program. To operate it correctly, the architect has to enter some of the angles in radians and some of the angles in degrees.

Recall the formula for the arc length s of an arc with measure $m°$ and radius r: $s = \dfrac{m°}{360°}(2\pi r)$. This formula can be applied to concentric circles.

7. Given the three concentric circles below, with radius 1 unit, 2 units, and 3 units, do the following.
   a. Calculate the arc lengths of each of the three arcs formed by the 60° angle.

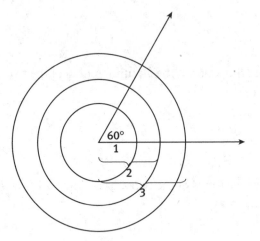

   b. Complete the following table for the three circles. Do not use an approximation for π.

Circle	Measure of Central Angle	Radius	Arc Length	Arc Length: Radius
1				
2				
3				

8. **Express regularity in repeated reasoning.** What pattern do you notice in the table?

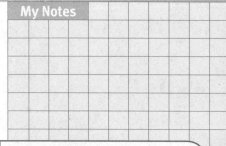
The architect points out that for a given fixed angle measure m, the length of the arc cut off by the central angle is proportional to the length of the radius. This constant of proportionality, $\frac{m^\circ}{360^\circ}(2\pi) = \frac{m^\circ}{180^\circ}\pi$, defines the *radian measure* of the angle.

Example A
Converting degrees to radians.

Convert 150° to radians.

Substitute $m = 150$ into the expression $\frac{m^\circ}{180^\circ}\pi$.

$$\frac{m^\circ}{180^\circ}\pi = \frac{150^\circ}{180^\circ}\pi = \frac{5\pi}{6}$$

So, $150^\circ = \frac{5\pi}{6}$ radians.

Example B
Converting radians to degrees.

Convert $\frac{\pi}{5}$ radians to degrees.

Multiply radians by $\frac{180^\circ}{\pi}$.

$$\frac{180^\circ}{\pi}\left(\frac{\pi}{5}\right) = 36^\circ$$

So, $\frac{\pi}{5}$ radians $= 36^\circ$.

Try These A-B
a. Complete: $20^\circ =$ _____ radians

b. Complete: $270^\circ =$ _____ radians

c. Complete: $\frac{2\pi}{3}$ radians $=$ _____ $^\circ$

d. Complete: $\frac{\pi}{9}$ radians $=$ _____ $^\circ$

My Notes

CONNECT TO SCIENCE

Units are an important part of scientific values and calculations. Scientists use one system of measurement—the SI system—to make it easier to communicate among themselves. The radian is the SI unit for angular measurement. Scientists often need to convert units using conversion ratios, as you may have done in your science classes.

Check Your Understanding

9. Alex states that all congruent circles are similar. Ethan states that all similar circles are congruent. With whom do you agree? Justify your reasoning.

10. What radian measure is equivalent to 0°? 180°?

LESSON 32-3 PRACTICE

11. **Make sense of problems.** Circle O is located at (2, 1). It has a radius of 4 units. Circle P is located at (−1, −1). It has a radius of 2 units.
    a. Are the circles congruent? How do you know?
    b. Can you prove that circle O and circle P are similar using only one similarity transformation? Explain.
    c. How can you prove that circle O and circle P are similar using more than one similarity transformation?

12. What degree measure is equivalent to the following radian measures?
    a. $\frac{\pi}{2}$
    b. $\frac{\pi}{4}$

13. What radian measure is equivalent to the following angle measures?
    a. 75°
    b. 150°
    c. 300°

ACTIVITY 32 PRACTICE
Write your answers on notebook paper.
Show your work.

Lesson 32-1

1. A circular ceramic plate has a circumference of 12π inches. What is the area of the plate?

2. What is the approximate largest circumference of a circular pond that could fit within a square walkway of sides 30 meters?
   A. 47 m
   B. 60 m
   C. 94 m
   D. 120 m

3. Levi boards a Ferris wheel with a diameter of 100 feet. What is the approximate distance, to the nearest foot, that Levi travels in six revolutions of the wheel?

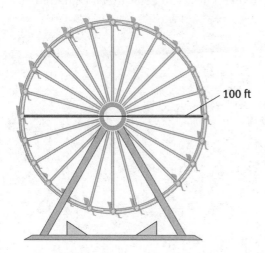

100 ft

4. A parallelogram has an area of 324 square feet. A circle has the same area. What is the approximate circumference of the circle?
   A. 10.2 ft
   B. 18.2 ft
   C. 31.8 ft
   D. 63.8 ft

5. Which of the following is equivalent to the ratio of the circumference to the radius of a circle?
   A. $\frac{\pi}{2}$
   B. π
   C. 2π
   D. 4π

6. The circumference of the thin metal band that protects the circular glass face of Dale's watch is 16π cm. What is the area of the glass face?

Lesson 32-2

Refer to the circle below for Items 7 and 8.

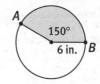

A
150°
6 in. *B*

7. Determine the area of the shaded region.

8. Determine the length of minor $\overarc{AB}$.

9. The measure of the arc of a sector is 72° and the area of the sector is 5π in.^{2} What is the radius of the circle?

   A. 5 in.
   B. 9 in.
   C. 10 in.
   D. 25 in.

10. Is it possible for an arc with a central angle of 30° in one circle to have a greater arc length than an arc with a central angle of 150° in another circle? Justify your reasoning.

11. Find the area, to the nearest tenth, of one-quarter of a circular mirror with diameter 8 meters.

Lesson 32-3

12. Circle Q is located at $(-5, 2)$. It has a radius of 5 units. Circle O is located at $(5, 2)$. It has a radius of 2 units.

    a. Describe the sequence of transformations that maps circle Q onto circle O to prove that the circles are similar.
    b. Describe another sequence of transformations that can be used to prove the circles are similar.

13. Circle S, with radius of 14 cm, is dilated using the scale factor 4 : 5. What is the radius of the new circle?

14. Which of the following is equivalent to 120°?

    A. $\frac{1}{3}\pi$ radians

    B. $\frac{2}{3}\pi$ radians

    C. 2π radians

    D. 3π radians

15. What degree measure is equivalent to $\frac{7\pi}{4}$ radians?

MATHEMATICAL PRACTICES
Reason Abstractly and Quantitatively

16. If the area of a sector is one-tenth of the area of the circle, what is the central angle of the sector? Explain how you determined your answer.

Some students are building the stage set for an upcoming school play. As they finalize some of the backdrops, they need to determine the budget for the cost of materials. The paint costs $12.50 per gallon, and one gallon of paint covers 350 square feet. Reflecting tape costs $4.50 per roll, and one roll of tape covers 40 linear feet.

1. The wooden backdrop for the opening scene shows a city skyline. One side of the backdrop is to be painted black. Find the area of the skyline. Then determine the budget for black paint if the backdrop is to be painted with two coats of paint.

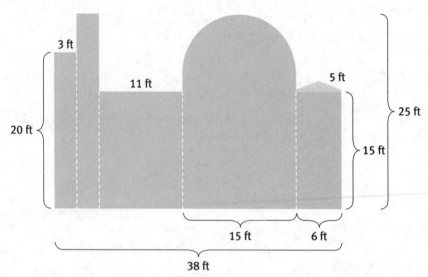

2. The second scene of the play takes place in a beehive. The backdrop is in the shape of a regular hexagon, as shown on the coordinate plane below. Each unit on the coordinate plane represents 5 feet.
   a. Determine the budget for painting one side of the backdrop with one coat of yellow paint.
   b. The perimeter of the hexagon is covered with reflecting tape. Determine the budget for the reflecting tape.

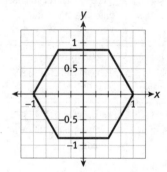

3. Part of the school's stage is shaped like a sector of a circle, as shown below. The students do not yet know the exact dimensions of this part of the stage, but they want to identify as many relationships as possible so that they will be able to decorate this part of the stage when the dimensions are available.

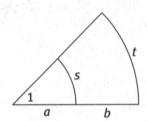

a. Explain why $\dfrac{s}{a} = \dfrac{t}{a+b}$.

b. The length of s is 12 feet, and the length of a is 10 feet. Determine the measure of $\angle 1$ in both degrees and radians.

Scoring Guide	Exemplary	Proficient	Emerging	Incomplete
	The solution demonstrates these characteristics:			
Mathematics Knowledge and Thinking (Items 1, 2, 3)	• Clear and accurate understanding of how to find the area and perimeter of plane figures, the proportional reasoning required to determine the budget for supplies, and arc length and conversions between degree and radian measures of angles	• A functional understanding of how to find the area and perimeter of plane figures, the proportional reasoning required to determine the budget for supplies, and arc length and conversions between degree and radian measures of angles	• Partial understanding of how to find the area and perimeter of plane figures, the proportional reasoning required to determine the budget for supplies, and arc length and conversions between degree and radian measures of angles	• Little or no understanding of how to find the area and perimeter of plane figures, the proportional reasoning required to determine the budget for supplies, and arc length and conversions between degree and radian measures of angles
Problem Solving (Items 1, 2, 3b)	• An appropriate and efficient strategy that results in correct answers	• A strategy that may include unnecessary steps but results in a correct answer	• A strategy that results in some incorrect answers	• No clear strategy when solving problems
Mathematical Modeling / Representations (Item 3a)	• Clear and accurate understanding of using arc length to create a proportion	• Mostly accurate understanding of using arc length to create a proportion	• Partial understanding of using arc length to create a proportion	• Little or no understanding of using arc length to create a proportion
Reasoning and Communication (Item 3a)	• Precise use of appropriate mathematics and language to justify $\dfrac{s}{a} = \dfrac{t}{a+b}$	• Mostly correct use of appropriate mathematics and language to justify $\dfrac{s}{a} = \dfrac{t}{a+b}$	• Misleading or confusing use of appropriate mathematics and language to justify $\dfrac{s}{a} = \dfrac{t}{a+b}$	• Incomplete or inaccurate use of appropriate mathematics and language to justify $\dfrac{s}{a} = \dfrac{t}{a+b}$

Three-Dimensional Figures

What's Your View?
Lesson 33-1 Prisms and Pyramids

Learning Targets:

- Describe properties and cross sections of prisms and pyramids.
- Describe the relationship among the faces, edges, and vertices of a polyhedron.

> **SUGGESTED LEARNING STRATEGIES:** Create Representations, Use Manipulatives, Self Revision/Peer Revision, Interactive Word Wall, Visualization

Len Oiler has gone into business for himself. He designs and builds tents for all occasions. Len usually builds a model of each tent before he creates the actual tent. As he builds the models, he thinks about two things: the frame and the fabric that covers the frame. The patterns for Len's first two designs are shown by the *nets* below.

1. Build a frame for each model.

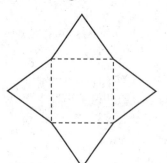

Figure 1

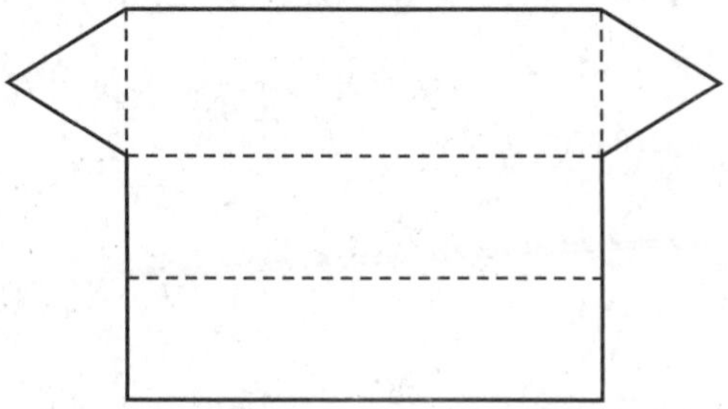

Figure 2

> ## MATH TERMS
>
> A **net** is a two-dimensional representation for a three-dimensional figure.
>
> **Faces** are the polygons that make up a three-dimensional figure.
>
> An **edge** is the intersection of any two faces.
>
> A **vertex** is a point at the intersection of three or more faces.
>
> In an **oblique prism**, the edges of the faces connecting the bases are not perpendicular to the bases. In a **right prism**, those edges are perpendicular to the bases.

2. A *prism* is a three-dimensional solid with two congruent, polygonal, and parallel bases, whose other *faces* are called lateral faces. Knowing that prisms are named according to their base shape and whether they are right or oblique, refer to the first tent frame you constructed based on Figure 1.
   a. What is the shape of the two congruent and parallel bases?

   b. What is the shape of the three lateral faces?

   c. What is the best name for the solid formed by the net in Figure 1?

   d. Use geometric terms to compare and contrast right prisms and oblique prisms.

> ## DISCUSSION GROUP TIP
>
> As you read and define new terms, discuss their meanings with other group members and make connections to prior learning.

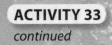
MATH TERMS

In an **oblique pyramid**, the intersection of the lateral faces (the top point of the pyramid) is not directly over the center of the base as it is in a right pyramid.

3. A *pyramid* is a three-dimensional solid with one polygonal base, whose lateral faces are triangles with a common vertex. Knowing that pyramids are named according to their base shape and whether they are right or oblique, refer to the second tent frame you constructed based on Figure 2 on the previous page.

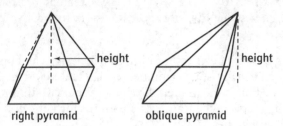

right pyramid   oblique pyramid

a. What is the shape of the base?

b. What is the best name for the solid formed by the net in Figure 2?

c. Use geometric terms to compare and contrast right pyramids and oblique pyramids.

4. The figure shown is a hexagonal pyramid. Locate the net for this solid on the worksheets your teacher has given you.

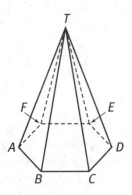

a. List the vertices of the pyramid.

b. List the base edges.

c. List the lateral edges.

d. List the lateral faces.

5. Complete the table below. Nets for the pentagonal prism and pyramid can be found on the worksheets your teacher has given you. All listed figures are examples of polyhedra (singular: *polyhedron*).

Figure Name	Number of Faces	Number of Vertices	Total Number of Edges
Triangular prism			
Rectangular prism			
Pentagonal prism			
Square pyramid			
Pentagonal pyramid			
	7	7	12
	8		18
	4	4	

6. List any patterns that you observe in the table above.

7. Make use of structure. Write a rule that expresses the relationship among *F*, *V*, and *E*.

8. Three views of the hexagonal pyramid are shown below.
   a. Label each view as *side*, *top*, or *bottom*.

  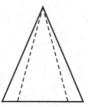

   b. Attend to precision. Explain the significance of the dashed segments in the views.

My Notes

MATH TERMS

A **polyhedron** is a three-dimensional figure consisting of polygons that are joined along their edges.

In any polyhedron, the intersection of any two faces is called an **edge**, and the vertices of the faces are the **vertices of the polyhedron**.

DISCUSSION GROUP TIPS

In your discussion groups, read the text carefully to clarify meaning. Reread definitions of terms as needed to help you comprehend the meanings of words, or ask your teacher to clarify vocabulary words.

CONNECT TO HISTORY

Leonard Euler (1707–1783) was one of the first mathematicians to write about the relationship between the number of faces, vertices, and edges in polyhedrons. Leonard Euler was not just a "one-dimensional" man; he made contributions to the fields of physics and shipbuilding, too.

My Notes

9. Sketch and label the bottom, top, and side views of this rectangular prism.

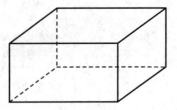

10. If the bottom of the solid formed by the net shown is face B, sketch the top, front, and side views.

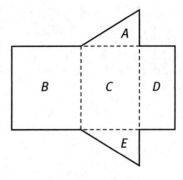

Lesson 33-1
Prisms and Pyramids

My Notes

11. Sketch the bottom, top, and side views of a square pyramid.

A **cross section** of a solid figure is the intersection of that figure and a plane.

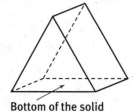 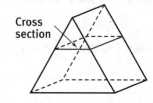

Bottom of the solid

Cross section

12. Make sense of problems. Below are several cross sections of a hexagonal right pyramid. Label each cross section as being *parallel* or *perpendicular* to the base of the pyramid.

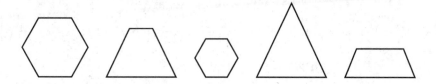

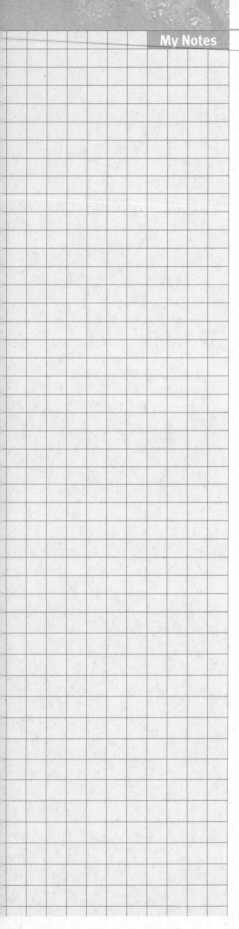

My Notes

13. Sketch several cross sections that are parallel to the base of a square pyramid. Sketch several cross sections that are perpendicular to the base of a square pyramid. What patterns do you observe?

Check Your Understanding

14. Use geometric terms to compare and contrast prisms and pyramids.
15. **Model with mathematics.** Consider the triangular prism below.

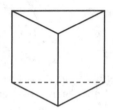

   a. Sketch several cross sections that are parallel to the bases of the triangular prism.
   b. Sketch several cross sections that are perpendicular to the bases of the prism.
   c. Describe the patterns you notice.

LESSON 33-1 PRACTICE

16. Consider the prism below.

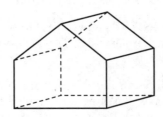

  a. Create a net for the figure.
  b. Sketch and label the top, bottom, and side views of the figure.

17. Consider the polyhedron below.

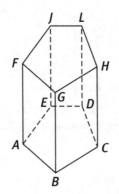

  a. Identify the vertices of the figure.
  b. Identify the shape of the two congruent and parallel bases.
  c. Identify the shape of the lateral faces.
  d. How many lateral edges compose the figure?
  e. Name each lateral face.
  f. List the base edges.
  g. What is the best name for the polyhedron?

18. A polyhedron has 10 edges. Explain how to determine the sum of the number of faces and vertices that compose the figure. Then name the polyhedron.

19. Critique the reasoning of others. The design for a new toy is shown in the net below. Jamal classifies the toy as a hexagonal prism since there are six lateral faces that meet at one point. Do you agree with Jamal? Justify your response.

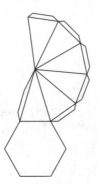

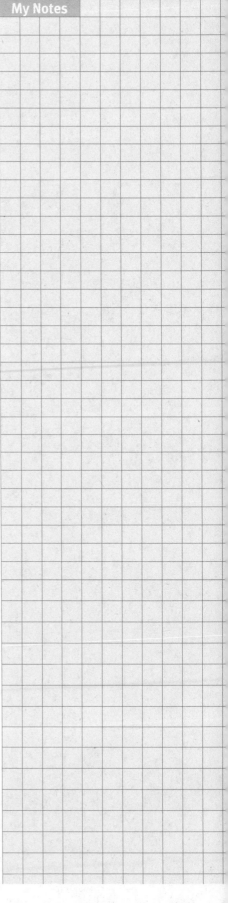

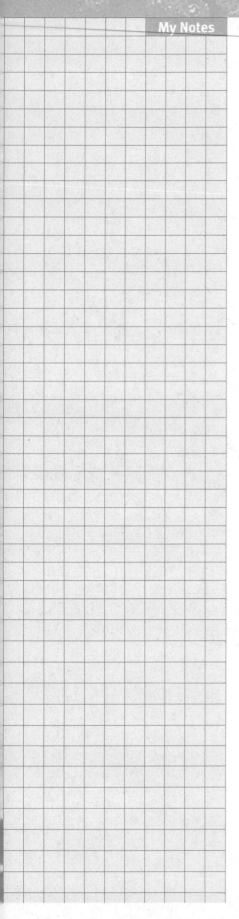

Learning Targets:

- Describe properties and cross sections of a cylinder.
- Describe properties and cross sections of a cone.

SUGGESTED LEARNING STRATEGIES: Group Presentation, Self Revision/Peer Revision, Visualization, Think-Pair-Share, Interactive Word Wall

A *cylinder* is the set of all points in space that are a given distance (radius) from a line known as the axis. Bases are formed by the intersection of two parallel planes with the cylinder. If the axis is perpendicular to each of the bases, the cylinder is called a right cylinder.

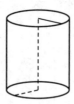

1. Label the axis, radius, and height in the diagram of the right cylinder.

2. Describe the shape and size of the cross sections that are parallel to the bases.

3. **Attend to precision.** Sketch an oblique cylinder.

4. Len is working on a pattern for a right cylinder. Which base is the correct size for this cylinder? Explain your answer.

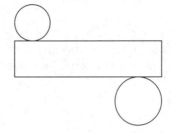

5. Explain how the dimensions of the rectangle in the net in Item 4 relate to the cylinder once it is constructed.

A *cone* is the union of all segments in space that join points in a circle to a point, called the **vertex** of the cone, that is not coplanar with the circle. The base of a cone is the intersection of a cone and a plane. If the segment that joins the center of the circle to the vertex is perpendicular to the plane that contains the center, the cone is a **right cone** and this segment is called the *height of the cone*. Otherwise, the cone is **oblique**.

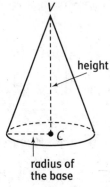
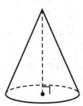
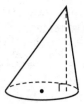
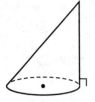
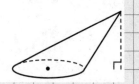

6. Compare and contrast the shape and size of the cross sections of a right cone that is parallel to the base with the cross sections of a cylinder that is parallel to its base.

7. Reason abstractly. Describe the cross section of a right cone that is perpendicular to the base and contains the vertex of the cone.

When the tent business gets slow, Len makes lampshades, which are formed when a plane parallel to the base intersects the cone.

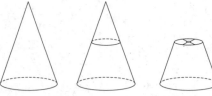

8. Len knows the height of the cone is 30 inches and the radius is 9 inches. He needs to know the area and circumference of the smaller circle, which is the top of the shade. (Assume the cross sections are 20 inches apart and parallel.)
   a. Label the center of the small circle *P*, and draw in $\overline{PQ}$. Identify two similar triangles in the figure. Explain why they are similar.

   b. Let *r* represent the radius of the small circle. Using corresponding sides of the similar triangles, write a proportion and solve for *r*.

   c. Find the circumference and area of the smaller cross section.

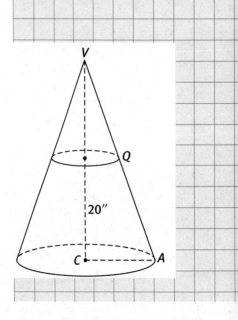

My Notes

Check Your Understanding

9. Describe the shape of the cross sections that are perpendicular to the bases of a right cylinder.

10. A figure has one base. The distance from the center of the base to the vertex is greater than the height. What is the best name for the figure?

11. Emma and Malia are both studying cross sections of the right cylinder shown. Emma states that all planes that pass through the axis of the cylinder form cross sections in the shape of a circle. Malia says this is not always true. Provide a counterexample of Emma's statement to prove that Malia is correct.

LESSON 33-2 PRACTICE

12. **Make sense of problems.** PVC is a type of plastic that is often used in construction. A PVC pipe with a 4 in. diameter is used to transfer cleaning solution into a process vessel. Explain how to compute the cross-sectional area of the pipe.

13. A graphic designer is working on a new label for a product that is packaged in a can. The radius of the cylinder is 12 cm. The distance between the top and bottom of the can is 15 cm.
    a. Describe the shape of the label prior to it being attached to the can.
    b. What are the dimensions of the label so that it completely covers the curved area of the can? Explain how you determined your answer.
    c. What is the area of the label, to the nearest square centimeter?

14. For each figure, determine the number of axes of symmetry and the number of planes of symmetry.

a.

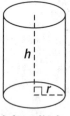

right cylinder

b.

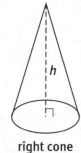

right cone

c.

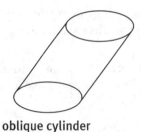

oblique cylinder

d.

oblique cone

Learning Targets:

- Describe properties and cross sections of a sphere.
- Identify three-dimensional objects generated by rotations of two-dimensional objects.

SUGGESTED LEARNING STRATEGIES: Interactive Word Wall, Vocabulary Organizer, Create Representations, Visualization, Think-Pair-Share

Len provides spherical-shaped paper lanterns for his customers to use on camping trips. A sphere is created when a circle is rotated in space about one of its diameters. A **sphere** is the set of all points in space that are a given distance (radius) from a given point (center).

1. Consider the cross sections of a sphere.
   a. Describe the shape and size of the cross sections.

   b. Where will the largest of these cross sections be located?

   c. Where is the center of the largest possible cross section of a sphere located in relation to the center of the sphere?

My Notes

MATH TERMS

The intersection of a plane through the center of a sphere is known as a **great circle**.

2. The figure shown is a sphere.

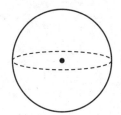

   a. Write a definition for a *chord of a sphere*. Draw and label a chord in the diagram.

   b. Write a definition for the *diameter of a sphere*. Draw and label a diameter in the diagram.

   c. Write a definition for a *tangent (line or plane) to a sphere*. Draw and label a tangent line and a tangent plane in the diagram.

   d. What must be true about a plane that is tangent to a sphere and a radius of the sphere drawn to the point of tangency? Explain your answer.

My Notes

A sphere is created by rotating a semicircle about a line, as shown in the figure below.

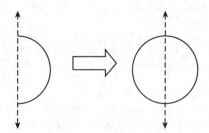

Rotating a plane about a given axis such that it forms a three-dimensional figure is known as a **solid of rotation**.

3. **Model with mathematics.** Sketch and name the solid generated by rotating rectangle *ABCD* about line *m*.

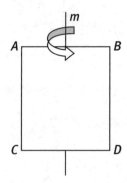

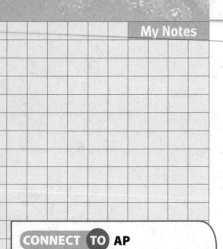

CONNECT TO AP

Right cylinders, cones, and spheres are often called *solids of rotation* because they can be formed by rotating a rectangle, triangle, or semicircle around an axis. In calculus, you will learn how to compute the volume of solids of rotation using a definite integral.

My Notes

4. Sketch and name the solid generated by rotating the triangle about the *x*-axis.

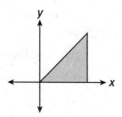

5. Describe how Figure B was created from Figure A. Then name the various three-dimensional figures that make up Figure B.

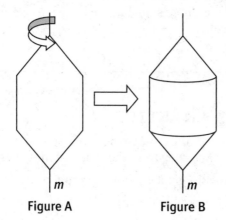

Figure A   Figure B

6. **Use appropriate tools strategically.** Cut out any two-dimensional shape, tape it to a string or wooden stick, then hold the string/stick vertically and twirl it between your fingers to see the three-dimensional solid it forms.
   a. Sketch the three-dimensional figure formed by your model.
   b. Compare your model with a partner's. Describe the differences in the figures formed. What accounts for these differences?
   c. Describe other tools you can use to create a solid of rotation model. Use your model to generate at least two more solid figures.

My Notes

Check Your Understanding

7. What is the ratio of the measure of the radius of a sphere to the measure of the radius of its great circle? Explain.

8. Two spheres intersect, as shown in the diagram below. Describe the intersection of the two spheres.

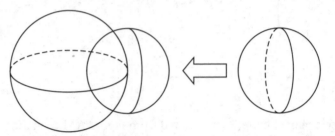

9. Can a solid of rotation about the *x*-axis generate the three-dimensional figure as shown? Explain.

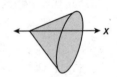

LESSON 33-3 PRACTICE

10. How do the areas of the cross sections of a sphere compare to each other as you move farther away from the center of the sphere?

11. Identify by name the greatest chord in a sphere.

12. What figure is formed by rotating a square about line *m*?

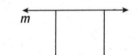

13. Which of the following two-dimensional figures was rotated about the *y*-axis to form the three-dimensional figure shown?

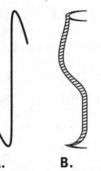
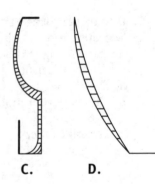

A.   B.   C.   D.

14. **Model with mathematics.** Keiko designed a pendant for a necklace by rotating a square about a diagonal, as shown. What is the width of the pendant at its widest point?

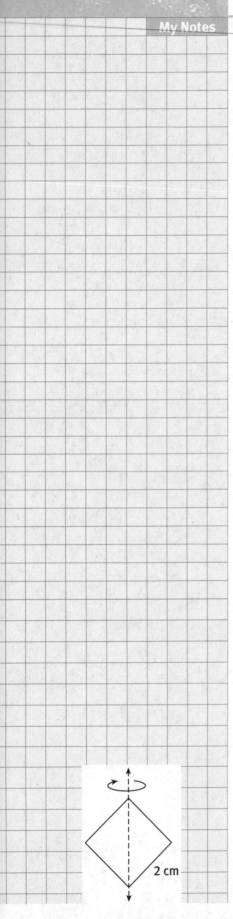

2 cm

ACTIVITY 33 PRACTICE
Write your answers on notebook paper.
Show your work.

Lesson 33-1

1. A pyramid has 24 edges and 13 faces. Find the number of vertices in the figure.

2. A polyhedron has 7 faces and 15 edges. How many vertices does it have?
   A. 8
   B. 10
   C. 22
   D. 24

3. Can you create a polyhedron with 17 vertices and 10 faces? Justify your reasoning.

4. An artist that specializes in metal work created the paperweight shown below.

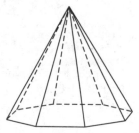

   a. Name the shape of the base.
   b. Classify the faces in the paperweight.

5. Which of the following nets represents a triangular prism with isosceles triangle faces?

A.

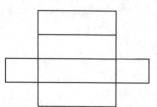

B.

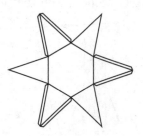

C.

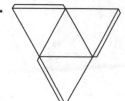

D.

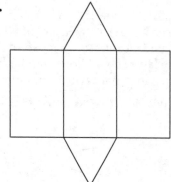

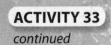
Lesson 33-2

6. Which of the following figures can be formed with two identical circular discs and a rectangular piece of aluminum foil?
   A. square pyramid
   B. right cylinder
   C. oblique cone
   D. rectangular prism

7. A plane intersects a cone, as shown below.

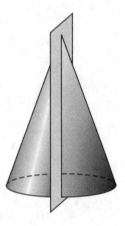

a. Describe the shape of the cross section formed.
b. The base of the shape you identified in part a is the same measure as what part of the cone?
c. What measure do the cone and the shape you identified in part a have in common?

8. Draw the possible cross sections of the cylinder shown.

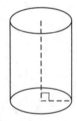

9. A graphic designer is creating a label for a three-dimensional figure. The net of the figure is shown on the coordinate grid.

What figure is represented by the net?

A.

B.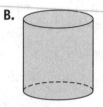

C.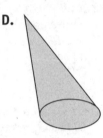

D.

Lesson 33-3

10. If the lines of latitude on a globe represent small circles, what feature on a globe represents a great circle?

11. Are spheres a type of polyhedron? Why or why not?

12. What type of shape is formed when a semicircle is revolved about its diameter?
    A. a cone
    B. a circle
    C. a sphere
    D. a hemisphere

13. Name the three-dimensional figure formed when rectangle $QRST$ is rotated about $\overline{ST}$.

14. The axis of symmetry of a cone is the x-axis. Describe, using solids of rotation, how the cone was formed.

MATHEMATICAL PRACTICES
Reason Abstractly and Quantitatively

15. Three different cross sections of a cone are shown below. Are the cross sections in each figure the same shape? Explain.

 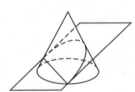

Prisms and Cylinders

Exterior Experiences

Lesson 34-1 Surface Area of Prisms and Cylinders

Learning Targets:

- Solve problems by finding the lateral area or total surface area of a prism.
- Solve problems by finding the lateral area or total surface area of a cylinder.

> **SUGGESTED LEARNING STRATEGIES:** Create Representations, Visualization, Think-Pair-Share

Brooke manages a group of tour guides and bush pilots for a company called Exterior Experiences. Brooke needs to order tents for a large group to be led into a wilderness area to view grizzly bears.

Mike is a bush pilot. He is planning to fly a group of Junior Rangers to a remote lake for a week of camping and trout fishing. They will be sleeping in tents that are in the shape of a triangular prism. The net below is a pattern for one of the Junior Ranger tents. Examine the two smaller right triangles at the bottom of the pattern. When they are zipped together, they form a triangle that is congruent to the equilateral triangle at the top of the pattern.

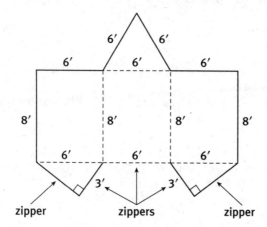

1. Find the area and perimeter of the equilateral triangular base.

2. To complete Item 1, you actually determined the missing zipper measure on the equilateral triangular base. Identify the theorem you used to determine the missing zipper measure.

3. Once the tent is constructed, what is the distance between the two bases?

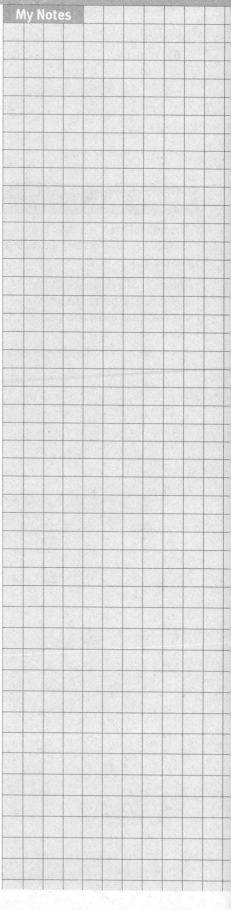

My Notes

4. Notice that the lateral faces of the prism form a larger rectangle.
  a. What are the dimensions of this larger rectangle?

  b. How do the dimensions of the larger rectangle relate to the triangular base and the distance between the two bases?

  c. The area of the largest rectangle is the sum of the areas of the lateral faces, known as the *lateral area*. Find the lateral area of this prism.

  d. If h represents the distance between the two bases in a prism, create a formula for finding the lateral area of a right prism in terms of h and the perimeter of the base, p.

MATH TERMS

The **lateral area** of a solid is the surface area of the solid, excluding the base(s).

The *faces* of a prism are its flat surfaces. The *bases* of a prism are the two congruent and parallel faces.

5. The *total surface area* of a prism is the sum of the lateral area and the area of the two bases.
  a. Calculate the total surface area for one of the Junior Ranger tents.

  b. Write a formula for calculating the total surface area, SA, in terms of the lateral area, LA, and the base area, B.

6. Reason abstractly. In the formula you generated for the surface area in Item 5b, why is there a 2 as the coefficient in front of the base, B?

7. Mike sleeps in a tent with a different-shaped front and back than those of the other tents, as shown below. Find the lateral area and the total surface area of Mike's tent (including the floor). Show your work.

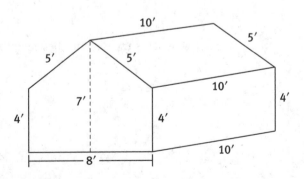

Check Your Understanding

8. Identify the figure formed with two square bases and four rectangular lateral faces.

9. Consider the triangular prism below.

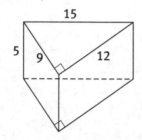

a. Identify the shapes and dimensions of the lateral faces.

b. Find the lateral area of the prism.

c. Identify the shapes and dimensions of each base.

d. What two measures can you now add together to find the total surface area of the prism? Compute the surface area of the prism.

Gino owns a company that manufactures cylindrical stuff sacks from water- and puncture-resistant fabric. Hikers and campers often use these stuff sacks to carry their tents and clothing when they go out on an excursion. The bases of the cylindrical sacks have a 6-inch radius, and the height is 15 inches.

10. Calculate the circumference and area of one of the bases of the stuff sack. Leave your answers in terms of π.

My Notes

MATH TERMS

The curved surface that lies between the two circular bases of a cylinder is known as the **lateral surface**.

11. If the sack is laid out on a table, what shape is the *lateral surface* of the cylinder? What are its dimensions?

12. How do the dimensions of the lateral surface of the sack relate to the circular base and the height of the cylinder?

13. Determine the lateral area of a stuff sack.

14. Write a formula for calculating the lateral area, LA, of a right cylinder in terms of the radius, r, the height, h, and π.

15. Calculate the total surface area of one of Gino's stuff sacks.

16. Write a formula for calculating the total surface area, SA, of a cylinder in terms of the lateral area, LA, and the base area, B.

Check Your Understanding

17. The pipe below is open on each end. Chester computes the surface area of the exterior surface of the pipe as 32π ft^2. Maria computes the surface area as 24π ft^2. Which student is correct? Justify your reasoning.

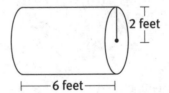

18. A manufacturing company produces plastic cylindrical trash cans with heights of 5 feet and diameters of 2 feet. A 10 ft-by-12 ft sheet of plastic is fed into a cutting machine. If each machine cuts the three shapes needed to make a trash can, how much scrap plastic is left once the plastic leaves the machine? Show your work.

LESSON 34-1 PRACTICE

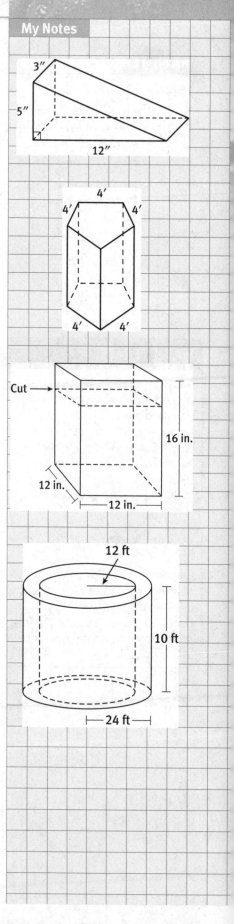

My Notes

19. Find the lateral and total surface areas of a prism whose base is a right triangle with legs 5 in. and 12 in. and whose height is 3 in.

20. A birdhouse in the shape of a right prism has a lateral area of 90 ft². The base of the birdhouse is a regular pentagon with 4 ft sides. Find the height of the prism.

21. **Reason quantitatively.** A company that manufactures GPS devices ships the product to their customers using the shipping container shown. To cash in on the rebate, the customer needs to cut 2 inches off of the top of the container and mail it back to the manufacturer, along with the receipt for the device.
    a. What is the surface area of the original shipping container?
    b. Darcy states that to find the surface area of the shipping container after the rebate section is removed, you just need to find the sum of the areas of the four 2 in. sides and subtract it from the surface area of the original container. Judd says that Darcy is forgetting to do something. Identify the step that Darcy needs to include. Explain.

22. In a convective type of heat exchanger, a smaller cylinder is placed inside a larger cylinder, as shown.
    a. Write the ratio of the lateral area of the smaller cylinder to the lateral area of the larger cylinder.
    b. Write the ratio of the surface area of the smaller cylinder to the surface area of the larger cylinder.

My Notes

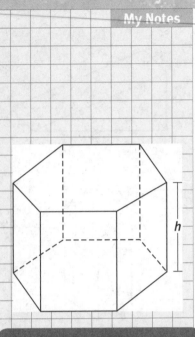

MATH TERMS

Cavalieri's Principle states that if two solids lying between two parallel planes have the same height, and all cross sections at equal distances from the bases have the same areas, then the solids have the same volume.

CONNECT TO Calculus

Cavalieri's Principle can be applied to more complicated shapes, such as when the width of a prism becomes smaller and smaller. This principle led to what is now known as integral calculus.

Learning Targets:

● Solve problems by finding the volume of a prism.
● Solve problems by finding the volume of a cylinder.

> **SUGGESTED LEARNING STRATEGIES:** Group Presentation, Self Revision/Peer Revision, Think-Pair-Share, Interactive Word Wall

Extreme Exteriors gives their tour guides a thermos before every excursion. Depending on the excursion, the thermos is either a right or an oblique cylinder. Sometimes the thermos is easier to carry on a bike or in a kayak if it is oblique.

Inside each thermos is a small filter in the shape of a hexagon, which uses thin, hexagonal-shaped filter paper. Extreme Exteriors always keeps a container of filter papers on hand.

Examine the filter paper container shown. The base of the container is congruent to each filter paper.

1. Name the figure that describes the container.

2. If the area of each filter paper is *B*, write a formula that finds the volume of filter paper the container holds.

3. Suppose the radius of the container is 2 in. and its height is 4 in. What is the volume of filter papers that fits in the container? Explain how you arrived at your answer.

Examine the two cylindrical-shaped thermoses below with radius *r* and height *h*.

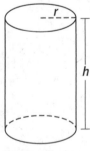

Right cylinder

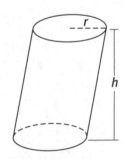

Oblique cylinder

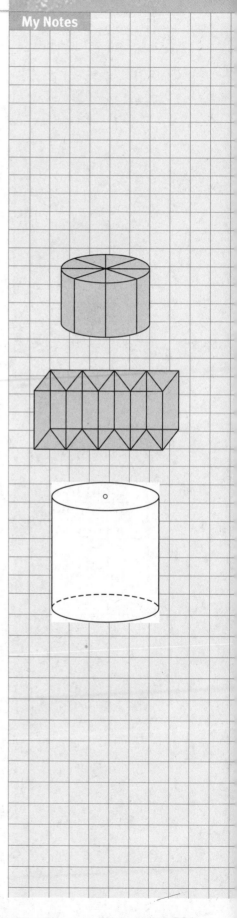

4. Suppose a plane parallel to the base of the cylinder passes through the cylinder.
  a. Describe the cross section of each cylinder.

  b. What is the area of the cross section of each cylinder?

5. Recall the volume formula for a prism in Item 2, where B is the base area and h is the height. What is the base area of the cylinder? How does this compare to your answer in Item 4b?

6. Suppose each cylinder was dissected into wedges and rearranged to form a solid, like that of a prism. Use what you know about the volume formula of a prism to determine the volume formula of a cylinder.

Example A

The volume of the cylinder shown is 450 ft^3 and the diameter is 8 ft. What is the height of the cylinder?

Use the volume formula for a cylinder, $V = Bh$, or $\pi r^2 h$, and substitute known values.

$$V = \pi r^2 h$$
$$\frac{V}{\pi r^2} = \frac{\pi r^2 h}{\pi r^2} \quad \text{Divide to isolate } h.$$
$$\frac{V}{\pi r^2} = h$$
$$\frac{450}{\pi (4)^2} = h$$
$$8.95 \approx h$$

The height of the cylinder is about 8.95 ft.

Try These A

a. The volume of a cylinder is 220 cm^3, and the radius is 5 cm. What is the height of the cylinder, to the nearest tenth?

b. The volume of a cylinder is 90 m^3, and the circumference of one of the bases is 27 m. Determine the height of the cylinder.

c. The volume of a rectangular prism is 120 ft. The width is 15 ft, and the height is 4 ft. What is the length of the prism?

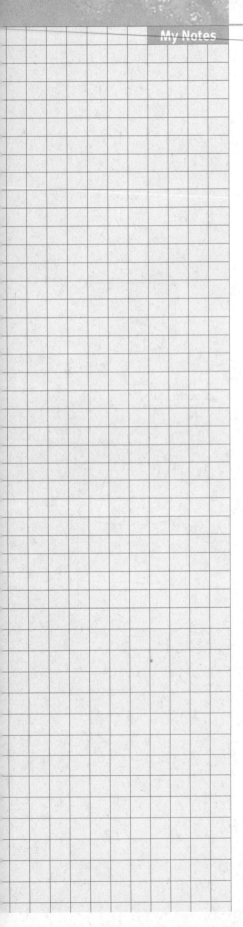

Brooke is looking to purchase one of two new styles of tents. One tent is in the shape of a half-cylinder, and one is in the shape of a triangular prism. Since the price of the tents is dependent on the area of material, Brooke wants to find the tent with the greatest volume (living area) using the least amount of material.

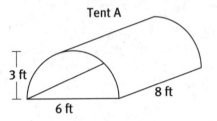
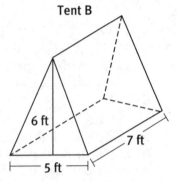

Tent A

3 ft
8 ft
6 ft

Tent B

6 ft
7 ft
5 ft

Now, work through a multipart problem that uses both surface area formulas and volume formulas.

7. First consider the volume of each tent.
   a. Write the formula for the volume of a cylinder. How can you adapt the formula to compute the volume of Tent A?

   b. Find the volume of Tent A. Show your calculations.

   c. Name the figure that describes the base of Tent B. What is the area of each base?

   d. Find the volume of Tent B. Show your calculations.

   e. Which tent has the greater volume?

My Notes

8. Next, consider the surface area of each tent. Keep in mind that each tent has a floor.

   a. Name the shapes that describe the base and the lateral faces of Tent A. How can you adapt the surface area formula of a cylinder to compute the surface area of Tent A?

   b. Find the surface area of Tent A. Show your calculations.

   c. Name the shapes that describe the base and the faces of Tent B. Find the dimensions of each face and base.

   d. Find the surface area of Tent B. Show your calculations.

   e. Which tent has the greater surface area?

9. **Make sense of problems.** Complete the table for the volume and surface area of each tent. Which tent has the greatest volume with the least amount of material? Explain how you determined your answer.

	Tent A	Tent B
Volume		
Surface Area		

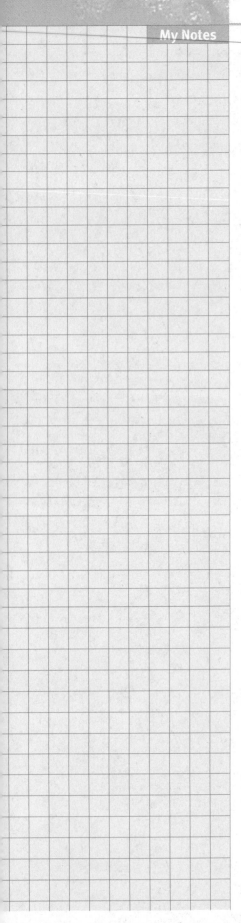

Check Your Understanding

10. **Attend to precision.** In Items 8 and 9, why are the units for perimeter, surface area, and volume different?

11. True or false? If a right prism and an oblique prism have congruent bases, then the volume of the right prism can never be equal to the volume of the oblique prism. If true, state the theorem that supports this fact. If false, provide proof.

12. If a cylindrical container does not have a lid, does it have an effect on the measure of the volume, the surface area, neither, or both? Justify your answer.

LESSON 34-2 PRACTICE

13. The length of the cylindrical tube shown is 10 ft. What is the volume of the tube given that the circumference of one of the bases is 48π ft?

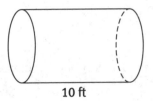

10 ft

14. **Model with mathematics.** A United States gold dollar has a radius of 26.5 mm and a thickness of 2 mm. Calculate the total volume of gold in a stack of 25 gold dollars, to the nearest mm^3.

15. The bases of a triangular prism are equilateral triangles with sides of 8 ft. The height of the prism is 5 ft. Determine the volume of the prism, to the nearest cubic foot.

16. The volume of a rectangular prism is 1200 ft^3. The bases are squares, as shown. What is the length of the prism?

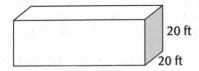

20 ft

20 ft

17. If two of the same type of three-dimensional figure have the same volume, is this a guarantee that the two figures have the same surface area? Explain.

ACTIVITY 34 PRACTICE
Write your answers on notebook paper.
Show your work.

Lesson 34-1

1. A cell phone is packaged in a rectangular cardboard container prior to shipment. The height of the container is 12 in., and the base has dimensions of 5 in. by 7 in.
   a. Compute the lateral area of the cardboard container.
   b. Compute the surface area of the cardboard container.
   c. The fee to ship the phone to a customer is $4.50 plus $0.05 per square inch of the exterior surface of the container. Compute the total shipping fee.

2. A stepping-stone has the shape of a right prism. It has a height of 10 ft and a base in the shape of a rhombus. The diagonals of the rhombus measure 12 ft and $12\sqrt{3}$ ft.

   Which of the following measures is the lateral area of the stepping-stone?
   A. 120 ft^2
   B. 480 ft^2
   C. 560 ft^2
   D. 960 ft^2

3. The lateral surface of the cylindrical can shown below is to be covered with a label. Determine the greatest area of label that can be used to cover the lateral surface of the can, without overlap.

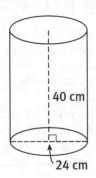

4. Consider the right triangular prism below.

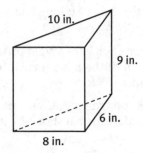

   a. Compute the lateral area of the prism.
   b. Compute the surface area of the prism.

5. A cereal company is designing a box for a new product. A right rectangular prism-shaped box stacks best on store shelves. The cereal will all fit into a prism that measures 10 in. long, 2.5 in. wide, and 14 in. high. The art department is designing graphics for the package and needs to know how much room they have to work with.

   What is the total surface area, in square inches, of the cereal box?
   A. 56 in.^{2}
   B. 105 in.^{2}
   C. 350 in.^{2}
   D. 400 in.^{2}

6. A pipe connects a soybean oil storage tank and a process vessel. Determine the lateral area of the pipe given that it is 12 ft long and 4 in. in diameter.

7. Determine the height of a right prism with lateral area 45 sq ft if the base is a regular hexagon each of whose sides is 5 ft.

8. What is the approximate surface area of the figure formed by the net shown?

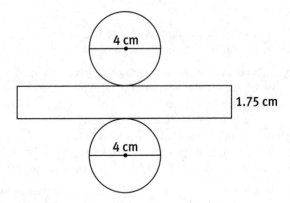

Lesson 34-2

9. Determine the volume of the right triangular prism.

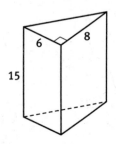

A. 29 cubic units
B. 306 cubic units
C. 360 cubic units
D. 720 cubic units

10. What is the radius of this cylinder if its volume is 2262 m³?

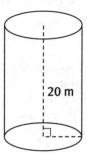

11. A cylindrical tank with a diameter of 8 feet and a height of 14 feet is being filled with water. If the water is entering the tank at a rate of 2 cubic feet per second, how long will it take for the tank to be half full?

12. A wooden storage trunk has a height of 4 ft, a length of 6 ft, and a width of 2 ft. The trunk is to be coated with two coats of polyurethane. What measure is needed to determine the total amount of polyurethane needed?
A. volume
B. weight
C. lateral area
D. surface area

13. The diameter of an oblique cylinder is 32 cm and the height is 4 cm. What is the volume of a right cylinder with the same dimensions?

MATHEMATICAL PRACTICES
Reason Abstractly and Quantitatively

14. The lateral areas, *LA*, of a cube and a right cylinder are equal. The figures even have the same height, *h*.
a. Write expressions for the lateral area of each figure.
b. Write an expression that can be used to determine the radius of the cylinder. Show how you determined your answer.

Pyramids and Cones

Perfect Packaging
Lesson 35-1 Surface Area of Pyramids and Cones

Learning Targets:
- Solve problems by finding the lateral area or total surface area of a pyramid.
- Solve problems by finding the lateral area or total surface area of a cone.

> **SUGGESTED LEARNING STRATEGIES:** Create Representations, Visualization, Think-Pair-Share

The way a product is packaged is an important marketing element for manufacturers, and in today's world, it is an important environmental concern for consumers.

Luis is leading a committee to change some of the current packaging materials used by his company that have been deemed nonrecyclable to more environmentally friendly materials. Many of the environmentally friendly materials, however, do not have the same strength or durability as the packaging materials currently in use. The committee realizes that if the materials are changed, then the shape of the actual package will likely have to change to ensure strength and durability.

The committee consists of representatives from the marketing department and the advertising department, a product engineer, and a packaging engineer. To begin, the marketing representative provides the committee with feedback that consumers are attracted to products packaged in pyramid- and cone-shaped containers.

Surface area is a critical concern for the advertising representative, as it dictates how much space is available for print. Before the committee goes any further, the advertiser wants to determine the surface area of a cone and pyramid.

1. Consider the *tetrahedron*, a special type of pyramid with an equilateral triangle for a base and equilateral triangles for each of its three sides. Suppose the length of each edge of the container is 8 ft.

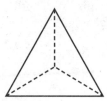

   a. Find the area of each face.

   b. Find the total surface area of the four faces.

> ## MATH TIP
> The formula for finding the area of an equilateral triangle, given the length of a side s, is $A = \dfrac{s^2\sqrt{3}}{4}$.

My Notes

c. Use the formula for calculating the area of an equilateral triangle to derive a formula for the *total surface area* of one of these pyramids in terms of the length of an edge, *s*.

d. The packaging engineer provides a 27.75 sq. yd sample of environmentally friendly material to create a model of this tetrahedron-shaped container. Find the dimensions of the pyramid.

2. Consider the square pyramid. Suppose each side of the square base of the pyramid is 12 ft, and the length of each lateral edge is 10 ft.

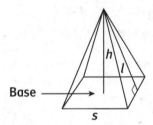

Base

s

a. Determine the perimeter and the area of the base.

b. How can you determine the height of a triangular face?

c. The height of a triangular face is the **slant height**. Draw one of the slant heights, and determine its length. Then calculate the area of one of the triangular faces.

MATH TERMS

The **slant height** of a regular pyramid, such as a square pyramid, is the distance between the vertex and the base edge of the pyramid. It is the altitude of a lateral face.

d. The **lateral area of a pyramid** is the sum of the areas of the lateral faces. Calculate the lateral area of the pyramid.

My Notes

e. If ℓ represents the slant height of the pyramid, create a formula for finding the lateral area, LA, of a right pyramid in terms of ℓ and the perimeter of the base, p.

f. The **total surface area of a pyramid** is the sum of the lateral area and the area of the base. Calculate the total surface area for the square pyramid.

g. Write a formula for calculating the total surface area, SA, of a right pyramid in terms of the lateral area, LA, and the base area, B.

3. Use your formulas in Items 2e and 2g to find the lateral area and total surface area for a regular tetrahedron, each of whose edges is 8 feet in length.

Check Your Understanding

4. Name the shapes of the lateral faces of a regular pyramid.

5. Can a pyramid ever have quadrilaterals for lateral faces? Explain.

6. Each side of the base of a square pyramid is 5 ft. The slant height of the pyramid is 4 ft.
   a. Calculate the lateral area of the pyramid.
   b. What is the surface area of the pyramid?

7. Each edge of a regular tetrahedron is 12 in.
   a. Calculate its lateral area.
   b. What is its surface area?

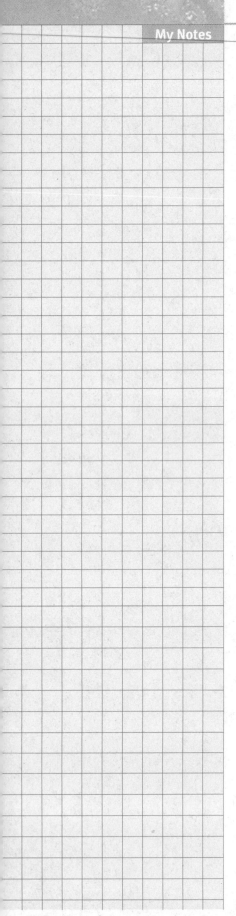

The advertising representative would like to have a formula for calculating the surface area for a cone-shaped package, in terms of the dimensions. She knows the formula for the area of the base of a cone, which is a circle. It's the lateral area that is troubling her. The packaging engineer guides her through an explanation by displaying several patterns for the curved surface of a cone, the **lateral surface**.

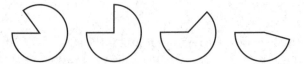

8. **Use appropriate tools strategically.** The engineer points out that each pattern is actually a sector of a circle. Find the patterns for the curved surface of several cones on the worksheet your teacher provided. Cut out each pattern and build the lateral surface for each cone. Trace each circular base on a sheet of paper and answer the questions below.

   a. As the lateral area of the cone decreases, what happens to the height of the cone?

   b. As the lateral area of the cone decreases, what happens to the radius of the base?

   c. As the lateral area of the cone decreases, what happens to the slant height of the cone?

   d. Which part of the cone corresponds to the radius of the sector?

The engineer starts each pattern for the lateral surface with a large circle with radius l. Then he cuts out a sector, as shown below.

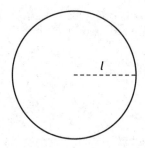 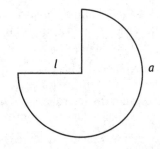

My Notes

9. **Make sense of problems.** Use the figures above to respond to each of the following.

   a. Write an expression for the area and circumference of the circle in terms of l and π.

   b. Write the ratio of the area of the sector A_S to the area of the circle.

   c. Write the ratio of the length of the arc of the sector a to the circumference of the circle.

   d. Explain why the two ratios in parts b and c can be used to create a proportion.

   e. Write the proportion from part d, and solve this proportion for A_S. Simplify your answer.

   f. How does a, the length of the arc of the sector, relate to the base of the cone?

   g. Write an expression for the lateral area of a cone, LA, in terms of l, the radius of the base, r, and π.

   h. Write a formula for calculating the total surface area, SA, in terms of the lateral area, LA, and the base area, B.

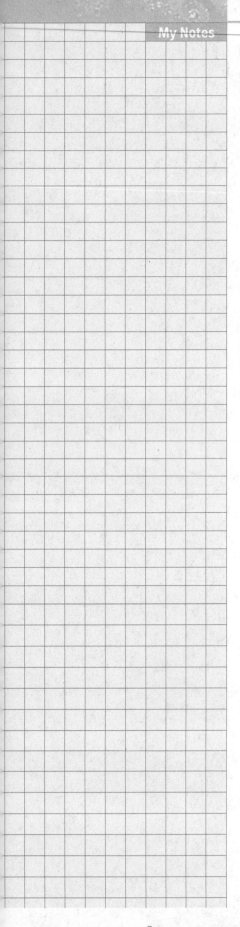

Check Your Understanding

10. Compare the formulas for surface area of cones and pyramids. Explain why the base area of a cone is not computed using the same formula as the base area for a pyramid.

11. The diameter of the base of a cone is 10 centimeters. The slant height of the cone is 7 centimeters.
    a. Determine the lateral area of the cone.
    b. What is the surface area of the cone?

12. A plastic cone-shaped package is 10 inches in diameter and 12 inches high.
    a. Make a sketch of the pyramid and label the dimensions.
    b. Find the lateral area.
    c. Compute the total surface area of the package.

13. Describe a step-by-step method you can use to find the height of a cone if you know the lateral area and the base area. Then use your method to find the height of a right cone whose lateral area is 136π ft^2 and base area is 64π ft^2.

LESSON 35-1 PRACTICE

14. Calculate the lateral area and surface area of a pyramid whose height is 8 ft and whose base is a square with 12 ft sides.

15. Find the lateral area of a right pyramid whose slant height is 18 mm and whose base is a square with area 121 mm^2.

16. **Reason quantitatively.** Calculate the surface area of the cylindrical rocket and "nose cone" if the slant height of the nose cone is 8 ft.

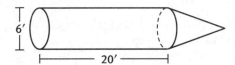

17. Find the lateral area and surface area for a right cone whose slant height forms a 45° angle with the base and whose radius is 8 mm.

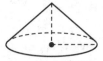

18. The product engineer shows the committee a product he is working on that is cylindrical in shape with a conical top. Find the total surface area of the product given the diameter is 24 ft, the height of the cylindrical portion is 6 ft, and the height of the conical portion is 5 ft.

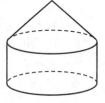

My Notes

Learning Targets:

- Solve problems by finding the volume of a pyramid.
- Solve problems by finding the volume of a cone.

> **SUGGESTED LEARNING STRATEGIES:** Visualization, Group Presentation, Self Revision/Peer Revision, Think-Pair-Share, Interactive Word Wall

For any new package design, the packaging engineer needs to confirm it can meet the volume requirements for the product. Luis asks the packaging engineer to explain how volume is computed for packages shaped like a pyramid or cone.

Consider the three potential package designs below. Each pyramid has the same base area and the same height.

1. **Model with mathematics.** The packaging engineer manipulates the pyramid into the figure shown. What figure do the three pyramids form?

My Notes

MATH TIP

There is a postulate that states that pyramids with the same base area and the same height have the same volume.

2. A cube is a type of prism.

   a. What is the formula for volume of a prism?

   b. How many pyramids form the cube?

   c. Do the pyramids within the cube have the same volume? How do you know?

   d. Describe how the formula from Item 2a can be adapted to create a formula for the volume of one of the square-based pyramids.

   e. Write the formula for the volume of one of the square-based pyramids.

MATH TERMS

Cavalieri's Principle states that two objects with the same height and the same cross-sectional areas at every height have the same volume.

The *height of an oblique pyramid* is the length of the perpendicular segment from its vertex to the plane of the base.

3. Describe how *Cavalieri's Principle* can be used to justify the formula in Item 2e for any square-based pyramid. Remember to use complete sentences and words such as *and, or, since, for example, therefore, because of, by the*, to make connections between your thoughts.

4. Critique the reasoning of others. Keith states that the formula in Item 2e does not apply to a pyramid with *any* polygonal base. Angela states that the formula does apply, and that only the formula used to compute B will be different. With whom do you agree and why?

Example A

Find the volume of a package shaped like a square pyramid, with the given measures.

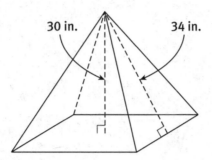

30 in.   34 in.

Step 1: Find the length of the base.

The distance between the height of the pyramid and the slant height is one-half the base. Use the Pythagorean Theorem to find this distance.

$$d^2 = 34^2 - 30^2$$
$$d = 16$$

The length of the base is 2(16) = 32 in.

Step 2: Use the volume formula for a pyramid, $V = \frac{1}{3} Bh$, and substitute known values.

$$V = \frac{1}{3} Bh$$
$$V = \frac{1}{3}(32)(32)(30)$$
$$V = 10,240 \text{ in.}^3$$

Solution: The volume of the pyramid is 10, 240 in.^{3}

Try These A

a. The height of a pyramid is 24 ft. The area of the base is 22 ft^2. Compute the volume of the pyramid.

b. The volume of a pyramid is 220 cm^3 and the base area is 10 cm^2. What is the height of the pyramid?

c. The slant height of a square pyramid is 10 feet. One side of the base of the pyramid is 12 feet. What is the volume of the pyramid?

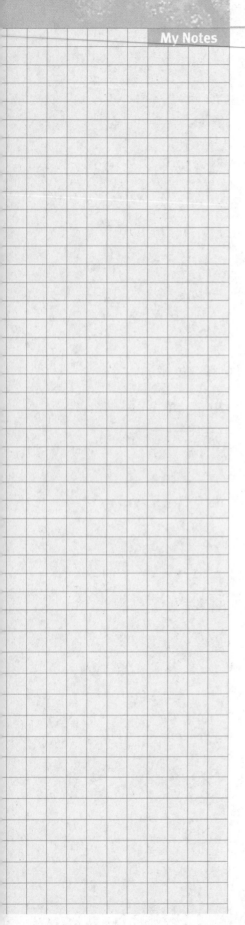

Now, consider a package design in the shape of a cone. The packaging engineer develops the volume formula by inscribing polygonal pyramids of varying bases in a cone.

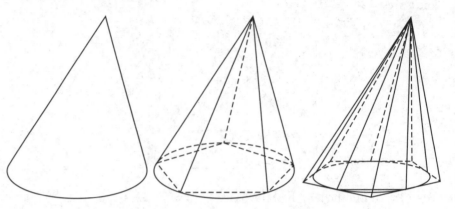

5. Write the formula for the volume of a pyramid.

6. Examine the base of each cone. As the number of sides increases in the polygonal pyramid, is the space between the pyramid base and the circular base of the cone increasing or decreasing?

7. Reason abstractly. Suppose the number of sides of the polygonal pyramid inscribed in the cone continued to increase. What shape would the base of the pyramid resemble?

8. Write the area formula for a circle.

9. Use the formulas in Items 5 and 8 to write the formula for volume of a cone.

My Notes

10. Compute the volume of the cone with a radius of 6 cm and a height of 15 cm, to the nearest tenth.

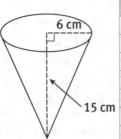

6 cm

15 cm

Check Your Understanding

11. A container of nuts in the shape of a right cone has a diameter of 18 cm. The height of the container is 7 cm. What is the volume of nuts that fits in the container?

12. Compare and contrast the volume formulas for cones and pyramids.

13. In terms of units of measure, how does the surface area of a cone differ from the volume of a cone?

14. A perfume bottle in the shape of a right cone has a diameter of 6 in. and a slant height of 5 in. How much perfume can the bottle hold, to the nearest cubic inch?

LESSON 35-2 PRACTICE

15. The height of a cone is 10 ft. The area of the base is 22 ft^2. Compute the volume of the cone.

16. The volume of a cone is 80 cm^3 and the base area is 5 cm^2. What is the height of the cone?

17. The volume of a right cone is 400 ft^3 and the height is 25 ft. Find the slant height of the cone, to the nearest tenth.

18. The base of a right pyramid has dimensions of 5 m by 6 m. The height of the pyramid is 12 m. What is the volume of the pyramid?

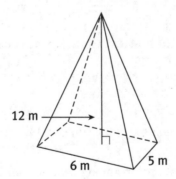

12 m

6 m

5 m

19. **Make sense of problems.** Peanuts are sold at the baseball game for $3.75. The peanuts are packaged in boxes shaped as rectangular prisms. The height of the box is 7 inches and the base of the box has an area of 3 in.^{2}. For the tournament games, management decided to package the peanuts in a pyramid design rather than as a prism. The pyramid has the same height and base area as the prism.
   a. Compare the volumes of the prism and the pyramid.
   b. Determine a price for the peanuts in the pyramid design that is proportionally fair to the original price. Explain your answer.

My Notes

Learning Targets:

- Apply concepts of density in modeling situations.
- Apply surface area and volume to solve design problems.

> **SUGGESTED LEARNING STRATEGIES:** Group Presentation, Self Revision/Peer Revision, Think-Pair-Share, Interactive Word Wall

Luis has learned that before they make any decisions about changing packaging materials, he needs to make sure he is within budget for the cost of the packaging materials and the cost of shipping the product.

The new material under consideration for packaging food products costs $0.45 per square foot. The shipping cost is $1.90 per pound. The table below shows the density for four different food products packaged in bulk and shipped from Luis's company.

Material	Density (lb/ft³)
Shelled almonds	30
Apple seeds	32
Coffee beans	22
Soybean hulls	6

Luis is analyzing the cost of the following two package designs to determine which package makes the most sense to use for coffee beans.

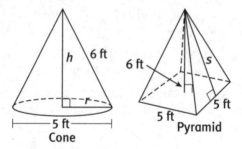

1. **Model with mathematics.** Consider the cone. The diameter is 5 ft and the slant height is 6 ft.

   a. Determine the surface area of the cone. Then find the cost of the packaging material.

   b. Determine the volume of the cone.

   c. What is the relationship among volume, density, and mass?

   d. Find the mass of the cone filled with coffee beans.

   e. Find the shipping cost of the cone.

   f. What is the total cost for packaging and shipping the cone-shaped package filled with coffee beans?

My Notes

2. Make a prediction as to whether the total cost for packaging and shipping the pyramid-shaped package will be greater than, less than, or the same as the cone-shaped package. Explain your reasoning.

3. Determine the validity of your prediction by analyzing the pyramid package.
   a. Find the cost of the packaging material for the pyramid design.

   b. Find the shipping cost of the pyramid.

   c. What is the total cost for packaging and shipping the cone-shaped package?

4. Compare the ratio of total cost to ship each package to volume shipped. How did your prediction in Item 2 compare to your findings?

5. Which food product in the table would be the least expensive to ship? Explain how you determined your answer.

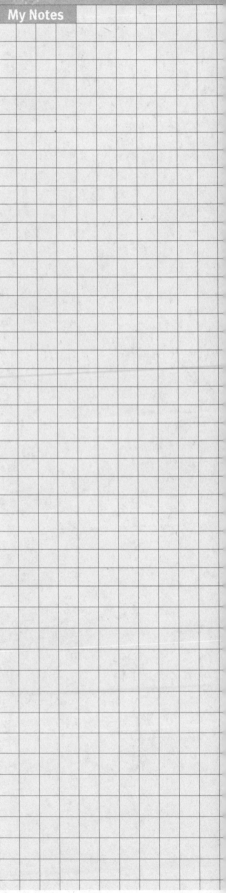

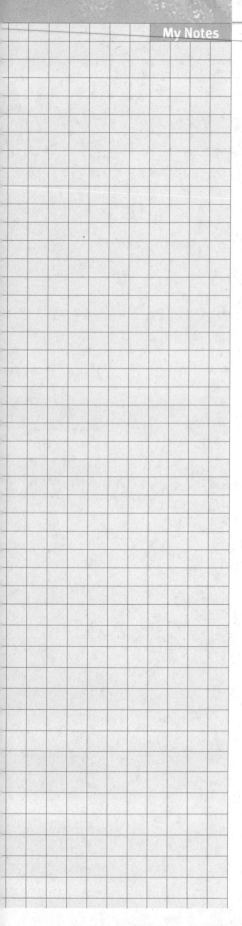

Check Your Understanding

6. Apple seeds are packaged in a container shaped like a square pyramid. Coffee beans are packaged in an identical container. Do the filled packages have the same mass? If not, explain how you can determine the product with the greater mass.

7. Shelled almonds are packaged in a cylindrical container with a 0.5-foot diameter and a height of 0.6 ft. What is the approximate mass of the almonds that fill the container, to the nearest tenth of a pound?

LESSON 35-3 PRACTICE

8. Butter has a density of 54 lb/ft³. It is packaged into a 5 in.-by-1.27 in.-by-1.27 in. cardboard prism. One package of butter contains four identical prisms. What is the approximate mass of one package of butter?

9. Two containers, a cone and a cylinder, both have a height of 6 ft. The bases have the same diameter of 4 ft. Both containers are filled with shredded paper that has a density of 12 lb/ft³.
   a. How do you know which container has the greatest mass?
   b. Make a generalized statement about the difference in volume of a cone and a cylinder given the same diameter and height.
   c. Determine the mass of each container. Are your answers reasonable? Explain how you know.

10. **Construct viable arguments.** A company needs to package crushed sandstone to send to a customer. Sandstone has a density of 1281 kg/m³. The customer asked if the company could send the sandstone in a Styrofoam container. Styrofoam has a density of 70 kg/m³. Should the company use a Styrofoam container to send the sandstone? Explain.

ACTIVITY 35 PRACTICE
Write your answers on notebook paper.
Show your work.

Lesson 35-1

1. The figure below is a square pyramid with height 10 cm and base edge 20 cm. Calculate each of the following:

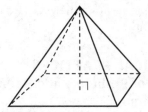

   A. the slant height
   B. the length of a lateral edge
   C. the length of the apothem of the base
   D. the length of the radius of the base

2. Paper cups used in some water dispensers are conically shaped. The cups have a diameter of 6 cm and a height of 8 cm. About how much paper is needed to make one of these cups, assuming there is negligible overlap?
   A. 24 cm^2 **B.** 48 cm^2
   C. 109 cm^2 **D.** 151 cm^2

3. Calculate the lateral and surface areas of a cone whose height is 12 in. and whose slant height is 15 in.

4. Consider the cone below.

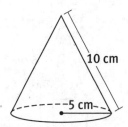

   a. Compute the lateral area of the cone.
   b. Compute the surface area of the cone.

5. What is the slant height of a right pyramid whose lateral area is 90 ft^2 and whose base is a regular hexagon with a 3 ft side?
   A. 3 ft   **B.** 10 ft
   C. 30 ft   **D.** 270 ft

Lesson 35-2

6. Compare and contrast the pyramid and prism formulas.

7. A square pyramid has a volume of 196 cm^3. Determine the height of the pyramid if the edges of the base measure 7 cm.

8. A cylinder has a volume of 200 in.^{3} Determine the volume of a cone whose radius and height are equal to that of the cylinder.

9. Determine the volume of the figure shown.

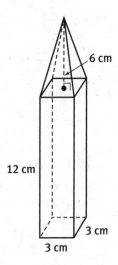

6 cm

12 cm

3 cm

3 cm

A. 114 cm^3 **B.** 126 cm^3
C. 340 cm^3 **D.** 648 cm^3

10. The volume of a square pyramid is $66\frac{2}{3}$ ft^3. The height is 8 feet. What are the dimensions of the base?

Lesson 35-3

11. The density of steel is approximately 0.28 lb/in.^{3} Find the mass of a solid cube of steel with 24 in. sides.

12. A cargo container in the shape of a rectangular prism has a height of 4 ft, a length of 6 ft, and a width of 3 ft. The container is filled to capacity with a solid material. The total mass of the container is 1080 lb. Which of the following is the most likely material in the container?
A. cat food: density 20 lb/ft^3
B. glass beads: density 120 lb/ft^3
C. golf tees: density 15 lb/ft^3
D. lima beans: density 45 lb/ft^3

13. The diameter of an oblique cylinder is 0.16 m and the height is 0.5 m. What is the approximate mass of a right cylinder with the same dimensions if it is filled with cottonseed? The density of cottonseed is 352 kg/m^3.

14. A large process vessel, in the shape of a cone, is filled with maple syrup. The density of maple syrup is 1362 kg/m^3. The height of the vessel is 4 m and the diameter is 1 m. What is the mass of the maple syrup in the vessel, to the nearest tenth?

MATHEMATICAL PRACTICES
Make Sense of Problems and Persevere in Solving Them

15. The figure below is a regular hexagonal right prism with a regular hexagonal pyramid carved into a base of the prism. Find the total surface area of the figure if the height of the prism and pyramid is 8 cm, and the length of one side of the hexagonal base of the prism and pyramid is 6 cm.

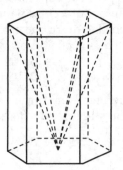

Play-Tel Toys has entered talks to create action figures for the latest Hollywood blockbuster film. The film's main character, a robot named Arigato, is the focus of the marketing campaign.

In order to do a cost analysis for creating the action figures, Play-Tel designers must determine the surface area and volume of the robot's body parts. Although the final shapes will be crafted in much greater detail, each body part will first be molded into the solids, as indicated in the diagram.

1. Complete the table based on the dimensions provided in the diagram.

	Surface Area	Volume
Cylindrical Head		
Conical Hat		
Right Cylinder Torso		
Right Cylinder Arm		
Square Prism Leg		

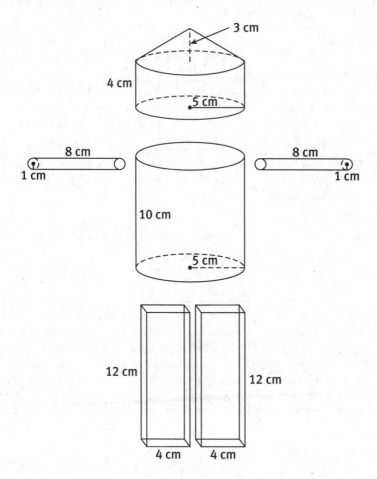

2. Each piece of the action figure will be painted before assembly. If it costs $0.02 per square centimeter to paint, determine the cost to paint each action figure.

3. The designers also need to determine the total amount of plastic to be used in the molds for each robot. If each cubic centimeter of plastic costs $0.03, determine the total cost to mold each action figure.

4. The designers are discussing the type of plastic material to use for the robot. The specified mass for the action figure is 1.34 kg. Use the density table to determine the type of plastic that would meet the mass specification. Justify your answer.

Plastic Material	Density g/cm^3
Polyethylene	0.96
Polypropylene	0.93
Poly Vinyl Chloride	1.47

*Source: http://www.dotmar.com.au/density.html

Scoring Guide	Exemplary	Proficient	Emerging	Incomplete
	The solution demonstrates these characteristics:			
Mathematics Knowledge and Thinking (Items 1, 2, 3, 4)	• Clear and accurate understanding of surface area, volume, and density • Accurate use of proportional reasoning to determine the cost of the action figure	• Mostly correct understanding of surface area, volume, and density • Mostly correct use of proportional reasoning to determine the cost of the action figure	• Partially correct understanding of surface area, volume, and density • Partially correct use of proportional reasoning to determine the cost of the action figure	• Little or no understanding of surface area, volume, and density • Incorrect or incomplete use of proportional reasoning to determine the cost of the action figure
Problem Solving (Items 1, 2, 3, 4)	• An appropriate and efficient strategy that results in correct answers	• A strategy that may include unnecessary steps but results in mostly correct answers	• A strategy that results in some incorrect answers	• No clear strategy when solving problems
Mathematical Modeling / Representations (Item 4)	• Clear and accurate understanding of creating an expression to determine density	• Mostly accurate understanding of creating an expression to determine density	• Partial understanding of creating an expression to determine density	• Little or no understanding of creating an expression to determine density
Reasoning and Communication (Item 4)	• Precise use of appropriate mathematics and language to justify which type of plastic should be used to meet mass specifications	• Mostly correct use of appropriate mathematics and language to justify which type of plastic should be used to meet mass specifications	• Misleading or confusing use of appropriate mathematics and language to justify which type of plastic should be used to meet mass specifications	• Incomplete or inaccurate use of appropriate mathematics and language to justify which type of plastic should be used to meet mass specifications

Spheres

Isn't That Spatial?
Lesson 36-1 Surface Area of Spheres

Learning Targets:

- Solve problems using properties of spheres.
- Solve problems by finding the surface area of a sphere.

> **SUGGESTED LEARNING STRATEGIES:** Create Representations, Visualization, Interactive Word Wall

"Cavalieri's Kitchen Wows Customers with Volumes of Food and Fun!" was the headline in the latest edition of *Food Critics* magazine. When asked the secret of the restaurant's success, head chef and owner Greta stated, "I combine my math background with my love of cooking to create interesting, appealing, and delicious food."

One of Greta's specialties is her ability to work with spherically shaped designs. A sphere is a three-dimensional shape such that all points are an equal distance from a fixed point. The fixed point is the center of the sphere and the distance from the fixed point is the radius of the sphere.

Example A

Greta is preparing a cake in the shape of a **_hemisphere_**, as shown below. She plans to wrap a piece of licorice around the cake, 4 inches up from the base. Given that the radius of the hemisphere is 6 inches, what is the total length of licorice needed?

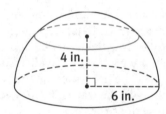

> **MATH TERMS**
>
> A **hemisphere** is one-half of a sphere.

Step 1: Use the Pythagorean Theorem to find the radius of the ring, *y*.

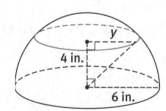

$$4^2 + y^2 = 6^2$$
$$y^2 = 20$$
$$y = \sqrt{20}$$

Step 2: To find the distance around the cake, use the circumference formula for a circle.

$$C = 2\pi r$$
$$C = 2\pi\sqrt{20}$$
$$C \approx 28.1 \text{ in.}$$

Solution: The length of licorice needed is 28.1 in.

Try These A

a. The diameter of a sphere is 40 ft. A plane, parallel to the center of the sphere, passes through the sphere at a distance of 12 ft from the center. Find the radius of the circular intersection.

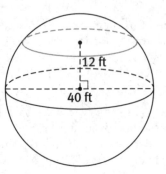

b. Find the circumference and area of the circular intersection of the plane in Part a.

Cavalieri's Kitchen is a popular restaurant with fishermen. Every day Greta's staff prepares lunches for fishermen to take on their charter fishing trips down the nearby river. Not only is the food delicious, but the fishermen appreciate that the lunches are packed by Cavalieri's Kitchen in waterproof, spherical-shaped containers. The fishermen tie the containers to their boats and allow them to float along in the water. The food and drinks inside the containers stay cold because the river's primary sources are spring water and melting snow.

The formula for calculating the surface area of a sphere is $A = 4\pi r^2$, where r represents the radius of the sphere.

1. Calculate the surface area for one of the spherical containers if the radius is 8 inches.

2. Attend to precision. Determine the radius of a sphere whose surface area is 1256.64 cm². Round your answer to the nearest centimeter.

Each evening, the fishermen return the empty containers to Cavalieri's Kitchen and typically stay for dinner. The restaurant is an interesting structure, as it is a hemisphere on a wooden platform.

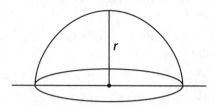

3. **Make use of structure.** Describe where a plane would have to intersect a sphere in order to form two hemispheres. Explain your answer.

MATH TERMS

When a plane passes through the center of a sphere, the intersection is known as a **great circle**.

4. Write a formula for calculating the surface area of the curved surface of the restaurant in terms of its radius, r.

5. Calculate the surface area of the curved surface of the hemisphere with radius 10 feet. Do not include the area of the floor.

CONNECT TO AP

In calculus, you will learn how to derive the formula used to calculate the surface area of a sphere using limits or a definite integral.

6. Use the formula from Item 4 to verify the formula for the surface area of a sphere in terms of its radius, r.

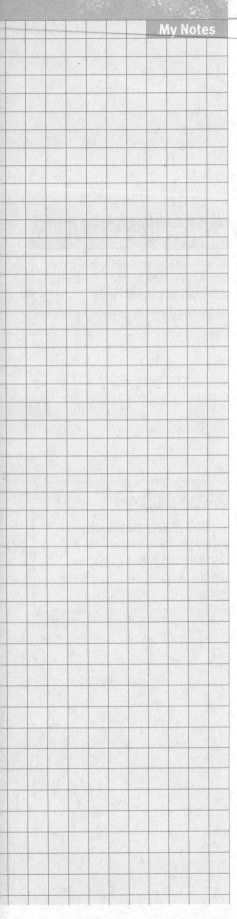

Check Your Understanding

7. Name the shape of the intersection when a plane intersects a sphere in more than one point.

8. A sphere can be divided into four equal quadrants. What is the surface area of each quadrant? Explain how you determined your answer.

9. Name the figure that forms the base of a hemisphere.

10. Write a formula for computing the total surface area of a hemisphere, including the base.

11. Calculate the surface area of a sphere whose radius is 6 cm.

12. A tent is made in the shape of a hemisphere with an 18 ft diameter. How much fabric is used to make the tent, including the floor?

LESSON 36-1 PRACTICE

13. Find the surface area of a sphere, in terms of π, given a radius of 15 in.

14. The surface area of a sphere is 144π ft^2. What is the radius?

15. A plane, parallel to the center of the sphere, passes through the sphere at a distance of 12 cm from the center. The radius of the circular intersection is 9 cm.
   a. Find the diameter of the sphere.
   b. What is the area of the great circle?

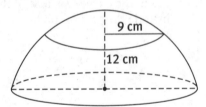

9 cm
12 cm

16. A sphere is inscribed in a cube. The surface area of the sphere is 196π in.^{2} What is the measure of the edge of the cube?

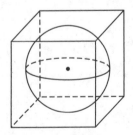

17. Make sense of problems. Cavalieri's Kitchen makes fresh orange juice each morning. The 64 oranges that Greta's staff peels each morning are spherical in shape. The radius of each orange is approximately 6 cm. The orange peels are discarded in a compost pile. How many square centimeters of orange peel are discarded each morning?

Learning Targets:

- Develop the formula for the volume of a sphere.
- Solve problems by finding the volume of a sphere.

SUGGESTED LEARNING STRATEGIES: Think-Pair-Share, Create Representations, Visualization

Greta is promoting a new menu item called the Blueberry Bubble. She tells her morning customers, "The hemisphere of blueberry pancakes that I am creating will absolutely melt in your mouth!" One of the fishermen, a regular morning customer, asks Greta to explain how the pancakes will follow the same mathematical principles as her other famous menu items. She states that, like a cone, a hemisphere is simply a fractional portion of a cylinder.

Greta uses three different stacks of vanilla pancakes to show her customers, placing one blueberry pancake in each stack, as shown below.

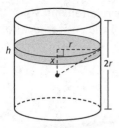 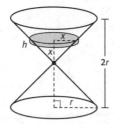 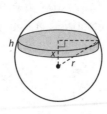

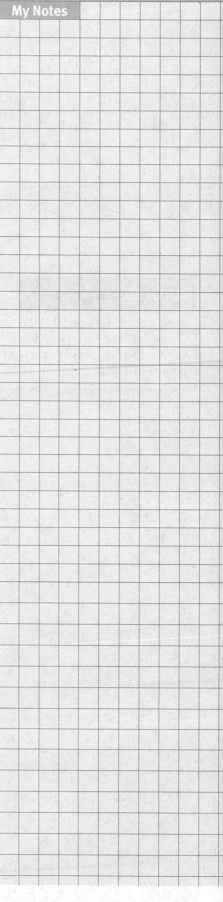

1. Describe the shape of each blueberry pancake.

2. Write the volume formula for the shape identified in Item 1.

3. How far is each pancake above the center of the corresponding figure?

4. Write expressions for the cylinder stack.
   a. Write an expression for the volume of the single blueberry pancake in the cylinder stack.

   b. Reason abstractly. Write an expression for the *number* of blueberry pancakes that will fill the entire cylinder.

   c. Use parts a and b to write an expression for the total volume of blueberry pancakes that will fill the cylinder stack.

My Notes

5. Notice that the radius of the blueberry pancake in the double cone is x. Write an expression for the volume of the single blueberry pancake in the double cone stack.

6. The volume of the single blueberry pancake in the sphere is equal to the volume of the one in the cylinder minus the volume of the one in the double cone. Write an expression for the volume of the single blueberry pancake in the sphere.

7. **Construct viable arguments.** Show that the relationship you identified in Item 6 holds true for the volumes of the entire stacks of pancakes in each figure as well.

MATH TIP

Previously, you learned that the volume of a cone is one-third the volume of a cylinder with the same base and height.

8. Write the formula for the volume of a sphere.

9. What is the formula for the volume of a hemisphere?

10. The Blueberry Bubble will have a base pancake with a radius of 3 inches, and each of the six pancakes in the hemisphere will have a thickness of 0.5 inch.
    a. Draw a diagram for the Blueberry Bubble.

    b. What is the volume of the Blueberry Bubble?

My Notes

Check Your Understanding

11. Suppose a sphere is divided into four equal quadrants. Write a formula to find the volume for $\frac{1}{4}$ of a sphere.

12. In terms of units of measure, explain why the surface area formula for a sphere has a squared radius and the volume formula for a sphere has a cubed radius.

13. The diameter of a sphere is 8 in. What is the volume of the sphere?

14. A sphere has a surface area of approximately 314 in.² What is the volume of the sphere to the nearest cubic inch?

LESSON 36-2 PRACTICE

15. Find the volume of the figure shown, to the nearest hundredth.

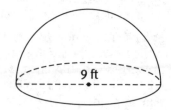

9 ft

16. Determine the volume of the sphere shown below, to the nearest tenth.

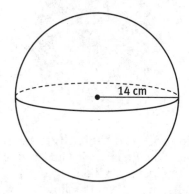

14 cm

17. Construct viable arguments. Four golf balls, each with radius 1 inch, fit snugly into a 2 in. × 2 in. × 8 in. box. Is the total volume left over inside the box greater than or less than the volume of a fifth golf ball? Justify your answer.

18. A spherical scoop of ice cream has been placed on top of a cone, as shown. If the ice cream melts completely, will it overflow the cone? Justify your answer.

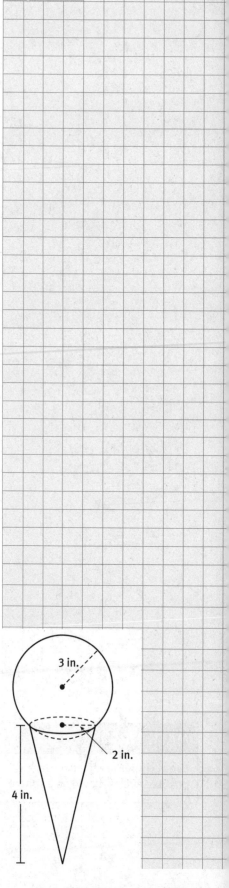

3 in.

2 in.

4 in.

Learning Targets:

● Compare parallelism in Euclidean and spherical geometries.
● Compare triangles in Euclidean and spherical geometries.

> **SUGGESTED LEARNING STRATEGIES:** Activating Prior Knowledge, Visualization, Create Representations, Look for a Pattern, Use Manipulatives

Greta has used various relationships among geometric figures such as lines, angles, polygons, circles, and three-dimensional objects to create interest in mathematics at her restaurant. She, like many others, has relied on an axiomatic system as the basis of many geometric theorems; Euclidean properties are sufficient for most real-world geometric applications. Greta does realize, however, that the study of mathematics goes well beyond Euclidean geometry—as the world, unlike Greta's pancakes, is not flat.

An understanding of spherical geometry is what allowed NASA engineers to perform the necessary calculations to get the rover to land on Mars in May 2008. Mathematicians, and curious folks like Greta, have pondered the existence of non-Euclidean geometries since the early 1800s. Research in these areas continues to be a considerable focus of study today.

Spherical geometry is one branch in the non-Euclidean field. It explores the geometric characteristics of figures on the surface of a sphere. There are significant differences in properties with this change in perspective. To understand the concepts related to spherical geometry, it is helpful to have a globe or a ball to contemplate these ideas.

1. **Use appropriate tools strategically.** Choose a point on the sphere provided by your teacher. Imagine that an ant walks on the sphere in a straight line so that it does not fall off.
   a. Trace the path that the ant would follow.
   b. Describe the path walked by the ant.
   c. Use a rubber band or masking tape to mark the path of the ant.

2. Choose a different point on the sphere. Imagine that a second ant walks in a straight line, trying to avoid the path of the first ant. Mark the path of the second ant.

3. How can the second ant choose a path that will not cross the path of the first ant?

MATH TIP

Great circles are the largest possible circles drawn on a sphere.

4. In Euclidean geometry, given a line and a point not on the line, there is exactly one line through the point parallel to the given line. Explain why no lines are parallel in spherical geometry.

5. In Euclidean geometry, if two lines intersect, they intersect in exactly one point. In spherical geometry, what is true about any two lines?

6. In spherical geometry, a **line** is defined to be a **great circle** of the sphere. Lines of longitude on a globe are examples of these. Why do you suppose that airlines design flight paths along spherical lines?

Antipodal points (also called antipodes) are two points that are diametrically opposite. A straight line through the center of the Earth connects them.

7. Locate the antipode for your city. State its location.

 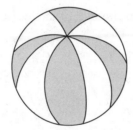

8. **Construct viable arguments.** Explain why most points on Earth have oceanic antipodes.

9. Choose a point on your sphere.
   a. Draw two great circles through the point.

   b. Use a protractor to measure the angles formed at the given point on the sphere by the great circles.

   c. What do you notice about the measures of the angles formed by the great circles?

My Notes

MATH TERMS

A **lune** is a region bounded by two great circles. The word is derived from the Latin word for *moon*.

10. **Model with mathematics.** Take a sphere. Choose a point N on your sphere.
   a. Draw a great circle through point N.
   b. Draw a second great circle through point N to create a *lune* with a 90° angle.
   c. Draw a great circle that does not contain point N to divide the lune into two congruent regions.
   d. How many nonoverlapping sections are created by the intersections of the three great circles?

   e. Each section is a spherical triangle. Use a protractor to measure the three angles of a triangle.

   f. What is the sum of the measures of those three angles?

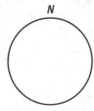

11. Choose any three random noncollinear points on the sphere. Draw the triangle through the points. Remember to draw the segments along a great circle.

12. Measure the three angles of the triangle and determine the sum of their measures.

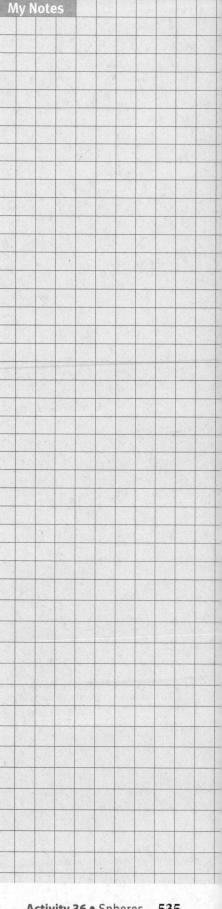

13. Use the given diagram with triangle *ABC*.
   a. What happens to the sum of the measures of the angles in the triangle as points *B* and *C* come closer and closer together?

   b. Based on your answer in Part a, what is the least possible sum for the three angles of a spherical triangle?

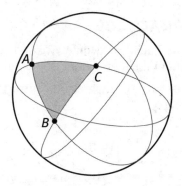

14. Use the given diagram with triangle *DQT*.

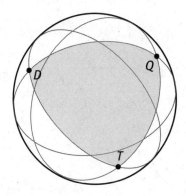

   a. What happens to the measure of each angle in the triangle as the points move outward and approach the same great circle?

   b. Based on your answer in part a, what is the greatest possible sum for the three angles of a spherical triangle?

15. Write the possible measurements for the sum of the measures of the angles of a triangle as a compound inequality.

My Notes

Check Your Understanding

16. Are the lines of the Earth's latitude considered lines in spherical geometry? Explain.

17. Locate two land-based antipodes on Earth.

18. Refer to Item 9. When two great circles intersect, how many points of intersection result? How many angles are formed at each point of intersection along with four lunes?

LESSON 36-3 PRACTICE

19. Why do you suppose Euclidean geometry is still considered to be an essential component of the high school curriculum?

20. **Make use of structure.** Compare and contrast Euclidean geometry and spherical geometry.

ACTIVITY 36 PRACTICE
Write your answers on notebook paper.
Show your work.

Lesson 36-1

1. Find the surface area of a sphere, in terms of π, given a radius of 2.5 in.

2. Paper lanterns are created and released each year to celebrate Jarrod's birthday. The lanterns are spherical in shape and have a diameter of 2 ft. About how much paper is needed to make one of these lanterns, assuming there is negligible overlap?
   A. 8.2 ft^2
   B. 12.57 ft^2
   C. 25.13 ft^2
   D. 50.24 ft^2

3. A large, spherical-shaped balloon is used by a local car lot to advertise the current car loan interest rate. The surface area of the balloon is 254.47 ft^2. What is the radius of the balloon?

4. For cancer awareness month, a pink stripe was painted around the balloon in Item 3. The stripe is parallel to the center of the sphere, and is located at a distance of 1.5 ft from the center.
   a. What is the radius of the pink stripe?
   b. What is the circumference of the pink stripe, to the nearest tenth?

5. Consider a sphere whose diameter is 50 cm. Compute the surface area of the sphere.

6. The figure below is a cone "topped" with a hemisphere. Calculate the total surface area if the radius of the cone and hemisphere is 10 cm and the height of the cone is 24 cm.

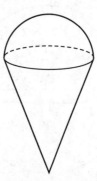

7. The park rangers maintain bear-proof trash containers at a local campground. These containers have a cylindrical shape with a hemisphere-shaped lid, as shown below. Every spring the park rangers paint the containers. Which of the following measures would help the park rangers the most in determining how much paint is needed to paint one trash container?

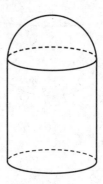

   A. weight   **B.** volume
   C. surface area   **D.** cross-sectional area

Lesson 36-2

8. Find the volume of the figure shown, in terms of π.

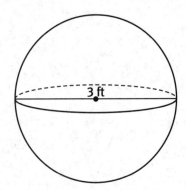

3 ft

9. Determine the approximate volume of one-half of the sphere shown below.

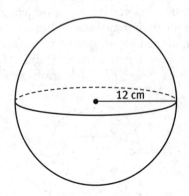

12 cm

10. The volume of a sphere is 62,500 ft^3. What is the diameter of the sphere?
  A. 25 ft
  B. 30 ft
  C. 50 ft
  D. 141 ft

11. The cylinder shown below has been capped with a hemisphere at each end. The height of the cylinder is 10 cm. The radius of each hemisphere is 2 cm. Calculate the volume of the figure.

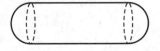

Lesson 36-3

12. Describe what is meant by non-Euclidean geometries.

13. Research hyperbolic geometry online. Describe the basis for this non-Euclidean geometry.

MATHEMATICAL PRACTICES
Make Sense of Problems and Persevere in Solving Them

14. A conical section has been carved into the flat surface of a hemisphere, as shown.

  a. What information is needed to calculate the total surface area?
  b. Write the steps for calculating the total surface area of this figure.

Changing Dimensions

Model Behavior
Lesson 37-1 Cubes and Spheres

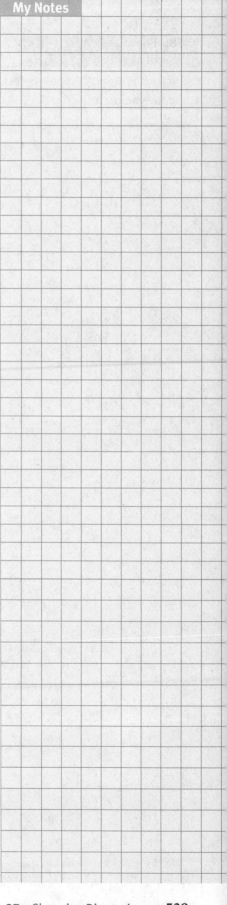

Learning Targets:

- Describe how changes in the linear dimensions of a shape affect its perimeter, area, surface area, or volume.
- Use geometric shapes and their measures to model real-world objects.

> **SUGGESTED LEARNING STRATEGIES:** Create Representations, Visualization, Predict and Confirm, Quickwrite

Howie Shrinkett builds scale models for museums. He was commissioned to build models of the solar system for the Hubble Planetarium, models of the Egyptian pyramids for the Ptolemy Natural History Museum, and models of the building that houses the Cubism Museum of Modern Art.

1. For the gift shop in the Cubism Museum of Modern Art, Howie created paperweights, key chains and planters. He began by investigating the dimensions, surface area, and volume of the cubes. Complete the table below.

Cubed-Shaped Item	Edge Length (in inches)	Area of Base (in square inches)	Surface Area (in square inches)	Volume (in cubic inches)
Key chain	1			
Paperweight	3			
Planter	9			

2. **Express regularity in repeated reasoning.** Howie observed that as the length of an edge increases, so does the resulting surface area.

   a. Make a conjecture about how the surface area changes when the edge of a cube is tripled.

   b. Use your conjecture and the information from the table to predict the surface area of a cube whose edge is 27 inches. Then verify or revise your conjecture from part a.

3. **Express regularity in repeated reasoning.** Howie also observed that as the length of an edge increases, so does the resulting volume.

   a. Make a conjecture about how the volume changes when the edge of a cube is tripled.

   b. Use your conjecture and the information from the table to predict the volume for a cube whose edge is 27 inches and verify or revise your conjecture from Part a.

My Notes

MATH TIP

The surface area of a sphere is $4\pi r^2$, and the volume is $\frac{4}{3}\pi r^3$.

4. For the Hubble Planetarium, Howie created scale models of Mars. Complete the table below for Howie's spheres.

Radius of Sphere (in feet)	Surface Area (in square feet)	Volume (in cubic feet)
12		
6		
3		

5. Howie observed that as the radius decreases, so does the resulting surface area.
   a. Make a conjecture about how the surface area changes when the radius is cut in half.

   b. Use your conjecture to predict the surface area of a sphere whose radius is 1.5 inches and verify or revise your conjecture from part a.

6. Howie also observed that as the radius decreases, so does the resulting volume.
   a. Make a conjecture about the way the volume changes when the radius is cut in half.

   b. Use your conjecture to predict the volume of a sphere whose radius is 1.5 inches and verify or revise your conjecture from part a.

7. **Reason abstractly.** Howie recalled that *similar* two-dimensional and three-dimensional figures are those that have the same shape but not necessarily the same size. Does this imply that all cubes are similar to all other cubes, and that all spheres are similar to all other spheres? Explain below.

My Notes

Check Your Understanding

8. The edge length of a cube is 4 feet.
   a. Find the surface area of the cube.
   b. Predict the surface area if the edge length of the cube is tripled.
   c. By what factor does the surface area increase?
   d. Suppose the edge length is quadrupled. By what factor will the surface area increase?
   e. Describe any pattern you notice between surface area and the scale factor of the edge length.

9. The radius of a sphere is 9 feet.
   a. Find the volume of the sphere, in terms of π.
   b. Predict the volume if the radius of the sphere is tripled.
   c. By what factor does the volume increase?
   d. Suppose the radius is quadrupled. By what factor will the volume increase?
   e. Describe any pattern you notice between volume and the scale factor of the radius.

10. Suppose the values in the table for the sphere had been given in yards. Explain how your conjectures in Items 5a and 6a would change.

LESSON 37-1 PRACTICE

11. One of the cubical display tables in the gift shop of a museum has side lengths of 6 feet. Howie wants to purchase a new table, but he wants each side to be reduced by 25%.

    a. What is the surface area of the new table?
    b. What is the volume of the new table?

12. A sphere with diameter 5 feet is being painted. How much more paint would be needed to paint a sphere that has four times the diameter?

13. Suppose the diameter of the sphere in Item 12 is tripled. What effect would that have on the volume of the sphere? Express your answer as an exponent.

14. Kendrick purchases a refrigerator for his college dorm. The sides of the refrigerator are congruent. The volume of the refrigerator is 5.832 cubic feet. The refrigerator in the dorm kitchen is a similar shape but has a volume of 157.464 cubic feet.
    a. Write the simplified ratio of the side length of the smaller refrigerator to that of the larger refrigerator.
    b. Write the simplified ratio of the surface area of the smaller refrigerator to that of the larger refrigerator.

15. **Critique the reasoning of others.** Buoys are used in the ocean as markers. The spherical-shaped markers in current use at a beach have a radius of 2 meters. One of the lifeguards stated that if the radius of the buoys were doubled, the buoys would have twice as much surface area and would be easier to see. Do you agree with the lifeguard's statement? Explain.

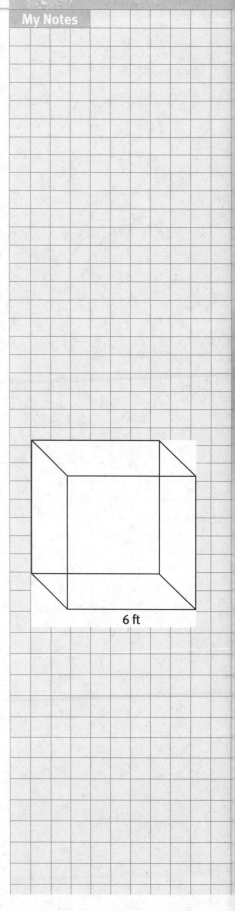

6 ft

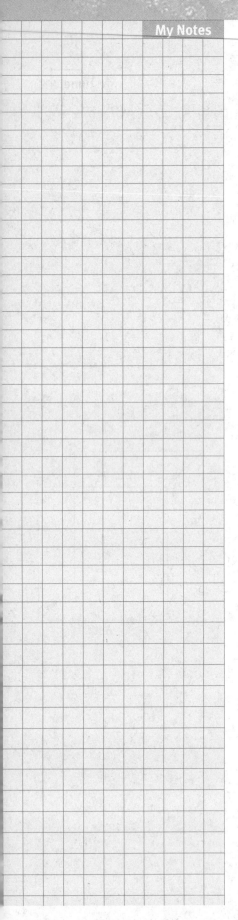

My Notes

Learning Targets:

- Describe how changes in the linear dimensions of a shape affect its perimeter, area, surface area, or volume.
- Use geometric shapes and their measures to model real-world objects.

SUGGESTED LEARNING STRATEGIES: Group Presentation, Self Revision/Peer Revision, Think-Pair-Share, Interactive Word Wall

As Howie begins his pyramid project for the Ptolemy Museum, he realizes that he needs more than one dimension to determine a scale model. The scale models must be geometrically similar.

1. **Make use of structure.** Which of the pyramids below are similar? Explain.

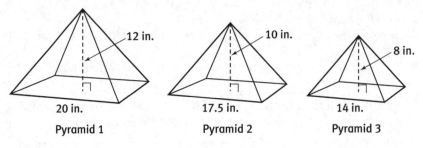

12 in.	10 in.	8 in.
20 in.	17.5 in.	14 in.
Pyramid 1	Pyramid 2	Pyramid 3

2. Howie has built a square pyramid. The base edge is 10 centimeters, and the height is 12 centimeters. He knows that he needs the height of the second pyramid to be 24 centimeters. Determine the scale factor of the small pyramid to that of the larger pyramid.

3. Determine the length of the base edge of the larger pyramid.

My Notes

4. Complete the table below for Howie's pyramids.

	Height of Pyramid (in.)	Length of the Base Edge (in.)	Slant Height (in.)	Perimeter of the Base (in.)	Area of the Base (sq. in.)	Lateral Area (sq. in.)	Surface Area (sq. in.)	Volume (cu. in.)
Pyramid 1								
Pyramid 2								
Ratio of Pyramid 1 / Pyramid 2								

5. Howie also designs models for cylindrical drums as shown below. Complete the table below, and justify whether or not the two cylinders are similar.

Cylinder 1

Cylinder 2

	Radius (cm)	Circumference of Base (cm)	Surface Area (square cm)	Volume (cubic cm)
Cylinder 1				
Cylinder 2				
Ratio of Cylinder 1 / Cylinder 2				

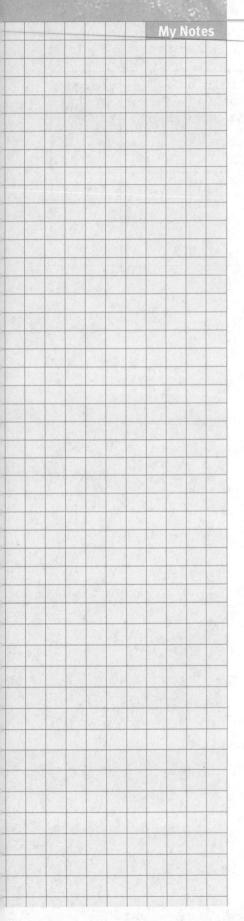

6. **Express regularity in repeated reasoning.** Complete the table below for any pair of similar solids with the scale factor *a:b*.

	Ratio of Sides/Edges or Other Corresponding Measurements	Ratio of Perimeters	Ratio of Areas	Ratio of Volumes
Similarity Ratios	$\frac{a}{b}$			

a. Write a conjecture about the ratio of corresponding perimeters in any pair of similar solids.

b. Write a conjecture about the ratio of corresponding areas in any pair of similar solids.

c. Write a conjecture about the ratio of the volumes of any similar solid.

7. **Model with mathematics.** Draw and label two solids whose corresponding dimensions do not have the same scale factors. Based on the conjectures you made in Item 6, verify that the two figures are not similar to one another.

8. A tetrahedron has four faces, each of which is an equilateral triangle. The diagram below shows two tetrahedrons. Suppose the tetrahedron on the left has 6-inch edges, and the tetrahedron on the right has 8-inch edges.

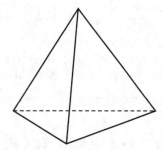

a. What is the ratio of the surface area of the smaller tetrahedron to the surface area of the larger tetrahedron?

b. What is the ratio of the volume of the smaller tetrahedron to the volume of the larger tetrahedron?

9. **Reason quantitatively.** Two similar cones have volumes of 125π in.^{3} and 64π in.^{3}
   a. Determine the scale factor for these cones.

   b. If the total area of the larger cone is 75π in.^{2}, calculate the total area of the smaller cone.

Check Your Understanding

10. In Item 8a, write the factor you used to determine the ratio of surface area with an exponent. Then write the factor you used in Item 8b to determine the ratio of volume with an exponent.

11. True or False? If the radius of a right cylinder is increased by a factor of 3, and the height stays the same, the volume of the cylinder will increase by a factor of 3. Explain your reasoning.

LESSON 37-2 PRACTICE

12. **Make sense of problems.** A small can of coffee is 3 in. tall with a 2 in. radius. It sells for $6.26. A larger can of coffee is 9 in. tall with a 6 in. radius. It sells for $12.52. Is the larger can of coffee priced proportionally in regard to the volume of the smaller can? Explain.

13. The radius and height of the cylinder shown is reduced by 75%. Describe the effect on the surface area.

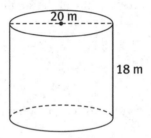

20 m

18 m

14. If the surface areas of two similar cylinders are 10π ft^2 and 160π ft^2, what is the ratio of the volume of the smaller cylinder to the volume of the larger cylinder?

15. **Attend to precision.** Describe the effect on the volume of a square pyramid if its height is doubled.

ACTIVITY 37 PRACTICE
Write your answers on notebook paper.
Show your work.

Lesson 37-1

1. If the surface area of two similar spheres is 256π ft^2 and 576π ft^2, what is the ratio of the volume of the smaller sphere to the volume of the larger sphere?

2. A modeling platform is in the shape of a cube. It has a surface area of 294 ft^2. Which of the following describes what happens to the surface area when the dimensions of the cube are doubled.
   A. The surface area is halved.
   B. The surface area stays the same.
   C. The surface area doubles.
   D. The surface area quadruples.

3. A cube has a volume of 1331 in.^{3} What are the approximate dimensions of the cube if the volume is increased by 1.5?

4. A packaging designer created a new container using two similar, three-dimensional figures. The scale used to create the figures was 2 : 5. Which of the following is the ratio of their volumes?
   A. 2 : 5
   B. 4 : 10
   C. 4 : 25
   D. 8 : 125

5. A sphere has a volume of $457\frac{1}{3}\pi$ m^3. The radius is halved.
   a. What is the new radius?
   b. What is the new volume of the sphere?

Lesson 37-2

6. A cylinder has a radius of 4 cm and a height of 9 cm. A similar cylinder has a radius of 6 cm.
   a. Find the scale factor of the smaller cylinder to the larger cylinder
   b. What is the ratio of the circumferences of the bases?
   c. What is the ratio of the lateral areas of the cylinders?
   d. What is the ratio of the volumes of the cylinders?
   e. If the volume of the smaller cylinder is 144π cm^3, what is the volume of the larger cylinder?

7. You purchased a scale model of the Eiffel Tower. The scale factor is 1 : 1180. The model is 10 inches high and has a surface area of 1.7 ft^2.
   a. What is the height of the Eiffel Tower?
   b. What is the surface area of the Eiffel Tower?

8. The volume of the cylinder, shown by the net below, needs to increase.
   a. What is the volume of the cylinder?
   b. What is the volume of the cylinder if the radius and height are doubled?
   c. Write the ratio of the volume of the current cylinder to the volume of the new cylinder if the measures of the current cylinder are doubled.

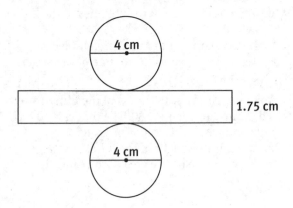

9. A pyramid has a height of 6 cm and base edge 8 cm, as shown.

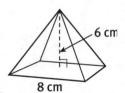

A pyramid similar to the one above has a height of 9 cm.
   a. Find the scale factor of the smaller pyramid to the larger pyramid.
   b. What is the ratio of the base edges?
   c. Find the base edge of the larger pyramid.
   d. What is the ratio of the lateral areas?
   e. What is the ratio of the volumes?
   f. If the volume of the larger pyramid is 130.5 cm³, what is the volume of the smaller pyramid?

10. The square base of a pyramid has side lengths x.

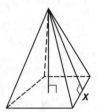

   a. What is the effect on the volume of the square pyramid if the sides change to $2x$?
   b. What is the effect on the volume of the square pyramid if the sides change to $\frac{1}{2}x$?

11. You purchased a scale model of the Statue of Liberty. The scale factor is 1 : 456. The model is 8 inches high and has a surface area of 0.052 ft².
   a. What is the height of the Statue of Liberty?
   b. What is the surface area of the Statue of Liberty?

12. The diameter of an oblique cylinder is 32 cm and the height is 4 cm. What is the volume of a right cylinder if the dimensions are halved?
   A. 8π cm³
   B. 128π cm³
   C. 512π cm³
   D. 1024π cm³

MATHEMATICAL PRACTICES
Look For and Make Use of Structure

13. The ratio of the edge lengths of two given cubes is $\frac{7}{2}$.
   a. Describe how to find the ratio for the area of the faces of the cubes.
   b. Describe how to find the ratio for the volumes of the cubes.

Changing Dimensions of Spheres
SPHERICAL STORAGE

Storage vessels containing organic liquids should be designed and built according to the American Petroleum Institute API-650 specification. Storage vessels come in various shapes and sizes, but in general most are installed within a containment basin for safety reasons. Some vessels need to be pressurized if they are being used to store organic liquids with high vapor pressures. Typically, the best design for this application, however costly, is a sphere.

A petroleum company plans to purchase some spherical pressurized storage vessels. The process-engineering group and the purchasing department are working together to analyze possible options.

1. Complete the table based on the dimensions provided.

Spherical Vessel	Diameter	Surface Area	Volume
Vessel A	20 m		
Vessel B			33,510.3 m^3
Vessel C		11,309.7 m^2	

2. The company plans to have the tanks painted after they are installed. Describe the effect that doubling the diameter has on the amount of paint needed to paint the tanks. What happens when the diameter is increased by a factor of 3?

3. Describe the effect that doubling the diameter has on the capacity of a spherical storage vessel. What happens to the volume when the diameter is tripled?

4. How would the amount of paint needed and the capacity change if the company chose a storage vessel with a diameter that was half as large as the diameter of Vessel A? Explain your reasoning.

The supports for the tanks are in the shapes of cylinders. The supports for Vessel A and Vessel C are similar. Each support for Vessel A has volume $450,000\pi$ cm^3 and surface area $60,450\pi$ cm^2.

5. If the volume of each cylindrical support for Vessel C is $1,518,750\pi$ cm^3, write a proportion that can be used to determine the surface area of each of Vessel C's supports. Explain how you arrived at your answer.

Scoring Guide	Exemplary	Proficient	Emerging	Incomplete
	The solution demonstrates these characteristics:			
Mathematics Knowledge and Thinking (Items 1, 2, 3, 4, 5)	• Clear and accurate understanding of surface area and volume of a sphere • Clear and accurate understanding of the relationships between scale factor, ratio of areas, and ratio of volumes of similar figures	• Mostly correct understanding of surface area and volume of a sphere • Mostly correct understanding of the relationships between scale factor, ratio of areas, and ratio of volumes of similar figures	• Partially correct understanding of surface area and volume of a sphere • Partially correct understanding of the relationships between scale factor, ratio of areas, and ratio of volumes of similar figures	• Little or no understanding of surface area and volume of a sphere • Little or no understanding of the relationships between scale factor, ratio of areas, and ratio of volumes of similar figures
Problem Solving (Items 1, 2, 3, 4)	• An appropriate and efficient strategy that results in correct answers	• A strategy that may include unnecessary steps but results in mostly correct answers	• A strategy that results in some incorrect answers	• No clear strategy when solving problems
Mathematical Modeling / Representations (Item 5)	• Clear and accurate understanding of creating a proportion to solve for the surface area of Vessel C's supports	• Mostly accurate understanding of creating a proportion to solve for the surface area of Vessel C's supports	• Partial understanding of creating a proportion to solve for the surface area of Vessel C's supports	• Little or no understanding of creating a proportion to solve for the surface area of Vessel C's supports
Reasoning and Communication (Items 4, 5)	• Precise use of appropriate mathematics and language to explain how the volume and surface area were affected by the dimension change • Precise use of appropriate mathematics and language to explain how the proportion is written	• Mostly correct use of appropriate mathematics and language to explain how the volume and surface area were affected by the dimension change • Mostly correct use of appropriate mathematics and language to explain how the proportion is written	• Misleading or confusing use of appropriate mathematics and language to explain how the volume and surface area were affected by the dimension change • Misleading or confusing use of appropriate mathematics and language to explain how the proportion is written	• Incomplete or inaccurate use of appropriate mathematics and language to explain how the volume and surface area were affected by the dimension change • Incomplete or inaccurate use of appropriate mathematics and language to explain how the proportion is written

Probability

Unit Overview
In this unit you will continue your study of probability. You will learn more about the language of probability, how to use the Addition Rule, how to calculate conditional probabilities, and the meaning of independence. You will also see how relevant these concepts are to everyday scenarios.

Key Terms
As you study this unit, add these and other terms to your math notebook. Include in your notes your prior knowledge of each word, as well as your experiences in using the word in different mathematical examples. If needed, ask for help in pronouncing new words and add information on pronunciation to your math notebook. It is important that you learn new terms and use them correctly in your class discussions and in your problem solutions.

Academic Vocabulary
- primates

Math Terms
- probability experiment
- outcome
- sample space
- event
- complement
- two-way frequency table
- intersection
- union
- mutually exclusive events
- conditional probability
- tree diagram
- dependent events
- independent events
- Fundamental Counting Principle
- *n* factorial
- permutation
- combination

ESSENTIAL QUESTIONS

? How does knowing that one event has happened change the probability of another event happening?

? How do such changes in probability influence the decisions we make?

EMBEDDED ASSESSMENTS

The two embedded assessments in this unit, following Activities 40 and 42, will allow you to demonstrate your ability to evaluate probabilities and your understanding of the relevance of these quantities.

Getting Ready

Write your answers on notebook paper.
Show your work.

1. Express the following percentages as decimals.
   a. 43%
   b. 8%
   c. 89.2%

2. Round the following decimals to three decimal places.
   a. 0.78326
   b. 0.78372
   c. 0.78354
   d. 0.78349
   e. 0.78021
   f. 0.70041
   g. 0.78968
   h. 0.79968

3. Express the following fractions in simplest form. (Do not use a calculator.)
   a. $\dfrac{3}{6}$
   b. $\dfrac{14}{35}$
   c. $\dfrac{24000}{36000}$

4. Evaluate the following. Express your answers as fractions in simplest form. (Do not use a calculator.)
   a. $\dfrac{3}{7} + \dfrac{2}{7}$
   b. $\dfrac{1}{6} + \dfrac{2}{3}$
   c. $\dfrac{5}{14} + \dfrac{1}{2}$
   d. $\dfrac{3}{8} + \dfrac{9}{10}$

5. Evaluate the following. Express your answers as fractions simplest form. (Do not use a calculator.)
   a. $\dfrac{2}{3} \cdot \dfrac{4}{5}$
   b. $\dfrac{2}{21} \cdot \dfrac{21}{37}$
   c. $\dfrac{2}{3} \cdot \dfrac{6}{7}$

6. Evaluate the following. Express your answers as fractions in simplest form. (Do not use a calculator.)
   a. $\left(\dfrac{1}{3}\right)\left(\dfrac{2}{3}\right) + \left(\dfrac{2}{3}\right)\left(\dfrac{1}{3}\right)$
   b. $\left(\dfrac{1}{3}\right)\left(\dfrac{5}{8}\right) + \left(\dfrac{2}{3}\right)\left(\dfrac{3}{8}\right)$

7. There are 36 students in a class, and 20 of them are girls. If a student is selected at random from the class, what is the probability that the selected student is a girl?

Sample Spaces

Springboard Superstar and More
Lesson 38-1 Probability of a Single Event

Learning Targets:
- Understand probability in real-world situations.
- Represent sample spaces as lists.
- Calculate the probability of a single event.

> **SUGGESTED LEARNING STRATEGIES:** Activating Prior Knowledge, Marking the Text, Visualization, Think-Pair-Share, Debriefing

1. Suppose that you have a cube with faces numbered 1 through 6. You will roll the cube 60 times.
   a. On roughly how many of the rolls would you expect to get a result that is an even number?

   b. On roughly how many of the rolls would you expect to get a 5?

   c. On roughly how many of the rolls would you expect to get a number that is 5 or more?

When we roll the cube, as described in Item 1, we expect to get an even number about half of the time. Another way of saying this is that, when you roll the cube, the probability of getting an even number is $\frac{1}{2}$. To write this using probability notation,

$$P(\text{even}) = \frac{1}{2}.$$

2. **a.** When you roll the cube, what is the probability that you get a 5? Write your answer using probability notation.

   b. When you roll the cube, what is the probability that you get a number that is 5 or more? Write your answer using probability notation.

DISCUSSION GROUP TIPS

As you share ideas in your group, ask your group members or your teacher for clarification of any language, terms, or concepts that you do not understand.

WRITING MATH

Probability Notation

The *probability* of an outcome is written in symbols as $P(\text{outcome})$, where the P stands for probability.

For example, the probability that the outcome is an even number can be written as $P(\text{roll results in an even number})$, or simply as $P(\text{even})$.

MATH TERMS

A **probability experiment** is the process of observing an outcome when the outcome is not known prior to the experiment.

An **outcome** is the result of a probability experiment.

The **sample space** is the set of all possible outcomes.

An **event** is any outcome or group of outcomes from a probability experiment.

The *probability* of an outcome tells you what part of the time you would expect the outcome to occur.

Rolling the cube is an example of a ***probability experiment***. A result of a probability experiment is called an ***outcome***. For the cube, the possible outcomes are 1, 2, 3, 4, 5, and 6.

The set of all possible outcomes is called the ***sample space***. Here the sample space is {1, 2, 3, 4, 5, 6}.

Getting an even number when you roll the cube is an example of an ***event***. To get an even number you have to roll a 2, a 4, or a 6. There are 3 outcomes that are even, out of a total of 6 possible outcomes. In the long run, $\frac{3}{6}$, or $\frac{1}{2}$, of the rolls of the cube will result in even numbers.

To generalize, if all the outcomes in the sample space are equally likely, then the probability of an event is given by

$$P(\text{event}) = \frac{\text{number of outcomes in the event}}{\text{number of outcomes in the sample space}}.$$

3. A regular solid is constructed with four faces. The faces are numbered 1 through 4, and the four outcomes are equally likely. We will roll this object once.
   a. What is the sample space for this probability experiment?

   b. Find the probability that the roll results in the following. Use probability notation in your answers.

   i. a 2   **iii.** a number greater than 4

   ii. a number that is at least 2   **iv.** a number greater than 0

If an event can never happen, then there are no outcomes in the event, and so the probability of the event is 0. If an event is sure to happen, then every element of the sample space is in the event, and so the probability of the event is 1.

The probability of any event is a number between 0 and 1. How large the probability is tells us how likely the event is to occur.

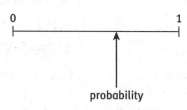

probability

> **MATH TIP**
>
> The probability of an outcome is a number between 0 and 1, inclusive. It can be written as a fraction, a decimal, or a percent.

Check Your Understanding

4. In probability, what is the word or phrase for the set of all possible outcomes?

5. How is the probability that an event does not happen related to the probability that the event happens?

6. What is the smallest possible value for a probability?

7. What is the largest possible value for a probability?

8. If a student is chosen at random from your class today, what is the probability that the student selected is male?

The contestants for the SpringBoard Superstar contest are as follows. (The genders and ages of the contestants are in parentheses.)

Aaron Kelly (Male, 17)   Lacey Brown (Female, 24)

Andrew Garcia (Male, 24)   Lee DeWyze (Male, 24)

Casey James (Male, 27)   Michael Lynch (Male, 26)

Crystal Bowersox (Female, 24)   Paige Miles (Female, 24)

Didi Benami (Female, 23)   Siobhan Magnus (Female, 19)

Katie Stevens (Female, 17)   Tim Urban (Male, 20)

9. Select one of the twelve contestants at random.
  a. What is the sample space for this probability experiment?

  b. Find the probability that the selected contestant:
    i. is Casey James.

    ii. is female.

    iii. has a last name beginning with Z.

    iv. is under 30 years old.

    v. has a last name beginning with B.

    vi. does not have a last name beginning with B.

  c. What do you get when you add the answers to Parts b(v) and b(vi)? Will the probability that an event happens and an event does not happen always add to 1? Explain.

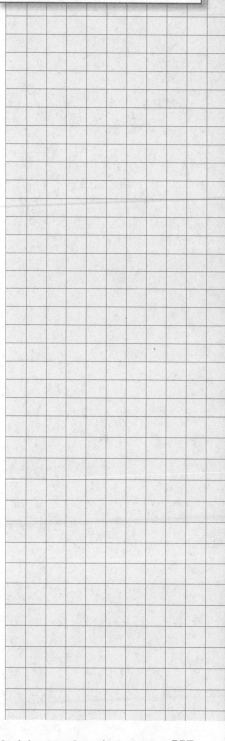

To generalize, when we add the probability that an event happens to the probability that it does not happen, we always get 1.

From this we can conclude that to find the probability that an event does <u>not</u> happen, we can subtract from 1 the probability that it <u>does</u> happen. This is called the *complement* of an event.

> (probability that an event does <u>not</u> happen) =
> 1 − (probability that the event <u>does</u> happen)

MATH TERMS

The **complement** of an event includes all possible outcomes of a probability experiment that are not outcomes of the event.

10. **Make sense of problems.** Jenna and James were recently married, and are planning on having three children. They are wondering how many girls and how many boys they will have in their family. Assume that they are equally likely to have a girl as a boy.
   a. Three of the possible outcomes are shown in the organized list. There are 8 possible outcomes. List the other five outcomes.

   GGG

   GGB

   GBG

   b. Find the probability that in their family they will have:
   i. three girls.

   ii. exactly two girls.

   iii. at least two girls.

   c. What is the probability that they will <u>not</u> have exactly two girls in the family?

Check Your Understanding

11. Iris rolled a five-sided number cube numbered 1 through 5. Find the probability that a roll will result in each of the following. Write your answer using probability notation.
  a. $P(\text{odd})$ **c.** $P(4)$
  b. $P(\text{not odd})$ **d.** $P(\text{not } 4)$

12. Fiona's dog Sunshine is expecting a litter of four pups. The chance that the pups will be male or female are equally likely. What is the probability that the litter will contain two males and two females? Make an organized list to determine the probability.

LESSON 38-1 PRACTICE

13. Rafael has a bag of marbles. There are 5 green marbles, 6 red marbles, and 4 white marbles. Rafael picks a marble out of the bag without looking. What is the probability of each of the following?
  a. $P(\text{green})$ **d.** $P(\text{not white})$
  b. $P(\text{not green})$ **e.** $P(\text{red})$
  c. $P(\text{white})$ **f.** $P(\text{not red})$

14. **Reason quantitatively.** The letters of a ten-letter word were placed in a box. Letters are chosen at random. Given that the probability of choosing a consonant is $\frac{3}{5}$, what is the probability of choosing a vowel? Explain.

15. Liam is tossing three coins in a game. He wants to determine the probability of tossing two heads.
  a. Make an organized list.
  b. What is the probability of tossing two heads? Explain.

Learning Targets:

- Understand probability in real-world situations.
- Describe events as subsets of a sample space using the characteristics of the outcomes.
- Represent sample spaces as tables of outcomes and as two-way frequency tables.
- Calculate the probability of events involving "and" and "or."

SUGGESTED LEARNING STRATEGIES: Activating Prior Knowledge, Marking the Text, Visualization, Think-Pair-Share, Debriefing

Consider probabilities that involve the words "and" and "or." Look again at the SpringBoard Superstar contestants.

Aaron Kelly (Male, 17)   Lacey Brown (Female, 24)

Andrew Garcia (Male, 24)   Lee DeWyze (Male, 24)

Casey James (Male, 27)   Michael Lynch (Male, 26)

Crystal Bowersox (Female, 24)   Paige Miles (Female, 24)

Didi Benami (Female, 23)   Siobhan Magnus (Female, 19)

Katie Stevens (Female, 17)   Tim Urban (Male, 20)

A contestant will be chosen at random.

1. Find the probability that the contestant will be female <u>and</u> under 21.
   a. How many of the contestants are females who are under 21?

   b. How many contestants are there in total?

   c. What is the probability that the randomly chosen contestant will be female <u>and</u> under 21?

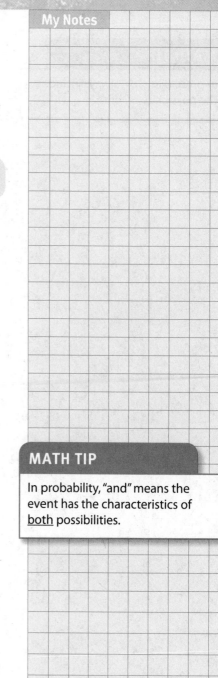

MATH TIP

In probability, "and" means the event has the characteristics of <u>both</u> possibilities.

My Notes

MATH TIP

In probability, "or" always includes the possibility of "both."

2. Now find the probability that the contestant will be female *or* under 21.
  a. Refer to the list of contestants. Put a check mark next to any contestant who is either female or under 21, or both. In probability, "or" always includes the possibility of "both."

  b. How many contestants are female *or* under 21?

  c. What is the probability that the randomly chosen contestant will be female *or* under 21?

3. A contestant will be chosen at random from the list of SpringBoard Superstar contestants. Find the probability that the contestant:
  a. has a first name after N (in the alphabetical order).

  b. has a first name after N <u>and</u> is male.

  c. has a first name after N <u>or</u> is male.

Very often, we show sample spaces using tables rather than lists.

4. Kathy likes Honey Crisp breakfast cereal. Each box of Honey Crisp contains a plastic animal—a monkey, an elephant, a caribou, or a bear—and each of these four animals is equally likely to be found in any given box. Kathy's younger brother, Brian, prefers Korn Invaders breakfast cereal. Each box of Korn Invaders contains either Hero Comic 1, Hero Comic 2, or Hero Comic 3, and each of the comics is equally likely to be found in any given box.

Tomorrow, Kathy will open a new box of Honey Crisp and Brian will open a new box of Korn Invaders. They will find out what prizes they have.

The table representing the sample space for this probability experiment is given.

	Hero Comic 1	Hero Comic 2	Hero Comic 3
Monkey			
Elephant			
Caribou			
Bear			

a. Using the eraser end of your pencil, locate the cell in the table that represents getting an elephant *and* Hero Comic 2.

b. Which cells of the table represent getting a caribou?

c. Which cells of the table represent getting Hero Comic 3?

d. How many outcomes are there in the sample space for this probability experiment?

e. Locate, again, the cell in the table that represents getting an elephant and Hero Comic 2. What is the probability of getting an elephant and Hero Comic 2?

f. Now find the probability of getting an elephant *or* Hero Comic 2.

Write stars in all the cells of the table that represent getting an elephant or Hero Comic 2. (Note: You are writing a star in any cell that represents getting an elephant, any cell that represents getting Hero Comic 2, and any cell that represents getting both. You should be writing 6 stars in total.)

What is the probability that they get an elephant *or* Hero Comic 2?

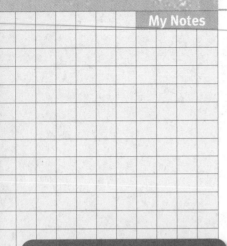

MATH TERMS

A **two-way frequency table** shows data that pertain to two different categories.

Check Your Understanding

5. If a student is chosen at random from your class, what is the probability that the student has a:
   a. first name beginning with a letter in the first half of the alphabet?
   b. first name beginning with a letter in the first half of the alphabet and is female?
   c. first name beginning with a letter in the first half of the alphabet or is female?

Sometimes, the sample space is represented using a table of counts.

6. A store has 48 different phones available with or without caller ID, and with or without a speakerphone. The numbers of phones with and without these features are shown in the **two-way frequency table** below.

	Speakerphone	No Speakerphone	Total
Caller ID	18	2	20
No Caller ID	16	12	28
Total	34	14	48

   a. How many of the phones have caller ID?

   b. What is the total number of phones that the store has available?

   c. If a phone is chosen at random, what is the probability that it has caller ID? Using a calculator, give your answer as a decimal rounded to three decimal places.

   d. A phone is chosen at random from the ones available at the store. To three decimal places, find the probability that the phone has a:
   i. speakerphone.

ii. speakerphone and caller ID.

iii. speakerphone but does not have caller ID.

iv. speakerphone or has caller ID.

Check Your Understanding

7. Students who take an AP Calculus exam can take either the AP Calculus AB exam or the more advanced AP Calculus BC exam. On each exam the highest possible grade is a 5 and the lowest is a 1. No student takes both exams. The approximate results (in thousands) for 2011 are summarized in the table below. (For example, the table tells us that 39,000 students took the AB exam and got a 5.)

	5	4	3	2	1	Total
AB	39	32	35	23	65	194
BC	28	10	12	4	8	
Total						

a. Complete the table by writing the row and column totals in the empty cells.
b. Suppose that one of these 256,000 students is chosen at random. Using a calculator, and giving your answers rounded to three decimal places, find the probability that the student:
   i. took the BC exam.
   ii. got a 5.
   iii. did not get a 5.
   iv. took the BC exam and got a 5.
   v. took the BC exam or got a 5.

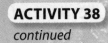

My Notes

LESSON 38-2 PRACTICE

8. Suppose that you are going to roll a red cube with faces numbered 1 through 6 and a blue cube with faces numbered 1 through 6.

   a. Draw a table to represent the sample space for this probability experiment.
   b. Giving your answers as fractions in their lowest terms, find the probability that:
      i. the red cube shows a 4 and the blue cube shows a 6.
      ii. the red cube shows a 4 <u>or</u> the blue cube shows a 6.
      iii. it is <u>not</u> the case that "the red cube shows a 4 or the blue cube shows a 6."
      iv. the sum of the numbers on the two cubes is 9.
      v. the sum of the numbers on the two cubes is more than 8.

9. Aslan's store has the following tablet computers in stock.

	Tablet Classic	Tablet Mini	Total
16 GB	75	95	
32 GB	42	63	
Total			

   a. Complete the table by writing the row and column totals in the empty cells.
   b. If a tablet is chosen at random, to the nearest thousandth, what is the probability it has 32 GB?
   c. If a tablet is chosen at random, to the nearest thousandth, what is the probability it is a Tablet Mini with 16 GB?
   d. If a tablet is chosen at random, to the nearest thousandth, what is the probability it is not a Tablet Mini?
   e. If a tablet is chosen at random, to the nearest thousandth, what is the probability it is a Tablet Classic?
   f. If a tablet is chosen at random, to the nearest thousandth, what is the probability it is a Tablet Classic or a Tablet Mini?

ACTIVITY 38 PRACTICE
Write your answers on notebook paper.
Show your work.

Lesson 38-1

1. A garden center has 20 plants in its "Special Offer" section. Information about these plants is given in the table below.

Plant Number	Type of Plant	Color of Flowers
1	Hyacinth	Pink
2	Hyacinth	White
3	Hyacinth	Blue
4	Hyacinth	Blue
5	Tulip	Pink
6	Tulip	White
7	Tulip	Pink
8	Pansy	Blue
9	Pansy	White
10	Pansy	Pink
11	Pansy	Pink
12	Zinnia	Pink
13	Zinnia	White
14	Zinnia	White
15	Daisy	White
16	Daisy	White
17	Daisy	Pink
18	Daisy	Blue
19	Orchid	Pink
20	Orchid	White

A customer picks a plant at random from the "Special Offer" section. Find the probability that the plant:
   a. is a hyacinth.
   b. has flowers that are blue.
   c. does not have flowers that are blue.
   d. is a rose.
   e. has flowers that are pink, white, or blue.

2. Each of the three spinners will be spun once. All outcomes are equally likely.

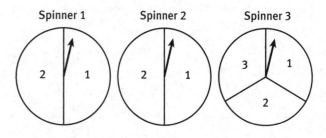

Spinner 1   Spinner 2   Spinner 3

   a. Complete the list of all the possible outcomes for the three spinners.

$$\begin{array}{ccc} 1 & 1 & 1 \\ 1 & 1 & 2 \\ 1 & 1 & 3 \\ 1 & 2 & 1 \\ & \cdots & \end{array}$$

   b. What is the probability that the sum of the scores for the three spinners will be more than 5?

3. A recently married couple are planning to have four children. They are equally likely to have a boy as a girl. What is the probability that they will have three boys and one girl?

   A. $\frac{1}{4}$

   B. $\frac{3}{8}$

   C. $\frac{3}{4}$

   D. $\frac{5}{8}$

Lesson 38-2

4. Refer to the information given in Item 1. A customer picks a plant at random from the "Special Offer" section. Find the probability that the plant is:
   a. a daisy with white flowers.
   b. not a daisy with white flowers.
   c. a daisy or has white flowers.
   d. a tulip with pink flowers or a zinnia with pink flowers.

5. Each of the spinners will be spun once. All outcomes are equally likely.

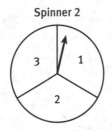

Spinner 1   Spinner 2

a. Draw a table to represent the sample space.
b. Find the probability of getting a D and a 2.
c. Find the probability of getting a D or a 2.

6. A high school current affairs club has members in all four grades (9, 10, 11, and 12) and of both genders. The numbers of students in the various grade/gender categories are given in the table below.

Grade	Gender		Total
	Male	Female	
9	8	6	
10	4	2	
11	3	7	
12	9	9	
Total			

a. Complete the table by entering all the totals in the empty cells.
b. A student from the club is chosen at random to make an announcement in assembly. Find the probability that the student is:
  i. in the 9th grade.
  ii. female.
  iii. an 11th-grade girl.
  iv. in the 11th grade or is a girl.

7. A recently married couple are planning to have three children. They are equally likely to have a boy as a girl. What is the probability that they will have all boys or all girls?

A. $\frac{1}{8}$

B. $\frac{1}{4}$

C. $\frac{1}{2}$

D. 1

MATHEMATICAL PRACTICES
Reason Abstractly and Quantitatively

8. Suppose that you're going to pick a student at random from your school. Put the following three events in order by how likely they are, from the most likely event to the least likely. Write a few sentences explaining why you ordered them the way you did.
  1. The student plays basketball.
  2. The student plays basketball and takes a music class.
  3. The student plays basketball or takes a music class.

Venn Diagrams and Probability Notation

Annabel High School

Lesson 39-1 Using a Venn Diagram to Represent a Sample Space

Learning Targets:

- Use Venn diagrams to represent events.
- Translate Venn diagrams of counts into Venn diagrams of probabilities.

> **SUGGESTED LEARNING STRATEGIES:** Activating Prior Knowledge, Close Reading, Create Representations, Visualization, Think-Pair-Share, Debriefing

We've represented sample spaces using lists and tables. We can also use Venn diagrams to represent sample spaces.

At Annabel High School, some students take Spanish and some do not. Some students take an art class, and some do not. Let *S* be the set of students who take Spanish, and let *A* be the set of students who take an art class. The numbers of students in these classes are shown in the Venn diagram.

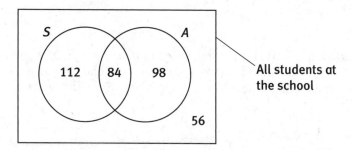

All students at the school

As you answer the following items, remember to use complete sentences and words such as *and, or, since, for example, therefore, because of, by the,* to make connections between your thoughts.

1. **a.** Look at the number "112" in the diagram. This number is inside the circle for *S* and outside the circle for *A*. It tells us that there are 112 students who take Spanish but do not take an art class. What does the number "98" tell us?

   b. What does the number "84" tell us?

   c. What does the number "56" tell us?

   d. What is the total number of students who take Spanish?

> **DISCUSSION GROUP TIPS**
>
> If you do not understand something in group discussions, ask for help or raise your hand for help. Describe your questions as clearly as possible, using synonyms or other words when you do not know the precise words to use.

> **DISCUSSION GROUP TIPS**
>
> As you listen to the group discussion, take notes to aid comprehension and to help you describe your own ideas to others in your group. Ask questions to clarify ideas and to gain further understanding of key concepts

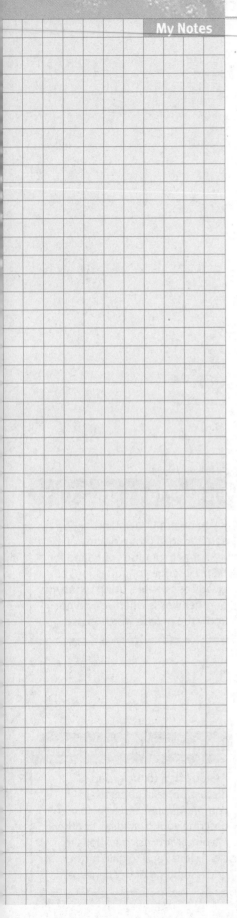

My Notes

e. What is the total number of students who take an art class?

f. How many students are there at the school?

g. How many students at this school take Spanish or an art class?

h. How many students do not take an art class?

2. **Reason quantitatively.** Now we can talk about probabilities.
   a. If a student is selected at random from the school, what is the probability that the selected student takes Spanish? Explain.

   b. A student is selected at random. Find the probability that the student selected:

   i. takes an art class.

   ii. takes Spanish *and* an art class.

   iii. takes an art class but does not take Spanish.

   iv. takes Spanish *or* an art class.

   v. takes neither Spanish nor an art class.

My Notes

3. **Model with mathematics.** Often, we write the probabilities in the Venn diagram, rather than the counts. Suppose a student is selected at random from Annabel High School. Let *S* be the event that the student takes Spanish and let *A* be the event that the student takes an art class.

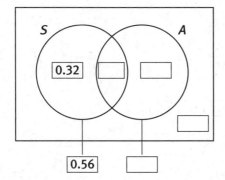

a. The number 0.32 in set *S* tells us the probability that the selected student takes Spanish and does not take an art class. How do you calculate this probability?

b. What does the "0.56" written in the box connected to the circle for event *S* tells us?

c. Write the appropriate probabilities in all the remaining empty boxes in the Venn diagram.

4. The most popular color for vehicles is white. Suppose that a vehicle is selected at random from a city, and let *C* be the event that the vehicle is a car and *W* be the event that the vehicle is white. Some of the relevant probabilities are shown in the Venn diagram below.

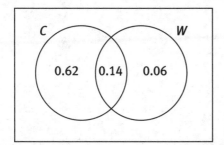

a. What two probabilities do you add to find the probability that the selected vehicle is a car? Find the probability.

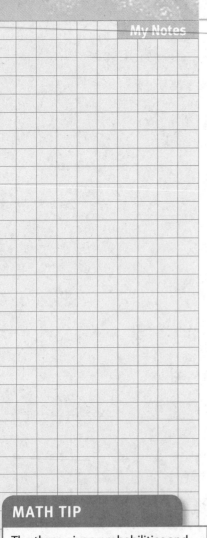

My Notes

b. Find the probability that the selected vehicle is:

  i. white.

  ii. a white car.

  iii. a car that is not white.

  iv. a car or is white.

c. What region in the Venn diagram represents the event that the vehicle selected is neither white nor a car? Find the probability of this event.

MATH TIP

The three given probabilities and the required probability added together must be 1, since the four probabilities cover all probabilities.

Check Your Understanding

5. At the beginning of this activity you were given a Venn diagram with the numbers (counts) of students who take the various combinations of Spanish (or not) and an art class (or not). From the counts you were given, how did you calculate the following?
  a. the total number of students in the school
  b. the probability that a randomly selected student takes Spanish
  c. the probability that a randomly selected student takes an art class but does not take Spanish

My Notes

6. Suppose that a student will be selected at random from Annabel High School. Let A be the event that the student takes an art class and let B be the event that the student plays basketball. The quantities p, q, r, and s given in the Venn diagram represent probabilities.

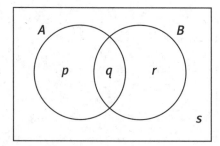

a. How would you calculate the probability that the student:
   i. plays basketball?
   ii. takes an art class and plays basketball?
   iii. plays basketball but does not take an art class?
   iv. takes an art class or plays basketball?
   v. does not take an art class?

b. If you knew the values of p, q, and r, how would you find the value of s? What does the probability s represent?

7. Suppose that a student will be selected at random from Annabel High School. Let F be the event that the student plays football and let M be the event that the student takes a music class. Some of the probabilities of the events are shown in the Venn diagram.

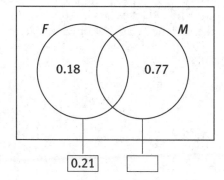

a. Complete the diagram.
b. What is the probability that the student will play football but will not take a music class?
c. What is the probability that the student will take a music class?

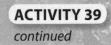
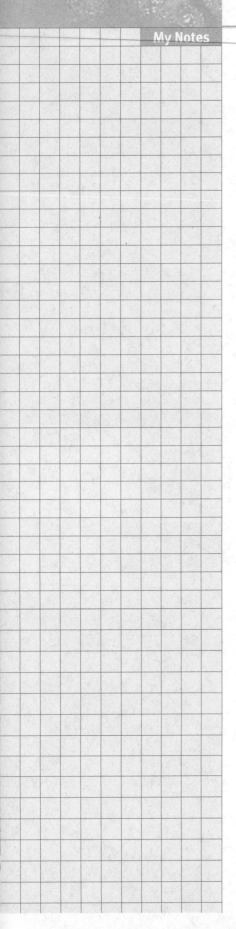

LESSON 39-1 PRACTICE

8. At Kennedy High School, some students take Italian and some do not. Some students take music and some do not. Let I be the set of students who take Italian, and let M be the set of students who take music.

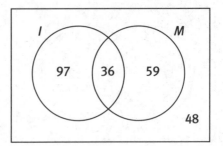

   a. What does the number "36" in the Venn diagram tell us?
   b. What does the number "59" tell us?
   c. What does the number "48" tell us?
   d. How many students take Italian or music?
   e. How many students do not take Italian?

9. If a student is selected at random from Kennedy High School, to the nearest thousandth, what is the probability that the selected student:
   a. takes Italian?
   b. takes Italian or music?
   c. does not take Italian and does not take music?
   d. only takes music?

10. **Make sense of problems and persevere in solving them.**
   Suppose that a student will be selected at random from the High School of Arts and Sciences. Let P be the event that the student takes physics and let D be the event that the student takes a dance class. The probability that the student takes physics is 0.28, while the probability that the student takes a dance class is 0.45. The probability that the student takes physics and a dance class is 0.07. What is the probability that the student takes a dance class but not a physics class?

Learning Targets:

● Use Venn diagrams to represent "and," "or," and "not."

● Use set notation to describe events.

> **SUGGESTED LEARNING STRATEGIES:** Activating Prior Knowledge, Close Reading, Create Representations, Visualization, Think-Pair-Share, Debriefing

1. Now look at the mathematical notation for "and," "or," and "not." Suppose that we're selecting a student at random from Annabel High School, and let *A* be the event that the student takes an art class and let *B* be the event that the student plays basketball.

   a. Shade the region representing the event that the selected student takes an art class <u>and</u> plays basketball.

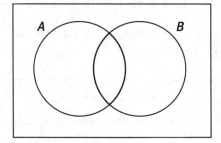

This region is called the ***intersection*** of the sets *A* and *B*, and can be written as $A \cap B$ (read as "A intersect B"). The probability that the selected student takes an art class and plays basketball can be written as $P(A \cap B)$.

MATH TERMS

The set of elements that are in *A* and in *B* is referred to as the **intersection** of *A* and *B*, written $A \cap B$.

b. Shade the region representing the event that the selected student takes an art class *or* plays basketball.

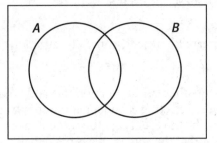

This region is called the **union** of the sets A and B, and can be written as $A \cup B$ (read as "A union B"). The probability that the selected student takes an art class or plays basketball can be written as $P(A \cup B)$.

c. Shade the region representing the event that the selected student does *not* take an art class.

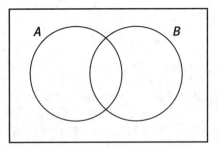

This region is the **complement** of the set A, and can be written as A^C (read as "A complement"). The probability that the selected student does not take an art class can be written as $P(A^C)$.

MATH TERMS

The set of elements that are in A or in B is referred to as the **union** of A and B, and is written $A \cup B$.

MATH TERMS

The set of elements that are not in A is referred to as the **complement** of A, and is written A^C.

These ideas are summarized in the table below.

Shading	In Words	In Probability Notation
A ⬤⬤ B (intersection shaded)	The probability that a randomly selected student takes an art class <u>and</u> plays basketball	$P(A \cap B)$
A ⬤⬤ B (both circles shaded)	The probability that a randomly selected student takes an art class <u>or</u> plays basketball	$P(A \cup B)$
A ⬤⬤ B (outside shaded)	The probability that a randomly selected student does <u>not</u> take an art class	$P(A^c)$

Check Your Understanding

2. Suppose that a student is selected at random from Annabel High School. Let *S* be the event that the student plays soccer and let *H* be the event that the student is on the honor roll. Copy each diagram and shade the region for each event.
   a. Shade the region that represents the event $S \cap H$.

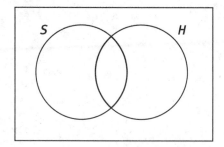

   b. Describe the event $S \cap H$ in words: "$S \cap H$ is the event that the student . . ."

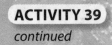

My Notes

c. Shade the region that represents the event $S \cup H$.

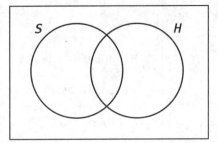

d. Describe the event $S \cup H$ in words.
e. Shade the region representing the event H^C.

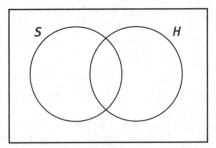

f. Describe the event H^C in words.

3. Consider picking a vehicle at random from a city. Denote the event that the vehicle is a sedan by S and the event that the vehicle is black by B. Write the following probabilities in probability notation. (Use the symbols $\cap$, $\cup$, and ^{C} where they apply.)
   a. the probability that the vehicle is black
   b. the probability that the vehicle is not black
   c. the probability that the vehicle is a black sedan
   d. the probability that the vehicle is either a sedan or is black
   e. the probability that the vehicle is a sedan and is not black
   f. the probability that the vehicle is a sedan or is not black

LESSON 39-2 PRACTICE

4. A student is selected at random from Annabel High School. Let *A* be the event that the student takes an art class and *B* be the event that the student plays basketball. Describe in words the event represented by each shaded region, and write the event in set notation.

a.

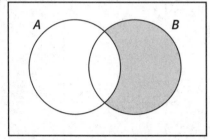

b.

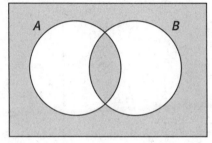

5. Suppose that a player will be selected at random from the roster of a local baseball team. Let the event that the player is a right-handed thrower be *R* and let the event that the player is a pitcher be *Q*. Some of the relevant probabilities are shown in the Venn diagram below.

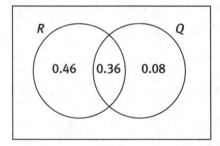

a. One probability has been omitted from the Venn diagram. Calculate this probability, and write the value in the appropriate place on the diagram.

My Notes

b. Reason abstractly and quantitatively. Complete the table below by writing the appropriate words, numbers, or probability notation in the empty cells.

Probability in Words	Probability Notation	Value of Probability
The probability that the player is a right-handed thrower	$P(R)$	0.82
The probability that the player is a pitcher		
The probability that the player is a right-handed thrower and is a pitcher		
	$P(R \cup Q)$	
	$P(Q^c)$	
The probability that the player is a right-handed thrower and is not a pitcher		
	$P(R^c \cap Q^c)$	

ACTIVITY 39 PRACTICE
Write your answers on notebook paper.
Show your work.

Lesson 39-1

1. A restaurant has a large fish tank. Some of the fish are goldfish, and some are not. Some of the fish are more than a year old, and some are not. Let the set of fish that are goldfish be G and let the set of fish that are more than a year old be M. The numbers of fish in various categories are shown below.

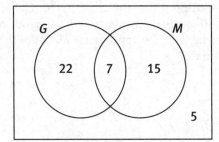

   a. How many fish are goldfish?
   b. How many fish are goldfish and are more than a year old?
   c. How many fish are goldfish or are more than a year old?
   d. How many fish are not goldfish and are not more than a year old?
   e. What is the total number of fish?
   f. How many fish are not goldfish?
   g. How many fish are less than or equal to a year old?
   h. What is the complement of set G? Describe the set in words.
   i. Compare the answers to Items 1e and 1f. Are they the same? Explain.

2. A fish will be selected at random from the tank. Complete the Venn diagram by writing the appropriate probabilities in the boxes. Give the probabilities as decimals to the nearest thousandth.

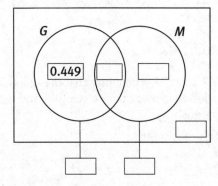

   a. Explain how you found P(goldfish less than or equal to a year old).
   b. What is the total of all the probabilities for this experiment? Explain.

Lesson 39-2

3. Refer to the Venn diagram you completed in Item 2. Describe each of the following probabilities in words. Then determine the value of the probability.
   a. $P(G)$
   b. $P(M)$
   c. $P(G \cap M)$
   d. $P(G \cup M)$
   e. $P(G^C)$
   f. What is the probability that the fish that is selected is more than a year old and is not a goldfish?

MATHEMATICAL PRACTICES
Model with Mathematics

4. The following table shows the numbers of phones available with and without speakerphone and with and without caller ID in Joe's Phone Store.

	Speakerphone	No Speakerphone
Caller ID	18	2
No Caller ID	16	12

Draw a Venn diagram to represent this information. Label the circles C (for Caller ID) and S (for Speakerphone). Write the four numbers in the table in the appropriate places in the diagram.

Addition Rule and Mutually Exclusive Events

Hector Street
Lesson 40-1 Applying the Addition Rule

Learning Targets:

- Learn the Addition Rule and understand why it applies.
- Use the Addition Rule to calculate probabilities.

> **SUGGESTED LEARNING STRATEGIES:** Activating Prior Knowledge, Think Aloud, Create Representations, Visualization, Think-Pair-Share, Debriefing

There are 100 houses on Hector Street. Some of the houses have attics, and some do not. Some of the houses have basements, and some do not. Let the set of houses that have attics be *A* and the set of houses that have basements be *B*. The numbers of houses with various combinations of attic and basement are shown.

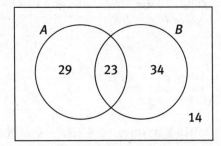

1. How many of the houses on the street have attics?

2. How many of the houses on the street have basements?

3. **Reason quantitatively.** If a house is selected at random from the street, what is the probability that it has an attic?

4. If a house is selected at random from the street, what is the probability that it has a basement?

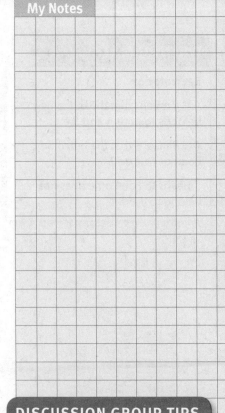

My Notes

DISCUSSION GROUP TIPS

Use your group discussions to clarify the meaning of mathematical concepts and other language used to describe problem information. With your group or your teacher, review background information that will be useful in applying concepts.

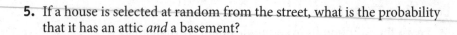

My Notes

WRITING MATH

Set Notation

$A \cap B$ means that the outcome belongs to both A **and** B.

$A \cup B$ means that the outcome belongs to A **or** B.

^{C} means the outcome does **not** belong to the set.

5. If a house is selected at random from the street, what is the probability that it has an attic *and* a basement?

6. Write the answers to Items 3–5 using probability notation. Use set notation as necessary.

7. What is the probability that it has an attic *or* a basement?
  a. What is the value of $P(A \cup B)$?

  b. What is the value of $P(A) + P(B)$?

  c. Construct viable arguments. Explain why $P(A) + P(B)$ is not equal to $P(A \cup B)$.

Complete the formula for the union of two intersecting sets.
$$P(A \cup B) = P(A) + P(B) - \underline{\hspace{1.5cm}}$$

Let's generalize. Suppose that various combinations of events A and B have the probabilities p, q, r, and s as shown in this Venn diagram.

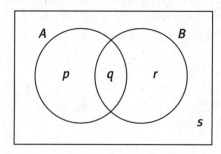

To calculate $P(A \cup B)$, find $p + q + r$.

To calculate $P(A)$, find $p + q$, and to calculate $P(B)$, find $q + r$.

If we calculate $P(A) + P(B)$, we get $p + q + q + r$, which includes <u>two</u> q's.

In $P(A \cup B)$ we only want <u>one</u> q.

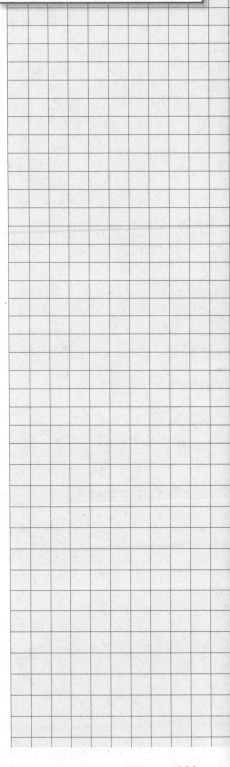

When we calculate $P(A \cup B)$ using $P(A)$ and $P(B)$, we have to subtract q, which is $P(A \cap B)$. This leads to the following formula:

$$P(A \cup B) = P(A) + P(B) - P(A \cap B)$$

MATH TIP

To find $P(A$ or $B)$, use the **Addition Rule:**

$P(A \cup B) = P(A) + P(B) - P(A \cap B)$

This formula is called the *Generalized Addition Rule*, and is often simply referred to as the Addition Rule.

Of the houses on Hector Street, 37% have central air conditioning, 52% have a security system, and 24% have both central air and a security system. Suppose that a house is selected at random from the street. Let C be the event that the house has central air and S be the event that the house has a security system. The given information is shown in the Venn diagram below.

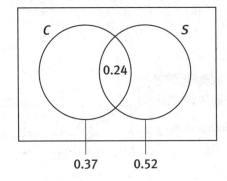

8. What is the value of each of the following?
   a. $P(C)$

   b. $P(S)$

   c. $P(C \cap S)$

9. **Make sense of problems.** Now use the Addition Rule to find $P(C \cup S)$. Express in words the meaning of the probability you just found.

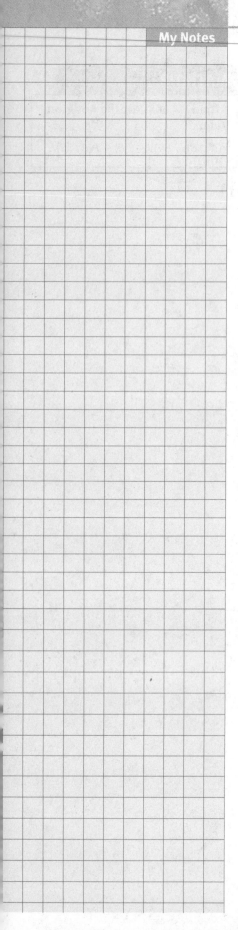

My Notes

10. **Model with mathematics.** Shade the region represented by $C \cup S$.

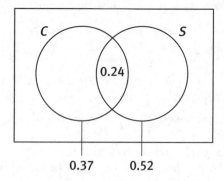

11. If a house is selected at random from this street, what is the probability that it has neither central air nor a security system?

Check Your Understanding

12. Write the Addition Rule.

13. Using the information given in the Venn diagram below, calculate $P(A \cup B)$.

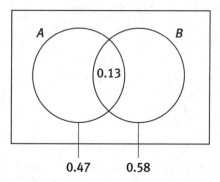

14. What is the probability of the complement of $P(A \cup B)$?

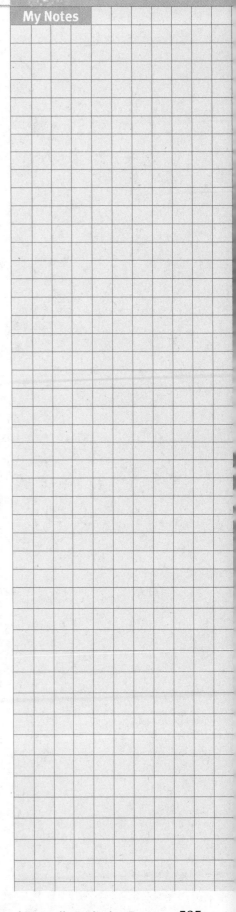

15. If a household is selected at random from Elm Street, the probability that the household has lagged pipes is 0.26 (lagged piping saves energy). The probability that the household recycles its refuse is 0.63. The probability that the household either has lagged pipes or recycles its refuse is 0.67.

 a. Write the given information using probability notation. Let the event that a household has lagged pipes be L and the event that a household recycles most of its refuse be R.

 b. Find the probability that a randomly selected household has lagged pipes *and* recycles its refuse. That is, find $P(L \cap R)$. Use the Addition Rule. Fill in the boxes with the given information and solve for $P(L \cap R)$.

$$P(L \cup R) \; = \; P(L) \; + \; P(R) \; - \; P(L \cap R)$$

$$\boxed{} = \boxed{} + \boxed{} - \boxed{?}$$

 c. What is the value of $P(L \cap R)$? Show your work.

Check Your Understanding

16. Reason quantitatively. For two intersecting sets, $P(C \cup D) = 0.85$. What is $P(C \cap D)$ if $P(C) = 0.7$ and $P(D) = 0.3$?

17. Calculate the three probabilities indicated by the question marks in the Venn diagram below.

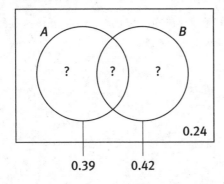

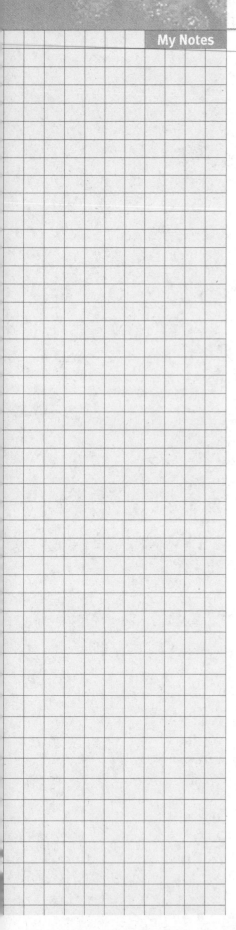

LESSON 40-1 PRACTICE

18. Dr. Zadok's Museum has a collection of cameras. If a camera is selected at random from the museum's collection, the probability that it is digital is 0.43 and the probability that it is a single lens reflex (SLR) camera is 0.51. The probability that the randomly selected camera is both digital and an SLR is 0.19.

    a. Let the event that a camera is digital be D and the event that a camera is an SLR be S. Draw a Venn diagram to illustrate the information that you were given.

    b. Suppose that a camera is selected at random from the museum's collection. Find the probability that it is
    i. either digital or an SLR.
    ii. digital but not an SLR.
    iii. an SLR but is not digital.
    iv. neither digital nor an SLR.
    v. not digital.

19. **Make sense of problems.** In the collection of clocks at Dr. Zadok's Museum, 28% run on electrical power, 45% have alarms, and 54% either run on electrical power or have alarms. If a clock is selected at random, what is the probability that it runs on electrical power and has an alarm? Show your work.

20. Dr. Zadok's Museum has a cafeteria. If a customer is selected at random, the probability that the customer orders a beverage is 0.74, the probability that the customer orders a dessert is 0.66, and the probability that the customer orders neither a beverage nor a dessert is 0.07.

    a. Draw a Venn diagram to represent this information.

    b. You are given that the probability that a randomly selected customer orders neither a beverage nor a dessert is 0.07. What does this tell you about the probability that the customer orders either a beverage or a dessert?

    c. Calculate the probability that a randomly selected customer orders a beverage and a dessert.

Learning Targets:

- Learn the meaning of "mutually exclusive" events.
- Use Venn diagrams to represent mutually exclusive events.
- Use the Addition Rule to calculate the probability of mutually exclusive events.

SUGGESTED LEARNING STRATEGIES: Activating Prior Knowledge, Marking the Text, Visualization, Think-Pair-Share, Debriefing

Mutually exclusive events are events that can't happen at the same time. They have no outcomes in common.

For example, suppose we have a cube with faces numbered 1 through 6. We will roll the cube once.

Let L = the event that the cube shows a number less than 3.

Let G = the event that the cube shows a number greater than 4.

On a roll of the cube, it is not possible that the result could be less than 3 <u>and</u> greater than 4. Therefore, L and G are mutually exclusive events.

1. **Reason abstractly.** A cube with faces numbered 1 through 6 will be rolled once.
   a. Let E be the event that the cube shows an even number and let F be the event that the cube shows a 5. Are E and F mutually exclusive events? Explain.

   b. Let E be the event that the cube shows an even number and let H be the event that the cube shows a number greater than 3. Are E and H mutually exclusive events? Explain.

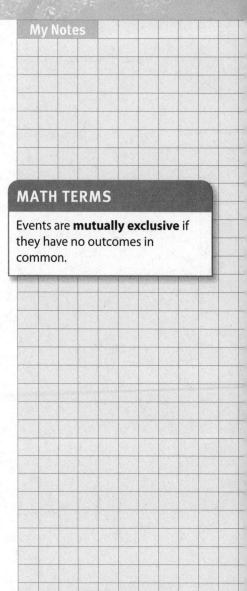

My Notes

MATH TERMS

Events are **mutually exclusive** if they have no outcomes in common.

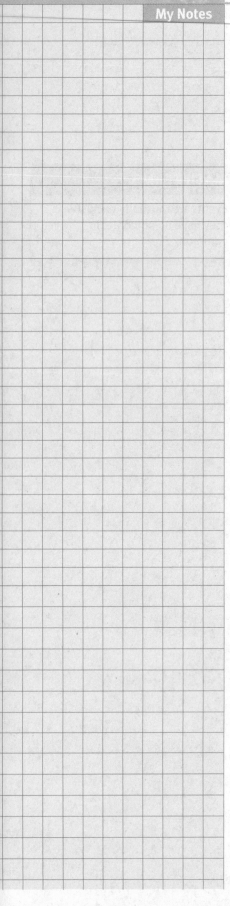

My Notes

2. Sam selects one car at random, and notes the color of the car.
   a. List five possible outcomes in this context.

   b. Give two events (in this context) that are mutually exclusive.

      Event A: The car is _____.
      Event B: The car is _____.
      Explain why your events are mutually exclusive.

3. Suppose that when you randomly choose a car, you note both its color and its make. Give two possible events that are not mutually exclusive.

   Event A: The car is _____.
   Event B: The car is _____.
   Explain why your events are not mutually exclusive.

Since mutually exclusive events have no outcomes in common, they can be represented in a Venn diagram where the circles do not intersect.

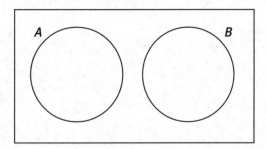

4. If the events A and B are mutually exclusive, what is the value of $P(A \cap B)$?

My Notes

5. The Addition Rule states that

$$P(A \cup B) = P(A) + P(B) - P(A \cap B).$$

Rewrite the Addition Rule for mutually exclusive events.

If the events A and B are mutually exclusive, then $P(A \cap B) = 0$. The Addition Rule for mutually exclusive events is as follows:

> If the events A and B are mutually exclusive, then
> $P(A \cup B) = P(A) + P(B).$

Check Your Understanding

6. Describe two events that are mutually exclusive.

7. Describe two events that are not mutually exclusive.

8. When a house is selected at random from Hector Street, the probability that it is a two-story house is 0.63 and the probability that it is a three-story house is 0.13. Let A be the event that a house has exactly two stories and let B be the event that a house has exactly three stories.
   a. Are A and B mutually exclusive events? Explain.
   b. Find the probability that a randomly selected house from Hector Street is a two- or three-story house.

9. **Make sense of problems.** When a student is selected at random from Annabel High School, the probability that the student plays soccer is 0.143 and the probability that the student takes a foreign language class is 0.682. Is it possible to use this information to find the probability that a randomly selected student plays soccer or takes a foreign language class? If so, explain how. If not, what extra information would enable you to answer the question?

10. **Construct viable arguments.** When would you use the Addition Rule $P(A \cup B) = P(A) + P(B)$?

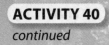

LESSON 40-2 PRACTICE

11. **Construct viable arguments.** Determine if each of the following events are mutually exclusive or not mutually exclusive. Explain your reasoning.
    a. On a visit to Fire Island, see the lighthouse. See the historical mansion.
    b. Take a car to the shore. Take a train to the shore.
    c. On a fishing trip, catch blue fish, sea bass, and fluke.
    d. Attend a baseball game and attend a football game on the same Saturday afternoon.

12. Using the information given in the Venn diagram, calculate each probability.

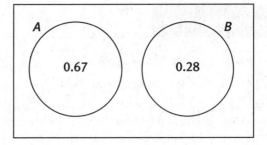

   a. $P(A \cup B)$
   b. $P(A)^C$
   c. $P(B)^C$
   d. $P(A \cup B)^C$
   e. $P(A \cap B)$

13. **Attend to precision.** At Annabel High School, 26.3% of the students are 9th graders and 22.8% of the students are 12th graders. If a student is selected at random from Annabel High School, what is the probability that the student is either a 9th grader or a 12th grader? Justify the method you use.

14. On average, 75% of the annual visitors to the lighthouse visit during the summer. Ten percent visit in the fall. The lighthouse is closed in the winter but open in the spring. Draw a Venn diagram that represents this information. Calculate the probability that a visitor selected at random from the visitor log last year visited the lighthouse in the spring or fall.

ACTIVITY 40 PRACTICE
Write your answers on notebook paper.
Show your work.

Lesson 40-1

1. State the generalized Addition Rule.

2. There are 58 houses on Elm Avenue. Some of the houses have hardwood flooring and some do not. Some of the houses have wall-to-wall carpeting and some do not. The numbers of houses with various combinations of flooring are shown in the Venn diagram.

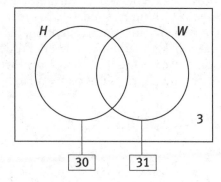

a. Complete the Venn diagram.
b. How many houses have hardwood flooring and carpeting?
c. How many houses have hardwood flooring or carpeting?

3. When a house is selected at random from Hector Street, the probability that the house has gas-fired central heating is 0.25, the probability that the house has off-street parking is 0.76, and the probability that the house has both gas-fired central heating and off-street parking is 0.19. Find the probability that a randomly selected house has either gas-fired central heating or off-street parking.

4. When a non-commercial vehicle is selected at random from a city, the probability that it is an SUV is 0.28, the probability that it is a hybrid is 0.22, and the probability that it is neither of these is 0.54.
a. Draw a Venn diagram to represent this information.
b. Suppose that a noncommercial vehicle is selected at random from this city. Find the probability that it is:
   i. either an SUV or a hybrid.
   ii. a hybrid SUV.
   iii. a hybrid car that is not an SUV.
   iv. not a hybrid.

Lesson 40-2

5. Suppose that you have a set of 40 cards consisting of

10 red cards labeled 1 through 10,

10 blue cards labeled 1 through 10,

10 green cards labeled 1 through 10, and

10 yellow cards labeled 1 through 10.

One card will be selected at random.

a. Let R be the event that the card is red and let G be the event that the card is green. Are R and G mutually exclusive events? Explain.
b. Let R be the event that the card is red and let T be the event that the card is a 10. Are R and T mutually exclusive events? Explain.
c. Let L be the event that the number on the card is at least 6 and let E be the event that the card shows an even number. Are L and E mutually exclusive events? Explain.

6. State the Addition Rule for the probability of mutually exclusive events.

7. The class had to solve this problem for homework. "What is the probability of rolling at least a 4 or an odd number when rolling a number cube?" Mical wrote the following solution:

$$P(\text{at least } 4) = \frac{3}{6}$$

$$P(\text{odd number}) = \frac{3}{6}$$

$$P(\text{at least } 4 \text{ or odd}) = \frac{3}{6} + \frac{3}{6} = \frac{6}{6}$$

Is Mical correct? Explain.

8. Colleen rolls a number cube and flips a coin. What is the probability that she will roll at least a 3 or flip heads?

   A. $\frac{1}{6}$

   B. $\frac{4}{6}$

   C. $\frac{5}{6}$

   D. $\frac{7}{6}$

9. At Annabel High School, 83% of the students take the bus and 6% drive themselves to school. If a student is selected at random from the school, what is the probability that the student either takes the bus or drives him/herself to school? Justify the method that you use.

MATHEMATICAL PRACTICES
Construct Viable Arguments and Critique the Reasoning of Others

10. The manager of an office building intends to replace the carpet in offices where the carpet is worn out and to replace the furniture in offices where the furniture is outdated. In order to find out how many offices need attention, the office manager plans to add the number of offices that need a new carpet to the number of offices that need new furniture. Is this correct? Explain.

Probability and the Addition Rule

DIANE'S BOOKS

1. Diane is organizing her collection of books. She has 91 novels in total, and has categorized them as shown in the table below.

	Hardcover	Paperback	Total
Detective Novels	12	20	
Romance Novels	8	28	
Other Novels	9	14	
Total			91

   a. Complete the table by writing the totals in the empty cells.
   b. Suppose that a book will be selected at random from these 91 novels. Find the probability that the book is:
      i. a detective novel.
      ii. a hardcover book.
      iii. a paperback detective novel.
      iv. a paperback or a detective novel.
      v. not a detective novel.
   c. If Diane selects one of these novels at random, are the events "is a detective novel" and "is a hardcover" mutually exclusive? Explain.
   d. If Diane selects one of these novels at random, are the events "is a detective novel" and "is a romance novel" mutually exclusive? Explain.

2. Diane also has a number of nonfiction books. Of those books, 28% are hardcover, 22% are reference books, and 13% are hardcover reference books. Diane will select a nonfiction book at random. Let the event that the selected book is a hardcover be H and the event that it is a reference book be R.
   a. Draw a Venn diagram to represent this information. (Show the probabilities as decimals.)
   b. Find the probability that the selected book is
      i. a hardcover *or* a reference book.
      ii. a hardcover that is not a reference book.
      iii. neither a hardcover nor a reference book.
   c. Write each of the following using probability notation. Use the symbols $\cap$, $\cup$, and ^{C} as necessary. (Note: You do not have to find the values of the probabilities.)
      i. the probability that the selected book is a hardcover and a reference book
      ii. the probability that the selected book is a hardcover or a reference book
      iii. the probability that the selected book is not a reference book

Scoring Guide	Exemplary	Proficient	Emerging	Incomplete
	The solution demonstrates these characteristics:			
Mathematics Knowledge and Thinking (Items 1, 2)	• Clear and accurate understanding of determining probabilities using a table of values or a Venn diagram • Clear and accurate understanding of the term *mutually exclusive*	• A functional understanding of determining probabilities using a table of values or a Venn diagram • A functional understanding of the term *mutually exclusive*	• Partial understanding of determining probabilities using a table of values or a Venn diagram • Partial understanding of the term *mutually exclusive*	• Little or no understanding of determining probabilities using a table of values or a Venn diagram • Little or no understanding of the term *mutually exclusive*
Problem Solving (Items 1, 2b)	• An appropriate and efficient strategy that results in correct answers	• A strategy that results in mostly correct answers	• A strategy that results in some correct answers	• No clear strategy when solving problems
Mathematical Modeling / Representations (Items 2a, 2c)	• Clear and accurate understanding of using probabilities to create a Venn diagram • Clear and accurate understanding of writing probability statements using appropriate mathematical symbols	• Mostly accurate understanding of using probabilities to create a Venn diagram • Mostly accurate understanding of writing probability statements using appropriate mathematical symbols	• Partial understanding of using probabilities to create a Venn diagram • Partial understanding of writing probability statements using appropriate mathematical symbols	• Little or no understanding of using probabilities to create a Venn diagram • Little or no understanding of writing probability statements using appropriate mathematical symbols
Reasoning and Communication (Items 1c, 1d)	• Precise use of appropriate mathematics and language to explain why the statements are or are not mutually exclusive	• Mostly correct use of appropriate mathematics and language to explain why the statements are or are not mutually exclusive	• Misleading or confusing use of appropriate mathematics and language to explain why the statements are or are not mutually exclusive	• Incomplete or inaccurate use of appropriate mathematics and language to explain why the statements are or are not mutually exclusive

Dependent Events
Coco Wildlife Conservation Trust
Lesson 41-1 Understanding Conditional Probability

Learning Targets:

- Understand the conditional probability of *A* given *B*.
- Determine conditional probabilities using two-way frequency tables and Venn diagrams.
- Interpret the answer in terms of the model.

> **SUGGESTED LEARNING STRATEGIES:** Summarizing, Paraphrasing, Think Aloud, Create Representations, Visualization, Think-Pair-Share, Debriefing

1. There are 90 cranes that belong to the Coco Wildlife Conservation Trust. The cranes have been categorized by gender and type as shown in the two-way frequency table.

	Male	Female	Total
Gray-crowned	16	13	
White-naped	17	14	
Stanley	11	19	
Total			90

   a. Complete the table by entering the other totals.

   b. If a female crane is selected at random, what is the probability that it is a Stanley crane?

   c. Calculate the probability that a crane is a Stanley crane given that it is female.

You found the probability that a crane is a Stanley crane *given that it is female*. This is a **_conditional probability_**. We know that the crane is female. Then we find the probability that it is a Stanley crane.

In probability notation we show conditional probabilities using a vertical line. The probability that a crane is a Stanley crane given that it is female is written *P*(Stanley | female). If we denote the events by their initial letters, this conditional probability is written *P*(*S* | *F*). *P*(*S* | *F*) is read "the probability of *S* given *F*."

MATH TERMS

A **conditional probability** is the probability that an event occurs given that another event occurs.

WRITING MATH

Probability Notation

The probability of *A* given *B* is written *P*(*A* | *B*).

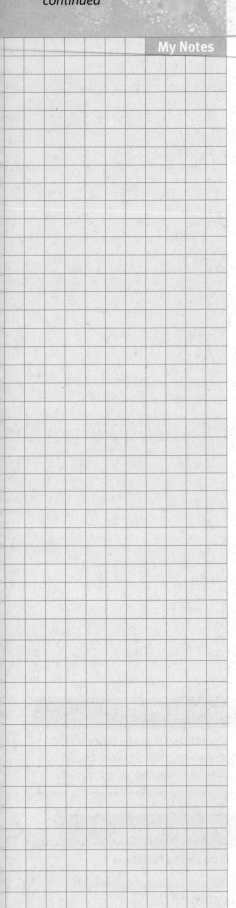

My Notes

2. Write the following probabilities using probability notation.
   a. the probability that a crane is male given that it is a gray-crowned crane

   b. the probability that a crane is a gray-crowned crane given that it is male

   c. the probability that a randomly selected white-naped crane is female

Check Your Understanding

3. The Coco Trust also has flamingos. The flamingos are categorized as shown in the table.

	Male	Female	Total
Chilean	16	13	
Greater	17	14	
Total			

   a. Complete the table by entering the totals.
   b. Suppose that a flamingo will be selected at random. The various possible events are denoted by their initial letters. Calculate the following probabilities to the nearest thousandth.
      i. $P(M)$
      ii. $P(M \mid C)$
      iii. $P(C \mid M)$
   c. If a female flamingo is selected at random, to the nearest thousandth, what is the probability that it is a greater flamingo? Use conditional probability notation to write your answer.

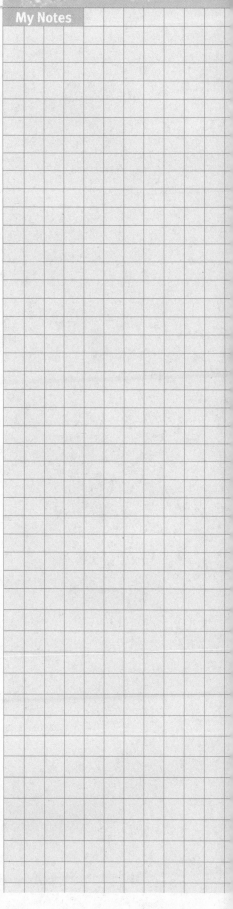

4. As part of their math course, Kate and Rob were required to do a statistical study. They selected a random sample of 80 students from their school. They asked all the selected students their grade level (9, 10, 11, or 12) and whether or not they had $5 or more with them. The results are shown in the table.

	9th Grade	10th Grade	11th Grade	12th Grade
Less than $5	13	10	9	3
$5 or more	8	9	17	11
Total				

a. Complete the table by entering the totals.
b. **Attend to precision.** A student will be selected at random from those in the sample. Find the following probabilities to the nearest hundredth.

   i. $P(\$5 \text{ or more} \mid 9\text{th grade})$

   ii. $P(\$5 \text{ or more} \mid 10\text{th grade})$

   iii. $P(\$5 \text{ or more} \mid 11\text{th grade})$

   iv. $P(\$5 \text{ or more} \mid 12\text{th grade})$

c. Since the sample was selected randomly, the students in the sample are likely to be representative of the school as a whole. What do the answers to Part b suggest to Kate and Rob about the amounts of money carried by students at the school?

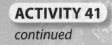

My Notes

Check Your Understanding

5. Suppose that a student is selected at random from your school. What would be the probabilities of each of the following events?
   a. the probability that the student plays the trumpet
   b. the probability that the student plays the trumpet given that the student is in the school band

6. Make sense of problems. Let T be the event that the student plays trumpet and let B be the event that the student is in the school band. Explain in words the meaning of each of the following probabilities.
   a. $P(T \cap B)$
   b. $P(T \mid B)$
   c. Are the probabilities in Parts a and b the same? Explain.
   (*Hint:* Use numbers.)

7. Some of the Trust's animals are tortoises. Some are not. Some of the animals are of known gender. Some are not. Let the set of tortoises be T and the set of animals of known gender be K. The numbers of animals falling into these categories are shown.

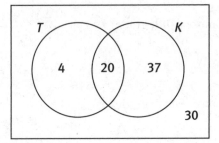

   a. How many animals are there at this location?

   b. How many of these animals are tortoises?

   c. How many of these animals are of known gender?

   d. How many of the animals of known gender are tortoises?

e. Find each of the following probabilities to the nearest thousandth. Use probability notation to write your answer.

   i. Suppose an animal of known gender is selected at random. What is the probability that this animal is a tortoise?

   ii. Calculate $P(K \mid T)$.

   iii. Do $P(T \mid K)$ and $P(K \mid T)$ represent the same region on the Venn diagram? Are the probabilities equal? Explain.

   iv. Suppose a tortoise is selected at random. What is the probability that its gender is not known?

MATH TIP

The phrase *its gender is not known* means that you should look for the complement of K.

Check Your Understanding

8. Reason quantitatively. Recall that at Annabel High School, some students take Spanish and some do not. Some students take an art class, and some do not. Let S be the set of students who take Spanish and A be the set of students who take an art class. The numbers of students in various combinations of these classes are given in the Venn diagram.

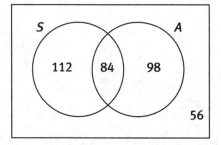

a. If a student is selected at random from the school, what is the probability that the student takes Spanish?

b. Find $P(S \mid A)$.

c. Find $P(A \mid S)$.

d. Which of the answers to Parts a and b is larger? Explain in your own words what this means.

e. Find $P(S \cap A \mid S^{C})$.

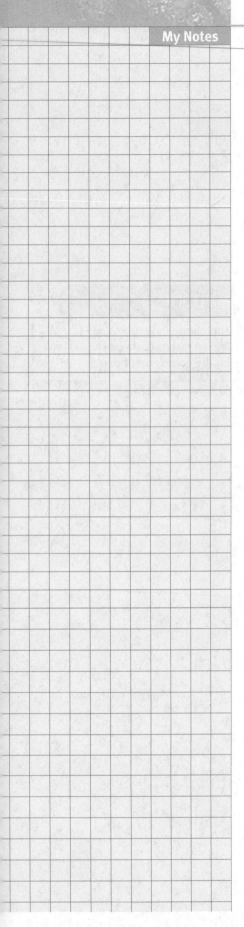

LESSON 41-1 PRACTICE

9. Recall the phone store. Some of the phones have caller ID. Some do not. Some have a speakerphone. Some do not. The numbers of phones with and without these features are shown in the table.
   a. Write the totals in the table.

	Speakerphone	No Speakerphone	Total
Caller ID	18	2	
No Caller ID	16	12	
Total			

Let C be the event that a phone has caller ID and let S be the event that a phone has a speakerphone. Calculate each probability to the nearest thousandth.
   b. If a phone is selected at random from those available at the store, what is the probability that it has a speakerphone?
   c. If you are now told that a phone has caller ID, does this make it more or less likely that it has a speakerphone?
   d. Find $P(C \mid S^C)$.

10. a. Draw a Venn diagram to illustrate the information in the table in Item 9.
    b. If a phone is selected at random from those available at the store, what is the probability that it has caller ID?
    c. If you are now told that a phone has a speakerphone, does this make it more or less likely that it has caller ID?

11. **Model with mathematics.** Recall the SpringBoard Superstar contest. This table shows four categories into which the contestants can be placed.

	Male	Female
Under 20	1	2
20 or Over	5	4

   a. Suppose that a contestant will be selected at random. Find the following probabilities to the nearest thousandth.
      i. $P(\text{female})$
      ii. $P(\text{female} \mid \text{under 20})$
      iii. $P(\text{female} \mid 20 \text{ or over})$
   b. Suppose you are a reporter for a newspaper. Write an article about the three probabilities you found in Part a. Compare these probabilities.

Learning Targets:

● Develop the conditional probability formula.
● Use conditional probability for everyday situations.

SUGGESTED LEARNING STRATEGIES: Marking the Text, Predict and Confirm, Summarizing, Paraphrasing, Discussion Groups, Think-Pair-Share, Note Taking

We have calculated conditional probabilities using *counts*. But often you are not given counts. You are only given probabilities. You can develop a formula to find conditional probability given probabilities. We begin with a Venn diagram showing counts.

1. Recall the tortoises and animals of known gender in the Coco Wildlife Preserve. The relevant counts are given in this Venn diagram where T is the set of tortoises and K is the set of animals of known gender.

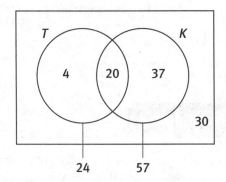

Write each probability as a fraction.

a. Find $P(T \mid K)$.

b. Now, find $P(T \cap K)$.

MATH TIP

The favorable outcomes of $P(T \mid K)$ and $P(T \cap K)$ are the same but the total possible outcomes are different. So the probabilities will be different.

c. Next, find $P(K)$.

d. Finally, find $\dfrac{P(T \cap K)}{P(K)}$. What do you notice?

To generalize, conditional probability can be found using this formula.

> For any two events A and B,
>
> $$P(A \mid B) = \dfrac{P(A \cap B)}{P(B)}$$

READING MATH

The formula for conditional probability is read:

"The probability of event *A* given event *B* is equal to the probability of event *A* and event *B* divided by event *B*."

CONNECT TO BIOLOGY

The *primates* are an order of placental mammals containing humans, apes, and monkeys.

Check Your Understanding

2. The Coco Foundation takes care of a number of *primates*. When a primate is selected at random, let T be the event that it is a tamarin and let N be the event that it is at least nine years old. Some of the relevant probabilities are shown in the Venn diagram.

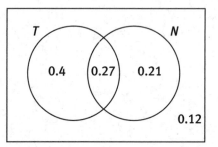

Write your answer to each question using probability notation.
a. What is the probability that a randomly selected primate is a tamarin *and* is at least nine years old?
b. What is the probability that a randomly selected primate is at least nine years old?
c. What is the probability that a randomly selected primate is a tamarin given that it is at least nine years old? Use the probability formula.

LESSON 41-2 PRACTICE

3. Of the Coco Foundation's lemurs, 39% are female, 54% are at least eight years old, and 21% are females who are at least eight years old. When a lemur is selected at random, let the event that it is female be F and let the event that it is at least eight years old be E.
   a. Write the values of $P(F)$, $P(E)$, and $P(F \cap E)$.
   b. **Model with mathematics.** Illustrate the information you have been given using a Venn diagram. Write decimals in your diagram, not percentages.
   c. When a lemur is selected at random, what is the probability that it is female given that it is at least eight years old?
   d. When a lemur is selected at random, what is the probability that it is at least eight years old given that it is female?
   e. When a lemur is selected at random, what is the probability that it is either a female or at least eight years old? (*Hint:* You may use the Addition Rule if you wish.)

4. Recall the information you were given about a local baseball team. R is the event that the player is a right-handed thrower and Q is the event that the player is a pitcher. The probabilities of various combinations of these events are shown in the Venn diagram.

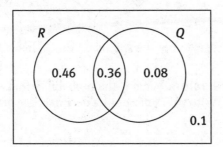

A player is selected at random.
   a. Calculate $P(R \mid Q)$.
   b. **Construct viable arguments.** What is the probability that the player is a pitcher given that he is a right-handed thrower? Explain the difference between this probability and the probability that a randomly selected player is a pitcher and a right-handed thrower.
   c. If a right-handed thrower is selected, what is the probability that he is not a pitcher?
   d. If a player who is not a pitcher is selected, what is the probability that he is a right-handed thrower? How would this probability be written using conditional probability notation?

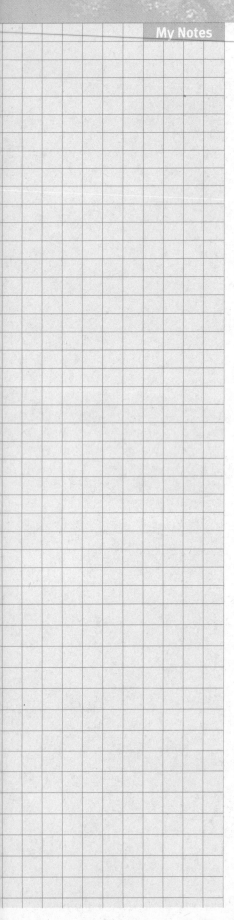

Learning Targets:
- Use tree diagrams to determine conditional probabilities.
- Apply the general Multiplication Rule.

SUGGESTED LEARNING STRATEGIES: Role Play, Shared Reading, Visualization, Discussion Groups, Debriefing, Close Reading, Marking the Text, Sharing and Responding

When problems involve conditional probabilities, it is often beneficial to use tree diagrams to illustrate the problem. A tree diagram can help you to find the conditional probabilities.

Anson is concerned that video games are interfering with his connecting with his friends. He has decided that, every day, when he's finished his homework, he will spin a spinner to decide if he should play video games or connect with his friends. The five outcomes on the spinner are equally likely.

He decided that if the result of the spin is a 4 or a 5, he will play video games; otherwise, he will not.

1. **Attend to precision.** What is the probability that Anson will play video games? Write your answer as a decimal. Use probability notation.

Anson found that if he plays video games, then the probability that he will connect with his friends is 0.3. If he doesn't play video games, the probability he'll connect with his friends is 0.9. You can use a ***tree diagram*** to illustrate this information.

Let V be the event that Anson plays video games, F be the event that he connects with his friends, V^C be the event that he doesn't play video games, and F^C be the event that he doesn't connect with his friends.

MATH TERMS

A **tree diagram** is a graphic organizer for listing the possible outcomes of an experiment.

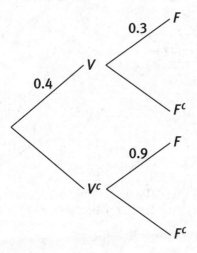

2. **Reason quantitatively.** Find each probability. Write the answer using probability notation. Then write the probability in the appropriate place on the tree diagram.

   a. What is the probability that Anson does not play video games?

   b. If Anson plays video games, what is the probability that he will not connect with his friends?

   c. If Anson doesn't play video games, what is the probability that he will not connect with his friends?

Notice that the conditional probability $P(F \mid V)$ is a ***dependent event***. We are looking for the probability of Anson connecting with friends once he has played video games.

MATH TERMS

Two events are said to be **dependent** if the result of the second event is affected by the result of the first **event**.

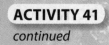

Now imagine 100 days, as shown in the tree diagram.

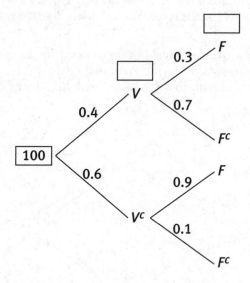

3. On how many of these 100 days would you expect Anson to play video games? Write this number in the box above "*V*".

4. On how many days would you expect Anson to play video games *and* connect with his friends? Write this number in the box above "*F*".

5. What is the probability of the event in Item 4?

6. What two probabilities can you multiply in order to find the probability of the event in Item 4?

7. Find each of the following probabilities using multiplication.
   a. Anson plays video games *and* does not connect with his friends.

   b. Anson does not play video games *and* connects with friends.

   c. Anson does not play video games *and* does not connect with his friends.

We'll now work out the probability that Anson connects with his friends. In order to connect with his friends, Anson has to either play video games and connect with his friends *or* not play video games and connect with his friends.

8. What is the probability that Anson connects with his friends? Use the Addition Rule for mutually exclusive events.

9. Notice the probability 0.3 in the tree diagram. This is a conditional probability. It is the probability of F given V. What is the probability of F given V^C? Use probability notation to write your answer.

Check Your Understanding

Bernadette also plays video games or does not, and connects with her friends or does not. The probabilities are shown in the diagram.

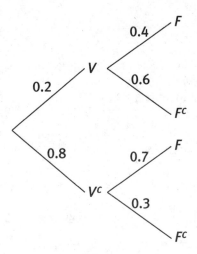

10. Find the probability that Bernadette plays video games and connects with her friends.

11. To find the probability that Bernadette connects with her friends, she has to either play video games and connect with her friends *or* not play video games and connect with her friends. What is the probability that she connects with her friends?

12. Why is it possible to add to find the probability in Item 11?

13. Write the probability that Bernadette connects with her friends given she does not play video games. Use probability notation to write your answer.

Consider another probability experiment involving *dependent events*.

In this experiment, the two events occur without replacement.

14. **Reason quantitatively.** Ms. Troy's math class consists of 18 girls and 12 boys. Ms. Troy is planning to choose two students at random to record the results of a survey on a poster. To do this, Ms. Troy will write the names of the students on identical slips of paper and will place the slips in a hat. She will randomly pick one slip from the hat, and then, without replacing the first slip, will randomly pick a second slip.
   a. What is the probability that the first student selected is a girl?

MATH TIP

Since the first slip of paper is not replaced, the sample space of the second event will be changed.

   b. If the first student selected is a girl, how many slips of paper for girls are now left in the hat? How many slips of paper are left in the hat? So, if the first student is a girl, what is the probability that the second student will also be a girl?

   c. If the first student selected is a boy, how many slips of paper for girls are now left in the hat? How many slips of paper are left in the hat? So, if the first student is a boy, what is the probability that the second student will be a girl?

   d. Write the relevant probabilities on the tree diagram below.

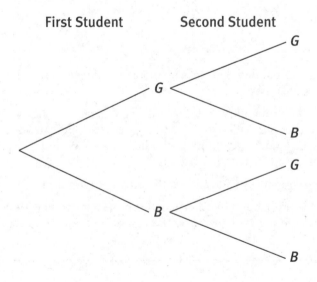

First Student   Second Student

G

G

B

G

B

B

e. Find the probability that both students chosen are girls. Use probability notation to write your answer.

My Notes

MATH TIP

Follow the branches of the tree diagram from *G* to *G* and multiply.

We have been using a tree diagram to find the probability of a compound event. This leads to the **Multiplication Rule**:

> If *A* and *B* are dependent events, then
>
> $P(A \text{ and } B) = P(A) \cdot P(B \mid A)$

f. Find the probability that a girl and a boy are chosen to represent the class. Use probability notation to write your answer.

MATH TIP

The probability that a girl and a boy are chosen can occur if the first student chosen is a girl or if the first student chosen is a boy.

Check Your Understanding

15. Mr. Santaella's class consists of 10 girls and 15 boys. He will choose two students at random to be hall monitors.
  a. Complete the tree diagram.

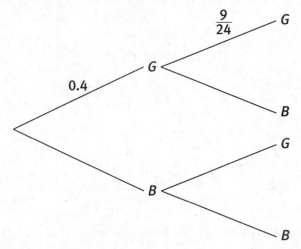

b. What is the probability that the students chosen will be:
  i. two girls?
  ii. a girl and a boy?
  iii. two boys?
  c. Why is this a probability experiment without replacement?

16. Owen has a bag of marbles with 3 red, 5 white, and 7 green marbles. He picks a marble from the bag without looking. He picks a second marble without putting the first marble back in the bag.
  a. Draw a tree diagram to represent this experiment.
  b. What is the probability that Owen will pick:
  i. two white marbles?
  ii. a red and a white marble?
  iii. two green marbles?

LESSON 41-3 PRACTICE

17. **Make sense of problems.** Gerry is developing a small ski resort. He has worked out that if there's a lot of snow this coming winter, the probability that the resort will make a profit is 0.9. However, if there's not a lot of snow this winter, then the probability that the resort will make a profit is 0.6. According to information Gerry found on the Internet, the probability that there will be a lot of snow this winter is 0.7.
    a. Draw a tree diagram to represent these possible outcomes. Include all the relevant probabilities.
    b. What is the probability that there will be a lot of snow and the resort will make a profit?
    c. What is the probability that there will not be a lot of snow and the resort will not make a profit?
    d. What is the probability that the resort will make a profit?

18. Coach Caroline's softball team has made the playoffs. The first game has not been scheduled yet, but Caroline knows that the first game is equally likely to be on any one of the seven days of the week. Caroline has different players available on different days of the week, and she has estimated that if the game is on a Monday, a Wednesday, or a Friday, the probability that her team will win is 0.6. If the game is on a Tuesday or a Thursday, the probability that her team will win is 0.5. If the game is on a Saturday or a Sunday, the probability that her team will win is 0.45.
    a. Complete the diagram below by writing the appropriate probabilities above the lines of the tree diagram.

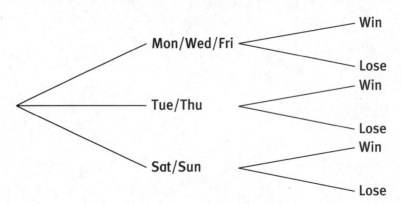

    b. What is the probability that Coach Caroline's team will win?

ACTIVITY 41 PRACTICE
Write your answers on notebook paper.
Show your work.

1. Recall the high school current affairs club that has members in all four grades (9, 10, 11, and 12) and of both genders (male and female). The numbers of students in the various grade/gender categories are given in the table.

	Male	Female	Total
9	8	6	
10	4	2	
11	3	7	
12	9	9	
Total			

a. Complete the table.
b. If a student is selected at random from the club's female members, what is the probability that she is a 9th grader?
c. When selecting a club member at random, what is the probability that the student is female given that the student is a 9th grader?
d. When selecting a club member at random, what is $P(\text{11th grade} \mid \text{male})$?

2. A random sample of 100 people was selected from the adults at a mall. Each person selected was asked whether he or she had used a mobile phone that day; people's ages were also noted. The results of the survey are summarized below.

	Age		
	18–35	36–55	56 or over
Had Used a Mobile Phone	34	27	10
Had Not Used a Mobile Phone	3	11	15
Total			

a. Complete the table.
b. Suppose that a person will be selected at random from those included in the sample. Find the following probabilities to two decimal places.
   i. $P(\text{used a mobile phone} \mid 18\text{–}35)$
   ii. $P(\text{used a mobile phone} \mid 36\text{–}55)$
   iii. $P(\text{used a mobile phone} \mid 56 \text{ or over})$
c. Since the sample was selected randomly from the adults at the mall, the results of the survey are likely to represent the population of all the adults at the mall. What do your answers in Part b suggest about this population?
d. Do you think it would be reasonable to use the sample result to make conclusions about all the adults in the town where the mall is located? Explain.

3. Suppose that you will select an American adult at random. Let S be the event that the person visited a supermarket last Wednesday, and let F be the event that the person is female.
a. Roughly, what do you think would be the value of $P(S)$? (Just make a rough guess! Any answer that is in any way reasonable will be accepted.)
b. Now think about the probability $P(S \cap F)$. Would this probability be larger or smaller than your answer to Part a? Explain.
c. Now think about the probability $P(S \mid F)$. Do you think this probability would be larger or smaller than your answer to Part b? Explain.

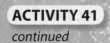

4. In an earlier exercise, a vehicle was to be selected at random from a city. Let the event that the vehicle is a car be C and the event that the vehicle is white be W. Some of the relevant probabilities are given in the Venn diagram.

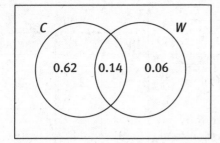

a. Calculate the value of the probability that has been omitted from the Venn diagram, and write that probability in the appropriate place.
b. Calculate $P(C \mid W)$.
c. What proportion of cars in this city is white?
d. If a non-white vehicle is selected at random, what is the probability that it is a car?

5. Janet is keeping her eye on a stock market index. If the index rises today, then the probability that she will make an investment tomorrow is 0.84. However, if the index does not rise today, then the probability that Janet will make an investment tomorrow is 0.58. This particular index rises on 70% of days.
a. Draw a tree diagram to represent this information. Complete the tree diagram by writing all the relevant probabilities next to the branches. Use decimals, not percentages, for the probabilities.
b. What is the probability that the index rises but Janet does not make an investment tomorrow? Show your work. Use probability notation.
c. What is the probability that Janet makes an investment tomorrow? Show your work. Use probability notation.

MATHEMATICAL PRACTICES
Reason Abstractly and Quantitatively

6. You spend your life making decisions. Though you may not realize it, many of your decisions are based on conditional probabilities. For example, a taxi driver thinks to himself, "If I take the interstate, it's likely that I'll get stuck in traffic, but if I take the back streets, it's much less likely that I'll get stuck in traffic. Therefore, I'll take the back streets." Describe a recent decision you've made that was based on conditional probability.

Independent Events
The Caribou, the Bear, and the Tyrannosaurus
Lesson 42-1 The Multiplication Rule

Learning Targets:
- Understand when two events are independent.
- Use the Multiplication Rule to determine if two events are independent.
- Understand independent and dependent events in real-world situations.

> SUGGESTED LEARNING STRATEGIES: Activating Prior Knowledge, Interactive Word Wall, Close Reading, Think Aloud, Shared Reading, Create Representations, Visualization, Think-Pair-Share, Debriefing

As you share your ideas, be sure to use mathematical terms and academic vocabulary precisely. Make notes to help you remember the meaning of new words and how they are used to describe mathematical ideas.

1. Suppose we have a set of 40 cards consisting of 10 blue cards (labeled 1 through 10), 10 green cards (labeled 1 through 10), 10 red cards (labeled 1 through 10), and 10 yellow cards (labeled 1 through 10). To summarize, this is what we have:

Blue:	1	2	3	4	5	6	7	8	9	10
Green:	1	2	3	4	5	6	7	8	9	10
Red:	1	2	3	4	5	6	7	8	9	10
Yellow:	1	2	3	4	5	6	7	8	9	10

   A card will be selected at random; if it's an 8, a 9, or a 10, you will win a prize.

   a. What is the probability that you will win a prize?

   b. Construct viable arguments. Suppose someone selects the card for you and tells you that the card is blue, but doesn't tell you what number is on the card. Does this change the probability that you will win a prize? Show the calculation that leads you to your answer.

   c. Using probability notation, the probability you found in Part a is written as $P(\text{prize})$. How would you use probability notation to write the probability in Part b?

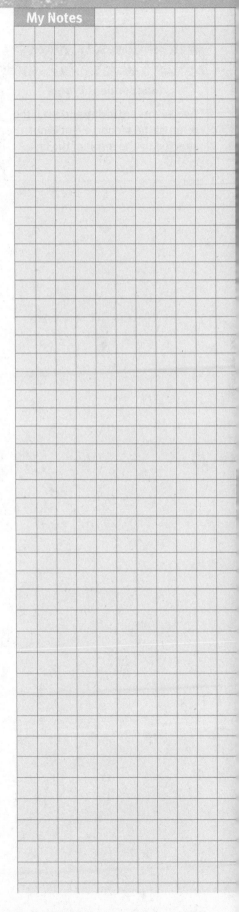

MATH TERMS

Independent Events

Two events are **independent** if the result of the second event is not affected by the result of the first event.

The fact that $P(\text{prize} \mid \text{blue})$ and $P(\text{prize})$ are equal tells us that the events "winning a prize" and "picking a blue card" are ***independent***. Knowing that the card is blue does not change the probability that you win a prize. If two events are independent, the following is true.

> Two events A and B are **independent** if
> $P(A \mid B) = P(A)$ and $P(B \mid A) = P(B)$.

We use this relationship to determine if two events are independent.

2. Suppose that you roll a cube with faces numbered 1 through 6.
   Let E be the event that the cube shows an even number.
   Let F be the event that the cube shows a number greater than 2.
   Let G be the event that the cube shows a number greater than 3.
   a. Find $P(E)$.

   b. Find $P(E \mid F)$. Are E and F independent events?

   c. Find $P(E \mid G)$. Are E and G independent events?

Sometimes you are only given the probabilities and you would like to determine if the events are independent or not. Based on the situation, you might think that the events are dependent. You need to do an analysis of the data to be sure.

3. Let the event that it is sunny tomorrow be S and let the event that Emily will go jogging be J. The probabilities are shown.

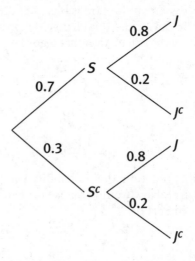

My Notes

a. Find $P(J)$. Show your work.

b. Find $P(J \mid S)$ and $P(J \mid S^C)$. Are J and S independent events? Are J and S^C independent events?

c. Reason abstractly. What conclusion can you draw regarding the probability of Emily jogging? Explain.

Now let's look at the probabilities of another jogger.

4. Let the event that it is sunny tomorrow be S and let the event that Chaya will go jogging be J. Suppose that the probabilities associated with these events are as shown in this tree diagram.

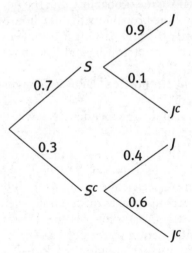

a. Find $P(J)$.

b. Find $P(J \mid S)$. Are J and S independent events?

c. Reason quantitatively. Is Chaya more or less likely than Emily to jog tomorrow? Explain.

CONNECT TO BIOLOGY

Biologists use this technique to interpret the results of clinical trials. They can determine if certain events affect the trial.

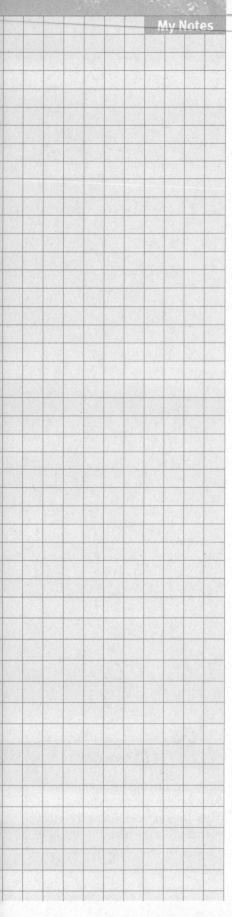

Check Your Understanding

5. A question in the previous activity told us about the Coco Trust's cranes. The cranes are categorized as shown in the table below.

	Male	Female	Total
Gray-crowned	16	13	29
White-naped	17	14	31
Stanley	11	19	30
Total	44	56	90

Suppose that a crane is selected at random. Find P(male) and P(male | Stanley). Are the events "is male" and "is a Stanley crane" in this population independent? Explain briefly.

6. In an earlier exercise, you were told that when a house is selected at random from Hector Street, the probability that the house has gas-fired central heating is 0.25, the probability that the house has off-street parking is 0.76, and the probability that the house has both gas-fired central heating and off-street parking is 0.19. Let G be the event that a house has gas-fired central heating and F be the event that it has off-street parking.
   a. **Model with mathematics.** Draw a Venn diagram to represent this information.
   b. Are the events G and F independent? Show the calculations that lead you to your conclusion.

7. In the country of Millipotamia, 68% of the population do strenuous exercise, 50% walk for pleasure, and 21% do neither of these two things.
   a. When a person is selected at random from Millipotamia, let E be the event that the person engages in strenuous exercise and W be the event that the person walks for pleasure. Draw a Venn diagram to illustrate the information you've been given.
   b. Find the probability that a randomly selected person from Millipotamia engages in strenuous exercise and walks for pleasure. (*Hint:* The Addition Rule could be used to answer this question.)
   c. Are the events E and W independent? Explain.

Lesson 42-1
The Multiplication Rule

In the first part of this lesson, we showed that for two independent events,

$$P(A \mid B) = P(A).$$

In a previous activity we showed that for any two events A and B,

$$P(A \mid B) = \frac{P(A \cap B)}{P(B)}.$$

Substitute $P(A)$ for $P(A \mid B)$ and rewrite the equation:

$$\frac{P(A \cap B)}{P(B)} = P(A)$$

Next, multiply both sides of the equation by $P(B)$. We see that this is equivalent to saying that

$$P(A \cap B) = P(A) \cdot P(B).$$

Now we know the following:

The events A and B are independent if and only if $P(A \cap B) = P(A) \cdot P(B)$.

So for independent events, in order to find the probability that both events will happen, you multiply the probabilities of the events. That is,

if A and B are independent events, then $P(A$ and $B) = P(A) \cdot P(B)$.

Note that the rule tells us two things:
First, if A and B are independent events, then $P(A \cap B) = P(A) \cdot P(B)$.
Second, if $P(A \cap B) = P(A) \cdot P(B)$, then A and B are independent events.

8. Recall the information about the houses on Hector Street, $P(G) = 0.25$, $P(F) = 0.76$, and $P(G \cap F) = 0.19$, and use the formula above to show that G and F are independent events.

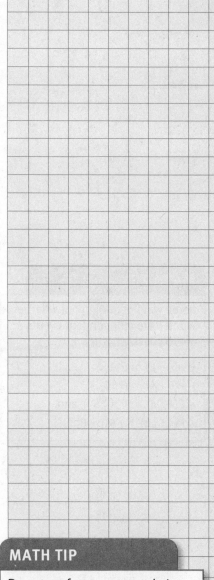

MATH TIP

Do not confuse two events being *independent* with their being *mutually exclusive*.

If two events are independent, then

$$P(A \cap B) = P(A) \cdot P(B).$$

If two events are mutually exclusive, then

$$P(A \cap B) = 0.$$

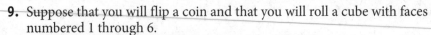

My Notes

9. Suppose that you will flip a coin and that you will roll a cube with faces numbered 1 through 6.
   a. **Make sense of problems.** Explain briefly in words how you know that the events "the coin lands heads up" and "the cube shows a 6" are independent.

   b. What is the probability that the coin will land heads up <u>and</u> the coin will show a six? Show your work.

10. When a student is selected at random from Annabel High School, let G be the event that the student's average grade is over 90 and let S be the event that the student lives in the southern part of town. You are given that $P(G) = 0.29$, $P(S) = 0.42$, and that G and S are independent events.
    a. When a student is selected at random from Annabel High School, what is the probability that the student has an average grade over 90 and lives in the southern part of town?

    b. When a student is selected at random from Annabel High School, what is the probability that the student has an average grade over 90 <u>or</u> lives in the southern part of town? (Note: The Addition Rule can be used to answer this question.)

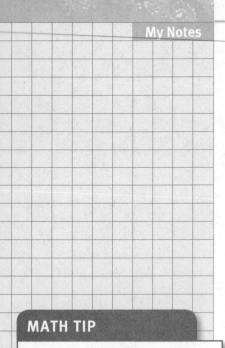

MATH TIP

Some ways of finding out whether A and B are independent events are to check whether

- $A(A \mid B) = P(A)$,
- $P(B \mid A) = P(B)$,
- $P(A \mid B) = P(A \mid B^C)$, and
- $P(A \cap B) = P(A) \cdot P(B)$.

Check Your Understanding

11. Suppose that you roll a cube with faces numbered 1 through 6. Let A be the event that the result for the cube is a 5, and let B be the event that the result is a 3.
    a. Explain in words how you know that A and B are independent events.
    b. What is the probability that event A is a 5 and event B is a 3?

12. Construct viable arguments. Suppose that the events *A* and *B* have probabilities as shown in the Venn diagram below. Are *A* and *B* independent events? Explain.

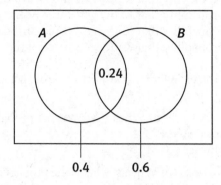

LESSON 42-1 PRACTICE

13. Kathy is still eating Crisp breakfast cereal, where each box contains a plastic monkey, elephant, caribou, or bear, and where these four animals appear with equal probability. Brian is eating Wheats breakfast cereal. Each box of Wheats contains one of five different plastic dinosaurs: Tyrannosaurus, Stegosaurus, Argentinosaurus, Giganotosaurus, and Iguanodon, and these five dinosaurs appear with equal probability. Each of the kids has one new box of cereal.

   a. Let *C* be the event that Kathy gets a caribou and let *T* be the event that Brian gets a Tyrannosaurus. Explain in words how you know that *C* and *T* are independent events.

   b. What is the probability that Kathy gets a caribou and Brian gets a Tyrannosaurus?

   c. What is the probability that Kathy gets a bear and Brian gets a Giganotosaurus?

   d. Remember that when two events are mutually exclusive you can find the probability that one event happens or the other event happens by adding the probabilities of the two events. What is the probability that Kathy gets a caribou and Brian gets a Tyrannosaurus <u>or</u> Kathy gets a bear and Brian gets a Giganotosaurus?

14. Reason quantitatively. Kathy has two new boxes of Crisp.

   a. What is the probability that both boxes contain caribous?

   b. What is the probability that the first box she opens contains a caribou and the second box she opens contains a bear?

   c. To get a caribou and a bear, Kathy can either get a caribou in the first box and a bear in the second box <u>or</u> she can get a bear in the first box and a caribou in the second box. What is the probability that Kathy gets a caribou and a bear?

15. Suppose that Kathy still doesn't have a caribou, and she really wants one. So her mother buys three boxes of Crisp, and Kathy opens the boxes one by one.
    a. What is the probability that Kathy gets three caribous?
    b. What is the probability that Kathy gets three bears?
    c. What is the probability that Kathy gets three caribous or three bears?
    d. What is the probability that Kathy gets three of the same type of animal?
    e. What will be the probability that Kathy doesn't get any caribous in the three boxes?

16. If Brian opens three boxes of Wheats, what is the probability that he gets:
    a. three Tyrannosauruses?
    b. no Tyrannosaurus?

17. If Brian opens two boxes of Wheats, what is the probability that he gets exactly one Tyrannosaurus? (*Hint:* The answer to this item is <u>not</u> 0.16.)

18. **Reason abstractly.** A survey found that 65 percent of Americans get enough exercise to meet a certain physical activity guideline. Suppose that two Americans will be selected at random. According to this guideline, find the probability that:
    a. they both get enough exercise.
    b. neither of them gets enough exercise.
    c. exactly one of them gets enough exercise.

19. Suppose that you have a red cube with faces numbered 1 through 6 and a blue cube with faces numbered 1 through 6. You roll both of the cubes. Find the probability that your total score is:
    a. 12.
    b. 11.
    c. 10.

Learning Targets:

- Discover ways probability is used in real-life situations.
- Determine the probability of an event involving area.
- Use a linear model to determine probability involving elapsed time.

SUGGESTED LEARNING STRATEGIES: Activating Prior Knowledge, Levels of Questions, Visualization, Discussion Groups, Debriefing

Wildlife biologists study animal populations to determine the possible effects of industrialization. Since it is impractical to attempt to count every animal in a population, samples are taken. The results are extrapolated to the entire population.

1. Ms. Takeuchi observed 23 wood ducks within a rectangular area along a river that was about 52 ft by 26 ft. The Coco Wildlife Trust wanted to determine if a protected area along a river in the preserve that was 60 ft by 40 ft could support the 36 wood ducks they had purchased. What is the probability that the protected area is sufficient for the 36 ducks? What might affect the survival of these ducks?

   a. How many wood ducks were observed in one square foot in the small area? First find the area of the sample space. Then find the number of ducks per square foot.

   b. How many wood ducks might be expected to be in the larger area?

   c. Find the probability that the protected area can support 36 ducks.

   d. What might account for a decline in the wood duck population?

CONNECT TO BIOLOGY

Wood ducks live in trees or bushes that grow along the shores of lakes, rivers, and streams. They need to be near water. When trees and bushes are cleared along the water, conservationists replace them with nesting boxes. For more information about wood ducks, go to *www.allaboutbirds.org/guide/ wood_duck/lifehistory*.

My Notes

2. Zelly plans to play the dart game at the county fair. The target is mounted on a dartboard that is 15 in. by 15 in. The small circle has a radius of 2 in. The large circle has the same center as the small circle and a radius of 6 in. If a dart lands in the shaded region, Zelly will win a grand prize. If a dart lands in the outer circular region, Zelly will win a smaller prize. Assume that it is equally likely that Zelly's dart will land on any point on the board.

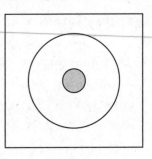

a. What is the probability Zelly will win the grand prize?

b. What is the probability Zelly will win the smaller prize?

The previous example is an example of an area model for probability. Now let's look at a linear model.

3. **Model with mathematics.** Mr. Torres catches a bus each morning for work. The bus runs every 20 minutes. If he arrives at his bus stop at a random time, what is the probability that he will have to wait 5 minutes or more? Assume the bus stops for an insignificant amount of time. This number line represents elapsed time. Point B is when the next bus will arrive.

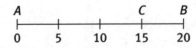

a. If Mr. Torres arrives at the bus stop between points C and B, how long will he have to wait for the next bus?

b. What happens if Mr. Torres arrives at any time between points A and C?

c. **Attend to precision.** What is the probability that Mr. Torres will have to wait 5 minutes or more? Show your work.

Check Your Understanding

4. Statistical information or data is used to calculate probabilities. The probabilities in turn help us to plan for future events such as earthquakes. How might knowing the probability that an earthquake may occur at a particular site be helpful?

5. Maggie wants to play darts at the school fair. The target is on a square dartboard that is 18 in. on a side. Maggie will score points if her dart lands in any of the concentric circles. She will score 25 points if her dart lands in the bull's-eye in the center. She will receive 15 points if her dart lands in the gray region, 10 points if her dart lands in the outer ring of the circles, and 0 points if her dart lands outside the circles on the dartboard. Write each probability as a decimal to the nearest ten thousandth and as a percent.

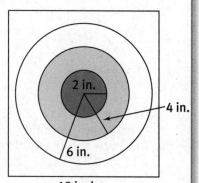

18 inches

a. What is the probability that her dart will hit a bull's-eye three times in a row?
b. What is the probability she will score 30 points in three attempts? Explain your work.

6. Mrs. Ciaccio takes a bus every Sunday to visit her mother in the next town. The bus leaves every 15 minutes. If she arrives at the bus stop at a random time, what is the probability that she will have to wait 10 minutes or more?

CONNECT TO GEOLOGY

The California Department of Conservation maintains a website on earthquake probabilities.

LESSON 42-2 PRACTICE

7. The members of the Math Club are designing dartboards. They experimented with different shapes. For which dartboard is the probability of hitting the bull's-eye the least? Note that the dartboards are not drawn to scale.

A.

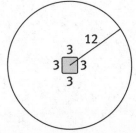

12
1.5
12

B.

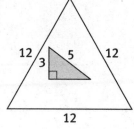

12   5   12
3
12

C.

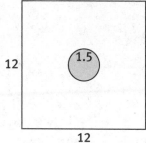

12
3
3   3
3

D.

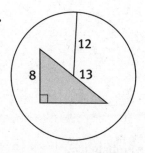

12
8   13

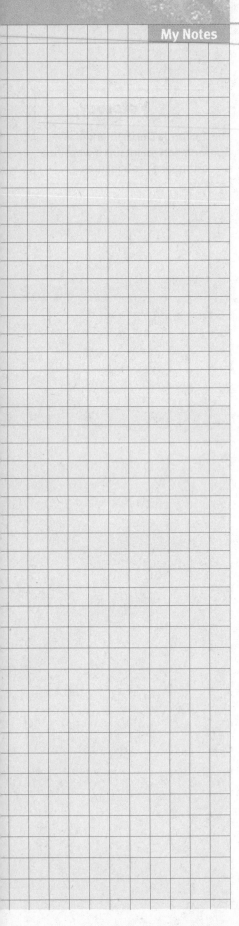

8. **Attend to precision.** Students will not play a dartboard game if it is too difficult to win a prize. Design a dartboard with the probability that a student will hit the bull's-eye about 15% of the time.

9. Darts are thrown at random at each dartboard. Find the probability that the dart will land in the shaded region. Write your answer as a percent.

a. 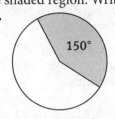 b. 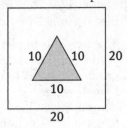 c.

10. Liam made a 3 × 3 target on a 10 × 10 dartboard.
    a. What is the probability that a dart will hit Liam's target?
    b. **Critique the reasoning of others.** Olivia made a 6 × 6 target on a 10 × 10 dartboard. She said that the probability of a dart landing in her target area would be twice as great as the probability that a dart will land in Liam's target area. Do you agree? Explain.

11. Amelia plants an 8 ft by 6 ft garden. She plants roses in a 2 ft by 3 ft section of the garden. If a robin randomly lands in the garden, what is the probability that the robin will land among the rosebushes? What is the probability that 2 robins will land among the rosebushes?

12. **Look for and make use of structure.** How would you find the probability of landing in the shaded region without knowing the length of the radii of the circles or the dimensions of the square? Show your work.

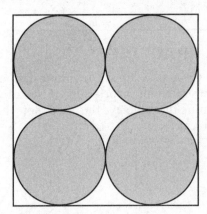

Learning Target:

● Use permutations and combinations to compute probabilities of compound events and solve problems.

SUGGESTED LEARNING STRATEGIES: Activating Prior Knowledge, Interactive Word Wall, Close Reading, Think Aloud, Marking the Text, Think-Pair-Share, Debriefing

Probability is based on counting. You have been introduced to various counting techniques such as listing, the Addition Rule, and the Multiplication Rule, as well as various ways of illustrating the counts such as two-way frequency tables, Venn diagrams, and tree diagrams. What you choose to use to find the probability of events depends on the problem and the information you are given.

For the techniques you will learn in this section, you need the *Fundamental Counting Principle.*

1. Suppose you have 2 pairs of jeans, 4 T-shirts, and 3 jackets. How many outfits do you have? You can multiply to find the total number of possible outfits.

What happens when the second event is influenced by the first event?

2. Suppose 5 children line up for a family portrait. It doesn't matter where each child stands. In how many different ways can the children pose for the portrait?

   a. How many choices are there for the first place in the photo?

   b. A child has been chosen for the first place. Now how many choices are there for the second place in the photo? Explain.

   c. Continue the pattern for the third, fourth, and fifth places. Use the Fundamental Counting Principle to determine the total possible ways the children can pose for a portrait.

> **MATH TERMS**
>
> The **Fundamental Counting Principle** states that if one event can occur in *m* different ways and a second event can occur in *n* different ways, then together the events can occur in *m* · *n* different ways, assuming that the second event is not influenced by the first event.

My Notes

MATH TERMS

The product $n(n-1)(n-2)$ $\ldots \cdot 3 \cdot 2 \cdot 1$ is called **n factorial** and is written **n!**.

A **permutation**, P, of a set of objects is any arrangement of the objects in a definite order. The number of arrangements is written

$$_nP_n = n!.$$

We now introduce a special mathematical notation called **n factorial**. This notation is shorthand for writing products such as the one in Item 2. We can write this product as 5!.

$$5! = 5 \cdot 4 \cdot 3 \cdot 2 \cdot 1 = 120$$

This notation is very helpful when you have to count all the possible outcomes for multiple events.

The problem in Item 2 is a **permutation**. The number of arrangements of the 5 children for the photo is 120 distinct arrangements. This is a simple permutation and can be written as $_5P_5$ or 5! Notice that there was no repetition in this event. The same child cannot stand in the first place and the second place at the same time.

3. Suppose the photographer wanted 3 of the children to sit on a bench in the photo. In how many different ways can 3 of the 5 children be seated on the bench? Begin with 5 children, but remember, you only want 3 to sit on the bench.

MATH TIP

The number of **permutations** of *n distinct* objects taken *r* at a time is given by the formula:

$$_nP_r = \frac{n!}{(n-r)!}$$

This is the number of permutations of 5 taken 3 at a time. We write and calculate

$$_5P_3 = 5 \cdot 4 \cdot 3 = 60 \text{ permutations.}$$

We can also write this using factorial notation in the following way:

$$_5P_3 = \frac{5 \cdot 4 \cdot 3 \cdot 2 \cdot 1}{2 \cdot 1} = \frac{5!}{(5-3)!}$$

When the objects to be arranged are not all distinct, the formula has to be adjusted.

4. Look at the word *bowwow*. The letters *o* and *w* are repeated. Thus, the letters in the word are not all distinct.
   a. How many permutations of the letters would there be if the letters were distinct?

MATH TIP

The number of *distinguishable* **permutations** P of *n* elements taken *n* at a time, with r_1 *like elements* of one kind, r_2 *like elements* of another kind, and so on, is given by the formula

$$P = \frac{n!}{r_1! r_2! r_3! \ldots}$$

Because some of the letters repeat, we would expect there to be fewer permutations. We adjust the formula:

$$P = \frac{6!}{2! 3!}$$

b. How many permutations of the letters are there in the word *bowwow*?

Each of the above examples is a problem that involves an event that occurs without replacement. How do we adjust the formula for permutations when there is replacement?

5. Al is creating a 3-digit secret code using the 4 digits 1, 3, 5, and 7. He decides that any of the digits can be repeated or replaced. So, 555 can be a code. Since the code 357 is different from the code 375, order matters. How many codes are possible? Explain.

> **MATH TIP**
>
> When n is the number of things to choose from and you choose r of them where *replacement* is allowed and order matters, the number of **permutations** is given by the formula
>
> $$n^r.$$

To solve a counting problem, you need to decide if order matters. If order matters, it's a permutation. Next you need to decide if the events involve replacement or not. Once you have made these two decisions, use the formula that is appropriate.

> **Check Your Understanding**
>
> **6. Use appropriate tools strategically.** Find the number of permutations for each of the following. Write the formula you used.
> **a.** How many different ways can 8 children be seated in a row of chairs?
> **b.** How many different ways can 8 children be seated in a row of 5 chairs?
> **c.** How many different ways can you arrange the letters in the word *Mississippi*?
> **d.** How many 4-digit secret codes can Brian create using the 5 digits 3, 4, 5, 6, and 7?
>
> **7. Make sense of problems.** Find the number of permutations of the letters in the words *dear* and *deer*. Use a permutation formula. Then make an organized list to verify your answers. Why are the permutations different for these 4-letter words?

My Notes

Let us look at a problem where order doesn't matter. How could we count the number of possible arrangements?

8. **Reason abstractly.** Suppose you have the four letters a, b, c, and d. You are asked to pick two letters. What is the number of possible arrangements:
   a. if order matters? That is, ab is different from ba. Explain.

   b. if order does *not* matter? That is, ab is the same as ba. You would expect there to be fewer arrangements. List all of the possible arrangements. Next, cross out the arrangements that are the same. Then count the number of arrangements that are left.

Arrangements where order doesn't matter are called **combinations**. Notice that part of the formula for combinations is the permutation formula $_nP_r$. Combinations are simpler than permutations. There are fewer of them.

MATH TERMS

A **combination** is a way of selecting several objects from a larger group, where order does not matter. The formula for combinations is

$$_nC_r = \frac{n!}{r!(n-r)!}$$

Check Your Understanding

9. What do you have to decide before you can solve a counting problem with multiple possibilities?

10. What is the difference between a permutation and a combination?

11. Write a problem involving permutations. Then rewrite the problem so that it is a problem involving combinations.

12. In a contest, 5 winners will get equal prizes. If 15 people enter the contest, how many different arrangements of 5 people can be chosen as winners? Why is this a combination?

13. How many different 4-digit numbers can be formed from the digits 1 through 9 inclusive? Is this a combination or permutation? Explain. Write the formula you can use to find the answer.

Now let's look at combinations with repetition.

14. There are 4 different kinds of donuts on the menu of Caroline's Café: chocolate, jelly, frosted, and plain. Jon wants to buy 3 donuts. How many ways can Jon choose his 3 donuts?

a. Does order matter? Give an example.

b. Is there repetition? Explain.

c. List the possible combinations Jon could have.

Listing a combination of 4 objects taken 3 at a time with repetition is doable. What if you list the number of combinations of 10 objects taken 4 at a time with repetition? A formula would be handy.

d. Use the formula to find out how many possible combinations there are if Jon chooses 3 donuts from a selection of 4 donuts.

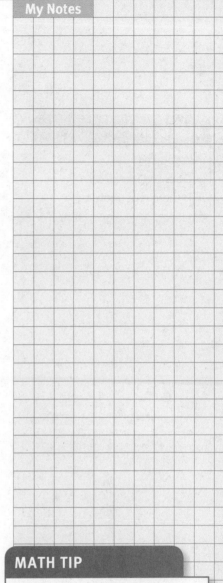

MATH TIP

The number of **combinations** of n objects taken r at a time *with repetition* is given by the formula

$$_nC_r = \frac{(n + r - 1)!}{r!(n - 1)!}.$$

e. Use the formula to find out how many possible combinations there are of 10 objects taken 4 at a time with repetition.

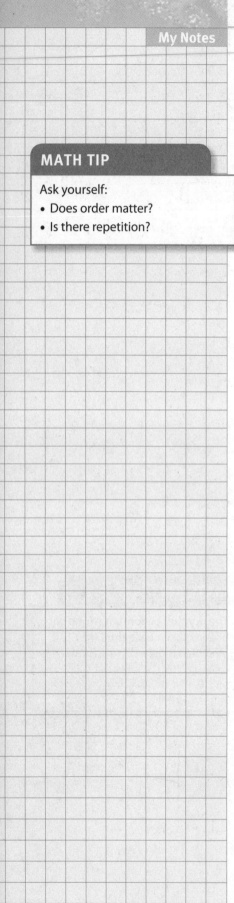

MATH TIP

Ask yourself:
- Does order matter?
- Is there repetition?

LESSON 42-3 PRACTICE

15. Identify the counting formula you can use to solve each problem. Then solve the problem.
    a. There are 10 questions on a multiple-choice test. Each question has 4 possible answers. How many ways can the test be completed?
    b. How many 3-letter code words can be made from the letters l, m, n, o, and p if repetition of a letter is allowed?
    c. How many lines can connect 6 points, no 3 of which are collinear? (*Hint:* Two points determine a line.) What is *n*? What is *r*?
    d. In how many different ways can the names of 11 players on a football team be listed in a column on the roster?
    e. How many different arrangements are there of the letters in the word *bedazzled*?

16. In a school library, there are 200 books. Neil wants to borrow 5 books. In how many ways can he make his choices?

17. How many different committees of 5 can be chosen from 12 people?

18. **Make use of structure.** A school club consists of 9 boys and 10 girls. How many committees of 3 boys and 2 girls can be formed? Show your work.

19. A box contains 5 red balls and 8 white balls. In how many ways can we choose 6 balls, 3 of which are white?

20. How many four-letter code words can be created from the letters l, m, n, o, and p? Letters can be repeated in a code word. Why is this a permutation?

21. How many ways can a president, vice president, treasurer, and secretary be picked from 15 students?

22. How many different 7-digit license plates can be made if the first digit must not be a 0 and no digits may be repeated?

23. How many different license plates can be made if there are 4 digits and 3 letters? No digit or letter is repeated, and the number 0 and the letter O are not used.

ACTIVITY 42 PRACTICE
Write your answers on notebook paper.
Show your work.

Lesson 42-1

1. When a student is selected at random from Annabel High School, the probability that the student plays soccer is 0.18, the probability that the student plays basketball is 0.32, and the probability that the student plays at least one of these sports is 0.42.
   a. Find the probability that a student selected at random from Annabel High School plays soccer, plays basketball, or plays soccer and basketball.
   b. Determine whether S and B are independent events. Explain.

2. The zoo's penguins are categorized as shown in this table.

	Known to Be Male	Known to Be Female	Unknown Gender	Total
Northern Rockhopper Penguin	15	12	5	
Magellanic Penguin	18	15	7	
Total				

   a. Copy the table above, and complete it by entering the totals.
   b. Suppose that a penguin will be selected at random.
      i. Find the probability that the selected penguin is known to be female.
      ii. Find the probability that the selected penguin is known to be female given that it is a northern rockhopper penguin.
      iii. Are the events "is known to be female" and "is a northern rockhopper penguin" independent? Explain using your answers to Parts b(i) and b(ii).

3. Dinah, one of the ducks at the zoo, is sick. The probability that Dinah will recover by next Thursday is 0.8. If Dinah recovers by next Thursday, the probability that Mr. Lee will go to the National Zoological Conference is 0.9. If Dinah doesn't recover by next Thursday, the probability that Mr. Lee will go to the conference is 0.4. In the tree diagram below, R denotes the event that Dinah recovers and Z denotes the event that Mr. Lee will go to the zoological conference.
   a. Write the appropriate probabilities next to the six branches.

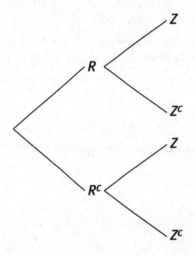

   b. Find the probability that Dinah recovers but Mr. Lee doesn't go to the conference.
   c. Find the probability that Mr. Lee goes to the conference.
   d. Are Z and R independent events? Explain.

Lesson 42-2

4. The shaded region is a square with side length of $5\sqrt{2}$ on a circular dartboard. Estimate the probability that a dart will hit the shaded region. Show your work.

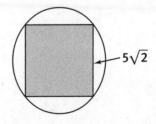

Lesson 42-3

5. How many permutations of the letters are there in the word *statistics*?

6. How many ways can 10 different books be arranged on a shelf that can hold 6 books?

7. There are 5 different-colored marbles in a bag. Sarah will pick out 3 marbles without looking. How many different combinations can she pick?

8. In how many ways can 7 children be seated in a row in the school auditorium?

9. In how many ways can a 4-digit code be created using the six digits 2, 3, 4, 6, 7, and 9 if repetition of a number is allowed?

10. In how many different ways can the letters a, b, c, d, e, and f be arranged in groups of 3?

MATHEMATICAL PRACTICES
Look For and Make Use of Structure

11. Choose an area you're interested in. It could be a sport, listening to or playing music, some other area of the arts, or any other interest.

   a. In your chosen context, describe two events that are mutually exclusive, and explain why they are mutually exclusive.

   b. In your chosen context, describe two events that you believe to be independent, and explain why you think this is the case.

Conditional Probability and Independent Events

DIANE'S e-BOOKS

1. Diane has a collection of 91 novels. They are categorized as shown in the table below.

	Hardcover	Paperback	Total
Detective Novels	12	20	32
Romance Novels	8	28	36
Other Novels	9	14	23
Total	29	62	91

   a. If Diane selects one of her novels at random, what is the probability that it is:

      i. a romance novel?

     ii. a romance novel given that it is a paperback?

   b. Use your answers to Parts a(i) and a(ii) to decide whether the two events are independent. Explain your reasoning.

2. Diane is looking at her collection of e-Books. She has worked out that 60% of her e-Books were downloaded from Company A, 68% are works of fiction, and 36% are works of fiction that were downloaded from Company A. When Diane selects one of her e-Books at random, let the event that it was downloaded from Company A be *A* and the event that it is a work of fiction be *F*.

   a. Draw a Venn diagram to represent the information you have been given. (As always, be sure to write the probabilities in your diagram and in your work as decimals, not percentages.)

   b. Complete your Venn diagram by writing on it any additional relevant probabilities.

   c. When Diane selects one of her e-Books at random, what is the probability that it is neither a work of fiction nor was downloaded from Company A?

   d. If Diane randomly selects a work of fiction, what is the probability that it was downloaded from Company A?

   e. If Diane randomly selects a book that was downloaded from Company A, what is the probability that it is not a work of fiction?

   f. What are the values of $P(A)$, $P(F)$, and $P(A \cap F)$?

   g. Use your answers to Part e to decide whether the events *A* and *F* are independent. Be sure to show any calculation that leads to your answer.

3. Books are classified as fiction or nonfiction, and Company A offers its books as either e-Books or printed books. When Diane goes to Company A's website, the probability that she will choose a work of fiction is 0.6. If she chooses a work of fiction, the probability that she will buy it as an e-Book is 0.8. If she chooses a book that is nonfiction, then the probability that she will buy it as an e-Book is 0.3.

a. Write the relevant probabilities next to the six branches on the tree diagram.

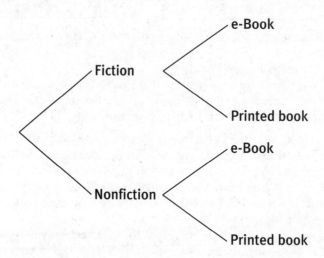

b. When Diane goes to Company A's website, what is the probability that she will buy a work of fiction as a printed book?

c. When Diane goes to Company A's website, what is the probability that she will buy an e-Book?

4. Company B has a very large number of books on its website, and 42% of the books are available as e-Books. Diane will select two books at random from Company B's website.

   a. Consider the event that the first book Diane selects is available as an e-Book and the event that the second book Diane selects is available as an e-Book. Explain in words how you know that these two events are independent.

   b. Find each probability. Write your answer as a percent to the nearest tenth of a percent.

      i. Both books are available as e-Books.

      ii. Neither book is available as an e-Book.

      iii. Exactly one of the two books is available as an e-Book.

5. Diane belongs to a book club. The club has just read their 10th novel and are planning a party to celebrate. Diane decides to make a copy of the front cover of one of the detective novels to use as a dartboard. The trim size of the cover is $5\frac{1}{2}$ by $8\frac{1}{2}$. On the cover is a moon with a $2\frac{1}{2}$ in. diameter. Estimate the probability that a club member will hit the moon on the dartboard.

6. Twenty of the hardcover books in Diane's collection are either detective novels or romance novels. Twelve are detective novels. How many permutations are possible for these two categories of hardcover books? Explain.

7. From her collection, Diane will choose, without looking, three hardcover detective novels to read during a school break. How many combinations of the three books are possible? Explain.

Scoring Guide	Exemplary	Proficient	Emerging	Incomplete
	The solution demonstrates these characteristics:			
Mathematics Knowledge and Thinking (Items 1, 2, 3, 4, 5, 6, 7)	• Clear and accurate understanding of determining probabilities using a table of values, a Venn diagram, a tree diagram, or area of plane figures • Clear and accurate understanding of independent events • Clear and accurate understanding of permutations and combinations	• A functional understanding of determining probabilities using a table of values, a Venn diagram, a tree diagram, or area of plane figures • A functional understanding of independent events • A functional understanding of permutations and combinations	• Partial understanding of determining probabilities using a table of values, a Venn diagram, a tree diagram, or area of plane figures • Partial understanding of independent events • Partial understanding of permutations and combinations	• Little or no understanding of determining probabilities using a table of values, a Venn diagram, a tree diagram, or area of plane figures • Little or no understanding of independent events • Little or no understanding of permutations and combinations
Problem Solving (Items 1a, 2b-f, 3bc, 4b, 5, 6, 7)	• An appropriate and efficient strategy that results in correct answers	• A strategy that results in mostly correct answers	• A strategy that results in some correct answers	• No clear strategy when solving problems
Mathematical Modeling / Representations (Items 2a, 3a)	• Clear and accurate understanding of using probabilities to create a Venn diagram • Clear and accurate understanding of using probabilities to complete a tree diagram	• Mostly accurate understanding of using probabilities to create a Venn diagram • Mostly accurate understanding of using probabilities to complete a tree diagram	• Partial understanding of using probabilities to create a Venn diagram • Partial understanding of using probabilities to complete a tree diagram	• Little or no understanding of using probabilities to create a Venn diagram • Little or no understanding of using probabilities to complete a tree diagram
Reasoning and Communication (Items 1b, 2g, 4a, 6, 7)	• Precise use of appropriate mathematics and language to explain why or why not the events are independent • Precise use of appropriate mathematics and language to explain the number of permutations or combinations possible for a given event	• Mostly correct use of appropriate mathematics and language to explain why or why not the events are independent • Mostly correct use of appropriate mathematics and language to explain the number of permutations or combinations possible for a given event	• Misleading or confusing use of appropriate mathematics and language to explain why or why not the events are independent • Misleading or confusing use of appropriate mathematics and language to explain the number of permutations or combinations possible for a given event	• Incomplete or inaccurate use of appropriate mathematics and language to explain why or why not the events are independent • Incomplete or inaccurate use of appropriate mathematics and language to explain the number of permutations or combinations possible for a given event

Symbols

$<$	is less than
$>$	is greater than
$\leq$	is less than or equal to
$\geq$	is greater than or equal to
$=$	is equal to
$\neq$	is not equal to
$\approx$	is approximately equal to
$\sim$	similar
$|a|$	absolute value: $|3| = 3$; $|-3| = 3$
$\perp$	perpendicular
$\parallel$	parallel
(x, y)	ordered pair
$\overset{\frown}{AB}$	arc AB
$\overleftrightarrow{AB}$	line AB
$\overrightarrow{AB}$	ray AB
$\overline{AB}$	line segment AB
$\angle A$	angle A
$m\angle A$	measure of angle A
$\triangle ABC$	triangle ABC
π	pi; $\pi \approx 3.14$; $\pi = \dfrac{22}{7}$

Formulas

Perimeter	
P	= sum of the lengths of the sides
Rectangle	$P = 2l + 2w$
Square	$P = 4s$
Circumference	$C = 2\pi r$, $C = \pi d$

Area	
Circle	$A = \pi r^2$
Parallelogram	$A = bh$
Rectangle	$A = lw$
Square	$A = s^2$
Triangle	$A = \frac{1}{2}bh$
Trapezoid	$A = \frac{1}{2}h(b_1 + b_2)$
Regular Polygon	$A = \frac{1}{2}ap$, where a is the apothem and p is the perimeter

Surface Area	
Cube	$SA = 6e^2$
Rectangular Prism	$SA = 2lw + 2lh + 2wh$
Cylinder	$SA = 2\pi r^2 + 2\pi rh$
Cone	$SA = \pi r^2 + \pi rl$
Regular Pyramid	$SA = B + \frac{1}{2}pl$
Sphere	$SA = 4\pi r^2$

Volume

Cylinder	$V = Bh, B = \pi r^2$
Rectangular Prism	$V = lwh$
Triangular Prism	$V = Bh, B = \frac{1}{2}bh$
Pyramid	$V = \frac{1}{3}Bh$
Cone	$V = \frac{1}{3}\pi r^2 h$
Sphere	$V = \frac{4}{3}\pi r^3$

Quadratic Equations

Standard form	$ax^2 + bx + c = 0$
Quadratic Formula	$x = \dfrac{-b \pm \sqrt{b^2 - 4ac}}{2a}$

Linear Equations

Slope	$m = \dfrac{y_2 - y_1}{x_2 - x_1}$
Slope-intercept form	$y = mx + b$
Point-slope form	$y - y_1 = m(x - x_1)$
Standard form	$Ax + By = C$

Other Formulas

Pythagorean Theorem	$a^2 + b^2 = c^2$, where c is the hypotenuse of a right triangle
Distance	$d = \sqrt{(x_2 - x_1)^2 + (y_2 - y_1)^2}$
Midpoint	$m = \left(\dfrac{x_1 + x_2}{2}, \dfrac{y_1 + y_2}{2} \right)$
Direct variation	$y = kx$
Inverse variation	$y = \dfrac{k}{x}$

Trigonometry
For an acute angle A in a right triangle: $$\sin A = \frac{\text{opposite}}{\text{hypotenuse}}$$ $$\cos A = \frac{\text{adjacent}}{\text{hypotenuse}}$$ $$\tan A = \frac{\text{opposite}}{\text{adjacent}}$$

Temperature	
Celsius	$C = \frac{5}{9}(F - 32)$
Fahrenheit	$F = \frac{9}{5}C + 32$

Properties of Real Numbers

Reflexive Property of Equality	For all real numbers a, $a = a$.
Symmetric Property of Equality	For all real numbers a and b, if $a = b$, then $b = a$.
Transitive Property of Equality	For all real numbers a, b, and c, if $a = b$ and $b = c$, then $a = c$.
Substitution Property of Equality	For all real numbers a and b, if $a = b$, then a may be replaced by b.
Additive Identity	For all real numbers a, $a + 0 = 0 + a = a$.
Multiplicative Identity	For all real numbers a, $a \cdot 1 = 1 \cdot a = a$.
Commutative Property of Addition	For all real numbers a and b, $a + b = b + a$.
Commutative Property of Multiplication	For all real numbers a and b, $a \cdot b = b \cdot a$.
Associative Property of Addition	For all real numbers a, b, and c, $(a + b) + c = a + (b + c)$.
Associative Property of Multiplication	For all real numbers a, b, and c, $(a \cdot b) \cdot c = a \cdot (b \cdot c)$.
Distributive Property of Multiplication over Addition	For all real numbers a, b, and c, $a(b + c) = a \cdot b + a \cdot c$.
Additive Inverse	For all real numbers a, there is exactly one real number $-a$ such that $a + (-a) = 0$ and $(-a) + a = 0$.
Multiplicative Inverse	For all real numbers a and b where $a \neq 0$, $b \neq 0$, there is exactly one number $\frac{b}{a}$ such that $\frac{b}{a} \cdot \frac{a}{b} = 1$ and $\frac{a}{b} \cdot \frac{b}{a} = 1$.
Multiplication Property of Zero	For all real numbers a, $a \cdot 0 = 0$ and $0 \cdot a = 0$.
Addition Property of Equality	For all real numbers a, b, and c, if $a = b$, then $a + c = b + c$.
Subtraction Property of Equality	For all real numbers a, b, and c, if $a = b$, then $a - c = b - c$.
Multiplication Property of Equality	For all real numbers a, b, and c, if $a = b$, then $a \cdot c = b \cdot c$.
Division Property of Equality	For all real numbers a, b, and c, $c \neq 0$ if $a = b$, then $\frac{a}{c} = \frac{b}{c}$.
Zero Product Property of Equality	For all real numbers a and b, if $a \cdot b = 0$ then $a = 0$ or $b = 0$ or both a and b equal 0.
Addition Property of Inequality*	For all real numbers a, b, and c, if $a > b$, then $a + c > b + c$.
Subtraction Property of Inequality*	For all real numbers a, b, and c, if $a > b$, then $a - c > b - c$.
Multiplication Property of Inequality *	For all real numbers a, b, and c, $c > 0$, if $a > b$, then $a \cdot c > b \cdot c$. For all real numbers a, b, and c, $c < 0$, if $a > b$, then $a \cdot c < b \cdot c$.
Division Property of Inequality*	For all real numbers a, b, and c, $c > 0$ if $a > b$, then $\frac{a}{c} > \frac{b}{c}$. For all real numbers a, b, and c, $c < 0$ if $a > b$, then $\frac{a}{c} < \frac{b}{c}$.

*These properties are also true for $<$, $\leq$, $\geq$.

Properties of Exponents

For any numbers a and b and all integers m and n,

$$a^m \cdot a^n = a^{m+n}$$

$$(a^m)^n = a^{mn}$$

$$(ab)^m = a^m b^m$$

$$\frac{a^m}{a^n} = a^{m-n}, a \neq 0$$

$$\left(\frac{a}{b}\right)^m = \frac{a^m}{b^m}, b \neq 0$$

$$a^{-n} = \frac{1}{a^n}, a \neq 0 \text{ and } \frac{1}{a^{-n}} = a^n, a \neq 0$$

$$a^0 = 1, a \neq 0$$

Properties of Radicals

In the expression $\sqrt[n]{a}$,

a is the radic and, $\sqrt{}$ is the radical symbol, and n is the root index.

$\sqrt[n]{a} = b$, if $b^n = a$ b is the nth root of a.

$a\sqrt{b} \pm c\sqrt{b} = (a \pm c)\sqrt{b}$, where $b \geq 0$.

$(a\sqrt{b})(c\sqrt{b}) = ac\sqrt{bd}$, where $b \geq 0, d \geq 0$.

$\dfrac{a\sqrt{b}}{c\sqrt{d}} = \dfrac{a}{c}\sqrt{\dfrac{b}{d}}$, where $b \geq 0, c \neq 0, d > 0$.

Table of Measures

Customary	Metric
Distance/Length	
1 yard (yd) = 3 feet (ft) = 36 inches (in.) 1 foot (ft) = 12 inches (in.) 1 mile (mi) = 1760 yards (yd) 1 mile (mi) = 5280 feet (ft) 1 acre (ac) = 43,560 square feet (ft)	1 meter (m) = 100 centimeters (cm) 1 meter (m) = 1000 millimeters (mm) 1 meter (m) = 10 decimeters (dm) 1 centimeter (cm) = 10 millimeters (mm) 1 kilometer (km) = 1000 meters (m)
Volume	
1 cup (c) = 8 fluid ounces (fl oz) 1 pint (pt) = 2 cups (c) 1 quart (qt) = 4 cups (c) = 2 pints (pt) 1 gallon (gal) = 16 cups (c) = 4 quarts (qt)	1 liter (L) = 1000 milliliters (mL) 1 liter (L) = 1000 cubic centimeters (cm³) 1 liter (L) = 100 centiliters (cL) 1 liter (L) = 10 deciliters (dL) 1 kiloliter (kL) = 1000 liters (L)
Weight/Mass	
1 pound (lb) = 16 ounces (oz) 1 ton (T) = 2000 pound (lb)	1 gram (g) = 1000 milligrams (mg) 1 kilogram (kg) = 1000 grams (g) 1 tonne (t) = 1000 kilograms (kg)
Time	
1 minute (min) = 60 seconds (sec) 1 hour (hr) = 60 minutes (min) 1 day (d) = 24 hours (hr)	1 year (yr) = 365 days (d) 1 year (yr) = 52 weeks (wk) 1 year (yr) = 12 months (mo)

Postulates and Theorems

POSTULATES

Postulate	Through any two points there exists exactly one line.
Postulate	Through any three noncollinear points there exists exactly one plane.
Postulate	A plane contains at least three noncollinear points.
Postulate	If there is a line and a point not on the line, then there is exactly one line through the point parallel to the given line.
	If there is a line and a point not on the line, then there is exactly one line through the point perpendicular to the given line.
The Ruler Postulate	a. To every pair of points there corresponds a unique positive number called the distance between the points. b. The points on a line can be matched with the real numbers so that the distance between any two points is the absolute value of the difference of their associated numbers.
Segment Addition Postulate	If B is between A and C, then $AB + BC = AC$. If $AB + BC = AC$, then B is between A and C.
The Protractor Postulate	a. To each angle there corresponds a unique real number between 0 and 180 called the measure of the angle. b. The measure of an angle formed by a pair of rays is the absolute value of the difference of their associated numbers.
Angle Addition Postulate	If P is in the interior of $\angle RST$, then $m\angle RSP + m\angle PST = m\angle RST$.
Alternate Interior Angles Theorem	If two parallel lines are cut by a transversal, then the pairs of alternate interior angles are congruent.
Corresponding Angles Postulate	When parallel lines are cut by a transversal, the corresponding angles will always have the same measure.

Postulates and Theorems
THEOREMS

Theorem	Vertical angles are congruent.
Theorem	The sum of the measures of the angles of a triangle is 180°.
Theorem	If two lines are parallel to the same line, then they are parallel to each other.
Theorem	In a plane, two lines perpendicular to the same line are parallel.
The Pythagorean Theorem	The square of the length of the hypotenuse of a right triangle is equal to the sum of the squares of the lengths of the legs of the right triangle.
Exterior Angle Theorem	The measure of an exterior angle is equal to the sum of the measures of the two nonadjacent angles.
The Hinge Theorem	If two sides of one triangle are congruent to two sides of another triangle, and the included angle in the first triangle is larger than the included angle in the other triangle, then the third side of the first triangle is longer than the third side of the other triangle.
Triangle Inequality Theorem	The sum of the lengths of any two sides of a triangle is greater than the length of the third side.
Centroid Measure Theorem	The centroid of a triangle divides each median into two parts so that the distance from the vertex to the centroid is twice the distance from the centroid to the midpoint of the opposite side.
AAS Theorem	If two angles and a non-included side of one triangle are congruent to the corresponding two angles and non-included side of another triangle, then the triangles are congruent.
Isosceles Triangle Theorem	If two sides of a triangle are congruent, then the angles opposite them are congruent.
Triangle Midsegment Theorem	The midsegment of a triangle is parallel to the third side, and its length is one half the length of the third side.
Trapezoid Median Theorem	The median of a trapezoid is parallel to the bases and its length is the average of the lengths of the bases.
Theorem	If both pairs of opposite sides of a quadrilateral are congruent, then the quadrilateral is a parallelogram.
Theorem	If one pair of opposite sides of a quadrilateral are congruent and parallel, then the quadrilateral is a parallelogram.

Postulates and Theorems

THEOREMS *continued*

Theorem	If both pairs of opposite angles of a quadrilateral are congruent, then the quadrilateral is a parallelogram.
Theorem	If the diagonals of a quadrilateral bisect each other, then the quadrilateral is a parallelogram.
Theorem	If a parallelogram has one right angle, then it has four right angles, and it is a rectangle.
Theorem	If a quadrilateral is equiangular, then it is a rectangle.
Theorem	If the diagonals of a parallelogram are perpendicular, then the parallelogram is a rhombus.
Theorem	If a quadrilateral is equilateral, then it is a rhombus.
Theorem	If the diagonals of a parallelogram are congruent, then the parallelogram is a rectangle.
Theorem	If a diagonal bisects a pair of opposite angles in a parallelogram, then the parallelogram is a rhombus.
AA Similarity Postulate	If two angles of one triangle are congruent to two angles of another triangle, then the triangles are similar.
Side-Angle-Side (SAS) Similarity Theorem	If an angle of one triangle is congruent to an angle of another triangle and the sides including those angles are in proportion, then the triangles are similar.
Side-Side-Side (SSS) Similarity Theorem	If the corresponding sides of two triangles are in proportion, then the triangles are similar.
Triangle Proportionality Theorem	If a line parallel to a side of a triangle intersects the other two sides, then it divides them proportionally.
Parallel Proportionality Theorem	If two or more lines parallel to a side of a triangle intersect the other two sides, then they divide them proportionally.
Angle Bisector Proportionality Theorem	An angle bisector in a triangle divides the side of the triangle opposite the angle into two segments that are in proportion to the adjacent sides.
Linear Pair Postulate	If two angles form a linear pair, then they are supplementary.
Right Triangle Altitude Theorem	If an altitude is drawn to the hypotenuse of a right triangle, then the two triangles formed are similar to the original right triangle and to each other.
Theorem	In a circle, two congruent chords are equidistant from the center of the circle.
Theorem	The tangent segments to a circle from a point outside the circle are congruent.
Inscribed Angle Measure Theorem	In a circle, the measure of an inscribed angle is one-half the measure of intercepted arc.

Postulates and Theorems

THEOREMS *continued*

Theorem	The measure of an angle formed by two secants drawn to a circle from a point in the exterior of the circle is equal to one-half the difference of the measures of their intercepted arcs.
Theorem	The measure of an angle formed by a secant and a tangent drawn to a circle from a point in the exterior of the circle is equal to one-half the difference of the measures of their intercepted arcs.
Theorem	If two chords of a circle intersect, then the product of the lengths of the segments of one chord equals the product of the lengths of the segments of the other chord.
Theorem	If two secant segments share the same endpoint outside a circle, then the product of the length of one secant segment and the length of its external segment equals the product of the length of the other secant segment and the length of its external segment.
Theorem	If a secant segment and a tangent segment share the same endpoint outside a circle, then the product of the length of the secant segment and the length of its external segment equals the square of the length of the tangent segment.

SpringBoard Learning Strategies
READING STRATEGIES

STRATEGY	DEFINITION	PURPOSE
Activating Prior Knowledge	Recalling what is known about a concept and using that information to make a connection to a new concept	Helps students establish connections between what they already know and how that knowledge is related to new learning
Chunking the Activity	Grouping a set of items/questions for specific purposes	Provides an opportunity to relate concepts and assess student understanding before moving on to a new concept or grouping
Close Reading	Reading text word for word, sentence by sentence, and line by line to make a detailed analysis of meaning	Assists in developing a comprehensive understanding of the text
Graphic Organizer	Arranging information into maps and charts	Builds comprehension and facilitates discussion by representing information in visual form
Interactive Word Wall	Visually displaying vocabulary words to serve as a classroom reference of words and groups of words as they are introduced, used, and mastered over the course of a year	Provides a visual reference for new concepts, aids understanding for reading and writing, and builds word knowledge and awareness
KWL Chart (Know, Want to Know, Learn)	Activating prior knowledge by identifying what students know, determining what they want to learn, and having them reflect on what they learned	Assists in organizing information and reflecting on learning to build content knowledge and increase comprehension
Marking the Text	Highlighting, underlining, and /or annotating text to focus on key information to help understand the text or solve the problem	Helps the reader identify important information in the text and make notes about the interpretation of tasks required and concepts to apply to reach a solution
Predict and Confirm	Making conjectures about what results will develop in an activity; confirming or modifying the conjectures based on outcomes	Stimulates thinking by making, checking, and correcting predictions based on evidence from the outcome
Levels of Questions	Developing literal, interpretive, and universal questions about the text while reading the text	Focuses reading, helps in gaining insight into the text by seeking answers, and prepares one for group and class discussions
Paraphrasing	Restating in your own words the essential information in a text or problem description	Assists with comprehension, recall of information, and problem solving
Role Play	Assuming the role of a character in a scenario	Helps interpret and visualize information in a problem
Shared Reading	Reading the text aloud (usually by the teacher) as students follow along silently, or reading a text aloud by the teacher and students	Helps auditory learners do decode, interpret, and analyze challenging text
Summarizing	Giving a brief statement of the main points in a text	Assists with comprehension and provides practice with identifying and restating key information
Think Aloud	Talking through a difficult text or problem by describing what the text means	Helps in comprehending the text, understanding the components of a problem, and thinking about possible paths to a solution
Visualization	Picturing (mentally and/or literally) what is read in the text	Increases reading comprehension and promotes active engagement with the text
Vocabulary Organizer	Using a graphic organizer to keep an ongoing record of vocabulary words with definitions, pictures, notes, and connections between words	Supports a systematic process of learning vocabulary

SpringBoard Learning Strategies
COLLABORATIVE STRATEGIES

STRATEGY	DEFINITION	PURPOSE
Critique Reasoning	Through collaborative discussion, respond to the arguments of others; question the use of mathematical terminology, assumptions, and conjectures to improve understanding and to justify and communicate conclusions	Helps students learn from each other as they make connections between mathematical concepts and learn to verbalize their understanding and support their arguments with reasoning and data that make sense to peers
Debriefing T	Discussing the understanding of a concept to lead to consensus on its meaning	Helps clarify misconceptions and deepen understanding of content
Discussion Groups	Working within groups to discuss content, to create problem solutions, and to explain and justify a solution	Aids understanding through the sharing of ideas, interpretation of concepts, and analysis of problem scenarios
Group Presentation	Presenting information as a collaborative group	Allows opportunities to present collaborative solutions and to share responsibility for delivering information to an audience
Jigsaw	Reading different texts or passages, students become "experts" and then move to a new group to share their information; after sharing, students go back to the original group to share new knowledge	Provides opportunities to summarize and present information to others in a way that facilitates understanding of a text or passage (or multiple texts or passages) without having each student read all texts
Sharing and Responding	Communicating with another person or a small group of peers who respond to a piece of writing or proposed problem solution	Gives students the opportunity to discuss their work with peers, to make suggestions for improvement to the work of others, and/or to receive appropriate and relevant feedback on their own work
Think-Pair-Share	Thinking through a problem alone, pairing with a partner to share ideas, and concluding by sharing results with the class	Enables the development of initial ideas that are then tested with a partner in preparation for revising ideas and sharing them with a larger group

WRITING STRATEGIES

Drafting	Writing a text in an initial form	Assists in getting first thoughts in written form and ready for revising and refining
Note Taking	Creating a record of information while reading a text or listening to a speaker	Helps in organizing ideas and processing information
Prewriting	Brainstorming, either alone or in groups, and refining thoughts and organizing ideas prior to writing	Provides a tool for beginning the writing process and determining the focus of the writing
Quickwrite	Writing for a short, specific amount of time about a designated topic	Helps generate ideas in a short time
RAFT (Role of Writer, Audience, Format, and Topic)	Writing a text by consciously choosing a viewpoint (role of the writer), identifying an audience, choosing a format for the writing, and choosing a topic	Provides a framework for communicating in writing and helps focus the writer's ideas for specific points of communication
Self Revision / Peer Revision	Working alone or with a partner to examine a piece of writing for accuracy and clarity	Provides an opportunity to review work and to edit it for clarity of the ideas presented as well as accuracy of grammar, punctuation, and spelling

SpringBoard Learning Strategies
PROBLEM-SOLVING STRATEGIES

Construct an Argument	Use mathematical reasoning to present assumptions about mathematical situations, support conjectures with mathematically relevant and accurate data, and provide a logical progression of ideas leading to a conclusion that makes sense	Helps develop the process of evaluating mathematical information, developing reasoning skills, and enhancing communication skills in supporting conjectures and conclusions
Create a Plan	Analyzing the tasks in a problem and creating a process for completing the tasks by finding information needed for the tasks, interpreting data, choosing how to solve a problem, communicating the results, and verifying accuracy	Assists in breaking tasks into smaller parts and identifying the steps needed to complete the entire task
Create Representations	Creating pictures, tables, graphs, lists, equations, models, and/or verbal expressions to interpret text or data	Helps organize information using multiple ways to present data and to answer a question or show a problem solution
Guess and Check	Guessing the solution to a problem, and then checking that the guess fits the information in the problem and is an accurate solution	Allows exploration of different ways to solve a problem; guess and check may be used when other strategies for solving are not obvious
Identify a Subtask	Breaking a problem into smaller pieces whose outcomes lead to a solution	Helps to organize the pieces of a complex problem and reach a complete solution
Look for a Pattern	Observing information or creating visual representations to find a trend	Helps to identify patterns that may be used to make predictions
Simplify the Problem	Using "friendlier" numbers to solve a problem	Provides insight into the problem or the strategies needed to solve the problem
Work Backward	Tracing a possible answer back through the solution process to the starting point	Provides another way to check possible answers for accuracy
Use Manipulatives	Using objects to examine relationships between the information given	Provides a visual representation of data that supports comprehension of information in a problem

Glossary
Glosario

A

acute angle (p. 8)   An angle whose measure is greater than 0° and less than 90°.

ángulo agudo (pág. 8)   Ángulo que mide más de 0° y menos de 90°.

adjacent angles (p. 46)   Coplanar angles that share a vertex and side but no interior points.

ángulos adyacentes (pág. 46)   Ángulos coplanares que comparten el vértice y un lado, pero ningún punto interior.

alternate interior angles (p. 74)   A pair of angles that are formed by two lines and a transversal and that are inside the two lines and on opposite sides of the transversal. When the two lines crossed by a transversal are parallel, the alternate interior angles are congruent.

ángulos alternos internos (pág. 74)   Par de ángulos formados por dos rectas y una transversal y que están dentro de las dos rectas y en lados opuestos de la transversal. Cuando las dos rectas cruzadas por una transversal son paralelas, los ángulos alternos internos son congruentes.

altitude of a triangle (p. 192)   A segment from a vertex of a triangle, perpendicular to the opposite side (or line containing the opposite side) of the triangle.

altura de un triángulo (pág. 192)   Segmento desde un vértice de un triángulo, perpendicular al lado opuesto (o recta que contiene el lado opuesto) del triángulo.

angle (p. 26)   The union of two rays with a common endpoint.

ángulo (pág. 26)   Unión de dos rayos con un extremo común.

angle bisector (p. 46)   A ray that divides an angle into two congruent adjacent angles.

bisectriz de un ángulo (pág. 46)   Rayo que divide un ángulo en dos ángulos adyacentes congruentes.

apothem (p. 457)   The perpendicular segment from a midpoint of a side of a regular polygon to the center of the circle circumscribed about the polygon.

apotema (pág. 457)   Segmento perpendicular que va desde el punto medio de un lado de un polígono regular hasta el centro del círculo circunscrito alrededor del polígono.

auxiliary line (p. 182)   A line (or ray or segment) added to a diagram to help in a proof or in determining the solution to a problem.

recta auxiliar (pág. 182)   Recta (o rayo o segmento) que se añade a un diagrama como ayuda en una demostración o para determinar la solución de un problema.

axiomatic system (p. 25)   A logical system based on undefined terms, definitions, axioms or postulates, and theorems.

sistema axiomático (pág. 25)   Sistema lógico basado en términos indefinidos, definiciones, axiomas o postulados y teoremas.

B

bases of a trapezoid (p. 209)   The parallel sides of a trapezoid.

bases de un trapecio (pág. 209)   Lados paralelos de un trapecio.

biconditional (p. 33)   Two statements connected by the words "if and only if."

doble implicancia (pág. 33)   Dos enunciados conectados por las palabras "si y sólo si".

bisect (p. 43)   To divide into two equal or congruent parts.

bisecar (pág. 43)   Dividir en dos partes iguales o congruentes.

bisecting ray (p. 349)   A ray whose endpoint is the vertex of the angle it divides into two congruent angles.

bisección de rayo (pág. 349)   Un rayo cuyo punto final es el vértice del ángulo se divide en dos ángulos congruentes.

C

central angle (p. 457)   An angle whose vertex is at the center of a circle and whose sides contain radii of the circle.

ángulo central (pág. 457)   Ángulo cuyo vértice está en el centro de un círculo y cuyos lados contienen radios del círculo.

centroid (p. 196)   The point of concurrency of the medians of a triangle.

centroide (pág. 196)   Punto de concurrencia de las medianas de un triángulo.

chord (p. 9)   A segment whose endpoints are points of a circle or points of a sphere.

cuerda (pág. 9)   Segmento cuyos extremos son puntos de un círculo o puntos de una esfera.

circle (p. 335)   The set of all points in a plane that are a given distance (the radius) from a given point (the center) in the plane.

círculo (pág. 335)   Conjunto de todos los puntos de un plano que están a una determinada distancia (radio) de un punto dado (centro) del plano.

circumcenter (p. 198)   The point of concurrency of the perpendicular bisectors of the sides of a triangle.

circuncentro (pág. 198)   Punto de concurrencia de las bisectrices perpendiculares de los lados de un triángulo.

circumscribed circle (p. 422)   A circle that contains all the vertices of a polygon.

círculo circunscrito (pág. 422)   Círculo que contiene todos los vértices de un polígono.

coincide (p. 186)   To correspond exactly.

coincidir (pág. 186)   Corresponder exactamente.

collinear points (p. 25)   Points that lie on the same line.

puntos colineales (pág. 25)   Puntos que yacen sobre la misma recta.

complement   The set of all outcomes in a sample space that are not included in a given event.

complemento   Conjunto de todos los resultados de un espacio muestral que no están incluidos en un suceso dado.

complementary angles (p. 8)   Two angles whose measures have a sum of 90°.

ángulos complementarios (pág. 8)   Dos ángulos cuyas medidas suman 90°.

compound event (p. 609)   An event that combines two or more events.

suceso compuesto (pág. 609)   Suceso que combina dos o más sucesos.

conclusion (p. 29)   The "then" clause in an if-then statement.

conclusión (pág. 29)   La cláusula "entonces" en un enunciado si-entonces.

concurrent lines (p. 382)   Three or more lines that intersect at one point.

rectas concurrentes (pág. 382)   Tres o más rectas que se intersecan en un punto.

conditional probability (p. 595)   The probability of an event *A*, given the occurrence of some other event *B*.

probabilidad condicional (pág. 595)   Probabilidad de un suceso *A*, dada la ocurrencia de algún otro suceso *B*.

conditional statement (p. 29)   A statement written in if-then form.

enunciado condicional (pág. 29)   Enunciado que se escribe en la forma si-entonces.

cone (p. 487)   The union of all segments in space that join points in a circle to a point, called the vertex, that is not coplanar with the circle plus the interior points of the circle.

cono (pág. 487)   Unión de todos los segmentos del espacio que unen los puntos de un círculo en un punto, llamado vértice, que no es coplanar con el círculo ni con los puntos interiores del círculo.

congruent angles (p. 46)   Angles that have the same measure.

ángulos congruentes (pág. 46)   Ángulos que tienen la misma medida.

congruent arcs (p. 288)   Arcs of a circle that have the same length.

arcos congruentes (pág. 288)   Arcos de un círculo que tienen la misma longitud.

congruent segments (p. 41)   Segments that have the same length.

segmentos congruentes (pág. 41)   Segmentos que tienen la misma longitud.

congruent triangles (p. 143)   Triangles in which all the corresponding sides and corresponding angles are congruent.

triángulos congruentes (pág. 143)   Triángulos en los que todos los lados correspondientes y los ángulos correspondientes son congruentes.

conjecture (p. 13)   An unproved statement that seems to be true.

conjetura (pág. 13)   Enunciado no demostrado que parece ser verdadero.

contrapositive (p. 32)   A version of a conditional statement formed by interchanging and negating both the hypothesis and conclusion of the statement.

contrapositivo (pág. 32)   Versión de un enunciado condicional que se forma al intercambiar y negar tanto la hipótesis como la conclusión del enunciado.

converse (p. 32)   A version of a conditional statement formed by interchanging the hypothesis and conclusion of the statement.

converso (pág. 32)   Versión de un enunciado condicional que se forma al intercambiar la hipótesis y la conclusión de un enunciado.

convex polygon (p. 455)   A polygon in which all interior angles have measures less than 180°.

polígono convexo (pág. 455)   Polígono en el que todos los ángulos interiores miden menos de 180°.

coordinate proof (p. 373) A proof that relates figures on the coordinate plane.

prueba de coordenadas (pág. 373) Prueba que relaciona figuras en el plano de coordenadas.

coplanar points (p. 25) Points that lie in the same plane.

puntos coplanares (pág. 25) Puntos que yacen en el mismo plano.

corollary (p. 268) A statement that results directly from a theorem.

corolario (pág. 268) Enunciado que resulta directamente de un teorema.

corresponding angles (p. 74) A pair of nonadjacent angles that are formed by two lines and a transversal such that the angles are on the same side of the transversal and one of the angles is outside the two lines while the other angle is between the two lines.

ángulos correspondientes (pág. 74) Par de ángulos no adyacentes que están formados por dos rectas y una transversal de modo tal que los ángulos están en el mismo lado de la transversal y uno de los ángulos está fuera de las dos rectas mientras que el otro ángulo está entre las dos rectas.

corresponding parts (p. 144) In congruent figures, the corresponding angles with equal measures and the corresponding sides with equal measures. In similar figures, the corresponding angles with equal measures and the corresponding sides whose lengths are in proportion.

partes correspondientes (pág. 144) En figuras congruentes, los ángulos correspondientes de igual medida y los lados correspondientes de igual medida. En figuras semejantes, los ángulos correspondientes de igual medida y los lados correspondientes cuyas longitudes están en proporción.

cosine (cos) (p. 309) The cosine of an acute angle in a right triangle is the ratio of the length of the adjacent side to the length of the hypotenuse.

coseno (cos) (pág. 309) El coseno de un ángulo agudo de un triángulo rectángulo es la razón de la longitud del cateto adyacente a la longitud de la hipotenusa.

counterexample (p. 30) An example or case that proves a conjecture or theory wrong.

contraejemplo (pág. 30) Ejemplo o caso que prueba que una conjetura o teoría es errónea.

cross section (p. 483) The intersection of a solid figure and a plane.

sección transversal (pág. 483) Intersección de un cuerpo geométrico con un plano.

cylinder (p. 486) The set of all points in space that are a given distance (radius) from a line, known as the axis, plus two bases formed by the intersection of two parallel planes with the cylinder.

cilindro (pág. 486) Conjunto de todos los puntos del espacio que están a una determinada distancia (radio) de una recta, conocida como eje, más dos bases formadas por la intersección del cilindro con dos planos paralelos.

D

deductive reasoning (p. 18) The use of facts, definitions, rules, and/or properties to prove that a conjecture is true.

razonamiento deductivo (pág. 18) El uso de datos, definiciones, reglas o propiedades para probar que una conjetura es verdadera.

dependent events (p. 605) Events in which the outcome of the first event affects the outcome of the second event.

sucesos dependientes (pág. 605) Sucesos en que el resultado del primer suceso afecta el resultado del segundo suceso.

diameter (p. 9) A chord containing the center of a circle or sphere, or the length of such a chord.

diámetro (pág. 9) Cuerda que contiene el centro de un círculo o esfera; también, la longitud de dicha cuerda.

dilation (p. 242) A transformation in which the image is similar (but not congruent) to the pre-image.

dilatación (pág. 242) Transformación en que la imagen es semejante (pero no congruente) a la imagen original.

discrete domain (p. 452) The domain for a function or graph that consists of discrete points.

dominio discreto (pág. 452) Dominio de una función o gráfica, que consta de puntos discretos.

E

edge (p. 479) The line segment formed by the intersection of two faces of a polyhedron.

arista (pág. 479) Segmento de recta formado por la intersección de dos caras de un poliedro.

equiangular (p. 453)   A polygon with all angles congruent.
equiangular (pág. 453)   Polígono con todos sus ángulos congruentes.

equilateral (p. 453)   A polygon with all sides congruent.
equilátero (pág. 453)   Polígono con todos sus lados congruentes.

event (p. 554)   Any outcome or set of outcomes.
suceso (pág. 554)   Cualquier resultado o conjunto de resultados.

exterior angle of a polygon (p. 455)   The angle formed by extending a side of a polygon.
ángulo exterior de un polígono (pág. 455)   Ángulo formado al extender un lado de un polígono.

F

face (p. 479)   One of the polygons that make up a three dimensional solid figure.
cara (pág. 479)   Uno de los polígonos que forman una figura geométrica tridimensional.

flowchart (p. 167)   A concept map showing a procedure, where boxes represent actions and connecting arrows show the flow of the logic behind the actions.
diagrama de flujo (pág. 167)   Mapa conceptual que muestra un procedimiento, donde las casillas muestran acciones y las flechas conectoras muestran el flujo de la lógica que hay detrás las acciones.

Fundamental Counting Principle (p. 625)   If one event can occur m ways and another event can occur n ways, then the first event followed by the second event can occur $m \cdot n$ ways; also called the Multiplication Principle.
Principio fundamental del conteo (pág. 625)   Si un suceso puede ocurrir de m maneras y otro suceso puede ocurrir de n maneras, entonces el primer suceso seguido del segundo suceso puede ocurrir de $m \cdot n$ maneras; llamado también Principio de la multiplicación.

G

geometric mean (p. 278)   The nth root of n factors. For example, 30 is the geometric mean of 18, 20, and 75 since $30 = \sqrt[3]{18 \cdot 20 \cdot 75}$.
media geométrica (pág. 278)   raíz enésima de n factores. Por ejemplo, 30 es la media geométrica de 18, 20 y 75, ya que $30 = \sqrt[3]{18 \cdot 20 \cdot 75}$.

great circle (p. 533)   The largest possible circle drawn on a sphere.
círculo mayor (pág. 533)   Círculo más grande posible dibujado sobre una esfera.

H

hemisphere (p. 525)   One half of a sphere.
semiesfera (pág. 525)   La mitad de una esfera.

hypothesis (p. 29)   The "if" clause in an if-then statement.
hipótesis (pág. 29)   La cláusula "si" en un enunciado si-entonces.

I

incenter (p. 198)   The point of concurrency of the angle bisectors of a triangle.
incentro (pág. 198)   Punto de concurrencia de las bisectrices de los ángulos de un triángulo.

independent events (p. 614)   Events in which the outcome of one event does not affect the outcome of the other event.
sucesos independientes (pág. 614)   Sucesos en que el resultado de un suceso no afecta el resultado del otro suceso.

indirect proof (p. 217)   A proof that begins by assuming the opposite of the conclusion. The assumption is used as if it were given until a contradiction is reached.
demostración indirecta (pág. 217)   Demostración que comienza suponiendo lo contrario de la conclusión. El supuesto se acepta como válido hasta llegar a una contradición.

inductive reasoning (p. 13)   The process of observing data, recognizing patterns, and making a generalization.
razonamiento inductivo (pág. 13)   Proceso de observar datos, reconocer patrones y hacer una generalización.

inscribed angle (p. 353)   An angle formed by two chords of a circle with a common endpoint.
ángulo inscrito (pág. 353)   Ángulo formado por dos cuerdas de un círculo con un extremo común.

inscribed circle (p. 432)   A circle drawn in the interior of a polygon and tangent to each side of the polygon.
círculo inscrito (pág. 432)   Círculo dibujado en el interior de un polígono y tangente a cada lado del polígono.

intercepted arc (p. 350)   An arc that connects the sides of an angle whose vertex is a point on the circle or in the interior of the circle; or an arc that connects the sides of an angle whose vertex is a point in the exterior of the circle and whose sides intersect the circle.
arco intersecado (pág. 350)   Arco que conecta los lados de un ángulo cuyo vértice es un punto del círculo o del interior del círculo; o arco que conecta los lados de un ángulo cuyo vértice es un punto que está en el exterior del círculo y cuyos lados intersecan el círculo.

inverse (p. 32)   A version of a conditional statement formed by negating both the hypothesis and conclusion of the statement.
inverso (pág. 32)   Versión de un enunciado condicional, formada al negar tanto la hipótesis como la conclusión del enunciado.

isosceles trapezoid (p. 210)   A trapezoid with congruent legs.
trapecio isósceles (pág. 210)   Trapecio de lados congruentes.

isosceles triangle (p. 186)   A triangle with two congruent sides.
triángulo isósceles (pág. 186)   Triángulo con dos lados congruentes.

K

kite (p. 206)   A quadrilateral with exactly two distinct pairs of congruent consecutive sides.

romboide (pág. 206)   Cuadrilátero que tiene exactamente dos pares distintos de lados consecutivos congruentes.

L

lateral area (p. 496)   The surface area of a solid excluding the base(s).

área lateral (pág. 496)   Área de la superficie de un cuerpo geométrico, excluyendo las bases.

legs of a trapezoid (p. 209)   The nonparallel sides of a trapezoid.

lados de un trapecio (pág. 209)   Lados no paralelos de un trapecio.

line segment (p. 25)   A part of a line bounded by two points on the line called endpoints.

segmento de recta (pág. 25)   Parte de una recta limitada por dos puntos de la recta llamados extremos.

logically equivalent (p. 33)   Two statements with the same truth value.

lógicamente equivalentes (pág. 33)   Dos enunciados que tienen el mismo valor de verdad.

M

major arc (p. 350)   An arc with a measure greater than 180°.

arco mayor (pág. 350)   Arco que mide más de 180°.

median of a trapezoid (p. 209)   A line segment that connects the midpoints of the legs of a trapezoid. The median is parallel to the bases.

mediana de un trapecio (pág. 209)   Segmento de recta que conecta los puntos medios de los lados de un trapecio. La mediana es paralela a las bases.

median of a triangle (p. 195)   A segment from a vertex of a triangle to the midpoint of the opposite side of the triangle.

mediana de un triángulo (pág. 195)   Segmento que va desde un vértice de un triángulo hasta el punto medio del lado opuesto del triángulo.

midpoint of a segment (p. 41)   The point on a segment that divides it into two congruent segments.

punto medio de un segmento (pág. 41)   Punto de un segmento que lo divide en dos segmentos congruentes.

minor arc (p. 350)   An arc with a measure less than 180°.

arco menor (pág. 350)   Arco que mide menos de 180°.

N

net (p. 479)   A two-dimensional drawing used to represent or form a three-dimensional object or solid.

red (pág. 479)   Dibujo bidimensional usado para representar o formar un objeto tridimensional o cuerpo geométrico.

O

oblique (p. 479)   Not perpendicular.

oblicuo (pág. 479)   Que no es perpendicular.

obtuse angle (p. 8)   An angle whose measure is greater than 90° and less than 180°.

ángulo obtuso (pág. 8)   Ángulo que mide más de 90° y menos de 180°.

orthocenter (p. 193)   The point of concurrency of the altitudes of a triangle.

ortocentro (pág. 193)   Punto de concurrencia de las alturas de un triángulo.

outcome (p. 554)   The result of a trial in an experiment.

resultado (pág. 554)   Resultado de una prueba en un experimento.

P

parallel lines (p. 73)   Coplanar lines that do not intersect.

rectas paralelas (pág. 73)   Rectas coplanares que no se intersecan.

parallelogram (p. 213)   A quadrilateral with both pairs of opposite sides parallel.

paralelogramo (pág. 213)   Cuadrilátero que tiene ambos pares de lados opuestos paralelos.

perpendicular (p. 84)   Figures that intersect to form right angles.

perpendiculares (pág. 84)   Figuras que se intersecan para formar ángulos rectos.

perpendicular bisector (p. 85)   A line, segment, or ray that intersects a line segment at its midpoint forming a right angle.

bisectriz perpendicular (pág. 85)   Recta, segmento o rayo que interseca un segmento de recta en su punto medio, formando un ángulo recto.

point of concurrency (p. 192)   The point where three or more lines intersect.

punto de concurrencia (pág. 192)   Punto donde se intersecan tres o más rectas.

point of tangency (p. 335)   The point at which a tangent line intersects a circle.

punto de tangencia (pág. 335)   Punto en que una recta tangente interseca un círculo.

polygon (p. 447)   A closed figure with sides formed by three or more coplanar segments that intersect exactly two other segments, one at each endpoint.

polígono (pág. 447)   Figura cerrada cuyos lados están formados por tres o más segmentos coplanares que intersecan exactamente otros dos segmentos, uno en cada extremo.

polyhedron (p. 481)   A closed three-dimensional figure consisting of polygons that are joined along their edges.

poliedro (pág. 481)   Figura tridimensional cerrada consistente en polígonos que están unidos a lo largo de sus aristas.

postulate (p. 39)   A statement that is accepted without proof.

postulado (pág. 39)   Enunciado que es aceptado sin demostración.

pre-image (p. 103)   The original graph or figure prior to a transformation.

preimagen (pág. 103)   Gráfica o figura original antes de una transformación.

prism (p. 479)   A solid with parallel congruent bases that are both polygons. The sides (faces) of a prism are all parallelograms or rectangles.

prisma (pág. 479)   Cuerpo geométrico que tiene dos bases paralelas congruentes que son ambas polígonos. Todas las caras de un prisma son paralelogramos o rectángulos.

probability experiment (p. 554)   The process of observing an outcome when it is not known prior to the experiment.

experimento de probabilidad (pág. 554)   El proceso de observar un resultado cuando no se sabe antes del experimento.

proof (p. 18)   An argument that transforms a conjecture to a theorem through the application of logical reasoning or deductive reasoning.

demostración (pág. 18)   Argumento que transforma una conjetura en un teorema por medio de la aplicación del razonamiento lógico o del razonamiento deductivo.

pyramid (p. 480)   A three-dimensional figure whose base is a polygon and whose other faces are triangles that share a common vertex.

pirámide (pág. 480)   Figura tridimensional cuya base es un polígono y cuyas otras caras son triángulos que comparten un vértice.

Pythagorean triplets (p. 284)   Three integers a, b, and c such that $c^2 = a^2 + b^2$.

tripletas pitagóricas (pág. 284)   Tres enteros a, b y c tales que $c^2 = a^2 + b^2$.

R

radius (p. 9)   A line segment connecting the center of a circle with a point on the circle, or the length of such a segment.

radio (pág. 9)   Segmento de recta que conecta el centro de un círculo con un punto del círculo; también, la longitud de dicho segmento.

ray (p. 25)   A part of a line consisting of an endpoint and all points on one side of that endpoint.

rayo (pág. 25)   Parte de una recta que consta de un extremo y todos los puntos a un lado de ese extremo.

rectangle (p. 216)   A parallelogram with four right angles.

rectángulo (pág. 216)   Paralelogramo que tiene cuatro ángulos rectos.

reflection (p. 112)   A transformation in which a figure is flipped over a line, called a line of reflection.

reflexión (pág. 112)   Transformación en que una figura se invierte en torno a una recta llamada eje de reflexión.

regular polygon (p. 453)   A polygon that is both equilateral and equiangular.

polígono regular (pág. 453)   Polígono que es tanto equilátero como equiangular.

rhombus (p. 218)   A parallelogram with four congruent sides.

rombo (pág. 218)   Paralelogramo que tiene cuatro lados congruentes.

right cylinder (p. 486)   A cylinder whose axis is perpendicular to each of the bases.

cilindro recto (pág. 486)   Cilindro cuyo eje es perpendicular a cada una de las bases.

rotation (p. 120)   A transformation in which each point of the pre-image travels clockwise or counterclockwise around a fixed point a certain number of degrees.

rotación (pág. 120)   Transformación en que cada punto de la preimagen se desplaza alrededor de un punto fijo un determinado número de grados en el sentido de las manecillas del reloj o en sentido contrario al de las manecillas del reloj.

S

sample space (p. 554)   The set of possible outcomes in an experiment.

espacio muestral (pág. 554)   Conjunto de resultados posibles de un experimento.

same-side interior angles (p. 74)   When two lines are cut by a transversal, a pair of angles in the interior between those two lines that are on the same side of the transversal.

ángulos colaterales internos (pág. 74)   Cuando dos rectas son cortadas por una transversal, un par de ángulos entre esas dos rectas, que están al mismo lado de la transversal.

scale factor (p. 242)   In similar figures and similar solids, the ratio of the lengths of any pair of corresponding sides or edges.

factor de escala (pág. 242)   En figuras semejantes y cuerpos geométricos semejantes, razón de las longitudes de cualquier par de lados o aristas correspondientes.

secant (p. 366)   A line, segment, or ray that intersects a circle in two points.

secante (pág. 366)   Recta, segmento o rayo que interseca un círculo en dos puntos.

sector of a circle (p. 464)   A region formed by two radii and an arc of a circle.

sector de un círculo (pág. 464)   Región formada por dos radios y un arco de un círculo.

similar polygons (p. 250)   Polygons with congruent corresponding angles and corresponding side lengths in proportion.

polígonos semejantes (pág. 250)   Polígonos cuyos ángulos correspondientes son congruentes y cuyas longitudes de los lados correspondientes son proporcionales.

sine (sin) (p. 309)   The sine of an acute angle in a right triangle is the ratio of the length of the opposite side to the length of the hypotenuse.

seno (sen) (pág. 309)   El seno de un ángulo agudo de un triángulo rectángulo es la razón de la longitud del cateto opuesto a la longitud de la hipotenusa.

slant height (p. 508)   The length of the shortest segment connecting the vertex of a cone or pyramid and a point on an edge along the base.

altura inclinada (pág. 508)   La longitud del segmento más corto que conecta el vértice de un cono o pirámide con un punto ubicado sobre una arista a lo largo de la base.

slope (p. 90)   The ratio of the vertical change of a line to the horizontal change of the line.

pendiente (pág. 90)   La razón del cambio vertical de una recta al cambio horizontal de la recta.

sphere (p. 525)   The set of all points (x,y,z) that are a given distance, the radius, from a point, the center.

esfera (pág. 525)   Conjunto de todos los puntos (x,y,z) que están a una determinada distancia, el radio, de un punto, el centro.

spherical geometry (p. 532)   A branch of non-Euclidean geometry that explores the geometric characteristics of figures on the surface of a sphere.

geometría esférica (pág. 532)   Rama de la geometría no euclidiana que explora las características geométricas de figuras sobre la superficie de una esfera.

square (p. 34)   A parallelogram with four right angles and four congruent sides.

cudrado (pág. 34)   Paralelogramo que tiene cuatro ángulos rectos y cuatro lados congruentes.

supplementary angles (p. 8)   Two angles whose measures have a sum of 180°.

ángulos suplementarios (pág. 8)   Dos ángulos cuyas medidas suman 180°.

surface area (p. 496)   The total area of all the surfaces of a three-dimensional figure.

área de la superficie (pág. 496)   Área total de todas las superficies de una figura tridimensional.

T

tangent (p. 309)   The tangent of an acute angle in a right triangle is the ratio of the length of the opposite side to the length of the adjacent side.

tangente (pág. 309)   La tangente de un ángulo agudo de un triángulo rectángulo es la razón de la longitud del cateto opuesto a la longitud del cateto adyacente.

tangent line (p. 335)   A line in the plane of a circle that intersects the circle in exactly one point; or a line that intersects a sphere in exactly one point.

recta tangente (pág. 335)   Recta en el plano de un círculo, que interseca el círculo en sólo un punto; también, recta que interseca una esfera en sólo un punto.

tangent segment (p. 345)   Part of a tangent line with one endpoint outside the circle and the other endpoint at a point of tangency to the circle.

segmento tangente (pág. 345)   Parte de una recta tangente con un extremo fuera del círculo y el otro extremo en un punto de tangencia al círculo.

tetrahedron (p. 545)   A polyhedron with four triangular faces.

tetraedro (pág. 545)   Poliedro que tiene cuatro caras triangulares.

theorem (p. 18)   A statement or conjecture that has been proven.

teorema (pág. 18)   Una declaración o conjetura que se ha probado.

theoretical probability (p. 554)   The ratio of the number of outcomes in the event being measured to the total number of possible outcomes.

probabilidad teórica (pág. 554)   Razón del número de resultados del suceso que se está midiendo al número total de resultados posibles.

translation (p. 108)   A transformation that moves each point of a figure the same distance and in the same direction.

traslación (pág. 108)   Transformación que mueve cada punto de una figura la misma distancia y en la misma dirección.

transversal (p. 74)   A line that intersects two or more coplanar lines in different points.

transversal (pág. 74)   Recta que interseca en diferentes puntos dos o más rectas complanares.

trapezoid (p. 209)   A quadrilateral with exactly one pair of parallel sides.

trapecio (pág. 209)   Cuadrilátero que tiene sólo un par de lados paralelos.

trigonometric ratios (p. 309)   Any ratio involving the side lengths of a right triangle.

razones trigonométricas (pág. 309)   Cuaquier razón que involucre las longitudes de los lados de un triángulo rectángulo.

truth values (p. 33) The truth or falsity of a proposition.

valores de verdad (pág. 33) La verdad o falsedad de una proposición.

two-column proof (p. 27) A deductive argument containing statements and reasons organized in two columns.

prueba de dos columnas (pág. 27) Un argumento deductivo que contienen declaraciones y razones organizado en dos columnas.

U

undefined terms (p. 25)   Fundamental terms used to define other terms and develop the system of geometry.

términos indefinidos (pág. 25)   Términos fundamentales se utilizan para definir otros términos y desarrollar el sistema de la geometría.

V

volume (p. 433)   The number of cubic units in a three-dimensional figure.

volumen (pág. 433)   Número de unidades cubicas de una figura tridimensional.

Verbal & Visual Word Association

Definition in Your Own Words	Important Elements

Academic Vocabulary Word

Visual Representation	Personal Association

Eight Circle Spider

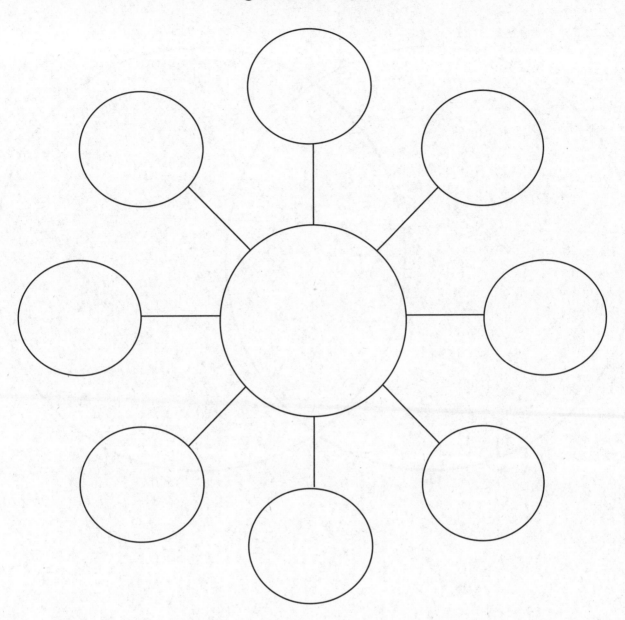

Venn Diagram

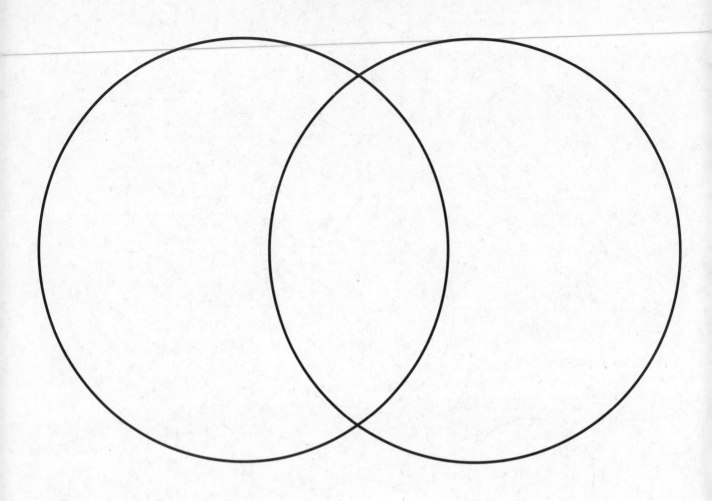

Net for a Cube

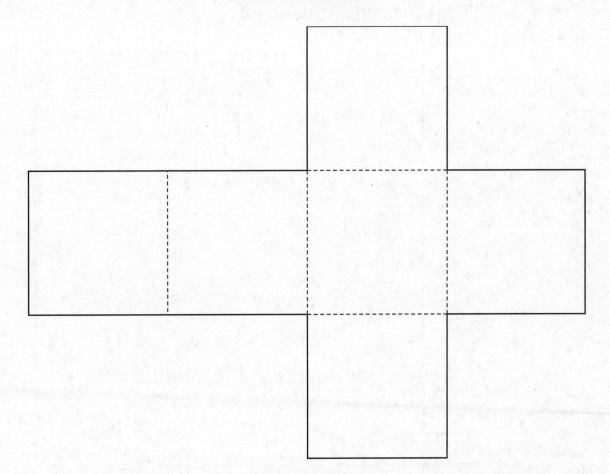

Rectangular Prism
With Open End

Triangular Prism
With Open End

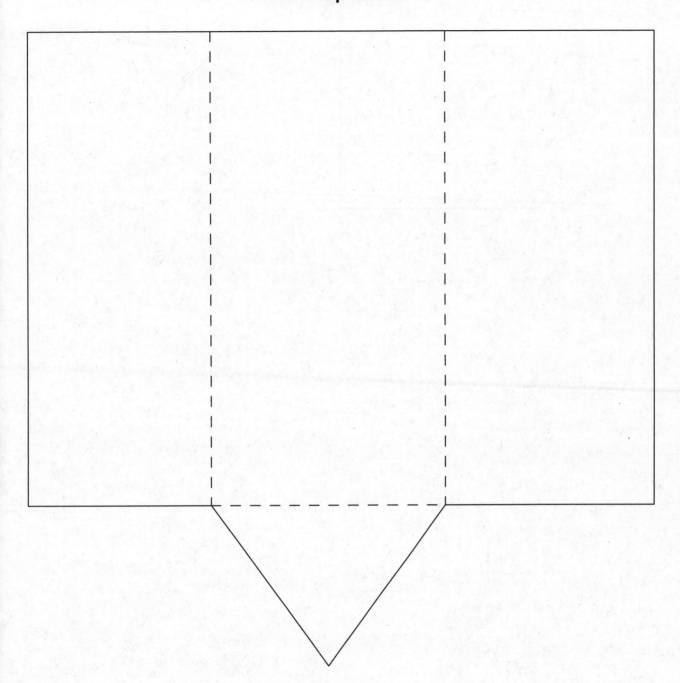

Net for a Cone

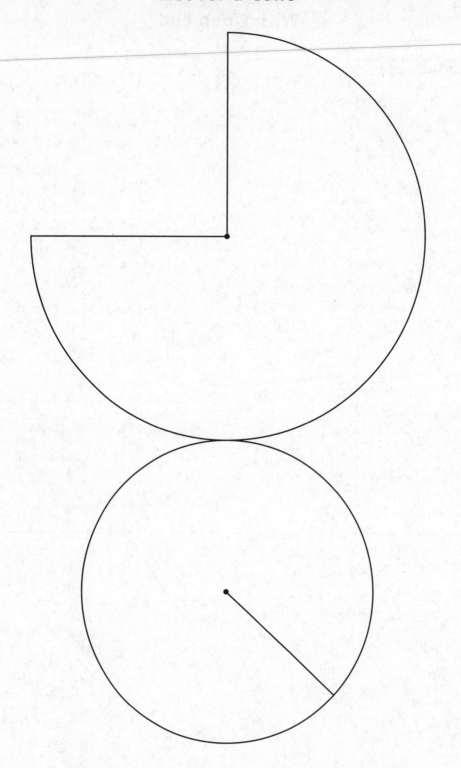

Index

A

AA Similarity Postulate, 258–259
AAS triangle congruence criteria, 151, 161–163
Acute angles, 7–8
Addition
  Addition Property of Equality, 26
  Distributive Property of Multiplication Over Addition, 20
Addition Rule
  applying, 583–585
  to calculate probability of mutually exclusive events, 589
  defined, 583
Adjacent angles, 46
Adjacent leg
  defined, 306
  in trigonometric ratio, 309–313
Alternate interior angle, 74
Alternate Interior Angles Theorem, 76, 79
Altitude of triangle
  defined, 192
  orthocenter, 193
  point of concurrency, 192–194
"And" events, 559–563, 575–576
Angle
  acute, 7–8
  adjacent, 46
  alternate interior, 74
  Angle Addition Postulate, 45–46
  bisector of, 46, 64
  central, 350
  complementary, 7–8, 47
  congruent, 46
  construction
    bisector of angle, 415–416
    of congruent angles, 413
  corresponding, 74
  exterior
  of polygons, 455–456
  of triangles, 183
  formed by chords, 358–361
  formed by secants, 365–366
  formed by tangents, 363–364
  inscribed, 353–357
  interior angles
  of polygons, 447–452
  of triangles, 183
  measure of, 45–48
  naming, 5–6
  obtuse, 7–8
  radian measure of, 473
  remote interior angle, 183
  right, 8

of rotational symmetry, 125
same-side interior, 74
straight, 8
supplementary, 7–8
vertex of, 5, 26
vertical, 48
Vertical Angles Theorem, 66
Angle Addition Postulate, 45–46, 63
Antipodal points, 533
Apothem, 457
Arc
  central angle, 350
  congruent, 351
  defined, 336
  major arc, 350
  minor arc, 350
Archimedes, 463
Area
  circle, 464–465
  composite figure, 435
  lateral, 496–499
  parallelogram, 433–435
  rectangles, 433–435
  regular polygon, 457–459
  rhombus, 441–443
  sector, 467
  trapezoid, 441–443
  triangle, 437–439
Argument
  in deductive reasoning, 18
ASA triangle congruence criteria, 151, 157–158
Auxiliary line, 182
Axiomatic system, 25

B

Base
  of prism, 496
  of trapezoid, 209
Base angle
  of isosceles triangle, 186
  of trapezoid, 209
Biconditional statement, 33, 377
Bisect, 41
Bisecting ray, 349
Bisector
  of angle, 46
    construction of, 415–416
  perpendicular, 85
  of segment
    construction perpendicular bisector, 414–415

C

Cartesian coordinate system, 51
Cavalieri's Principle, 500, 514
Center of dilation, 244
Central angle, 350
Centroid, 196–197
Centroid Measure Theorem, 197
Chord, 9–10
  angles formed by, 358–361
  congruent, 340–342
  defined, 336
  intersecting, 342–343
  of sphere, 489
Circles
  arc
    congruent, 351
    defined, 336
    major arc, 350
    minor arc, 350
  area, 464–465
  center
    complete the square to find, 396–397
  chord, 9–10
    angles formed by, 358–361
    congruent, 340–342
    defined, 336
    intersecting, 342–343
  circumference of, 463–465
  circumscribed circle, 199, 463
  concentric, 470–472
  constructions
    hexagon inside, 422–423
    square inside, 423
    triangle inside, 424
  on coordinate plane, 391–394
  defined, 335
  diameter, 9–10, 336
  equation of, 391–393, 396–397
  great circle, 489, 527, 532, 533
  inscribed angles, 353–357
  inscribed circle, 199, 463
  radius, 9–10, 335
    complete the square to find, 396–397
  secant line
    angles formed by, 365–366
  sector
    area, 467
    defined, 464
    length of, 468
    similarity and, 470–472
  tangent line
    angles formed by, 363–364
    defined, 335
    tangent segment, 345–346

Circumcenter, 198–199
Circumference
  of circle, 463–465
  sphere, 525–526
Circumscribed circle, 199, 463
Circumscribed polygon, 422
Closure, 20
Coincide, 186
Combinations, 628–629
Compass, 411
Complementary angles, 7–8, 47
  definition of, 64
  two-column proof, 68
Complement of event, 557
Complement of set, 574
Complete the square
  to find center and radius of circle,
    396–397
  steps of, 396
Composite figure
  area of, 435
  defined, 435
Composition of transformations
  defined, 129
  find image and pre-image under,
    129–131
  inverse transformation, 132–133
  notation for, 129
Concentric circles, 470
Conclusion, 29
Conditional probability
  defined, 595
  formula for, 601–602
  tree diagrams, 604–609
  two-way frequency table, 597
  Venn diagram, 598–599
Conditional statement
  contrapositive, 32
  converse, 32
  defined, 29
  inverse, 32
  logically equivalent, 33
Cone
  characteristics of, 487
  density and, 518–519
  height of, 487
  lateral area, 510–511
  lateral surface, 510
  oblique, 487
  right, 487
  as solid of rotation, 490–491
  surface area, 510–511
  vertex of, 487
  volume, 516–517
Congruence, 134

Congruent angle
  construction of, 413
  defined, 46
  two-column proof, 68
Congruent arc, 351
Congruent chords, 340–342
Congruent figures
  determining with rigid motion,
    134–136
Congruent segments
  construction of, 411, 412
  defined, 41
Congruent Supplements Theorem, 77
Congruent triangles, 143–164
  congruence criteria
    AAS, 151, 161–163
    ASA, 151, 157–158
    developing, 147–153
    extending, 160–164
    proving, 154–159
    SAS, 137, 151, 156
    SSS, 151, 154–155
  corresponding parts, 144
  defined, 143
  find unknown angle of, 144–146
  flowchart, paragraph and two-column
    proof for, 167–176
  hypotenuse-leg, 163
  kite, 206
  parallelogram, 213–214
  rectangle and, 216
  rhombus and, 218
  Conjecture, 339
  in deductive reasoning, 18–22
  defined, 13
Constructions, 411–426. See also
    Geometric constructions
Contrapositive statement, 32
Converse statement, 32
Convex polygon, 455
Coordinate plane
  circles on, 391–394
  dilations, 241–244
  distance on, 51–54
  midpoint on, 56–57
  parabola on, 401–407
  Pre-image, 103
  reflection on, 112–114
  rotations on, 120–122
  translation, 108–109
  triangle congruence criteria, 160
Coordinate proof, 207
  concurrency of medians of triangles,
    382–386
  defined, 373

  midpoint formula, 373–375
  slope criteria for parallel and
    perpendicular lines, 377–380
Corollary, 214
Corresponding angles, 74
Corresponding Angles Theorem, 76, 79
Corresponding parts, 144
Cosine (cos)
  defined, 309–310
  inverse function, 315–316
  Law of Cosines, 324–328
Counterexample, 30, 147
Criterion, 151
Cross Product Property, 320
Cross section, 483
Cube
  linear dimension changes and, 539
  volume, 513–514, 539
Cylinder
  Cavalieri's Principle, 500
  characteristics of, 486
  lateral area, 498–499
  linear dimension changes and, 543–544
  net, 486
  right, 486
    as solid of rotation, 490–491
  surface area, 498–499
  volume, 502–504

D

Decagon
  interior angles sum, 450–453
Deductive reasoning, 18–22
  argument, 18
  biconditional statement, 33
  conclusion, 29
  conditional statement, 29
  conjecture, 18
  contrapositive statement, 32–33
  converse statement, 32–33
  counterexample, 30
  defined, 18
  hypothesis, 29
  inverse statement, 32–33
  postulates, 39
  proof, 18
  proofs, 63–69
  theorem, 18
  truth value, 32–33
Defined terms, 25
  using to justify statements in
    two-column proof, 63–64
Density
  package design and, 518–519

Density formula, 443
Dependent event, 605
Descartes, René, 51
Diameter, 9–10
   defined, 336
   of sphere, 489
Dilations, 241–247
   center of, 244
   defined, 242
   origin-centered, 244
Directed line segment, 108–111, 387
Directrix, 401
Discrete domain, 452
Distance
   along a line, 39
   on coordinate plane, 51–54
   on number line, 41–42
   between two points
      formula for, 54
      Pythagorean Theorem, 52–54
Distance Formula, 54, 207
Distributive Property, 26
Division
   Division Property of Equality, 26
Dodecagon
   interior angles sum, 450–453
Domain, discrete, 452
Drawing, 411

E

Edge, 479, 481
Elimination method, 193
Endpoints, 25
Equality
   Addition Property of Equality, 26
   Division Property of Equality, 26
   Multiplication Property of Equality, 26
   Subtraction Property of Equality, 26,
      64, 67
Equiangular, 453
Equidistant, 340
Equilateral, 453
Euclid, 182, 187
Euclidean geometry, 532–536
Euler, Leonard, 481
Events
   defined, 554
   dependent, 605

independent, 614–618
involving "and" and "or," 559–563
mutually exclusive, 587–589
Exterior angle
   of polygons, 455–456
   of triangle, 183
Exterior Angle Theorem, 183–184

F

Face, 479
Fibonacci, 13
Flips. *See* Reflections
Flowchart, 169
Flowchart proofs
   to create two-column proof, 167–168,
      173
   statement and reason in, 169
   steps in writing, 167–175
Focus, of parabola, 401
Format, 55
45°-45°-90° right triangle, 291–293
Fundamental Counting Principle, 625

G

Generalized Addition Rule, 583
Geometric constructions, 411–426
   angle congruent to given angle, 413
   bisector of angle, 415–416
   circle inside triangle, 424
   defined, 411
   hexagon in circle, 422–423
   parallel lines, 418–419
   perpendicular bisector of given
      segment, 414–415
   of perpendicular lines, 419
   segment congruent to segment, 411
   square in circle, 423
   tools for, 411
   of triangle, 412
Geometric mean
   defined, 278
   Right Triangle Altitude Theorem,
      278–279
Geometric probability, 621–623
Geometry
   as axiomatic system, 25
Great circle, 489, 527, 532, 533

H

Hemisphere, 525
Heptagon
   exterior angle sum, 455
   interior angles sum, 447–453
Hexagon
   construction of, inside circle, 422–423
   exterior angle sum, 455
   interior angles sum, 447–453
Hexagonal prism, 481
Hexagonal pyramid, 481
Horizontal line
   point-slope form, 193
   slope of, 192
Hypotenuse
   finding midpoint, 53–54
   Pythagorean Theorem and, 283–284
Hypotenuse-leg (HL), 163
Hypothesis, 29

I

Image, 103
Incenter of triangle, 198–199
Independent event, 614–618
Indirect measurement, 262–264
Indirect proofs, 217
Inductive reasoning, 13–17
Inscribed angles, 353–357
Inscribed circle, 199, 463
Inscribed polygon, 422
Interchange, 32
Interior angles
   of polygons, 447–454
   of triangle, 183
Intersecting chords, 342–343
Intersection of sets, 573
Inverse statement, 32
Inverse trigonometric functions, 315–316
Isosceles trapezoid, 210–212
Isosceles triangles
   area of, 437
   base angle of, 186
   Isosceles Triangle Theorem, 186
   right, 291–293
   vertex angle of, 186
Isosceles Triangle Theorem, 186–188

Perimeter
    of parallelogram, 434
    of rectangle, 434
    of regular polygon, 458
Permutations, 625–628, 626
Perpendicular bisector, 85
    of sides of triangle, 198
Perpendicular Bisector Theorem, 155
Perpendicular lines
    construction of, 419
    definition of, 64, 84
    proof on slope criteria for, 377–380
    slope equation and, 92–95
    slope of, 192
Perpendicular Postulate, 84
Perpendicular Transversal Theorem, 85
Pi
    Archimedes' calculation of, 463
Plane
    naming, 4
Point
    naming, 4
Point of concurrency
    altitude of triangle, 192–194
    centroid, 196–197
    circumcenter, 198
    defined, 192
    incenter, 198
Point of tangengy, 345
Point-slope form
    defined, 93, 193
    horizontal line, 193
    vertical line, 193
Polygon
    circumscribed, 422
    convex, 455
    defined, 447
    exterior angle of, 455
    inscribed, 422
    interior angles
        defined, 447
        sum of, 447–452
    regular
        area, 457–459
        defined, 453
        interior angle, 453–454
        perimeter, 458
Polyhedron
    defined, 481
    edge, 481
    vertices of, 481
Postulates
    AA Similarity Postulate, 258–259
    Angle Addition Postulate, 63

defined, 39
Parallel Postulate, 84, 182
Perpendicular Postulate, 84
Protractor Postulate, 45
Ruler Postulate, 39
Same-Side Interior Angles Postulate, 76, 79
Segment Addition Postulate, 40, 64
using to justify statements two-column proof, 63–64
Pre-image, 103
Primates, 602
Prism
    base of, 496
    characteristics of, 479
    defined, 479
    hexagonal, 481
    lateral area, 496–497
    nets, 479
    oblique, 479
    pentagonal, 481
    rectangular, 481, 482
    right, 479
    surface area of, 495–497
    triangular, 481
    volume, 500–501
Probability
    Addition Rule
        applying, 583–585
        calculate probability of mutually exclusive events, 589
    combinations, 628–629
    complement of event, 557
    conditional
        defined, 595
        formula for, 601–602
        tree diagrams, 604–609
        understanding, 595–599
    defined, 554
    events
        defined, 554
        dependent, 605
        independent, 614–618
        involving "and" and "or," 559–563
        mutually exclusive, 587–589
    geometric, 621–623
    linear model to determine, for elapsed time, 622
    Multiplication Rule
        defined, 609
        independent event determination, 614–618
    outcome, 554
    permutations, 625–628

probability experiment, 554
    sample space, 554
    of single event, 553–558
    two-way frequency table, 562, 597
    Venn diagram
        complement of sets, 574
        conditional probability, 598–599
        intersection of sets, 573
        mutually exclusive events, 587–589
        representing "and," "or" and "not," 574–577
        to represent sample space, 567–571
        union of sets, 574
Probability experiment, 554
Proofs
    AAS congruence criteria, 161–163
    categories of valid reasons, 169
    concurrency of medians of triangles, 382–386
    coordinate, 207, 373
    defined, 18
    flowchart proofs, 167–175
    indirect, 217
    midpoint formula, 373–375
    paragraph proofs, 175
    prove statement, 27
    Pythagorean Theorem, 283–284
    quadrilateral is parallelogram, 223–226
    quadrilateral is rectangle, 227–229
    quadrilateral is rhombus, 230–232
    quadrilateral is square, 233–234
    requirements for good proof, 63
    Right Triangle Altitude Theorem, 276
    slope criteria for parallel and perpendicular lines, 377–380
    triangle congruence criteria, 154–159
    Triangle Proportionality Theorem, 266
    two-column proofs, 27, 63–69, 176
    writing, 63–69
Properties
    Addition Property of Equality, 26
    Cross Product Property, 320
    Distributive Property, 26
    Distributive Property of Multiplication Over Addition, 20
    Division Property of Equality, 26
    Multiplication Property of Equality, 26
    Reflexive Property, 26
    Substitution Property, 26, 67
    Subtraction Property of Equality, 26, 64, 67
    Symmetric Property, 26
    Transitive Property, 26, 63
    Transitive Property of Congruence, 67

using to justify statements two-column proof, 63–64

Proportionality
  Parallel Proportionality Theorem, 268
  Triangle Proportionality Theorem, 265–267

Protractor Postulate, 45

Prove statement, 27

Ptolemy, Claudius, 45

Pyramid
  Cavalieri's Principle, 514
  characteristics of, 480
  density and, 518–519
  hexagonal, 481
  lateral area, 508–509
  linear dimension changes and, 542–545
  net, 479–481
  oblique, 480
  pentagonal, 481
  right, 480
  slant height, 508
  square, 481, 483
  surface area, 507–508
  triangular, 481
  volume, 513–515

Pythagorean Theorem
  converse of, 286–287
  defined, 52, 283
  distance between two points, 52–54
  Law of Cosine and, 325
  proof for, 283–284

Pythagorean triple, 284, 286

Q

Quadrilaterals
  interior angles sum, 447–453
  kite
    congruent triangles, 206
    properties of, 206
  parallelogram
    congruent triangles and, 213–214
    proving quadrilateral is parallelogram, 223–226
  parallelograms
    properties of, 213–214
  rectangle
    properties of, 216–217
    proving quadrilateral is rectangle, 227–229
  rhombus
    properties of, 218–219
    proving quadrilateral is rhombus, 230–232
  square
    properties of, 219
    proving quadrilateral is square, 233–234

trapezoid
  isosceles, 210–212
  properties of, 209–212

R

Radian measure, 473

Radius, 9–10
  complete the square to find, 396–397
  defined, 335

Ray
  bisecting, 349
  naming, 4

Reading Math, 4, 29, 39, 48, 51, 77, 104, 602

Reason, in flowchart proof, 169

Reasoning
  deductive, 18–22
  inductive, 13–17
  logical, 18

Rectangles
  area, 433–435
  congruent triangles, 216
  defined, 216
  perimeter of, 434
  properties of, 216–217
  proving quadrilateral is rectangle, 227–229

Rectangular prism, 481, 482

Reflectional symmetry, 117

Reflections, 112–119
  on coordinate plane, 112–114
  defined, 112, 116
  line of reflection, 112, 117
  notation for, 116
  reflectional symmetry, 117

Reflexive Property, 26

Regular polygon
  area, 457–459
  defined, 453
  interior angle, 453–454
  perimeter, 458

Remote interior angle, 183

Replicate, 450

Rhombus
  area of, 441–443
  congruent triangle, 218
  defined, 110, 218
  properties of, 218–219
  proving quadrilateral is rhombus, 230–232
  translation of, 110

Right angle, 8
  defined, 8
  definition of, 63

Right cone, 487

Right cylinder, 486

Right prism, 479

Right pyramid, 480

Right triangle
  adjacent leg, 306
  area of, 437
  congruent
    hypotenuse-leg, 163
  45°-45°-90° right triangle, 291–293
  geometric mean, 278–279
  inverse trigonometric functions, 315–316
  isosceles, 291–293
  opposite leg, 306
  Pythagorean Theorem, 283–284
    distance between two points, 52–54
  Right Triangle Altitude Theorem, 275–277, 278–279
  similar, 303–306
  30°-60°-90° right triangle, 295–297
  trigonometric ratio
    cosine, 309–313
    sine, 309–313
    tangent, 309–313

Right Triangle Altitude Theorem, 275–277
  corollaries of, 278–279
  geometric mean, 278–279

Rigid motion
  to determine congruence, 134–136
  in transformations, 104–106

Rotational symmetry, 125

Rotations, 120–126
  angle of rotation, 120, 122
  center of, 120–121
  on coordinate plane, 120–122
  defined, 120, 124
  rotational symmetry, 125
  of solids, 490–491

Ruler Postulate, 39

S

Same-side interior angle, 74

Same-Side Interior Angles Postulate, 76, 79

Sample space
  defined, 554
  Venn diagram to represent, 567–571

SAS (side-angle-side), 137

SAS Similarity Theorem, 259–260

SAS triangle congruence criteria, 151, 156
  Secant line
    angles formed by, 365–366
    defined, 365

Sector
  area of, 467
  defined, 464
  length of, 468

Photo Credits

Unit 1: Steel Dragon (p. 91), Jeff Rogers www.coastergallery.com

Unit 4: wind farm (p. 391), Terrance Emerson, iStockphoto; Table of Geometry (p. 411), Cyclopaedia, 1728; circular garden (p. 463), iStockphoto

Unit 5: earth rendering (p. 532), Jan Rysavy/iStockphoto